LINEAR NETWORK ANALYSIS

Sundaram Seshu

Assistant Professor of Electrical Engineering
Syracuse University

Norman Balabanian

Associate Professor of Electrical Engineering
Syracuse University

LINEAR NETWORK ANALYSIS

1959

New York · John Wiley & Sons, Inc.   London · Chapman & Hall, Ltd.

To

Lily Seshu and Jean Balabanian

PREFACE

This book has evolved from a set of notes used in a graduate course on network analysis at Syracuse University for the last three years. The course follows a first-term graduate course in functions of a complex variable and Laplace transforms. Hence, in the book we assume that the student will come equipped with this background. Nevertheless, we have provided an appendix on these subjects which serves as a convenient reference. The Appendix also serves the purpose of acquainting the student with the level of the prerequisites assumed in the main text.

The need for a first-year graduate-level textbook on network theory has been apparent for some time. In the past, by network (or circuit) analysis was almost invariably meant a-c steady-state analysis. This was to be distinguished from transient analysis. Guillemin's *Communication Networks* and Gardner and Barnes' *Transients in Linear Systems* have been the classic works in these two areas. But network theory is much more than simply the addition of steady-state analysis and transient analysis. In this book we have attempted to develop the foundations of network theory carefully and to smooth out the transitions among (a) steady-state and transient responses, (b) time and frequency responses, and (c) analysis and synthesis.

The development starts from the basic fundamentals (Kirchhoff's laws, the number of independent equations, etc.) and leads the student to the thresholds of some of the most advanced concepts in network theory: network synthesis, realizability conditions, feedback and control systems, etc. Almost all results are carefully proved, and all assumptions that are made in the development are clearly enunciated. Whenever a result is used with merely a "reasonableness" type proof, the conditions under which the results apply and the results themselves are carefully stated.

In the past, a fairly sharp division has existed between the "passivists" and the "activists." In this book, active and passive networks are treated simultaneously from the first chapter. All discussions, theorems, etc., are phrased to encompass both types of networks (except those which are not valid for active networks, of course).

The purpose of network theory is to be able to predict the value of voltage or current at any point and at any instant of time, in an interconnection of electrical devices when the voltage or current at some other point is known. The first problem that must be faced when attempting this task is the establishment of an adequate model which will account for all observable effects under specified conditions of operation of the devices. Such a model has been built up over the years. Here we are content with a postulational approach; we postulate the behavior of the elements which go to make up the model. For example, we spend no time with considerations of magnetic field and flux in order to show the reasonableness of the voltage-current relationships of a transformer.

It may be possible to represent a physical device by one element of the model, or by an interconnection of several such elements, under certain conditions of operation. However, under other conditions the model for that device may require modification. Whether or not the interelectrode capacitances of a vacuum tube need to be considered in a given problem, for example, depends on the frequency range of interest. Considerations such as this will influence an engineer in choosing models for the devices encountered in a given problem. Desire for simplicity will also influence his choice. But no matter what considerations are involved, the network that is drawn on paper as a candidate for analysis is a model. The techniques that we use in analyzing the model will be independent of these considerations.

In this book we will not be concerned with the considerations that are involved in selecting an appropriate model in a given case under specified conditions of operation; our starting point will be a model. However, this does not imply that "physical" considerations and "device theory" are unimportant. It simply means that this is one of the topics, together with a host of other topics in electrical engineering, which we choose to omit from this book. On the other hand, a teacher using this book can easily make up for this "deficiency" in his lectures.

The important topic of transmission lines (distributed systems) has been omitted from this book. To treat any more than the most trivial cases of lossless and distortionless lines is a major commitment because of the complexity of the contour integration problems that arise. We did not feel it justifiable to include a chapter on transmission lines, only to treat these simple cases.

The core of the text consists of the first five chapters around which the rest of the structure is built. After a precise formulation of the fundamental equations—Kirchhoff's laws and the definitions of network elements—in Chapter 1, Chapter 2 is devoted to a review of elementary network theory, but from a mature point of view. The complex plane is introduced here and is used throughout the rest of the book. No generality is sought in this chapter, but the student is given plenty of opportunity to solve relatively simple loop and node systems of equations, with emphasis on the *complete* solution.

As a prelude to the general loop and node analyses in Chapter 4, the elementary aspects of matrix algebra and network topology are taken up in Chapter 3. Chapter 4 attempts to complete the routine analysis of networks. To this end, very general formulations of loop and node equations are given, as well as methods of computing initial conditions in singular problems. The problem of computing network functions from loop and node equations is also taken up here, as well as a brief treatment of duality. Chapter 5 winds up the classical aspects of network analysis by taking up the more important network theorems and relating steady state and transient response. The chapter concludes with a discussion of the steady-state response to general periodic driving functions.

Chapters 6 and 7 give the modern points of view in the time and frequency domains, respectively. The "excitation-response" point of view is exploited in Chapter 6 to get the superposition integral representations for the response function. At the end of this chapter the main results are summarized as a set of uniqueness theorems. The discussion of network functions in the complex frequency plane is the main theme of Chapter 7. After an introductory section, the sufficiency of the real part, magnitude and angle as specifications of the network function, are taken up. The latter half is devoted to the integral relationships between the real and imaginary parts, generally referred to as "Bode formulas." The last section explains the analogy between network functions and potential fields.

Chapter 8 is more or less a classical treatment of two-port parameters, except that the discussion is not restricted to reciprocal two ports, and scattering parameters are also included.

Network functions of passive structures are singled out for special treatment in Chapter 9. This chapter contains the contributions of Brune, Foster, Cauer, and Gewertz, in so far as network analysis is concerned. An initial treatment of positive real functions, introduced by means of the energy functions of the network, is followed by Foster's Reactance Theorem and its restatements for RC and RL networks. The realizability criteria for the two-port parameters follow. The last section is devoted to the topological formulas of Kirchhoff and Maxwell.

Chapter 10 is a collection of topics of special interest in active network analysis. A brief treatment of block diagrams is followed by a somewhat more detailed study of signal flow graphs and topics in stability—the Nyquist criterion and the root locus.

Chapter 11 treats classical filter theory based on image parameters. This is a generalized treatment and is not based on the characteristics of a particular structure as in Zobel's theory.

A textbook at the first-year graduate level is unlikely to contain any original material. In a few places our point of view or method of attack might be considered novel, but the results are all well known. We have tried to give credit to the original contributors wherever it was appropriate. It is almost certain that we have failed to give proper credit in some places, and we apologize to the authors for this oversight.

A project of this magnitude necessarily reflects the authors' experiences under their teachers and in discussions with their colleagues and their students. It is virtually impossible to acknowledge them all. We would like to single out for specific acknowledgment Wilbur LePage who gave us continuous encouragement during the progress of this work, and Harry Gruenberg who patiently taught an initial version of the notes and gave us numerous suggestions for improvement, which we have incorporated. Professors Myril B. Reed and Wilbur R. LePage have also contributed indirectly by virtue of having been the teachers of the two authors.

SUNDARAM SESHU
NORMAN BALABANIAN

March 1959

CONTENTS

Contents

Contents

1 · FUNDAMENTAL CONCEPTS

In the last two decades network theory has "graduated" from a "useful approximation in a large number of practical cases" to the status of an "exact science." This remark of course, applies to the attitude of engineers towards the subject rather than to any metamorphosis of the subject itself. This change in viewpoint is in a large measure due to the vastly increased emphasis in both mathematics and physics that is placed in the education of present-day electrical engineers, and the increased understanding of the nature of physical sciences which inevitably accompanies this training. An example of the demand for more mathematical training occurs right here, since we are assuming some knowledge of the theory of functions of a complex variable and of Laplace transforms as prerequisites to network theory.

In this text we will study network theory from precisely this modern point of view. In the first two chapters we will lay the groundwork, by reexamining the fundamental ideas and methods of circuit analysis. These were undoubtedly "covered" in an undergraduate course on circuit theory. Nevertheless, it is quite likely that some very important ideas were either glossed over or else not quite understood or appreciated in that course. In any case our point of view here will be much more mature than is possible in an undergraduate course.

1.1 Current and Voltage References

The variables, in terms of which the behavior of electric networks is described, are voltage and current. Although other quantities, such as charge and magnetic flux, are also encountered, the former two are the most useful ones. These quantities are functions of time and we will designate them by the symbols $v(t)$ and $i(t)$. Although the notation we use here and throughout the book does not have any intrinsic merit, use of careless notation is usually a consequence of, and in turn leads to, sloppy and improper patterns of thinking. In order to foster clear thought, we will stress the importance of consistent notation. (Lower

1

case letters will consistently be used to represent functions of time.)

The fundamental laws on which network theory is founded express relationships among currents and voltages at various places in the network. Before we can formulate these laws, we must clear up a certain matter having to do with the so-called "assumed positive direction of current" and "assumed positive polarity of voltage."

The function $i(t)$ is a real-valued function of time which characterizes the variation of a current with time. It can take on negative values as well as positive values in the course of time. Figure 1a shows a sinu-

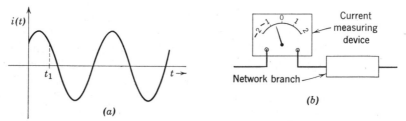

Fig. 1.   Current reference.

soidal function of time which might represent the current in a branch of a network. Suppose we use a device to measure the current, which is sensitive to the instantaneous value of the current.

For the purposes of this discussion we assume this device to be a center-zero D'Arsonval ammeter. It is perfectly clear that at any time, say t_1, shown in the figure, two different readings will be obtained on the meter depending on the two ways in which the meter can be connected. One of these two readings will be the negative of the other, but either one of them will tell us the magnitude and sense (direction) of the current at t_1, provided there is a mark on the terminals of the meter which indicates the direction of the current through the meter when the needle swings one way (positive) or the other (negative). Let's assume that one of the terminals has a + mark on it, indicating that the current is oriented from this terminal to the other through the meter when the needle swings positive. Then, if the terminals of the meter are so connected that the needle swings positive at time $t = t_1$, a positive value of $i(t)$ will correspond to a positive reading of the meter. However, it is not necessary that the meter be so connected. If the meter is connected in the opposite direction, the needle will swing negative at time $t = t_1$. But since the meter terminals are interchanged, we still find the sense of the current through the branch to be the same as before. Thus it does not matter how the meter is connected, *so long as we know how it is* by some kind of a mark.

A completely analogous discussion is appropriate for the voltage across a network branch.

Now it would be impractical to show an ammeter and a voltmeter with suitably marked terminals for each branch in a network diagram; so we adopt some other convention that will supply the same information. The symbols that we will use in this text are shown in Fig. 2. The convention adopted here is to draw the arrow for $i(t)$ from the + terminal of the ammeter to the other terminal. The

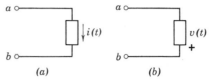

Fig. 2. Current and voltage references.

+ for $v(t)$ is placed at the same end of the branch as the + on the voltmeter. Thus, the arrow indicates that $i(t)$ will be positive at those times when the actual current in the network branch is in the direction of the arrow. Alternatively we can say that the arrow indicates the actual (instantaneous) sense of the current when an ammeter is connected in such a way that it reads positive; and the arrow is drawn according to the meter connection. Similarly the plus sign indicates the actual instantaneous voltage polarity when the voltmeter is connected in such a way that it reads positive; and the plus sign conforms to the meter connection.

These two symbols, the arrow and the plus sign, are respectively called current and voltage *references*. As we mentioned above, it is completely arbitrary how the current and voltage references are chosen (just as it is unimportant how the meters are connected). Hence, it is not important *how* the references are chosen, but it *is* important *that a current and voltage reference be assigned to a network element;* otherwise the functions $i(t)$ and $v(t)$ for that element have no real significance.

An apparent contradiction of this statement may be discovered by turning to later chapters of this book and noting that the branches in network diagrams have not been assigned current and voltage references. This is not really a contradiction, however, since we use the very arbitrariness of the references to make conventions on their assignment for the purpose of simplifying network equations. After making these conventions, we can dispense with the reference symbols, being confident that our desires on this score are understood.

1.2 Kirchhoff's Laws

Electric network theory, like all scientific theories, attempts to describe the phenomena occurring in a portion of the physical world by setting up a mathematical model. This model, of course, is based on observations in the physical world, but it also utilizes other mathematical models which have stood the test of time so well that they have come to be regarded as physical reality themselves. As an example, the picture of electrons flowing in conductors and thus constituting an electric current is so vivid that we lose sight of the fact that this is just a theoretical model of a portion of the physical world.

The purpose of a model is to permit us to understand natural phenomena. But more than this, we expect that the logical consequences to which we are led will enable us to predict the behavior of the model under conditions which we establish. If we can now duplicate in the physical world the conditions that prevail in the model, our predictions can be experimentally checked. If our predictions are verified we gain confidence that our model is a good one. If there is a difference between the predicted and experimental values which cannot be ascribed to experimental error, and we are reasonably sure that the experimental analog of the theoretical model duplicates the conditions of the model, we must conclude that the model is not "adequate" for the purpose of understanding the physical world and must be overhauled.*

In the case of electric network theory, the model has had great success in predicting experimental results. As a matter of fact, the model has become so real that it is difficult for students to distinguish between the model and the physical world.

The first step in establishing a model is to make intimate observations of the physical world. Experiments are performed attempting to establish universal relationships among the measurable quantities. From these experiments general conclusions are drawn concerning the behavior of the quantities involved. These conclusions are regarded as "laws," and are usually stated in terms of the variables of the mathematical model.

A. Kirchhoff's Current Law. In network theory the fundamental "laws" are Kirchhoff's two laws. Consider the portion of a network shown in Fig. 3. Several branches are shown connected together at a node, the current references in the branches being clearly indicated. In Fig. 3a all the references are directed away from the node. Let us remember that the reference indicates that if an instantaneous value-reading meter is connected with its + marked terminal at the tail of the arrow it will read positive when the instantaneous current is in the arrow direction. Assuming meters so connected, experimental observation

---

* An example of such a revision occurred after the celebrated Michelson-Morley experiment, where calculations based on Newtonian mechanics did not agree with experimental results. The revised model is relativistic mechanics.

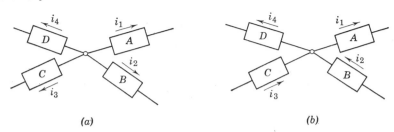

(a)   (b)

Fig. 3.   Kirchhoff's current law.

shows us that the sum of all the meter readings is zero (within experimental accuracy). If we interchange the terminals of one of the meters (equivalently, reverse the corresponding current reference) we should of course change the sign of that particular reading. Thus, with the current references shown in Fig. 3b, we find

$$i_1(t) - i_2(t) - i_3(t) + i_4(t) = 0 \qquad (1)$$

Each current with reference directed away from the node is preceded with a plus sign while each current with reference directed toward the node is preceded with a minus sign.

Based on many observations such as this, we draw the general conclusion that expressions such as Eq. (1) will hold at all nodes of a network no matter how many branches are connected at each node. This is then really in the form of an assumption, or *postulate*. A whole theory is built up on this, and several other, postulates. If at any time it is found that logical results that are derived based on the postulates cannot be verified experimentally, then we will have to seek a modification of the postulates. Fortunately, such a circumstance has not yet transpired in network theory (and most probably is not likely to). As a matter of fact, we may consider that the validity of equations similar to Eq. (1) at any node is a direct consequence of the principle of conservation of charge, which is itself a fundamental postulate.

Let us now state Kirchhoff's current law formally. For this purpose it is convenient to include in the equation for each node all branches of a network, whether or not the branch is connected to the particular node.

Kirchhoff's Current Law

If a network has N_b branches and N_v (v for vertex) nodes, then

$$\sum_{j=1}^{N_b} a_{kj} i_j(t) = 0; \qquad k = 1, 2, \cdots, N_v \qquad (2)$$

where the coefficients a_{kj} have the values $+1$, -1 or zero:

$a_{kj} =$ 1 if branch j is connected to node k and its current reference is directed away from the node;

$a_{kj} = -1$ if branch j is connected to node k and its current reference is directed toward the node;

$a_{kj} =$ 0 if branch j is not connected to node k.

In stating this law no cognizance is taken of the constituents of a branch; they may be active or passive, linear or nonlinear, although in this book we will be restricted to linear networks.

In defining the a_{kj} coefficients we have chosen the branch currents with reference *away* from the node to be exalted with positive coefficients; those branch currents with reference toward the node have been assigned a lowly negative coefficient. We can actually reverse this convention if we like, since such a practice would be equivalent to multiplying Eqs. (2) by -1 throughout. It may be helpful to think that a node has two possible orientations, *away* and *toward*, and we choose one of these as the node orientation.

According to Eq. (2) we will have as many equations from the current law as there are nodes in the network. The question arises whether all of these equations are independent. We shall next answer this question.

Let us denote the left side of the equations with the symbol y; thus, y_k stands for the left side of the kth equation. A set of homogeneous equations is said to be *linearly dependent* if at least one of the equations can be expressed as a linear combination of the others; that is, if we can write

$$y_k = K_1 y_1 + K_2 y_2 + \cdots + K_{k-1} y_{k-1} + K_{k+1} y_{k+1} + \cdots + K_{N_v} y_{N_v} \quad (3)$$

or, equivalently,

$$K_1 y_1 + K_2 y_2 + \cdots + K_{N_v} y_{N_v} \equiv 0 \quad (4)$$

where the K's are constants, *not all zero*.

To help in visualizing the argument, let us consider a specific example. Figure 4 shows a network with four nodes and five branches which have been numbered arbitrarily. The Kirchhoff current law equations (abbreviated KCL) can be written as follows.

Node 1:	$i_1(t)$	$+i_2(t)$				$= 0$
Node 2:	$-i_1(t)$		$-i_3(t)$	$+i_4(t)$		$= 0$
Node 3:				$-i_4(t)$	$-i_5(t)$	$= 0$
Node 4:		$-i_2(t)$	$+i_3(t)$		$+i_5(t)$	$= 0$

$$(5)$$

The vertical bars in these equations have no significance other than to emphasize the systematic manner of writing the equations. We have omitted writing the terms with zero coefficient for clarity. Note that only one branch current appears in each column, and it appears exactly twice, once with a plus sign, once with a minus sign. This circumstance should be expected since each branch is connected between exactly two nodes, and its current reference is away from one node and toward the other.

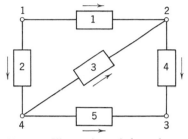

Fig. 4. Illustration of dependence of KCL equations.

Now let us add all the equations. Each term on the left will be matched by another term having the opposite sign. Hence, the sum will be identically zero. This result has the form of Eq. (4) with all the K's equal to unity. Hence, the equations are linearly dependent. Any one of the equations can be expressed as the negative sum of all the others. If we know three of the equations, we immediately know the fourth one as well. Expressed in terms of the number of nodes, we can say that *at most* $N_v - 1$ of the equations are independent. For this particular example we can easily see that exactly $N_v - 1$ (or 3) of the equations are independent. As a matter of fact, this is a general result which we will use from now on without proof. The proof will be given in section 3.3.

B. Kirchhoff's Voltage Law. The second fundamental law, or postulate, of network theory is Kirchhoff's Voltage Law (abbreviated KVL). Consider the portion of a network shown in Fig. 5. This con-

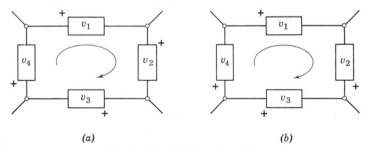

(a)   (b)

Fig. 5.   Kirchhoff's voltage law.

sists of several branches connected to form a simple closed path or loop. From the two possible orientations we must choose an orientation or reference for the loop, just as we did for the node. The orientation of the loop is shown by means of an arrow.

The voltage references of the branches are clearly indicated in the figure. In Fig. 5a the plus marks are all located at the tail of the loop orientation arrow. If we connect instantaneous value-reading voltmeters across the branches of the experimental analog of the model shown in the diagram, with the + marked terminals at the indicated voltage references, then we observe that the sum of all the voltmeter readings at each instant of time is zero. Again, if we interchange the terminals of a meter, or reverse the corresponding voltage reference, we should change the sign of that particular reading. Thus, in terms of the references shown in Fig. 5b we will find

$$v_1(t) - v_2(t) - v_3(t) + v_4(t) = 0 \qquad (6)$$

Each voltage with a reference plus at the tail of the loop orientation arrow is preceded with a plus sign, while each voltage with a reference at the head of the loop orientation arrow is preceded with a minus sign.

Based on many experimental observations such as this, we postulate that expressions such as Eq. (6) will hold for each closed path in a network. To formalize the statement of the law let us include in the equation for each loop all the branches of the network, whether or not a branch appears on the contour of a particular loop. If a branch is not in a loop, then the corresponding branch voltage will have a zero coefficient in the equation for that loop.

Kirchhoff's Voltage Law

If a network has N_b branches and $N_m(m$ for mesh) loops, then

$$\sum_{j=1}^{N_b} b_{kj} v_j(t) = 0; \qquad k = 1, 2, \cdots, N_m \qquad (7)$$

where the coefficients b_{kj} have the values $+1$, -1, or 0:

$b_{kj} = \quad 1 \quad$ if branch j is in loop k and its voltage reference is at the tail of the loop orientation arrow;

$b_{kj} = -1 \quad$ if branch j is in loop k and its voltage reference is at the head of the loop orientation arrow;

$b_{kj} = \quad 0 \quad$ if branch j is not in loop k.

Just like the current law, this law is also valid for passive, active, linear, or nonlinear branches.

In order to avoid some possible misunderstandings (or clear up existing confusions) we need to make some remarks about the statement of Kirchhoff's voltage law as given here. Frequently, Kirchhoff's voltage law is stated as

$$\Sigma \text{ voltage rises} = \Sigma \text{ voltage drops} \tag{8}$$

for any closed loop. There is nothing wrong with this statement provided we interpret the words "rise" and "drop" properly. The drops correspond to voltage references being at the tail of the loop reference arrow, and the rises correspond to voltage references being at the head of the loop reference arrow. The voltage of a given branch may be a drop in one loop and a rise in another. In this text we will not use the words "rise" and "drop," since they may carry connotations that we wish to avoid.

Finally one remark about the loop reference. As far as Kirchhoff's voltage law is concerned, this arrow is nothing more than a specification of the loop and its orientation. It is *not* a loop current, something we have yet to define. It may be interpreted as such, in due course, when we come to write loop equations, but it does not play the role of a loop current in Kirchhoff's voltage law.

According to the voltage law there will be as many equations as there are closed paths in a network. Again the question of dependence arises. In the present case it is more difficult to answer this question than it is for the KCL equations. If the network contains N_b branches and N_v nodes, then the number of independent equations that can be written from Kirchhoff's voltage law is $N_b - (N_v - 1)$. We will use this result without proof, leaving the proof to section 3.3. We will, however, show that there are *at least* this many independent equations. To do this let us make some definitions.

A *connected* network is one which consists of only one part. A *tree* of a connected network is a connected subnetwork which contains all the nodes of the network but does not contain any closed paths.

Any connected network contains at least one tree. Each branch of a network may or may not be on a tree depending on how the tree is chosen. For example, Fig. 6 shows two trees of the network which was originally

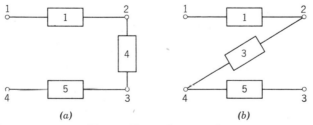

Fig. 6.   Trees of a network.

shown in Fig. 4. In Fig. 6*a* branch 4 is on the tree while in Fig. 6*b* it is not. For a particular choice of a tree the branches on the tree are called *tree branches* (strangely enough), whereas those that are not on the tree are called *links* or *chords*. Since there are N_b branches and N_v nodes, there must be $N_v - 1$ tree branches and $N_b - (N_v - 1)$ links. (The proof that a tree of N_v vertices contains $N_v - 1$ branches is not given here, but may be found in section 3.3.)

Let us choose any tree of a given connected network and consider any one of the links. This link has two nodes, and these are certainly on the tree. We can always find an open path consisting of tree branches only, connecting these two nodes, since the tree is connected. This open path of tree branches, together with the link, forms a closed loop. For each link we can find one such closed loop. Since there are $N_b - (N_v - 1)$ links, there will be the same number of such closed loops. This set of loops is referred to as the *fundamental system of loops*. The orientations of the loops are chosen such that the link voltage reference is at the tail of the loop reference arrow.

It is now clear that if we write KVL equations for the fundamental system of loops, the resulting set of equations will be independent. This is true because each equation contains a voltage (that of the link) which does not appear in any other equation. No linear combination of any number of the remaining equations can ever include this particular voltage. Hence, at least $N_b - (N_v - 1)$ KVL equations are independent.

For any given network the correct number of independent equations will always be obtained if we choose a tree and form the fundamental system of loops. However, in the case of *planar* networks (networks which can be drawn on paper without having any branch cross over other branches), it is simpler to choose all the internal meshes, or "windows," as closed loops. This procedure will give the correct number of equations.

Let us now summarize the discussion in this section. We have stated the two laws of Kirchhoff as fundamental postulates of network theory. These laws express the equilibrium of branch currents at the nodes of a network and the equilibrium of branch voltages around closed loops in the network. If a network contains N_b branches and N_v nodes, then the number of independent KCL equations is $N_v - 1$ and the number of independent KVL equations is $N_b - (N_v - 1)$.

1.3 Network Elements

In the statement of Kirchhoff's laws, no cognizance is taken of the constituents of a branch. To complete the description of the model of electric networks which we are building up, we must now *postulate* the existence of certain components. These components must be endowed with such properties that our model will be able to account for observable electrical phenomena, such as the spark produced by an induction coil, the heating of a wire which is carrying current, etc. Of course, this model has been established over the years; there is no need for us to review all the physical considerations which eventually led to the model in its present form.

We define three *network elements* in our model: resistance, inductance, and capacitance.* The diagrammatic representations are shown in Fig. 7.

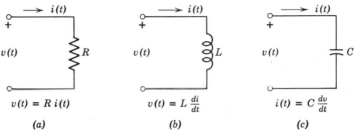

$$v(t) = R\,i(t)$$

$$v(t) = L\frac{di}{dt}$$

$$i(t) = C\frac{dv}{dt}$$

(a)   *(b)*   *(c)*

Fig. 7.   Network elements.

The precise definitions of the elements are given in terms of the relationships between the current and the voltage at the element terminals. These definitions are shown in Fig. 7 and are tabulated in Table 1.

TABLE 1

Element	Symbol	Voltage-current relationships
Resistance	R	$v = Ri$ $i = \dfrac{1}{R}v = Gv$
Inductance	L	$v = L\dfrac{di}{dt}$ $i(t) = \dfrac{1}{L}\displaystyle\int_0^t v(x)\,dx + i(0)$
Capacitance	C	$i = C\dfrac{dv}{dt}$ $v(t) = \dfrac{1}{C}\displaystyle\int_0^t i(x)\,dx + v(0)$

* Mutual inductance is treated separately.

Note that these expressions are valid only for the voltage and current references shown on the diagrams. Reversing either a current or a voltage reference will reverse the sign of the corresponding expression.*

The element can be thought of as a two-terminal (paper) device. It is characterized by a parameter; in case of the resistance element, for example, the parameter is denoted by R and is called resistance. It is perhaps unfortunate that the element and the parameter have the same name, but this does not often lead to confusion.†

We see that the first two relationships in the figure express $v(t)$ in terms of $i(t)$, while the third one gives $i(t)$ in terms of $v(t)$. It is sometimes necessary to invert the v-i (short for voltage-current) relationships to solve for current or voltage as the case may be. This is easily done for the resistance, but is somewhat more difficult for the other two.

Consider the inductance element. Its voltage depends only on the derivative of the current. Figure 8 shows a family of curves each mem-

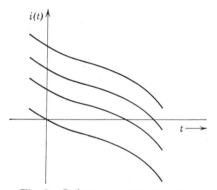

Fig. 8.   Inductance-current curves.

ber of which might be the current in the inductance. These curves will all lead to the same voltage across the inductance, since at each value of time the slopes are identical. For a given voltage, then, we will be unable to tell which one of these curves represents the current, *unless a value of current is specified at some particular time.* This will locate a point on the appropriate curve and, thus, fix the current. It is immaterial for what particular value of time the current is specified. Usually, we are interested in the state of a network after some particular event

---

* Note that in all cases the voltage is a linear function of the current, or its derivative, or its antiderivative. For this reason, these elements are called *linear* elements.

† There are three entities to be considered—the black box in the laboratory, the wiggly line on paper and the number R—for all of which we have only two names, "resistor" and "resistance." So, two of them have to share a name. We choose to use the same name for the last two.

in time, such as the opening or closing of a switch. Since the origin of time is arbitrary, we usually choose it to coincide with the value at which the current is specified. With this convention, inversion of the v-i relationship of the inductance leads to

$$v(t) = L\frac{di}{dt} \qquad (a)$$

$$i(t) = \frac{1}{L}\int_0^t v(x)\,dx + i(0) \qquad (b)$$

(9)

In the last expression the lower limit is approached from positive values so that for $i(0)$ we really should write $i(0+)$.

Quite often the inverse relationship is written as an indefinite integral (or antiderivative) instead of a definite integral, as we have written here. Such an expression is incomplete unless we add to it a specification of $i(0+)$, and in this sense is misleading. Normally one thinks of the voltage $v(t)$ as being expressed as an explicit function such as $\epsilon^{-\alpha t}$, $\sin \omega t$, etc., and the antiderivative as being something unique, $-\frac{1}{\alpha}\epsilon^{-\alpha t}$, $-\frac{1}{\omega}\cos \omega t$, etc., which is certainly not true. Also, in many of the cases that we shall consider, the voltage may not be expressible in such a simple fashion for all t, the analytic expression for $v(t)$ depending upon the particular interval of the axis on which the point t falls. In such a case the definite integral is certainly preferable. Some such waveshapes are shown in Fig. 9.

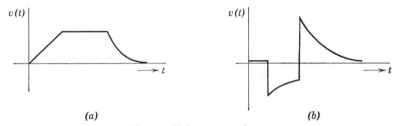

(a)   *(b)*

Fig. 9.   Voltage waveshapes.

Another important result becomes apparent if we again consider Eqs. (9). So long as the current is a continuous, differentiable function, the voltage will remain bounded. Or, considering it from the inverse viewpoint, the current in an inductance will be continuous so long as the voltage remains bounded. Thus, the value of the current at "zero plus" will be the same as its value at "zero minus" so long as the voltage remains bounded. This is usually expressed by stating that the current in an inductance cannot change instantaneously. This statement will be true only if the voltage across the inductance remains bounded. In most networks this will be the case. We will defer to a later chapter the discussion of cases in which the inductance current can be discontinuous.

What we have said for the inductance will be equally true for the capacitance but with the words voltage and current interchanged. Thus, the v-i relationships for the capacitance are

$$i(t) = C \frac{dv}{dt} \qquad (a)$$

$$v(t) = \frac{1}{C} \int_0^t i(x) \, dx + v(0) \qquad (b)$$

$$(10)$$

The voltage across the capacitance will be continuous so long as the current remains bounded. Thus the capacitance voltage at zero plus will equal its value at zero minus so long as the current remains bounded, which will be true in most networks. We will consider the general case in a later chapter.

The elements we have defined in our model do not have their exact counterparts in the physical world. The electrical behavior of physical devices can be described in terms of a model which consists of several (ideal) elements that are interconnected in various ways. For example, the behavior of a coil of wire can be approximately described (and predicted) by the network shown in Fig. 10. Very often the required

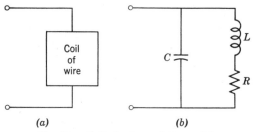

(a)   *(b)*

Fig. 10.   Coil of wire and its model.

capacitance is small and a good approximation to the behavior of the coil of wire is obtained if the capacitance is completely removed. Physical coils can be made whose behavior is closely approximated by that of an inductance alone (as in RF chokes) or of a resistance alone (as in a potentiometer or wire-wound resistance).

Physical devices whose electrical behavior can be represented approximately by one of the elements in our model are given special names. These are *resistor*, *inductor*, and *capacitor*, represented by the elements resistance, inductance, and capacitance, respectively. Such devices are designed so that only one effect, resistive, inductive, or capacitive, predominates.

We find, however, that not all physical devices can be described in terms of the three elements we have discussed. One such device is a *transformer*. A simple transformer consists of two coils of wire which are in close proximity. We say that the two coils are *coupled* (mutually or magnetically). We observe that a voltage will appear at the terminals of one coil when the current in the other coil varies with time. This effect cannot be accounted for by any combination of the three elements we have defined. We need to introduce another element. In contrast with the two-terminal elements appearing in our model so far, this one must have two pairs of terminals. The element is called a *transformer*, the same as the physical device of which it is to be a model. It is defined

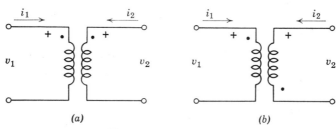

(a) (b)

Fig. 11.   A transformer.

in terms of the diagram shown in Fig. 11a and the following voltage-current relationships.

$$v_1 = L_1 \frac{di_1}{dt} + M \frac{di_2}{dt} \qquad (a)$$

(11)

$$v_2 = M \frac{di_1}{dt} + L_2 \frac{di_2}{dt} \qquad (b)$$

Note that the signs appearing in these equations are valid only for the voltage and current references shown. Reversing a voltage or current reference will reverse the signs of corresponding terms.

This element is characterized by *three* parameters instead of only one: the two *self-inductances* L_1 and L_2, and the *mutual inductance* M. The self-inductance parameter is identical with the previously defined inductance. The mutual inductance is a measure of the voltage that can be produced at one pair of terminals by a current variation at the other pair. In contrast with the self inductance, it is an algebraic quantity which can have a negative or a positive value. The actual sign is indicated by polarity marks on the transformer diagram. A dot (or other symbol) is placed at one terminal of each pair. Then, M will be positive if each current reference is directed toward or away from the corresponding dot-marked terminal. It will be negative if one current reference is directed toward a dot while the other one is directed away. In writing the v-i relationships of a transformer it is not necessary to know how the dots are positioned on the terminals. This information will be necessary, however, when numerical values are required for the mutual inductance.

We should here mention that there is another convention in common use. Under this convention M is always positive, like L. However, the signs preceding the terms involving M in the v-i relationships must be adjusted depending on the sense of the current references relative to the dots. The two conventions are, of course, completely equivalent. The second one, however, requires knowledge of the dot locations even when the v-i relationships are written.

Let us note here that we have made very little attempt to justify establishing the transformer model that we did, starting from physical considerations and experimental evidence. We assume that these experimental results (Faraday's law, Lenz's law), and their implications are known. We will leave it to you to show how the dot positions in the model are related to relative winding directions of the coils in an actual physical transformer. Another question that may be asked is: why choose the same parameter M in both of the expressions in Eqs. (11) instead of writing M_{12} and M_{21}, respectively? Our viewpoint is that we are establishing a model. We are free to choose the components of our model and endow them with any characteristics we like. The only test of the model is its ability to describe and predict phenomena in the physical world. Our justification, then, must be our ability to corroborate experimentally the results of our assumption. We will leave to you the problem of devising an experiment that can be performed on an actual transformer, whose results will show that it is reasonable to choose $M_{12} = M_{21}$ in the model.*

We have stated that the mutual inductance is a measure of the voltage that can be produced at one pair of terminals of a transformer by a current variation in the other pair. Although this is true, more

---

* This equality can also be established by appealing to Faraday's law, which is outside our scope, or by using a rather involved energy argument.

useful information will be obtained if we have a comparison of the voltages produced at both pairs of terminals by current in one pair of terminals. This can be done by considering the v-i relationships in Eqs. (11) alternately for the cases $i_2 \equiv 0$ and $i_1 \equiv 0$. For these two cases we find

$$\left.\frac{v_1}{v_2}\right|_{i_2 \equiv 0} = \frac{L_1}{M} \qquad (a)$$

$$(12)$$

$$\left.\frac{v_1}{v_2}\right|_{i_1 \equiv 0} = \frac{M}{L_2} \qquad (b)$$

If we now take the ratio of these two expressions, we will get

$$\frac{\left.\dfrac{v_1}{v_2}\right|_{i_1=0}}{\left.\dfrac{v_1}{v_2}\right|_{i_2 \equiv 0}} = \frac{M^2}{L_1 L_2} = k^2 \qquad (13)$$

We find that this ratio is a positive constant, which we have labelled k^2. Either of the ratios in Eqs. (12) can take on any real value. However, based on experimental observations on actual transformers, we should expect the ratio of v_1 to v_2, due to a variation of current i_2, to be no greater than the same ratio due to a variation of current i_1. Thus, $k^2 \leq 1$. The number k is called the *coupling coefficient*. It gives a measure of the *tightness* or *closeness* of coupling between the two pairs of terminals.*

No physical transformer has yet been built that has a coefficient of coupling equal to unity, although this value has been approached quite closely. However, in the model, we admit the possibility of such a transformer and we dignify it with the name *perfect transformer* or *unity-coupling transformer*. For such a transformer the self and mutual inductances satisfy the condition

$$L_1 L_2 - M^2 = 0 \qquad (14)$$

Some authors use the name *ideal transformer* to denote the same thing. However, we will use the name *ideal transformer* for another element in our model. This element, like the plain, ordinary transformer, has two pairs of terminals, as shown in Fig. 12. We define the ideal transformer in terms of the following v-i relationships.

---

* The generalization of the restriction on k to multiwinding transformers is given in section 9.3.

$$i_2 = ni_1 \qquad (a)$$

$$v_2 = \frac{1}{n} v_1 \qquad (b) \tag{15}$$

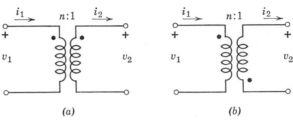

(a)   (b)

Fig. 12.   An ideal transformer.

Thus, the ideal transformer is characterized by a single parameter n called the *turns ratio*. For the references and polarities of Fig. 12a, n is positive, whereas for Fig. 12b, n is negative. This is the more common usage of the term ideal transformer.

Let us see how closely a perfect transformer and an ideal transformer are related. Turn back to Eqs. (11) and take the ratio of v_2 to v_1. At the same time, insert the perfect transformer condition given in Eq. (14). In order to make the diagrams in Figs. 11 and 12 agree, reverse the reference directions of i_2 in Fig. 11. This will change the sign before the second term in Eqs. (11). The result for a perfect transformer will be

$$\frac{v_2}{v_1} = \frac{\sqrt{L_1 L_2}\, \dfrac{di_1}{dt} - L_2 \dfrac{di_2}{dt}}{L_1 \dfrac{di_1}{dt} - \sqrt{L_1 L_2}\, \dfrac{di_2}{dt}} = \sqrt{\frac{L_2}{L_1}} \tag{16}$$

Comparing this with the second one of Eqs. (15) we see that they will be identical if we set

$$n = \sqrt{\frac{L_1}{L_2}} \tag{17}$$

Now in the case of actual coils of wire, the inductance is proportional to the square of the number of turns in the coil. This is the origin of the name *turns ratio* for n.

So far it appears that a perfect transformer and an ideal transformer are the same. However, we still need to compare the relationships between the currents in the two cases. In order to do this, turn again to Eq. (11a), still assuming the sign before the second term to be negative, corresponding to a reversal of the reference of i_2 in Fig. 11. Let us integrate this equation from 0 to t. We will get

$$\int_0^t v_1(x)\, dx = L_1 i_1(t) - L_1 i_1(0) - M i_2(t) + M i_2(0) \tag{18}$$

We have still not used the perfect transformer condition of Eq. (14). If we do so, and rearrange terms, we will get

$$i_1(t) = \frac{1}{n} i_2(t) + \frac{1}{L_1} \int_0^t v_1(x)\, dx + i_1(0) - \frac{1}{n} i_2(0) \tag{19}$$

This equation is to be compared with the first one in Eqs. (15). Two differences are noted: first the appearance of the initial values of the currents, and second, the appearance of the term involving a voltage. The first of these is not serious. The major difference between an ideal transformer and a perfect transformer is in the appearance of the middle term on the right side of Eq. (19).

If we denote by i_a everything on the right side but the first term, the form of the equation will suggest that it is the KCL equation at a node, one branch of which consists of an inductance L_1, as shown in Fig. 13.

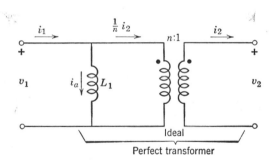

Fig. 13.   Relationship between perfect and ideal transformers.

This figure satisfies both Eqs. (16) and (19). It shows how a perfect transformer is related to an ideal transformer. If in a perfect transformer we permit L_1 and L_2 to approach infinity, but in such a way that their ratio remains constant, the result will be an ideal transformer.

All of the elements that we have discussed up till now can be characterized by the word *passive*. To complete our model we will need to define other elements, elements which may be labeled *active* and which will account for our ability to generate voltage and current. We call such elements *sources* or *generators*. We define two types of source, as follows.

1. A *voltage source* is a two-terminal element whose voltage at any instant of time is independent of the current at its terminals.

2. A *current source* is a two-terminal element whose current at any instant of time is independent of the voltage across its terminals.

The diagrammatic representations are shown in Fig. 14. It does not matter what network is connected at the terminals of a voltage source, its voltage will be unmodified. Of course, the current will be affected by the network. Similarly, the network connected at the terminals of a current source will affect the voltage across these terminals but will leave the current unmodified. For this reason they are called *independent* sources.

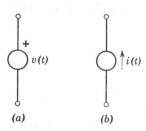

Fig. 14.   Voltage and current sources.

In the physical world there is no exact counterpart of the sources we have defined, any more than there are pure resistances or inductances. Physical generators may be approximated by one or the other of these two sources, to some degree. As an example, we are familiar enough with the dimming of the house lights when a large electrical appliance is switched on the line to know that the voltage of a physical source varies under load.

In an actual physical source the current or voltage generated may depend on some nonelectrical quantity, such as the speed of a rotating machine, or the concentration of acid in a battery, or the light intensity incident on a photoelectric cell. These relationships are of no interest to us in network analysis, since we are not concerned with the internal operation of sources, only with their terminal behavior. Thus, our idealized sources take no cognizance of the dependence of voltage or current on nonelectrical quantities; they are called independent sources.

However, it is found that the behavior of certain electrical devices, vacuum tubes and transistors, for example, cannot be explained in terms of a model consisting of interconnections of the independent sources and passive elements which we have so far defined. To account for these devices as well, we define another type of source, a dependent source.

A *dependent voltage source* is a source whose terminal voltage is dependent on other voltages or currents. Similarly, a *dependent current source* is a source whose terminal current is dependent on other voltages or currents. Examples of such sources are shown in Fig. 15. The first two are dependent voltages, one being voltage-dependent the other current-dependent. The second two are dependent currents, one being

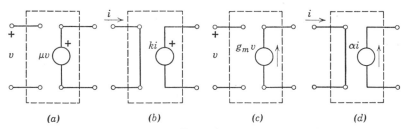

Fig. 15.   Dependent sources.

voltage-dependent, the other current-dependent. In contrast with independent sources, the dependent sources have two pairs of terminals instead of one. In each of these examples the source voltage or current is directly proportional to another voltage or current. This type of dependence is, of course, very simple. The model can be expanded by including other types of dependence, as well; for instance, the source output voltage may be the derivative of the input current. However, we will omit detailed consideration of any other type of dependence in our model.

The introduction of dependent sources into our model leads to many additional results not possible with the previous elements alone. As an example, consider the parallel connection of a resistor and a dependent current source shown in Fig. 16. Application of KCL at one of the nodes shows that the current through R is $(1 - \alpha)i$. Hence, the voltage-current relationship at the input terminals will be

$$v = (1 - \alpha)Ri \qquad (20)$$

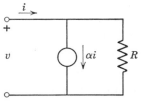

Fig. 16. A negative resistance converter.

The presence of the dependent source seems to have the effect of changing the value of R. If α is greater than one, the network behaves like a negative resistance. For this reason it is called a *negative resistance converter*.

For certain ranges of voltage and current the behavior of certain vacuum tubes and transistors can be approximated by a model consisting of the interconnection of dependent sources and other network elements. Figure 17 shows two such models. These models are not valid representations of the physical devices under all conditions of operation. For example, at high enough frequency the interelectrode capacitances of the tube would need to be included in the model.

The last point brings up a question. When an engineer is presented with a physical problem concerned with calculating certain voltages and currents in an interconnection of various physical electrical devices, his

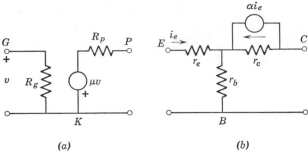

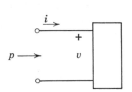

Fig. 17.　Models representing vacuum triode and transistor.

first task must be one of representing each device by a model. This model will consist of interconnections of sources and/or passive components which we have defined in this chapter. The extent and complexity of the model will depend on the type of physical devices involved and the conditions under which they are to operate. Considerations involved in choosing an appropriate model to use, under various given conditions, do not form a proper part of network analysis. This is not to say that such considerations and the ability to choose an appropriate model are not important; they are. However, many other things are important in the total education of an engineer, and they certainly cannot all be treated in one book. In this book we will make no attempt to construct a model of a given physical situation before proceeding with the analysis. Our starting point will be a model.

1.4　Power and Energy

The concept of *energy* is one of the most fundamental concepts in physical science. The principle of conservation of energy, which states that energy can neither be created nor destroyed but can be transformed into different forms, is another fundamental postulate on which much of physical science is founded.

The time rate of change of energy is *power p*. From elementary considerations we know that electrical power is related to voltage and current by the expression

Fig. 18.　Reference for power.

$$p(t) = v(t)i(t) \qquad (21)$$

Since voltage and current have references, so must power in order for this expression to be valid. The reference for power is shown in Fig. 18 relative to the references of voltage and current. If either reference is reversed, the reference for power will also reverse.

Let us now turn to the elements in our model and determine their behavior in terms of power and energy. First consider the independent sources; let the branch in Fig. 18 be an independent source. According to Fig. 18, the power entering the source is $p = vi$. But, if this is a voltage source, the voltage will be a given function of time, whereas the current will depend on the network which is connected at the terminals. The energy which enters the source between the time t_1 and t_2 is found by integrating the power.

$$\text{Energy entering} = \int_{t_1}^{t_2} v(t)i(t)\, dt \qquad (22)$$

This energy will be either positive or negative depending on the function $i(t)$, which, in turn, depends upon the network connected across the terminals of the source. A similar statement is true if the source is a current source.

The preceding paragraph seems to indicate that an independent source can generate (or create) energy and can destroy energy. This would be catastrophic, if true. Our interpretation is that the source can transform into nonelectrical energy the electrical energy which it absorbs. Likewise, the energy which it apparently generates is transformed from some other, nonelectrical form.

Let us now consider the passive elements. If the branch shown in Fig. 18 is a resistance, then $v = Ri$ and the energy entering the resistance between time t_1 and t_2 will be

$$\text{Energy entering} = \int_{t_1}^{t_2} Ri^2(t)\, dt \qquad (23)$$

Since $i(t)$ is a real function of t, the integrand is always positive; hence, so is the energy. Thus, the resistance *absorbs* or *dissipates* energy. Again we interpret this as a conversion of energy into a non-electrical form, heat in this case. Note that the negative resistance converter shown in Fig. 16 is a device which continually supplies energy (for $\alpha > 1$); it cannot absorb.

Letting the branch in Fig. 18 be an inductance and a capacitance in turn, we find for the energy

$$\text{Energy entering } L = \int_{t_1}^{t_2} L\frac{di}{dt}i\, dt = \int_{i_1}^{i_2} Li\, di$$

$$= \tfrac{1}{2}L(i_2{}^2 - i_1{}^2) \qquad (24)$$

We have labelled i_1 and i_2 the currents at the times t_1 and t_2, respectively.

Similarly

$$\text{Energy entering } C = \int_{t_1}^{t_2} C \frac{dv}{dt} v \, dt = \int_{v_1}^{v_2} Cv \, dv$$

$$= \tfrac{1}{2}C(v_2{}^2 - v_1{}^2) \tag{25}$$

Thus, the energy entering these elements may be positive or negative over a period of time. We say that these elements *store* energy, the instantaneous values of the energy stored being, respectively,

$$T = \tfrac{1}{2}Li^2(t) \tag{26}$$

$$V = \tfrac{1}{2}Cv^2(t) \tag{27}$$

The functions T and V are called the *energy functions*. They are never negative for any value of time. (The use of the symbol V for the capacitive energy is deplorable, but it is quite standard.) In a later chapter we will use the properties of the energy functions to deduce the behavior of the corresponding networks.

Let us now summarize the results of this chapter. We stated as postulates the laws which express the equilibrium of currents at any node of an electric network and the equilibrium of voltages around all closed loops at every instant of time. These laws are independent of what constitutes a branch. We found that not all the equations resulting from the application of these laws are independent, and we discussed ways of finding the correct number of independent ones in any given network. We next discussed the voltage-current relationships of the elements which go to make up our model of electric networks. The next step in the development is to insert these v-i relationships into Kirchhoff's laws and then attempt a solution of the resulting equations. This will be the subject of the next chapter.

2. LOOP AND NODE SYSTEMS OF EQUATIONS

In the last chapter we found that an application of the two fundamental laws of Kirchhoff leads to two different sets of simultaneous equations. In one of these sets the variables are branch currents, while in the other they are branch voltages. Our ultimate purpose is to be able to solve for all the branch voltages and currents in the network, knowing the values of the network parameters, including the source voltages and currents, and the initial conditions.

2.1 Loop Equations

Consider the Kirchhoff current law equations. We found that these are $N_v - 1$ independent equations in the N_b branch currents. Since there are more unknowns than there are equations, a unique solution of these equations does not exist. If we assign values to $N_b - (N_v - 1)$ of the branch currents (suitably chosen), then all the rest of the currents can be expressed uniquely in terms of these. The number $N_b - (N_v - 1)$ rings a bell; this is precisely the number of independent Kirchhoff voltage law equations. However, these equations are in the branch voltage variables, of which there are again N_b. If we can express these branch voltage variables in terms of $N_b - (N_v - 1)$ current variables, then we will have the same number of unknowns as we have equations and a possible solution will be in view. This is what we plan to do.

We will illustrate the procedure by means of an example. Figure 1 shows a Wheatstone bridge circuit. For this example $N_v = 4$ and $N_b = 6$. Hence, there will be 3 independent KCL equations and 3 independent KVL equations. [The voltage source with R_1 in series is counted as one branch. If we count them as two branches N_b will be 7; but now there will be a node at their junction, thus making $N_v = 5$, leaving $N_b - (N_v - 1)$ unchanged.] The branches have been numbered according to the subscripts on the parameters.

To avoid complicated notation, we will use similar symbols, i and v, with numerical subscripts for both branch variables and loop or node

25

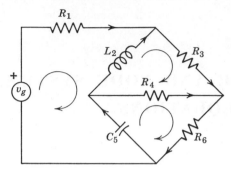

Fig. 1.   Wheatstone bridge.

variables.   When it is necessary to distinguish between them (as it will be, if we need both sets within the same development) we will use i_b and v_b with a second numerical subscript for branch variables.

Suppose we choose a tree consisting, say, of branches 2, 4, and 5; then, branches 1, 3, and 6 will be links.   If we apply Kirchhoff's current law at the nodes, we will find that all the branch currents can be expressed in terms of the link currents i_1, i_3, and i_6.   Thus,

$$i_2 = i_3 - i_1$$

$$i_4 = i_6 - i_3 \qquad (1)$$

$$i_5 = i_6 - i_1$$

In Fig. 1, the three circular arrows indicate the orientations of the loops that we have chosen for writing KVL equations.   They do not carry any implication of current (as yet).   But suppose we think of circulating *loop currents* with references given by the loop orientations. A consideration of the figure shows that these loop currents are identical with the link currents i_1, i_3, and i_6.   All branch currents can be expressed in terms of the loop currents.   The set of equations which relate the branch currents to the loop currents, such as Eqs. (1), is called the *mesh transformation*.

Let us now write KVL equations for the three loops shown in the figure. Assuming that the branch voltage references are at the tail of the branch current references, we will get

$$v_1 - v_2 \qquad\qquad - v_5 \qquad = 0$$

$$v_2 + v_3 - v_4 \qquad\qquad = 0 \qquad (2)$$

$$v_4 + v_5 + v_6 = 0$$

The next step is to invoke the voltage-current relationships of the branches in order to express the branch voltages in terms of the branch currents. Following this, the mesh transformation is used, leaving only the loop currents as unknowns. However, since the mesh transformation is usually obvious in simple examples, these two steps can be performed simultaneously. Thus, Eqs. (2) become

$$i_1 R_1 - v_g - L_2 \frac{d}{dt}(i_3 - i_1) - \frac{1}{C_5} \int_0^t (i_6 - i_1)\, dx - v_5(0) = 0 \quad (a)$$

$$L_2 \frac{d}{dt}(i_3 - i_1) + R_3 i_3 - R_4(i_6 - i_3) = 0 \quad (b) \qquad (3)$$

$$R_4(i_6 - i_3) + \frac{1}{C_5} \int_0^t (i_6 - i_1)\, dx + v_5(0) + R_6 i_6 = 0 \quad (c)$$

Presumably the source voltage v_g and the initial capacitance voltage are known. These can be transposed to the right side of the equations and the rest of the terms can be collected to give

$$i_1 R_1 + L_2 \frac{di_1}{dt} + \frac{1}{C_5} \int_0^t i_1(x)\, dx - L_2 \frac{di_3}{dt} - \frac{1}{C_5} \int_0^t i_6(x)\, dx$$

$$= v_g(t) + v_5(0) \quad (a)$$

$$- L_2 \frac{di_1}{dt} + (R_3 + R_4)i_3 + L_2 \frac{di_3}{dt} - R_4 i_6 = 0 \quad (b) \qquad (4)$$

$$- \frac{1}{C_5} \int_0^t i_1(x)\, dx - R_4 i_3 + (R_4 + R_6)i_6 + \frac{1}{C_5} \int_0^t i_6(x)\, dx$$

$$= -v_5(0) \quad (c)$$

Consider the form of these equations. They are ordinary linear integrodifferential equations in the three unknown loop currents. When the terms are collected in this manner, we say that the equations are in *standard form*. The solution of such equations will occupy a large amount of our time. At the moment, however, let us assume that the solution can be found. Then the three loop currents will become known for all values of t. Since all the branch currents can be expressed in terms of the loop currents, they in turn, will become known. The v-i relationships of the branches will then permit determination of the branch voltages. The analysis of the network will thus be complete.

Let us now go back and examine this sequence of events. Since we have six branch current variables and only three independent KCL equations, some $6 - 3 = 3$ of the branch current variables can be chosen arbitrarily (as far as the KCL equations are concerned) and all the others can be expressed in terms of these three. Within wide limits, it is immaterial which three are chosen in terms of which the remaining ones are expressed. We can perhaps more easily visualize the situation if we think in terms of loop currents instead of branch currents. The question then becomes, how do we choose the loop currents? In the example we worked out, the loops for choosing loop currents were the same as the loops for writing the KVL equations. This is really not necessary; the loops that define the loop currents can be different from the loops used in writing the KVL equations. However, if they are chosen the same, then the standard form of the loop equations will possess certain symmetries (when no dependent sources are present). Hence, it is certainly convenient to choose the loop currents in this manner, and we shall always do so. With the loop currents chosen in this manner, the terms involving loop current i_j in equation k are identical with the terms involving i_k in equation j. We will have more to say about this symmetry later.

The procedure which we have illustrated (and to which we will refer as *loop analysis*) is a general procedure which can be followed for any network. However, two specific situations warrant special attention. These are: (1) the presence of current sources, and (2) the presence of dependent sources in the network. Neither of these introduces any insurmountable difficulties. We will illustrate by means of examples the peculiarities introduced into the loop equations by these situations.

Consider the network shown in Fig. 2a. Since the point we wish to illustrate does not depend on the constituents of the branches, we have

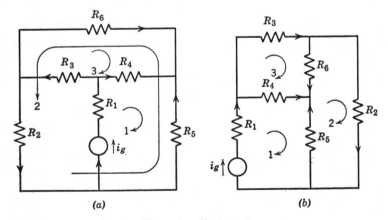

Fig. 2.   Network with current source.

chosen all the branches to be resistances for simplicity. There are again six branches and four nodes, leaving three independent KVL equations. Let us choose the loop currents such that the current of the current source is identical with one of the loop currents. This can always be done in any solvable problem; a redrawing of the diagram as in part (b) helps to visualize this. With the choice of loops shown, the loop currents are identical with branch currents i_1, i_2, and i_3. Let us now write the KVL equations while at the same time we insert the v-i relationships of the branches. As a matter of fact, we can also perform the mesh transformation simultaneously. The result will be

$$R_1 i_1 + R_4(i_1 - i_3) + R_5(i_1 - i_2) + v_g = 0 \quad (a)$$

$$R_5(i_2 - i_1) + R_2 i_2 + R_6(i_2 - i_3) = 0 \quad (b) \qquad (5)$$

$$R_4(i_3 - i_1) + R_6(i_3 - i_2) + R_3 i_3 = 0 \quad (c)$$

Here we have three equations in what might appear to be four unknowns, the three loop currents and the voltage across the current source which we have labelled v_g. However, loop current i_1 is identical with i_g, which is known, thus leaving only three unknowns. However, note that the last two equations do not contain v_g; only i_2 and i_3 are unknown in these equations. Let us rewrite these in standard form. The result will be

$$(R_2 + R_5 + R_6)i_2 - R_6 i_3 = R_5 i_1 \qquad (a)$$

$$\qquad\qquad\qquad\qquad\qquad\qquad\qquad\qquad (6)$$

$$-R_6 i_2 + (R_3 + R_4 + R_6)i_3 = R_4 i_1 \qquad (b)$$

These are two equations in two unknowns, and we can proceed to solve them by methods we will discuss shortly. (Because we chose all the branches to be resistances, we can effect the solution of these equations readily right now.) Once we have the solutions for i_2 and i_3, we can substitute these into the first equation and solve for the voltage across the current source.

Note that if we had not chosen the loops such that the current source appeared in only one loop, then the unknown v_g would have appeared in more than one equation, thus not permitting the simplification that we found. To summarize, we observe that when current sources are present in a network and a loop analysis is carried out, far from encountering difficulties, the solution is simplified by the fact that the number of equations that must be solved simultaneously is reduced by the number of current sources present. After this set of equations is solved, substitution into the remaining equation yields the solution for the unknown v_g.

Let us now consider the modification of loop equations when dependent sources are present. Consider the network shown in Fig. 3. (This is

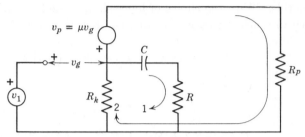

Fig. 3.   Network with dependent source.

the equivalent circuit of a cathode follower with some additional elements in the cathode circuit.) In this network $N_b = 4$, whereas $N_v = 3$, so that there will be two independent KVL equations. Choosing loop currents as indicated by the arrows, we write KVL equations around these loops, mentally substituting the *v-i* relationships of the branches and the mesh transformation. The result will be

$$Ri_1 + \frac{1}{C}\int_0^t i_1(x)\,dx + v_c(0) + R_k(i_1 + i_2) = 0 \quad (a)$$

$$(7)$$

$$R_p i_2 + R_k(i_1 + i_2) + v_p = 0 \quad (b)$$

We must now express the voltage of the dependent source, which is $v_p = \mu v_g$, in terms of the currents i_1 and i_2. From the diagram this expression is

$$v_p = \mu[v_1 + R_k(i_1 + i_2)] \tag{8}$$

Using this expression in Eq. (7) and collecting terms, we get

$$(R + R_k)i_1 + \frac{1}{C}\int_0^t i_1(x)\,dx + R_k i_2 = -v_c(0) \quad (a)$$

$$(9)$$

$$R_k(\mu + 1)i_1 + [R_k(\mu + 1) + R_p]i_2 = -\mu v_1 \quad (b)$$

This is the desired set of equations. Note that these equations do not exhibit the type of symmetry we found when there are no dependent sources.

The presence of dependent sources does not seriously affect our procedure for writing loop equations. There is an additional task of expressing the voltages (or currents) of dependent sources in terms of the loop currents, but this is very easily accomplished.

2.2   Node Equations

Let us return now to a consideration of the Kirchhoff voltage law equations. We found that there are $N_b - (N_v - 1)$ independent equations in the N_b branch variables. If we assign values to a suitable set of $N_b - [N_b - (N_v - 1)] = N_v - 1$ of the variables, the remaining ones can be expressed uniquely in terms of these. We recognize $N_v - 1$ to be the number of independent KCL equations. But these equations themselves involve N_b branch current variables. If it were possible to express these N_b current variables in terms of $N_v - 1$ voltage variables, then there would be the same number of equations as unknowns. This procedure is clearly quite similar to the one we used in arriving at the loop system of equations. In that case we substituted the KCL equations (written as the mesh transformation) and the v-i relationships of the branches into the KVL equations. Now, we shall reverse this pattern and substitute the KVL equations together with the v-i relationships of the branches into the KCL equations. We shall illustrate the procedure with an example.

Consider the network shown in Fig. 4. Counting v_{g1} in series with

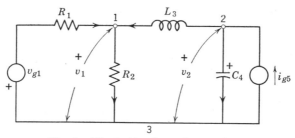

Fig. 4.   Illustration for node equations.

R_1 as one branch, there are five branches and three nodes. Let us choose one of the nodes (any one) as a reference (or datum) node and consider the voltages between each of the other nodes and the reference node, with the voltage reference $+$ away from the datum node. These voltages are the *node* voltages. Any branch voltage can be written as the difference between two node voltages. (One of these two may be the reference node so that the branch voltage becomes identical with the node voltage except possibly for sign.) For the present example, with node 3 chosen as reference, we have

$$\text{Branch voltage } 2 = - \text{ branch voltage } 1 = v_1$$

$$\text{Branch voltage } 4 = - \text{ branch voltage } 5 = v_2 \qquad (10)$$

$$\text{Branch voltage } 3 \qquad\qquad\qquad = v_2 - v_1$$

These expressions, which relate the branch voltages to the node voltages are called the *node transformation*. They are equivalent to the KVL equations, as you can verify.

Let us now write the KCL equations. There will be $3 - 1 = 2$ independent equations. We can choose any two of the three nodes for writing the KCL equations. *The node we omit need not be the node chosen as reference in defining the node voltages.* However, if we make this choice the standard form of the equations will take on a symmetrical form (when there are no dependent sources). Hence, we will always make this choice. The KCL equations for nodes 1 and 2 are

$$-i_1 + i_2 - i_3 \qquad\qquad = 0 \qquad (a)$$
$$\qquad\qquad\qquad\qquad\qquad\qquad\qquad (11)$$
$$i_3 + i_4 - i_5 = 0 \qquad (b)$$

We now insert the v-i relationships of the branches into these expressions to obtain a result involving the branch voltages. Then we use the node transformation given in Eqs. (10) to convert to node voltages. Since the relationships between branch and node voltages are so simple, both of these steps can be performed simultaneously, yielding the result

$$\frac{v_1 + v_{g1}}{R_1} + \frac{v_1}{R_2} - \frac{1}{L_3} \int_0^t (v_2 - v_1)\, dx - i_3(0) = 0 \quad (a)$$
$$\qquad\qquad\qquad\qquad\qquad\qquad\qquad (12)$$
$$\frac{1}{L_3} \int_0^t (v_2 - v_1)\, dx + i_3(0) + C_4 \frac{dv_2}{dt} - i_{g5} = 0 \quad (b)$$

If we now collect terms and transpose known quantities to the right, the result will be

$$\left(\frac{1}{R_1} + \frac{1}{R_2}\right) v_1(t) + \frac{1}{L_3} \int_0^t v_1(x)\, dx - \frac{1}{L_3} \int_0^t v_2(x)\, dx = -\frac{v_{g1}}{R_1} + i_3(0)$$
$$\qquad\qquad\qquad\qquad\qquad\qquad\qquad (a) \qquad (13)$$
$$-\frac{1}{L_3} \int_0^t v_1(x)\, dx + C_4 \frac{dv_2}{dt} + \frac{1}{L_3} \int_0^t v_2(x)\, dx = i_{g5}(t) - i_3(0)$$
$$\qquad\qquad\qquad\qquad\qquad\qquad\qquad (b)$$

These equations, just like the loop equations, are ordinary integro-differential equations. The source currents and voltages, and the initial conditions, are known; the unknowns are the node voltages. Suppose now that we solve these equations for the node voltages. The node transformation will then give us the solutions for the branch voltages. The branch currents will also be known from the $v\text{-}i$ relationships of the branches. The analysis of the network is then complete.

We refer to the procedure we have just discussed as *node analysis*. Like loop analysis, this is also a general procedure which can always be used, even when voltage sources or dependent sources are present. In fact, in our example a voltage source was present.

There is one situation which might lead to difficulty when carrying out a node analysis. Consider a network which includes a transformer. The KCL equations can be written without difficulty. The next step in the analysis is to substitute the $v\text{-}i$ relationships of the branches into the KCL equations. Here we encounter some difficulty. The $v\text{-}i$ relationships for a simple transformer are

$$v_1(t) = L_1 \frac{di_1}{dt} + M \frac{di_2}{dt} \qquad (a)$$

$$v_2(t) = M \frac{di_1}{dt} + L_2 \frac{di_2}{dt} \qquad (b)$$

$$(14)$$

These expressions give the voltages in terms of the currents. In order to use these in the KCL equations we will have to invert them. Suppose we integrate both sides between the limits 0 and t. The result will be

$$\int_0^t v_1(x)\, dx = L_1 i_1(t) - L_1 i_1(0) + M i_2(t) - M i_2(0) \qquad (a)$$

$$\int_0^t v_2(x)\, dx = M i_1(t) - M i_1(0) + L_2 i_2(t) - L_2 i_2(0) \qquad (b)$$

$$(15)$$

Transposing the initial value terms leads to

$$L_1 i_1(t) + M i_2(t) = \int_0^t v_1(x)\, dx + L_1 i_1(0) + M i_2(0) \qquad (a)$$

$$M i_1(t) + L_2 i_2(t) = \int_0^t v_2(x)\, dx + M i_1(0) + L_2 i_2(0) \qquad (b)$$

$$(16)$$

Each of these equations contains both i_1 and i_2. Let us now solve these for i_1 and i_2. Perhaps the easiest way is to multiply the first equation by L_2 and the second by M and subtract. This will eliminate i_2. Similarly, i_1 can be eliminated by multiplying the first equation by M, the second by L_1, and then subtracting the two equations. The results of these operations will be

$$i_1 = \frac{L_2}{L_1 L_2 - M^2} \int_0^t v_1(x)\, dx - \frac{M}{L_1 L_2 - M^2} \int_0^t v_2(x)\, dx + i_1(0) \quad (a)$$

$$(17)$$

$$i_2 = \frac{L_1}{L_1 L_2 - M^2} \int_0^t v_2(x)\, dx - \frac{M}{L_1 L_2 - M^2} \int_0^t v_1(x)\, dx + i_2(0) \quad (b)$$

Clearly, these expressions are valid only for a nonperfect transformer.

Thus, we have succeeded in inverting the v-i relationships of a transformer. With these expressions available, we can proceed on the nodal analysis of a network containing transformers without difficulty. This same approach can be used to invert the v-i relationships of multiwinding transformers, but the expressions will become very unwieldy. In Chapter 4 we will discuss a method based on matrix algebra which will make the expressions look simple. For the present, let us be content with the knowledge that nodal analysis can be carried out even when mutual coupling is present; however it involves a little extra work.

Let us now consolidate our thoughts on the subject of loop and node analyses. We see that both procedures are made up of the same ingredients: Kirchhoff's voltage law equations, Kirchhoff's current law equations, and the voltage-current relationships of the network elements. In loop analysis it is the *current law* which permits us to express, by means of the mesh transformation, all branch currents in terms of certain of them which we identify as loop currents. If we then substitute the v-i relationships into the voltage law equations and use the mesh transformation, the result is a set of $N_b - (N_v - 1)$ integrodifferential equations in the same number of loop current unknowns.

This order is reversed in node analysis. It is the *voltage law* which permits us to express, by means of the node transformation, all the branch voltages in terms of the node voltages. If we then substitute the v-i relationships into the current law equations and use the node transformation, the result is again a set of integrodifferential equations, this time $N_v - 1$ of them, in the same number of node voltage unknowns.

For any given network, whether it contains current or voltage sources, or dependent sources, or transformers, either method of analysis—loop or node—may be used. They are both very general tools. The number of equations obtained might influence the choice, as $N_v - 1$ and $N_b - (N_v - 1)$ may be different. If the objective of the analysis is to obtain complete solutions to all branch voltages and currents, as we assume here, there is very little difference between one method of analysis and another. All of them—loop, node, or any of the other known methods—involve roughly the same amount of work. In the usual practical problem this is not the case. If only the steady state solution is required, the number of equations is a prime consideration. If only the solution to one variable is required, the choice may depend upon whether this is a current or voltage. Presence of mutual inductances or dependent generators may also guide the choice. In some special network geometries a mixture of loop and node equations is more useful than either. (In network analysis, there are a very large number of special cases, and each of them has a "best method of attack." We shall stress the general procedures more in this text and refrain from just compiling "tricks of the trade." We shall mention a few of these special cases in Chapter 4, and a few more as we go along, especially in Chapter 10.)

2.3   Solution by Laplace Transforms

In the preceding sections of this chapter we have seen that in our attempt to find the voltages and currents in an electric network we are led to a set of simultaneous, ordinary, linear, integrodifferential equations with constant coefficients. (Of course, for simple networks this set might reduce to a single equation.) We are now faced with the problem of solving such a set of equations. In this book we will consider only one method of solution—the Laplace transformation method. We assume that you are familiar with the principles of the Laplace transform and of functions of a complex variable.*

The basic procedure of the Laplace transform method of solution is quite simple and straight-forward. The first step involves taking the Laplace transform of the set of integrodifferential equations. In doing this we assume that the solutions of the equations are transformable. This step converts the set of integrodifferential equations, in which the unknowns are time functions (representing currents or voltages), into a set of algebraic equations in which the unknowns are the transforms of voltage or current. This set of equations is then solved for the unknown transforms by algebraic methods. Finally, taking the inverse transform leads to the desired solution of the original integrodifferential equations.

Perhaps we can best illustrate this process by considering a few illustrative examples. For a simple example, consider the network shown in Fig. 5. The capacitance has a voltage $v_C(0) = -V_0$ before the switch

---

* An appendix on this subject has been provided, p. 505, for those who desire a "refresher course" in the theory of functions of a complex variable and Laplace transforms.

is closed at $t = 0$. It is desired to find the current $i(t)$ after the close of the switch.

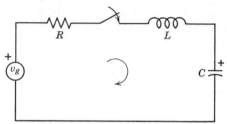

Fig. 5.   Series RLC network.

There is only one loop in this network and all the branch currents can be chosen equal to the loop current $i(t)$. We can write Kirchhoff's voltage law around the single loop, at the same time substituting the voltage-current relationships to obtain

$$L\frac{di}{dt} + Ri(t) + \frac{1}{C}\int_0^t i(x)\,dx + v_C(0) - v_g(t) = 0 \qquad (18)$$

In examining Eq. (18) we see that two types of terms are present. The last two terms, the initial capacitance voltage and the source voltage, are referred to as *driving functions* or *excitation functions*. If we were to write node voltage equations, then the initial inductance current would appear explicitly. This also is an excitation. Any voltage or current which is unknown before a solution is obtained is referred to as a *response function*. In the present case we are mainly interested in the current $i(t)$ and we call it the current response. Thus, the equation contains driving functions and terms which involve the response function.

We now take the Laplace transform of this equation. In this book we shall use a capital letter to designate the Laplace transform of a function which is itself represented by the corresponding lower case symbol. Thus the Laplace transform of a function $f(t)$ is

$$\mathcal{L}\{f(t)\} = \int_0^\infty f(t)\epsilon^{-st}\,dt = F(s) \qquad (19)$$

Since the $\mathcal{L}$-transform operation is distributive, the Laplace transform of the left side of Eq. (18) can be written as the sum of the transforms of each term, *assuming each term is $\mathcal{L}$-transformable*. This is a step which needs justifying, since we do not yet know the solution and so do not know whether it, or its derivative or its integral, are $\mathcal{L}$-transformable. If we proceed under the assumption that this step is justified, and we

obtain a solution for $i(t)$ which satisfies the equation, then this is justification enough.*

Let us examine Eq. (18) in detail, assuming that the driving function
is piecewise continuous and of exponential order. Most of the functions
we deal with, such as sinusoids (truncated or otherwise), exponentials,
step functions, pulses of various shapes, etc., are of this nature. It
follows that the desired solution $i(t)$ must be continuous, for otherwise
Eq. (18) could not be satisfied (at a discontinuity). This statement
applies everywhere except possibly at $t = 0$. Under some conditions,
which we will discuss in Chapter 4, it is possible for the current in an
inductance to be discontinuous across $t = 0$. This fact does not violate
the above statement if we interpret the equation to be valid for $t > 0$.
This is in line with our discussion of the lower limit of the integral in
Eq. (18).

Let us now proceed with the solution. Taking the Laplace transform
of each term in Eq. (18) and transposing known quantities to the right
yields

$$LsI(s) + RI(s) + \frac{1}{sC} I(s) = V_g(s) - \frac{v_C(0)}{s} + Li(0)$$

or, finally, setting $i(0) = 0$ and $v_C(0) = -V_0$,

$$I(s) = \frac{sV_g(s) + V_0}{L\left(s^2 + \frac{R}{L}s + \frac{1}{LC}\right)} \tag{20}$$

This is the Laplace transform of the desired result. Note that the numerator contains terms that involve the excitation functions, including the
initial conditions, while the denominator involves the network parameters.

Since $V_g(s)$ is a $\mathcal{L}$-transform function, it is an analytic function of
the complex variable s. Hence, $I(s)$ is also an analytic function. Its
singularities include the singularities of $V_g(s)$ and the zeros of the
quadratic in the denominator.

The next step in the solution involves finding the inverse transform
of $I(s)$. For this purpose the inversion integral, given by

$$i(t) = \frac{1}{2\pi j} \int_{Br} I(s) \epsilon^{st} \, ds \tag{21}$$

is always available. However, the transform functions whose inverses
we need to evaluate in lumped network analysis are very often rational

---

* The basis of this justification lies in the "uniqueness theorems" for the solutions
of such equations, which can be found in any treatise on differential equations.

functions (the ratio of two polynomials). For such functions, no integration is needed. Application of the residue theorem yields the result that $i(t)$ is simply the sum of residues of $I(s)\epsilon^{st}$ at all its poles, for $t > 0$.

Another approach is to decompose the transform function into a sum of additive terms, each term of which is simple enough that its inverse transform is easily recognized. The inverse transform of the original function is then the sum of the inverse transforms of each additive term. This process involves forming a partial fraction expansion of $I(s)$ (which therefore involves the evaluation of the same residues).

In order to proceed with our illustration, let us insert some numerical values in Eq. (20). Let $V_0 = 1$, $L = 1$, $R = 5$, $C = \frac{1}{6}$, and

$$v_g(t) = \sin t \qquad (a)$$

$$V_g(s) = \mathcal{L}(\sin t) = \frac{1}{s^2 + 1} \qquad (b)$$

(22)

With these values, Eq. (20) becomes

$$I(s) = \frac{\dfrac{s}{s^2 + 1} + 1}{s^2 + 5s + 6} = \frac{s^2 + s + 1}{(s^2 + 1)(s + 2)(s + 3)} \qquad (23)$$

This is a good time for us to illustrate a few practical computational "tricks" that come in handy. We notice that the function $I(s)$ has one pair of complex conjugate poles and two real poles. Now it is better to keep the conjugate poles together, since the response is going to be a real function of t. (Otherwise we would have to recombine the resulting two complex functions in t, after separating them in s—certainly a wasted effort.) Also it is easier to compute the residue at a real pole than to compute the residue at a complex pole (numerically). Keeping these facts in mind, we compute the residues at the real poles first. Since the real poles are both of order one, the computation is very simple.

$$\text{Residue of } I(s) \text{ at } -2 = \lim_{s \to -2} (s + 2)I(s)$$

$$= \frac{s^2 + s + 1}{(s^2 + 1)(s + 3)}\bigg|_{s=-2}$$

$$= \tfrac{3}{5} \qquad (24)$$

Similarly,

$$\text{Residue at } (s = -3) = \frac{s^2 + s + 1}{(s^2 + 1)(s + 2)}\bigg|_{s=-3}$$

$$= -\tfrac{7}{10} \qquad (25)$$

Now instead of finding the residues at $s = \pm j$, we shall merely subtract the principal parts at the real poles.

$$I(s) - \left[\frac{\frac{3}{5}}{s+2} + \frac{-\frac{7}{10}}{s+3}\right] = \frac{s^2+s+1}{(s^2+1)(s+2)(s+3)} - \frac{\frac{3}{5}}{s+2} + \frac{\frac{7}{10}}{s+3}$$

$$= \frac{1}{10}\frac{s^3+6s^2+11s+6}{(s^2+1)(s+2)(s+3)} \qquad (26)$$

At first the right side of this expression looks worse than what we started with. However we know that the numerator must be divisible by $(s+2)(s+3)$, because we have subtracted the principal parts at these poles; the poles are no longer present. So we divide the numerator by $(s+2)(s+3)$, getting finally:

$$I(s) - \left[\frac{\frac{3}{5}}{s+2} + \frac{-\frac{7}{10}}{s+3}\right] = \frac{1}{10}\frac{s+1}{s^2+1} \qquad (27)$$

Remembering the transforms of sine and cosine functions, we separate the right side into two terms. After transposing, the expression for $I(s)$ becomes finally

$$I(s) = \frac{1}{10}\left[\frac{s}{s^2+1} + \frac{1}{s^2+1} + \frac{6}{s+2} - \frac{7}{s+3}\right] \qquad (28)$$

Equation (28) is not a partial fraction expansion but is a form that is convenient for inversion. We can recognize each term easily and write down the inverse transform as:

$$i(t) = \tfrac{1}{10}[\cos t + \sin t + 6\epsilon^{-2t} - 7\epsilon^{-3t}] \qquad (29)$$

You should verify that this expression satisfies the integrodifferential Eq. (18) and the given initial value for the inductance current. (The capacitance voltage is satisfied automatically. Why?)

We could have obtained the partial fraction expansion of $I(s)$ easily from Eq. (27) by computing the complex residues. This expansion is

$$I(s) = \frac{1}{20}\left\{\frac{1-j}{s-j} + \frac{1+j}{s+j} + \frac{12}{s+2} - \frac{14}{s+3}\right\} \qquad (30)$$

Let us here digress temporarily to discuss a point which the numerical values in this problem force upon our attention. The given element values do not correspond to values which are normally available in physical devices. But with these element values the expression for $I(s)$ in Eq. (23) is pleasantly free of large numbers, involving powers of 10. The poles and zeros of $I(s)$ are conveniently located close to the origin in the s-plane. This circumstance leads to computational convenience and is certainly desirable.

It is always possible to reduce the tediousness of computation with large numbers by a suitable scale change in the s-plane. Consider the impedance of an inductance sL. For given values of L and s, this impedance will have a certain value. Suppose we multiply L by a real positive number ω_0 and we simultaneously divide s by the same number. The impedance will remain unchanged. Similarly, the impedance of a capacitance $1/sC$ will remain unchanged if we multiply C by ω_0, while at the same time dividing s by ω_0. What this process does is to change the scale in the s-plane, the frequency scale. We refer to it as a *frequency normalization*.

Another useful normalizing device involves amplitude. Note that if all resistance, inductance, and reciprocal capacitance values in a network are divided by a constant R_0, then the current in each branch of the network in response to a voltage excitation will be multiplied by that same constant. But this is simply a change in scale. Such a procedure is referred to as *impedance normalization*.

Numerical computation can be considerably simplified by use of frequency and impedance normalization. Let us designate normalized values of R, L, and C with a subscript n. Then, if frequency is normalized with respect to ω_0 and impedance is normalized with respect to R_0, the normalized element values will be given by .

$$R_n = \frac{R}{R_0}$$

$$L_n = \frac{\omega_0 L}{R_0}$$

$$C_n = R_0 \omega_0 C$$

These expressions show that the normalized element values are dimensionless. When, in the numerical illustrative examples we give values such as $C = 2$, we do not mean 2 farads; we mean a normalized, dimensionless value of 2. Now let us return to our mainstream of thought.

The partial fraction expansion of $I(s)$ puts into evidence all the poles of $I(s)$. Some of these poles (the first two terms in Eq. (30)) are contributed by the driving function, while the remainder are contributed by the network. In the inverse transform we find terms that resemble the driving function and other terms which are exponentials. There is an abundance of terminology relating to these terms which has been accumulated from the study of differential equations in mathematics, from the study of vibrations in mechanics, and from the study of a-c circuit theory, so that today we have a number of names to choose from. These are

Forced response—natural or free response

Particular integral—complementary function

Steady state—transient

Perhaps we are most familiar with the terms *steady state* and *transient*. When the driving function is a sinusoid, as in our example, there will be a sinusoidal term in the response which goes on for all time. In our example the other terms present die out with time; they are ephemeral, transient. Thus, eventually the sinusoidal term will dominate. This leads to the concept of steady state. If the driving function is not a sinusoid, but is still periodic, we can extend the idea of steady-state response to this case as well. However, if the driving function is not periodic the concept of steady-state loses its significance. Nevertheless, the poles of the transform of the driving function contribute terms to the partial fraction expansion of the response transform and so the response will contain terms due to these poles. These terms constitute the *forced response*. In form they resemble the driving function. The remaining terms represent the *natural* response. They will be present in the solution (with different coefficients) no matter what the driving function is; even if there is no driving function except initial capacitance voltages or initial inductance currents. This leads to the name natural or free response. The exponents in the natural response are called the *natural modes* (or *normal* nodes).

In the illustrative example the exponents in the natural response, the natural modes, are negative real. If there were positive exponents, or complex ones with positive real part, then the natural response would increase indefinitely with time instead of dying out. A network with such a behavior is said to be *unstable*. We define a *stable* network as *one whose natural modes lie in the closed left half s-plane*, that is, in the left half plane or on the j-axis.* Actually, some people prefer to exclude networks with j-axis natural modes from the class of stable networks. This is simply a matter of preference.

Let us now clearly define the various classes of responses. The complete response of a network consists of two parts; the forced response and the natural, or free, response. The forced response consists of all those terms which are contributed by poles of the driving functions, whereas the free response consists of all the terms which are contributed

---

* This definition is applicable to all lumped, linear, time-invariant systems.

by the natural modes [the zeros of $\Delta(s)$]. *In case the driving functions are periodic, the forced response is also called the steady-state. If there are no j-axis natural modes, then the free response is also called the transient.* In this book we shall not use the words particular integral or complementary function, since they do not convey the meanings which are important to us.

Let us now return to the illustrative example and assume that the driving function is changed to

$$v_g(t) = \epsilon^{-2t} \qquad (a)$$

$$V_g(s) = \frac{1}{s+2} \qquad (b)$$

(31)

everything else remaining the same. Then, instead of Eq. (23), we will get

$$I(s) = \frac{\dfrac{s}{s+2} + 1}{s^2 + 5s + 6} = \frac{2(s+1)}{(s+2)^2(s+3)} \qquad (32)$$

We now have a pole of order two at $s = -2$, and a simple pole at $s = -3$. Again we can increase computational efficiency by separating the simple pole at $s = -3$ first. By inspection the residue at $s = -3$ is -4. The remainder is:

$$I(s) + \frac{4}{s+3} = \frac{4s^2 + 18s + 18}{(s+2)^2(s+3)} = \frac{4s+6}{(s+2)^2} \qquad (33)$$

The last step follows by cancelling $(s+3)$. The standard procedure now is to write

$$\frac{4s+6}{(s+2)^2} = \frac{A}{(s+2)^2} + \frac{B}{s+2} \qquad (34)$$

and compute A and B as

$$A = \frac{(s+2)^2(4s+6)}{(s+2)^2}\bigg|_{s=-2} \qquad (a)$$

$$B = \frac{d}{ds}\left[(s+2)^2\frac{4s+6}{(s+2)^2}\right]\bigg|_{s=-2} \qquad (b)$$

(35)

We can, if we like, repeat our procedure of subtracting the term that is easier computed, namely $A/(s+2)^2$. However in this simple case the standard procedure is easier. A and B are found by inspection from Eq. (35) to be

$$A = -2 \qquad B = 4 \qquad (36)$$

Therefore, the partial fraction expansion of $I(s)$ is finally

$$I(s) = 2\left(\frac{2}{s+2} - \frac{1}{(s+2)^2} - \frac{2}{s+3}\right) \qquad (37)$$

In this case we see that the transform of the driving function has a pole at one of the natural modes of the network. The response transform, therefore, has a double pole. Taking the inverse transform of $I(s)$, we get

$$i(t) = \epsilon^{-2t}(4 - 2t) - 4\epsilon^{-3t} \qquad (38)$$

In this case it is not quite so simple to distinguish between the forced response and the natural, because the driving function has a pole at one of the natural modes of the network. Referring to specific terms in this solution as "transient" also does not make sense, since the entire response dies out with time.

Let us now consider a slightly more complicated example. Figure 6

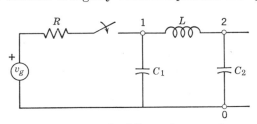

Fig. 6.   Network of illustrative example.

shows a common interstage, the series-peaked circuit. The network is initially relaxed, which means that prior to the closing of the switch at $t = 0$ there is no current in the inductance and no voltages on the capacitances. It is desired to find the voltage across capacitance C_2 after the closing of the switch. By counting the branches and nodes we see that there are two independent KVL equations and the same number of KCL equations. Since the desired response is a voltage it would be slightly more convenient to use a node analysis. Let us choose the node numbered 0 as a reference and write KCL equations at the other two nodes. We can mentally insert the v-i relationships of the branches, while at the same time expressing the branch voltages in terms of the node voltages. The result will be

$$\frac{v_1(t) - v_g(t)}{R} + C_1\frac{dv_1}{dt} + \frac{1}{L}\int_0^t (v_1 - v_2)\, dx = 0 \quad (a)$$

$$\frac{1}{L}\int_0^t (v_2 - v_1)\, dx + C_2\frac{dv_2}{dt} = 0 \quad (b)$$

$$(39)$$

Since the initial inductance current is zero, this term has not been written. In standard form these equations are

$$\frac{v_1(t)}{R_1} + C_1 \frac{dv_1}{dt} + \frac{1}{L} \int_0^t v_1(x)\, dx - \frac{1}{L} \int_0^t v_2(x)\, dx = \frac{v_g(t)}{R} \quad (a)$$

$$-\frac{1}{L} \int_0^t v_1(x)\, dx + \frac{1}{L} \int_0^t v_2(x)\, dx + C_2 \frac{dv_2}{dt} = 0 \quad (b)$$

(40)

The next step is to take the $\mathcal{L}$-transform of these equations. This leads to

$$\left(C_1 s + \frac{1}{R_1} + \frac{1}{Ls} \right) V_1(s) - \frac{1}{Ls} V_2(s) = \frac{V_g(s)}{R} \quad (a)$$

$$-\frac{1}{Ls} V_1(s) + \left(C_2 s + \frac{1}{Ls} \right) V_2(s) = 0 \quad (b)$$

(41)

Again, we did not write the initial values of v_1 and v_2 since they are zero. These equations are a set of simultaneous algebraic equations. To solve for $V_2(s)$ in this simple case, we can solve the second equation for $V_1(s)$ and substitute into the first. We can also solve for $V_2(s)$ by Cramer's rule in terms of determinants. Let $\Delta(s)$ be the determinant of this set of equations. Then, the solution for $V_2(s)$ is

$$V_2(s) = \frac{1}{\Delta(s)} \frac{V_g(s)}{RLs} \quad (42)$$

where

$$\Delta(s) = \begin{vmatrix} C_1 s + \dfrac{1}{R} + \dfrac{1}{Ls} & -\dfrac{1}{Ls} \\[2mm] -\dfrac{1}{Ls} & C_2 s + \dfrac{1}{Ls} \end{vmatrix}$$

$$= \frac{C_1 C_2}{s} \left(s^3 + \frac{1}{C_1 R} s^2 + \frac{C_1 + C_2}{C_1 C_2 L} s + \frac{1}{RLC_1 C_2} \right) \quad (43)$$

For purposes of illustration let us take

$$v_g(t) = \epsilon^{-2t} \quad (a)$$

$$V_g(s) = \frac{1}{s+2} \quad (b)$$

(44)

and $C_1 = 1$, $C_2 = 5$, $R = \frac{1}{3}$, $L = \frac{3}{10}$. With these values, $\Delta(s)$ becomes

$$\Delta(s) = \frac{5}{s}(s^3 + 3s^2 + 4s + 2) = \frac{5}{s}(s+1)(s^2 + 2s + 2) \quad (45)$$

Finally, $V_2(s)$ becomes

$$V_2(s) = \frac{2}{(s+2)(s+1)(s^2+2s+2)} \tag{46}$$

It is evident that the singularities of $V_2(s)$ include the singularity of the driving function and the zeros of $\Delta(s)$. The equation $\Delta(s) = 0$ is called the *characteristic equation* and its zeros are the natural modes.

In order to proceed we again expand the response transform in partial fractions. The result will be

$$V_2(s) = \frac{2}{s+1} - \frac{\frac{1}{2}(1-j)}{s+1-j} - \frac{\frac{1}{2}(1+j)}{s+1+j} - \frac{1}{s+2}$$

$$= \frac{2}{s+1} - \frac{s+2}{s^2+2s+2} - \frac{1}{s+2} \tag{47}$$

In the second line the two terms contributed by the complex pair of poles are combined into a single term.

The final step requires finding the inverse transform of $V_2(s)$. From the first line of Eq. (47) it is apparent that the desired result will be a sum of exponential functions. However, some of the exponents, as well as the coefficients, will be complex. These complex exponentials can be combined into real terms. The same result is more easily obtained from the second line of Eq. (47) by writing the term involving the complex poles as

$$\frac{s+2}{s^2+2s+2} = \frac{s+1}{(s+1)^2+1} + \frac{1}{(s+1)^2+1} \tag{48}$$

The final result is

$$v_2(t) = 2\epsilon^{-t} - \epsilon^{-t}(\cos t + \sin t) - \epsilon^{-2t} \tag{49}$$

All the terms but the last in this result constitute the natural response, since they are the contributions of the zeros of $\Delta(s)$. The last term is the forced response. The terms steady state and transient do not convey any real significance in this case.

2.4 Summary

Let us now summarize the discussion of this chapter. We have seen that a complete solution for all the branch voltages and currents can be obtained by the simultaneous solution of all the equations resulting from an application of Kirchhoff's voltage law, Kirchhoff's current law, and the branch voltage–current relationships. However, it is not neces-

sary to do this.   Two general methods of analysis can always be used:
the loop system and the node system.

In the first of these methods, the branch currents are expressed in
terms of loop currents.   These expressions are inserted into the branch
v-i relationships which, in turn, are inserted into the KVL equations.
In the node system, the branch voltages are expressed in terms of the
node voltages.   These expressions are inserted into the branch v-i
relationships which, in turn, are inserted into the KCL equations.

Each of these methods of analysis leads to an independent set of
ordinary linear integrodifferential equations with constant coefficients;
$N_b - (N_v - 1)$ equations in loop analysis, $N_v - 1$ in node analysis.
These equations are solved by the method of Laplace transforms.

In this chapter we illustrated the Laplace transform method of solution by means of numerical examples.   We did not attempt to formulate
the technique in a general way but shall do so after you have become
familiar with the solution of network equations in relatively simple cases
and after we have discussed in the next chapter a procedure which will
considerably simplify the notation.

PROBLEMS

2.1 Write the loop and node systems of equations for the networks of Fig.
P2.1.   (Include initial conditions and insert any references you need.)

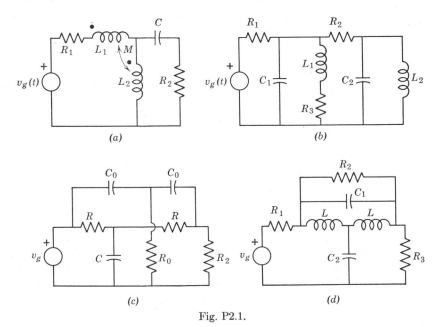

Fig. P2.1.

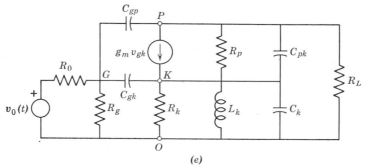

(e)

Fig. P2.1 (*continued*).

2.2 In Fig. P2.2 the switch has been closed for a long time when it is opened at $t = 0$. The source voltage is $v_g(t) = V_0$. Find the voltage across the switch under the condition $RC = k^2L/R$, with

(a) $k^2 = 1$
(b) $k^2 = \frac{25}{16}$
(c) $k^2 = \frac{16}{25}$

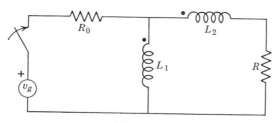

Fig. P2.2.

2.3 In Fig. P2.3 the switch is closed at $t = 0$. Find the voltage across resistance R if

(a) $v_g(t) = 1$
(b) $v_g(t) = \sin 2t$

Take $L_1 = 1$, $L_2 = 5$, $M = 2$, $R = 3$, $R_0 = 2$.

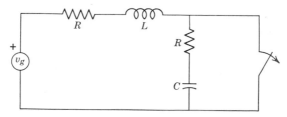

Fig. P2.3.

2.4 The outer loop in Fig. P2.4 has been closed for a long time when at $t = 0$ the switch is closed. Find the voltage $v(t)$ after the closing of the switch. Take $L = 1$, $R = 1$, $R_0 = \frac{1}{2}$, $C = \frac{1}{4}$, $v_g(t) = 2 \sin 2t$.

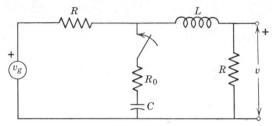

Fig. P2.4.

2.5 In the network of Fig. P2.5 $R_1 = 1$, $R_2 = 10$, $C_1 = C_3 = 1$, $C_2 = 20$.

For $i_g = \begin{cases} \cos t, & t > 0 \\ 0, & t < 0 \end{cases}$

find the current in R_2 and the voltage across C_2.

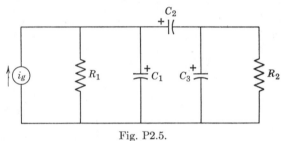

Fig. P2.5.

2.6 (Read this problem carefully.) In the network of Fig. P2.6 choose the "windows" as the closed loops for writing KVL equations. Obtain loop equations: (*a*) by choosing the same loops to define loop currents; (*b*) by choosing one "window" and the outside loop to define loop currents.

Note the symmetry, or lack of it in the resulting equations.

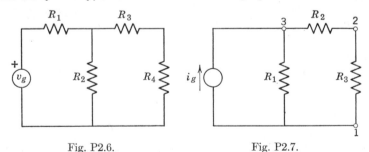

Fig. P2.6.   Fig. P2.7.

2.7 (Read this problem carefully.) In the network of Fig. P2.7 write the KCL equations for all nodes but node 1. Now obtain node equations by: (*a*) choosing node 1 as a datum node; (*b*) choosing node 2 as a datum node.

Note the symmetry or lack of it in the resulting equations.

2.8 In the network of Fig. P2.8

$$R_1 = 1\ \Omega \qquad L_3 = 1\ \text{mh}$$
$$R_2 = 4\ \Omega \qquad L_4 = 4\ \text{mh}$$

Coupling coefficient $k = 1/\sqrt{2}$; all currents are zero for $t < 0$.

(a) With $v_g = 1,\ t > 0$
$\qquad = 0,\ t < 0$, find $i_{b2}(t)$.

(b) Repeat with $v_g = \sin 10t,\ t \geq 0$
$\qquad\qquad = 0,\qquad t < 0$

(c) Repeat part (a) with everything unchanged except for k which is now $k = 1$.

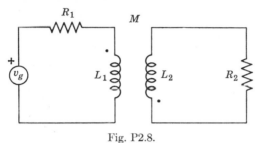

Fig. P2.8.

2.9 In the network of Fig. P2.9 the initial capacitance voltages are zero.

With $v_g = 1,\ t \geq 0$
$\qquad = 0,\ t < 0$

Find the branch current in the $3R$ resistance.

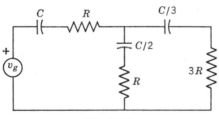

Fig. P2.9.

2.10 In the network of Fig. P2.10 the initial inductance currents are zero.

$$R_1 = 100 \qquad\qquad\qquad L_1 = 1$$
$$R_2 = 200 = R_3 \qquad\quad L_2 = 2$$
$$v_g = 100,\quad t \geq 0$$
$$\quad = 0\ ,\quad t < 0$$

Find the branch currents in R_1 and R_3.

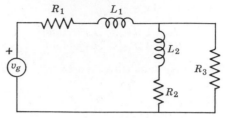

Fig. P2.10.

2.11 Repeat Problem 2.10 when the source is placed in the second loop as shown in Fig. P2.11. Everything else is the same.

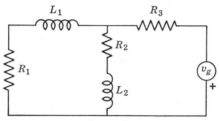

Fig. P2.11.

2.12 The response of an audio amplifier to an input "step" is very important, as hi-fi enthusiasts know. The network of Fig. P2.12 is an audio stage. Typical values for the parameters are:

$R_k = 1000$ ohms $R_L = 500,000$ ohms
$C_k = 10$ microfarads $C_c = 0.1$ microfarad
$R_p = 10,000$ ohms $R_g = 1$ megohm
$$\mu = 20$$

The input is a unit step; i.e.,

$$v_1(t) = 0, \quad t < 0$$
$$v_1(t) = 1, \quad t \geq 0$$

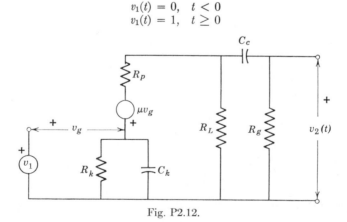

Fig. P2.12.

Find the output voltage $v_2(t)$ for $t > 0$, assuming zero initial conditions. Sketch the input and output voltages for the first 0.02 second. Remove C_K from the network. Again find $v_2(t)$ with everything else unchanged. Plot $v_2(t)$ for $0 < t < 0.02$, on the same sheet as the first two curves. (Normalize each curve with respect to the steady state value.)

2.13 As compared with the RC interstages of Problem 2.12, the transformer-coupled stages have relatively poor transient responses. To illustrate this, compute the output voltage $v_2(t)$ of the network shown in Fig. P2.13 (which is a simplified output stage) with the same input step. Plot $v_2(t)$ for $0 < t < 0.02$ sec. Compare with Problem 2.12. (Normalization is again advised.) All initial values are zero.

$$L_1 = 10 \text{ henries} \qquad L_2 = 1 \text{ henry} \qquad M = 3 \text{ henries}$$
$$R_2 = 100 \text{ ohms} \qquad R_p = 10{,}000 \text{ ohms} \qquad R_k = 1000 \text{ ohms}$$

$$\mu = 20$$

$$v_1(t) = 0, \quad t < 0$$
$$v_1(t) = 1, \quad t \geq 0$$

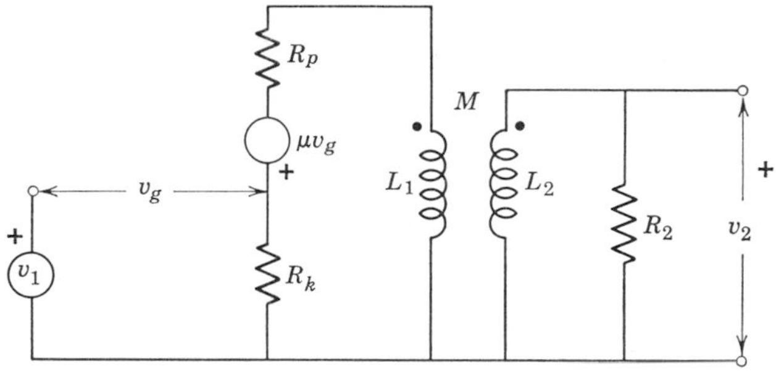

Fig. P2.13.

2.14 Repeat Problem 2.13 with 0.00001 microfarad connected across the primary and sketch $v_2(t)$ for $0 < t < 0.0002$ sec. The result you see is the "singing" in the loudspeaker when percussion instruments (drums for instance) are played. (The capacitance represents the distributed capacitance in the transformer primary.)

2.15 (Transient response of the simple tuned circuit.) In Fig. P2.15

$$v_1(t) = 1, \quad t > 0 \qquad R_1 = 1000$$
$$v_1(t) = 0, \quad t < 0$$

keeping $\omega_0{}^2 = 1/LC$ and $\zeta = (R/2)\sqrt{C/L}$ as parameters, compute $v_2(t)$. Assume all initial conditions to be zero. Sketch three typical curves for $v_2(t)$ one for each of the three cases $\omega_0{}^2 \gtrless R^2/4L^2$. For one fixed value, $\omega_0 = 10$ and $\zeta = 0.1$, compute the time taken for the response to go from 10 per cent to 90 per cent of its steady-state value (the *rise time*) and the maximum value reached by the response in per cent above the steady-state value (the *overshoot*).

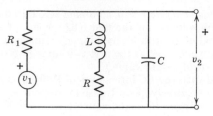

Fig. P2.15.

2.16 In Problem 2.15, plot the location of the poles and zeros of $V_2(s)$ in the complex plane. Sketch the locus of the poles of $V_2(s)$ as R varies from 0 to ∞. Interpret the three ranges for R as used in the first part of Problem 2.15. Interpret ζ and ω_0 in the complex plane for the case $\omega_0^2 > R^2/4L^2$.

2.17 Figure P2.17 illustrates one type of automobile ignition system. The contact K is cam operated when the engine turns over, opening and closing the gap. S denotes the spark gap in the spark plug. (The distributor is not shown.) Suppose the system is in steady state when the contact K opens. Write the integrodifferential equations that hold before the spark occurs together with the initial conditions (assuming continuity for inductance currents and capacitance voltages). Solve for $v_s(t)$ and sketch the form of $v_s(t)$ for $0 \le t < 0.1$ sec.

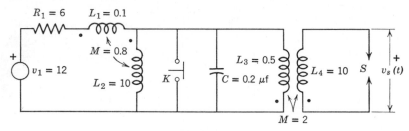

Fig. P2.17.

2.18 The network of Fig. P2.18 is in steady state when switch S opens. Find the voltage $v_0(t)$ across the switch after the switch opens.

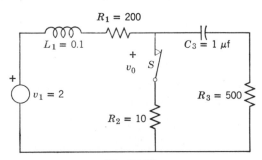

Fig. P2.18.

2.19 The network of Fig. P2.19 is the power supply filter of a cheap broadcast receiver. The input voltage $v_1(t)$ is a half rectified sine wave (rectifier output).

$$v_1(t) = 200 \sin 400t \qquad 0 \le t < \frac{\pi}{200}$$

$$= 0 \qquad \frac{\pi}{200} \le t < \frac{2\pi}{200}$$

$$v_1\left(t + \frac{2\pi}{200}\right) = v_1(t).$$

R_L represents the load (consisting of all the vacuum tubes). Assuming all initial conditions to be zero, find the voltage across R_L and sketch it for the first period.

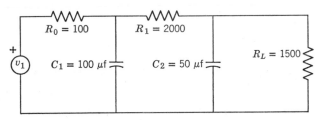

Fig. P2.19.

2.20 In the network of Fig. P2.20, the input voltage is a rectangular pulse of one volt and one second duration. That is

$$v_g(t) = \begin{cases} 0 & t < 0 \\ 1 & 0 \le t < 1 \\ 0 & t > 1 \end{cases}$$

Find $v_C(t)$ if the initial voltage on the capacitance is (i) 0, (ii) 1 volt.

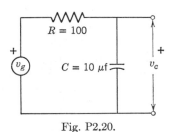

Fig. P2.20.

3 · MATRIX ALGEBRA
AND ELEMENTARY TOPOLOGY

In network analysis, we have to deal with systems of linear (algebraic or differential) equations. Matrix notation is a very convenient method of writing such equations. And, as with every convenient notation, it incidentally gives us new points of view and a better understanding. In this respect we might compare it with vector analysis or with Laplace transformation. It is certainly possible to study electromagnetic field theory without ever writing down a vector equation. However, if this is done Maxwell's equations will occupy a whole page and we cannot really "see" what they mean. It is only when we learn to think of certain field quantities as single vectors that we get any real intuition or "physical feel" for electromagnetic fields. Similarly, it is possible to treat the subject of transient analysis of networks on the basis of classical theory of differential equations. However, the real intuition about the behavior of lumped linear networks comes only when we consider Laplace transforms, the classical theory appearing artificial by comparison. Matrix algebra serves a similar purpose with regard to systems of linear equations. It unifies a number of concepts, especially those that are common to linear algebraic equations and linear differential equations. Just as one learns to think of a vector with three components as one "entity," one can learn to think of a system of equations as one matrix equation. Much of the value of the matrix notation is a consequence of this particular point of view.

It is on these grounds that we shall justify our adventure into this new branch of mathematics. For matrix algebra does not make it any *easier* for us to solve numerical problems. We still have to do the same amount of work as always. But we can "see" what we are doing and understand why we are doing it.

Since it is not our purpose to write a treatise on matrix algebra, many of the proofs of theorems shall be omitted. Nor shall any comprehensive coverage of matrix theory be attempted. Several excellent detailed treatments of the subject exist.*

3.1 Definitions

A matrix is a rectangular array of quantities. The quantities involved may be real or complex numbers, functions, derivative operators etc. In defining the operations of matrix algebra we will assume that the entries obey an algebra similar to the algebra of real numbers. (In the language of the mathematician, the entries are chosen from a "field.") For example the arrays

$$\begin{bmatrix} 1 & 0 \\ 0 & -1 \\ 4 & 7 \end{bmatrix}, \begin{bmatrix} \dfrac{s}{s+2} & 2s \\ 2s & 3s^2 \end{bmatrix}, [4+3j \quad 3 \quad 5j]$$

are matrices. It is important to note that the whole rectangular array is *a matrix*. It is one entity. We place square brackets around the array to indicate this fact. There are also other notations in common use for a matrix. Two of these are shown below.

$$\begin{pmatrix} as+b & cs \\ cs & ds+e \end{pmatrix}, \begin{Vmatrix} \dfrac{s^2}{s^2+1} & \dfrac{2s}{s+2} \\ s+\dfrac{1}{s} & 2s \end{Vmatrix}$$

We should be very careful to distinguish between matrices and determinants. A determinant is one single number. A matrix is a whole array of numbers.

The horizontal lines of a matrix are called *rows* and the vertical lines *columns*. The *order* of a matrix is given as (m,n) where m is the number of rows and n is the number of columns. The order may also be written as $(m \times n)$, read "m by n." Since we wish to consider a matrix as a single entity, we use a single symbol like A, B, etc., for a matrix. (In this text bold face letters will be used to denote matrices.) The entries of a matrix are denoted by small letters a, b, c, etc. We specify the position of an entry in a matrix by an ordered pair of subscripts. Thus in the matrix A, the element a_{23} is in the second row, third column. When we wish to talk about the elements of a matrix in general terms, as we would in definitions, proofs, etc., we use the notation

$$A = [a_{ij}]_{m,n} \tag{1}$$

* Perlis, S., *Theory of Matrices*, Addison-Wesley Publishing Co., Boston, 1955. Hohn, F. E., *Elementary Matrix Algebra*, Macmillan Co., New York, 1958.

This notation means the following. A is a matrix of order (m,n). The entries are a_{11}, a_{12}, etc. In other words, equation (1) means the same thing as

$$A = \begin{bmatrix} a_{11} & a_{12} & a_{13} \cdots a_{1n} \\ a_{21} & a_{22} & a_{23} \cdots a_{2n} \\ \cdot & \cdot & \cdot \cdot \cdot \cdot \cdot \cdot \cdot \cdot \cdot \\ a_{m1} & a_{m2} & a_{m3} \cdots a_{mn} \end{bmatrix} \tag{2}$$

The symbol a_{ij} is called the "typical element" of the matrix A since the subscripts i and j may stand for any position in the matrix. We are now ready for a few of the matrix operations.

Two matrices $A = [a_{ij}]$ and $B = [b_{ij}]$ are called equal if they are of the same order and if the entries of the two matrices are identical. That is,

$$a_{ij} = b_{ij} \qquad \text{all } i, j$$

We should utter a word of warning here. Matrices obtained by appending rows or columns of zeros to a matrix A are not equal to A. They are different matrices. For example

$$\begin{bmatrix} 1 & 1 \\ 2 & 0 \end{bmatrix} \neq \begin{bmatrix} 1 & 1 & 0 \\ 2 & 0 & 0 \end{bmatrix} \tag{3}$$

In order to distinguish matrices from ordinary numbers, we call the latter *scalars*.

The next operation that we shall define is the multiplication of a matrix by a scalar. If α is a scalar and $A = [a_{ij}]$ is a matrix,

$$\alpha A = A\alpha = [(\alpha a_{ij})] \tag{4}$$

That is, to multiply a matrix by a scalar we multiply each element of the matrix by the scalar. The rule is, thus, very different from the corresponding rule for determinants.

The matrix obtained by multiplying a matrix A by the scalar (-1) is denoted as $-A$. We will presently see that this notation is consistent with our concept of a negative.

To add two matrices we add corresponding entries. Thus, addition is defined only for matrices of the same order. Formally, if

$$A = [a_{ij}]_{m,n} \quad \text{and} \quad B = [b_{ij}]_{m,n} \tag{5}$$

then

$$A + B = [(a_{ij} + b_{ij})] \tag{6}$$

Obviously

$$A + B = B + A \tag{7}$$

and

$$A + (B + C) = (A + B) + C \qquad (8)$$

from the corresponding properties of the entries. Subtraction is immediately defined as

$$A - B = A + (-B) \qquad (9)$$

Now we see that

$$A - A = [(a_{ij} - a_{ij})] = [0] \qquad (10)$$

The matrix [0] which has 0 for each entry, is called the *zero matrix*. For each order we have a zero matrix. However it is usual to let the symbol **0** itself stand for all zero matrices. There will normally be no confusion introduced thereby. The zero matrix has the familiar property of zero, namely

$$0 + A = A + 0 = A \qquad \text{all } A \qquad (11)$$

The next operation of interest is multiplication of two matrices. This operation is somewhat more complicated than the ones introduced so far.

If

$$A = [a_{ij}]_{m,n} \quad \text{and} \quad B = [b_{ij}]_{n,p}$$

then

$$AB = C = [c_{ij}]_{m,p} \qquad (12)$$

where the entries are given by

$$c_{ij} = \sum_{k=1}^{n} a_{ik} b_{kj} \qquad (13)$$

Thus the element in the (i,j) position of the product is obtained by multiplying the corresponding elements of the ith row of the first matrix and the jth column of the second matrix and adding the products obtained. Thus, multiplication is defined only when the number of columns in the first matrix is equal to the number of rows in the second matrix.

Example:

$$\begin{bmatrix} a_{11} & a_{12} & a_{13} \\ a_{21} & a_{22} & a_{23} \end{bmatrix} \begin{bmatrix} b_{11} & b_{12} & b_{13} \\ b_{21} & b_{22} & b_{23} \\ b_{31} & b_{32} & b_{33} \end{bmatrix} =$$

$$\begin{bmatrix} (a_{11}b_{11} + a_{12}b_{21} + a_{13}b_{31}) & (a_{11}b_{12} + a_{12}b_{22} + a_{13}b_{32}) & (a_{11}b_{13} + a_{12}b_{23} + a_{13}b_{33}) \\ (a_{21}b_{11} + a_{22}b_{21} + a_{23}b_{31}) & (a_{21}b_{12} + a_{22}b_{22} + a_{23}b_{32}) & (a_{21}b_{13} + a_{22}b_{23} + a_{23}b_{33}) \end{bmatrix}$$

$$(14)$$

When the product AB is defined, i.e., when the number of columns in A is equal to the number of rows in B, we say that the product AB

is *conformable*. The product has the same number of rows as the first matrix and the same number of columns as the last matrix. Immediately we see that AB may be a conformable product while BA is not, as in the example of Eq. (14). But that is not all. Both AB and BA may be defined without being equal. For example, let

$$A = \begin{bmatrix} 1 & -1 \\ 1 & 0 \end{bmatrix}$$

and

$$B = \begin{bmatrix} 1 & 0 \\ 1 & 1 \end{bmatrix}$$

Then

$$AB = \begin{bmatrix} 0 & -1 \\ 1 & 0 \end{bmatrix} \tag{15}$$

and

$$BA = \begin{bmatrix} 1 & -1 \\ 2 & -1 \end{bmatrix} \tag{16}$$

It is clear that

$$AB \neq BA \tag{17}$$

so that matrix multiplication is not *commutative* as a general rule. Hence, when referring to the product of A and B we must specify how they are to be multiplied. In the product AB, A is *postmultiplied* by B and B is *premultiplied* by A. In special cases, of course, a matrix product may be commutative.

In contrast with the noncommutative property, matrix multiplication is *associative* and *distributive* over addition. Thus, if the products AB and BC are defined, then

$$(AB)C = A(BC) \tag{18}$$

and

$$A(B + C) = AB + AC \tag{19}$$

Having defined a matrix with properties similar to the number 0, we should also define a matrix with properties similar to the number 1. This matrix, known as the *unit* (or *identity*) matrix is defined as follows: The unit matrix of order n is defined by

$$U_n = [u_{ij}]_{n,n} \tag{20}$$

where

$$u_{jj} = 1, j = 1, 2, \cdots n \quad (a)$$
$$u_{ij} = 0, \text{ if } i \neq j \quad\quad\quad (b) \tag{21}$$

For example the unit matrices of order 2, 3, and 4 are, respectively,

$$\begin{bmatrix} 1 & 0 \\ 0 & 1 \end{bmatrix}, \begin{bmatrix} 1 & 0 & 0 \\ 0 & 1 & 0 \\ 0 & 0 & 1 \end{bmatrix}, \begin{bmatrix} 1 & 0 & 0 & 0 \\ 0 & 1 & 0 & 0 \\ 0 & 0 & 1 & 0 \\ 0 & 0 & 0 & 1 \end{bmatrix}$$

We can easily verify that U does have the property of the number 1, namely if A is any matrix of order (m,n) then

$$U_m A = A U_n = A \tag{22}$$

For simplicity of notation the order of the unit matrix is often omitted.

The real number 1 is also associated with a different operation. If $a \neq 0$, there is a number b such that

$$ab = ba = 1 \tag{23}$$

The number b is called the reciprocal of a, written

$$b = 1/a = a^{-1} \tag{24}$$

Since matrix multiplication is noncommutative, the notation A^{-1} is used rather than $1/A$. Thus we would like to find the matrix A^{-1} with the property that

$$A^{-1}A = AA^{-1} = U \tag{25}$$

It is possible to show that such a matrix A^{-1} will exist if and only if the matrix A is *square* and the *determinant of the matrix A is nonzero.*

It is quite evident that we can associate a determinant with a square matrix. The determinant of a square matrix A is written as det A or as $|A|$, the former notation being preferable. For example

$$\det \begin{bmatrix} 1 & -1 \\ 2 & 1 \end{bmatrix} = \begin{vmatrix} 1 & -1 \\ 2 & 1 \end{vmatrix} = 3 \tag{26}$$

As a word of warning, if two matrices A and B have the same determinant, this does not imply that $A = B$; the two may even be of different orders. The matrix and its determinant are completely different species of animal.

A square matrix with a nonzero determinant is called a *nonsingular* matrix. All other matrices, square or not, are *singular* matrices.

Suppose a matrix A is nonsingular. Let Δ be the determinant of A and let Δ_{ij} be the cofactor of the element a_{ij}. The determinant obtained by deleting row i and column j from the matrix A is known as the minor M_{ij}. Then Δ_{ij} is related to M_{ij} by the equation

$$\Delta_{ij} = (-1)^{i+j} M_{ij} \tag{27}$$

Let us define a new matrix B as follows.

$$B = [\alpha_{ij}] \tag{28}$$

where

$$\alpha_{ij} = \frac{\Delta_{ji}}{\Delta} \tag{29}$$

Then, by direct multiplication we can show that

$$BA = AB = U \tag{30}$$

It is apparent that B is the inverse of A. The details of the proof are left as a problem. To find the inverse of a matrix A, then, we proceed as follows. We replace each entry of A by its cofactor divided by det A; then we interchange the rows and columns of the result.

This process of interchanging rows and columns of a matrix is an operation called *transposing*. If A is a matrix

$$A = [a_{ij}]_{m,n} \tag{31}$$

then the *transpose* of A, denoted A'(or A_t), is defined by

$$A' = [\alpha_{ij}]_{n,m} \tag{32}$$

where

$$\alpha_{ij} = a_{ji} \tag{33}$$

In network theory we meet matrices with the property

$$A = A' \tag{34}$$

that is, the matrix is equal to its transpose. This means that $a_{ij} = a_{ji}$. Such matrices (which obviously have to be square) are known as *symmetric* matrices.

The operation transpose, satisfies the following properties.

$$(A')' = A \tag{35}$$

$$(A + B)' = A' + B' \tag{36}$$

$$(A \cdot B)' = B' \cdot A' \tag{37}$$

$$(\alpha A)' = \alpha A' \tag{38}$$

$$\det A' = \det A \qquad (A \text{ square}) \tag{39}$$

Using the operation transpose, we can define the inverse matrix more concisely as

$$A = [a_{ij}]_{n,n}; \quad \det A \neq 0,$$

$$A^{-1} = \frac{1}{\Delta} [\Delta_{ij}]' \tag{40}$$

As an example let us find the inverse of the matrix:

$$A = \begin{bmatrix} 1 & -1 & 0 \\ 2 & 0 & 4 \\ -1 & 3 & -1 \end{bmatrix}$$

By the usual computations

$$\Delta = -10 \qquad \Delta_{22} = -1$$
$$\Delta_{11} = -12 \qquad \Delta_{23} = -2$$
$$\Delta_{12} = -2 \qquad \Delta_{31} = -4$$
$$\Delta_{13} = 6 \qquad \Delta_{32} = -4$$
$$\Delta_{21} = -1 \qquad \Delta_{33} = 2$$

Hence

$$A^{-1} = \begin{bmatrix} \frac{12}{10} & \frac{1}{10} & \frac{4}{10} \\ \frac{2}{10} & \frac{1}{10} & \frac{4}{10} \\ -\frac{6}{10} & \frac{2}{10} & -\frac{2}{10} \end{bmatrix}$$

3.2 Linear Algebraic Equations

We are now ready to consider linear algebraic equations—which are our main interest. Suppose we have a system of linear algebraic equations

$$a_{11}x_1 + a_{12}x_2 + a_{13}x_3 + \cdots + a_{1n}x_n = y_1$$
$$a_{21}x_1 + a_{22}x_2 + a_{23}x_3 + \cdots + a_{2n}x_n = y_2$$
$$\cdot \quad \cdot \quad \cdot \quad \cdot \quad \cdot \quad \cdot \quad \cdot \quad \cdot \quad \cdot \quad \cdot \quad \cdot \quad \cdot \quad \cdot \quad \cdot \quad \cdot \quad \cdot \quad \cdot$$
$$a_{m1}x_1 + a_{m2}x_2 + a_{m3}x_3 + \cdots + a_{mn}x_n = y_m$$

Such a system of equations may be written in matrix notation as

$$\begin{bmatrix} a_{11} & a_{12} & \cdots & a_{1n} \\ a_{21} & a_{22} & \cdots & a_{2n} \\ \cdot & \cdot & \cdots & \cdot \\ a_{m1} & a_{m2} & \cdots & a_{mn} \end{bmatrix} \begin{bmatrix} x_1 \\ x_2 \\ \cdot \\ \cdot \\ x_n \end{bmatrix} = \begin{bmatrix} y_1 \\ y_2 \\ \cdot \\ \cdot \\ y_m \end{bmatrix} \qquad (41)$$

which you can verify by carrying out the multiplication on the left. We now see by our definitions of matrix multiplication and equality that

Eq. (41) is the same as the set of equations immediately preceding it. Note that we refer to Eq. (41) as a *single equation*, a *matrix equation*. This equation may be written more elegantly and concisely as:

$$AX = Y \tag{42}$$

with an obvious definition of the matrices A, X, and Y. Once we get used to the concept of a matrix, i.e., once equations like (42) begin to mean something, we will appreciate the economy of thought offered by the matrix notation.

Let us see some more of the elegance of matrix notation by solving Eq. (42) using matrix algebra. First let us consider the simplest case, when $m = n$ and det $A \neq 0$. That is, the coefficient matrix A is nonsingular. Then, premultiplying Eq. (42) on both sides, by A^{-1} we get

$$A^{-1}(AX) = A^{-1}Y \tag{43}$$

From the associative property and the definition of inverse it follows that

$$X = A^{-1}Y \tag{44}$$

Thus we have solved Eq. (42). Let us write out Eq. (44) in detail, using the formula for inverse. We get

$$
\begin{bmatrix} x_1 \\ x_2 \\ \cdot \\ \cdot \\ \cdot \\ x_n \end{bmatrix}
=
\begin{bmatrix}
\dfrac{\Delta_{11}}{\Delta} & \dfrac{\Delta_{21}}{\Delta} & \dfrac{\Delta_{31}}{\Delta} & \cdots & \dfrac{\Delta_{n1}}{\Delta} \\
\dfrac{\Delta_{12}}{\Delta} & \dfrac{\Delta_{22}}{\Delta} & \dfrac{\Delta_{32}}{\Delta} & \cdots & \dfrac{\Delta_{n2}}{\Delta} \\
\cdot & \cdot & \cdot & \cdot & \cdot \\
\dfrac{\Delta_{1n}}{\Delta} & \dfrac{\Delta_{2n}}{\Delta} & \dfrac{\Delta_{3n}}{\Delta} & \cdots & \dfrac{\Delta_{nn}}{\Delta}
\end{bmatrix}
\begin{bmatrix} y_1 \\ y_2 \\ \cdot \\ \cdot \\ \cdot \\ y_n \end{bmatrix}
\tag{45}
$$

A little reflection will show that this solution is nothing more than Cramer's rule for solving linear algebraic equations. It is merely economy of thought to express the solution in compact form as in Eq. (44).

We see, incidentally, that if the coefficient matrix is nonsingular, the solution is unique. In particular if $Y = 0$, the unique solution is $X = 0$.

For the next case let us consider the system which has more unknowns than equations, i.e., $m < n$, under the hypothesis that the equations are independent. Independence implies that at least one $(m \times m)$ determinant chosen from A is nonzero. Let us straighten out the terminology of this statement by defining a submatrix. Given a matrix A, *a submatrix* of A is obtained by deleting a set of rows and a set of columns of A (including the possibility of not deleting any rows or not deleting any columns). Let us now restate the condition of linear dependence. The system of equations given in Eq. (42), in which A is of order (m, n), is linearly independent if and only if A contains a nonsingular submatrix of order m (where m is the number of equations).

Returning to our problem, we are given that the system is independent and $m < n$. Y may or may not be zero. By hypothesis A contains (at least) one nonsingular submatrix of order m. Let $j_1, j_2, \cdots, j_m$ be the columns of this submatrix. By rearranging the variables we can rewrite the same equation as

$$
\begin{bmatrix}
a_{1j_1} & a_{1j_2} & \cdots & a_{1j_m} & \vdots & a_{1j_{m+1}} & \cdots & a_{1j_n} \\
a_{2j_1} & a_{2j_2} & \cdots & a_{2j_m} & \vdots & a_{2j_{m+1}} & \cdots & a_{2j_n} \\
\cdot & \cdot & \cdot & \cdot & & \cdot & \cdot & \cdot \\
a_{mj_1} & a_{mj_2} & \cdots & a_{mj_m} & \vdots & a_{mj_{m+1}} & \cdots & a_{mj_n}
\end{bmatrix}
\begin{bmatrix}
x_{j_1} \\
x_{j_2} \\
\cdot \\
\cdot \\
x_{j_m} \\
--- \\
x_{j_{m+1}} \\
\cdot \\
\cdot \\
x_{j_n}
\end{bmatrix}
=
\begin{bmatrix}
y_1 \\
y_2 \\
\cdot \\
\cdot \\
y_m
\end{bmatrix}
\tag{46}
$$

You should verify that this is the same system of equations with which we started. If we call the submatrix consisting of the first m columns of the coefficient matrix of Eq. (46) A_{11} and that consisting of the last $n - m$ columns A_{12}, and similarly let X_1 and X_2 stand for the corresponding sets of unknowns, we can rewrite Eq. (46) as

$$
[A_{11} \quad A_{12}]\begin{bmatrix} X_1 \\ X_2 \end{bmatrix} = Y \tag{47}
$$

The technique we are using here is known as *matrix partitioning* and is a very useful tool. The matrices A and X are said to be *partitioned* and the partitioning is shown by the dashed lines in Eq. (46). If we consider the submatrices A_{11}, A_{12}, X_1, X_2 as *elements*, the product on the left side of Eq. (47) may be written as

$$
[A_{11} \quad A_{12}]\begin{bmatrix} X_1 \\ X_2 \end{bmatrix} = A_{11}X_1 + A_{12}X_2 \tag{48}
$$

This is a legitimate operation and does give the correct answer provided the products on the right are conformable and we preserve the order.

You can verify this by direct computation. Matrices partitioned in this fashion are said to be *conformally partitioned*.

Then we can rewrite Eq. (47) as

$$A_{11}X_1 + A_{12}X_2 = Y$$

or

$$A_{11}X_1 = Y - A_{12}X_2 \tag{49}$$

By our hypothesis and construction, A_{11} is nonsingular. Then, premultiplying both sides of Eq. (49) by A_{11}^{-1}, we get

$$X_1 = A_{11}^{-1}(Y - A_{12}X_2) \tag{50}$$

which is the general solution of Eq. (42). For the homogeneous case $Y = 0$, the solution becomes

$$X_1 = -A_{11}^{-1}A_{12}X_2 \tag{51}$$

The variables in X_2, in both solutions (50) and (51) are arbitrary "constants." Thus we have solved for m variables in terms of the other $(n - m)$ variables.

As an example, consider the following set of equations, which are the Kirchhoff current law equations of the network of Fig. 1.

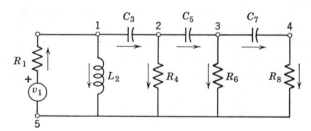

Fig. 1.   Illustrative example.

$$\begin{bmatrix} -1 & 1 & 1 & 0 & 0 & 0 & 0 & 0 \\ 0 & 0 & -1 & 1 & 1 & 0 & 0 & 0 \\ 0 & 0 & 0 & 0 & -1 & 1 & 1 & 0 \\ 0 & 0 & 0 & 0 & 0 & 0 & -1 & 1 \end{bmatrix} \begin{bmatrix} I_1 \\ I_2 \\ I_3 \\ I_4 \\ I_5 \\ I_6 \\ I_7 \\ I_8 \end{bmatrix} = 0 \tag{52}$$

We notice that columns 2, 4, 6, and 8 form a unit matrix, which is non-singular. Rewriting the equations as suggested, we get

$$
\left[\begin{array}{cccc:cccc}
1 & 0 & 0 & 0 & -1 & 1 & 0 & 0 \\
0 & 1 & 0 & 0 & 0 & -1 & 1 & 0 \\
0 & 0 & 1 & 0 & 0 & 0 & -1 & 1 \\
0 & 0 & 0 & 1 & 0 & 0 & 0 & -1
\end{array}\right]
\left[\begin{array}{c}
I_2 \\ I_4 \\ I_6 \\ I_8 \\ \hline I_1 \\ I_3 \\ I_5 \\ I_7
\end{array}\right] = 0
\qquad (53)
$$

(Notice the rearrangement of variables.)

Multiplying according to the indicated partitioning and transposing the second term leads to

$$
\left[\begin{array}{cccc}
1 & 0 & 0 & 0 \\
0 & 1 & 0 & 0 \\
0 & 0 & 1 & 0 \\
0 & 0 & 0 & 1
\end{array}\right]
\left[\begin{array}{c}
I_2 \\ I_4 \\ I_6 \\ I_8
\end{array}\right]
= -
\left[\begin{array}{cccc}
-1 & 1 & 0 & 0 \\
0 & -1 & 1 & 0 \\
0 & 0 & -1 & 1 \\
0 & 0 & 0 & -1
\end{array}\right]
\left[\begin{array}{c}
I_1 \\ I_3 \\ I_5 \\ I_7
\end{array}\right]
\qquad (54)
$$

Since the inverse of the unit matrix is itself, the solution of this equation is

$$
\left[\begin{array}{c}
I_2 \\ I_4 \\ I_6 \\ I_8
\end{array}\right]
=
\left[\begin{array}{cccc}
1 & -1 & 0 & 0 \\
0 & 1 & -1 & 0 \\
0 & 0 & 1 & -1 \\
0 & 0 & 0 & 1
\end{array}\right]
\left[\begin{array}{c}
I_1 \\ I_3 \\ I_5 \\ I_7
\end{array}\right]
\qquad (55)
$$

Finally, if we include the remaining variables, we get

$$
\left[\begin{array}{c}
I_2 \\ I_4 \\ I_6 \\ I_8 \\ I_1 \\ I_3 \\ I_5 \\ I_7
\end{array}\right]
=
\left[\begin{array}{cccc}
1 & -1 & 0 & 0 \\
0 & 1 & -1 & 0 \\
0 & 0 & 1 & -1 \\
0 & 0 & 0 & 1 \\
1 & 0 & 0 & 0 \\
0 & 1 & 0 & 0 \\
0 & 0 & 1 & 0 \\
0 & 0 & 0 & 1
\end{array}\right]
\left[\begin{array}{c}
I_1 \\ I_3 \\ I_5 \\ I_7
\end{array}\right]
\qquad (56)
$$

The last four rows of Eq. (56) merely state that $I_1 = I_1$, $I_3 = I_3$, etc., which is certainly true. They are included to show a complete solution of Eq. (52). For each set of values of I_1, I_3, I_5, and I_7, we have a solution of Eq. (52). In a physical problem, the values of these variables are chosen to satisfy other conditions, and so are not completely arbitrary.

There is one case which we have not considered so far, namely $m > n$. That is, a system in which there are more equations than unknowns. This case is more complicated than the other two, since we are faced with a new question which is very basic. There is no assurance in general that such a system of equations will have any solution at all. A system of equations which has at least one solution is said to be *consistent*. If it has no solution it is an *inconsistent* system of equations. For example the system of equations

$$\begin{bmatrix} 1 & 1 \\ 1 & -1 \\ 2 & 3 \end{bmatrix} \begin{bmatrix} x_1 \\ x_2 \end{bmatrix} = \begin{bmatrix} 0 \\ 0 \\ 1 \end{bmatrix} \tag{57}$$

has no solution at all. The first two equations demand that $x_1 = x_2 = 0$, which does not satisfy the third equation. To answer the question of existence of solutions, we have to introduce the concept of *rank*. The *rank* of a matrix A is the order of the largest nonsingular submatrix of A. In terms of this concept we can unify the theory of linear equations very elegantly. We will state three typical results to illustrate this remark.

1. The system of equations

$$AX = Y \tag{58}$$

is consistent if and only if

$$\text{Rank of } A = \text{rank of } [A \quad Y] \tag{59}$$

(The matrix $[A \quad Y]$ is obtained by appending the column Y to the matrix A and is known as the *augmented* matrix.)

2. The system of equations

$$AX = Y \tag{60}$$

where A is of order (m,n) is linearly independent if and only if

$$\text{Rank of } A = m$$

3. The homogeneous system of linear equations

$$AX = 0 \tag{61}$$

is always consistent (with the trivial solution $X = 0$). If A is of order (m,n), this system has nontrivial solutions if and only if

$$\text{Rank of } A < n$$

The proofs of these results will not be given here.

Thus for the case $m > n$, we have to check for consistency. If the system is consistent, then it is dependent. It is obvious that the matrix cannot contain a nonsingular submatrix of order $> n$. If the rank of A is r ($\leq n$), we select r independent equations from the set (by finding a nonsingular submatrix of order r of A and choosing the equations defined by these r rows) and solve them by earlier procedures. The solutions will automatically satisfy the other equations.

3.3 Elementary Topology

Several times in Chapter 1 we had to use the phrase "this fact will not be proved here," because we had not developed the necessary topological concepts. Network topology is a generic name referring to all properties having to do with the geometry of the network. In the present section we shall attempt an elementary discussion of network geometry as a prelude to the general discussion of loop and node systems of equations which follows in the next chapter. We will at the same time tie up the loose ends concerning the number of independent KCL and KVL equations, which were left dangling in Chapter 1. This section is by no means an exhaustive treatment of network topology, it is intended merely to give a general idea of the subject. For a more complete treatment, see Seshu.[*]

The geometrical properties of a network are independent of the constituents of a branch and so in topological discussions it is usual to replace each network branch by a line segment. The resulting structure is known as a *linear graph*. For example the graph associated with the network of Fig. 2a is shown in Fig. 2b. Notice that we take the current references over to the linear graph. We say that the linear graph is *directed;* that is, we interpret the arrowhead as an orientation associated with the line segments. In the literature on graph theory many different terminologies are in vogue. Some of these are listed below.

Branch   edge, 1-cell, arc, element.
Node   vertex, 0-cell.
Loop   circuit, simple closed path.

Our brief study of network topology will be concerned primarily with

[*] S. Seshu, *Theory of Linear Graphs with Applications in Electrical Engineering*, published by Electrical Engineering Department, Syracuse University, 1958.

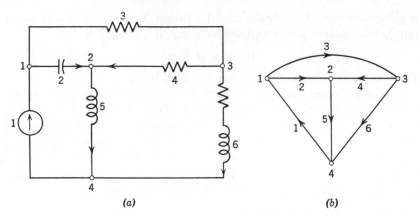

Fig. 2.   A network and its associated linear graph.

the coefficient matrices of Kirchhoff's current and voltage law equations. As we observed in Chapter 1, Kirchhoff's laws are independent of the constituents of a branch, and thus can be defined for the linear graph as well.   The fact that we have transferred only the current reference and not the voltage reference is no serious handicap, as we can make a simple convention about it.   We make the convention that the reference plus for the branch voltage is at the tail of the reference arrow for the branch current.   Such a convention is permissible since the references are arbitrary.

If we write the current law equations for the network of Fig. 2 in matrix notation, we get

$$\begin{array}{c} 1 \\ 2 \\ 3 \\ 4 \end{array} \begin{bmatrix} -1 & 1 & 1 & 0 & 0 & 0 \\ 0 & -1 & 0 & -1 & 1 & 0 \\ 0 & 0 & -1 & 1 & 0 & 1 \\ 1 & 0 & 0 & 0 & -1 & -1 \end{bmatrix} \begin{bmatrix} i_1(t) \\ i_2(t) \\ i_3(t) \\ i_4(t) \\ i_5(t) \\ i_6(t) \end{bmatrix} = \begin{bmatrix} 0 \\ 0 \\ 0 \\ 0 \end{bmatrix} \qquad (62)$$

This equation can be written concisely as:

$$A_a i_b(t) = 0 \qquad (63)$$

The coefficient matrix A_a is the incidence matrix (also called the vertex-edge incidence matrix or the vertex matrix) of the linear graph.   The incidence matrix

$$A_a = [a_{ij}] \qquad (64)$$

is of order $N_v \times N_b$ (i.e., it has one row for each node and one column for each branch) and its elements a_{ij} are defined by Eq. 2 of Chapter 1.

As we observed in Chapter 1, each column of the incidence matrix contains exactly one $+1$ and one -1. Therefore any row of the incidence matrix is the negative sum of the others. Thus the rank of the incidence matrix A_a is at most $N_v - 1$. One of the statements that we should prove now is that the incidence matrix of a connected graph has a rank equal to $N_v - 1$, so that exactly $N_v - 1$ of the KCL equations are linearly independent. It is possible to prove this statement directly by reducing the matrix A_a by elementary operations (addition of one row to another). However, we shall take this opportunity to introduce an important topological concept, namely the *cut set*, and devise a devious proof for the rank of A_a.

To motivate the discussion, let us add some of the KCL equations of Fig. 2, say the equations for nodes 1 and 2. The resulting equation is

$$-i_1(t) + i_3(t) - i_4(t) + i_5(t) = 0 \qquad (65)$$

Let us see what this equation represents. A little thought will reveal that branches 1, 3, 4, and 5 which appear in this equation, are exactly those branches which have one node in the set of nodes $\{1,2\}$ and the other node in the set of nodes $\{3,4\}$. In other words, if we remove these branches from the network, the network will be separated into two pieces, nodes 1 and 2 being in one part and nodes 3 and 4 in the other. Alternatively, if we *cut* these branches, the network is also *cut* into two pieces. For this reason, we call such a set of branches a *cut set*. In Fig. 3, this cut set is shown by means of a dotted line.

Equation (65) can also be interpreted as follows: The total current crossing the dotted line in the direction of the arrow of Fig. 3 is zero. This statement is a familiar one and you may have used it many times before. (For instance, the directed sum of line currents in a three phase system is zero.)

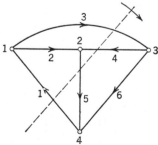

Fig. 3. A cut set.

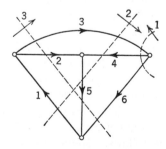

Fig. 4. Some cut sets of Fig. 3.

Evidently the graph of Fig. 3 has many cut sets besides the one that we have shown in Fig. 3. Some of these are represented in Fig. 4. Some of these cut sets are merely the sets of branches connected to a node, which is understandable, since a node is isolated from the rest of the network by cutting the branches connected to it. For each of these cut sets, a KCL equation can be written (which equation would naturally be the sum of the KCL equations at the nodes on the "tail side" of the cut set reference arrow). For instance, for the cut sets of Fig. 4, we get the equations

$$\text{Cut set 1.} \qquad -i_3(t) + i_4(t) + i_6(t) = 0 \qquad (a)$$

$$\text{Cut set 2.} \quad -i_1(t) + i_3(t) - i_4(t) + i_5(t) = 0 \qquad (b) \qquad (66)$$

$$\text{Cut set 3.} \quad i_2(t) + i_3(t) - i_5(t) - i_6(t) = 0 \qquad (c)$$

Our objective here is to show that there are $N_v - 1$ linearly independent cut set equations. This will prove that there are $N_v - 1$ KCL equations, since cut set equations are linear combinations of KCL equations (at the nodes), and we cannot increase the number of linearly independent equations by taking linear combinations of these. To do this we shall make use of the concept of a tree introduced in Chapter 1.

In Chapter 1 we stated that a tree of N_v nodes contains $N_v - 1$ branches, but did not prove this fact. Let us first establish this result by induction on the number of nodes.

First we observe that a tree of two nodes ($N_v = 2$) can have only one branch, since it must be connected and must not contain any loops. Next suppose that every tree of $N_v = k$ nodes contains $k - 1$ branches. Now consider any tree of $k + 1$ nodes. Such a tree must contain at least one node with only one branch connected to it. We can prove this fact by starting from any node of the tree and constructing a maximal path. Since a tree contains no loops, such a path must end, and when it ends, we have a node with only one branch connected to it. If we remove this end node and the single branch connected to it, we have a tree of k nodes. By the induction hypothesis this tree contains $k - 1$ branches. Putting back the end node and branch, we see that the tree of $k + 1$ nodes contains k branches, which proves the result.

Getting back to our main objective, we shall now define a set of $N_v - 1$ *fundamental cut sets* for a connected network, which are analogous to the fundamental loops of Chapter 1, and which have independent KCL equations. Suppose the network is connected. We first find a tree of the network. For each branch b_k of the tree we construct a cut set as follows. Removing b_k from the tree disconnects the tree into two pieces (one, or in trivial cases both, of which may consist of an isolated node). Now we find all the links (chords) that go from one part of this disconnected tree to the other. These links, together with the branch b_k constitute the fundamental cut set for b_k. For each branch of the tree, we have a fundamental cut set. For example, consider the graph of Fig. 5. Choosing the tree of branches 3, 4, 5, 6, we get the fundamental cut sets shown in the figure, the cut set number corresponding to the branch number. The cut set references are chosen to agree with the corresponding tree branch reference.

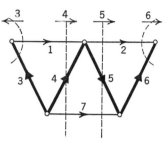

Fig. 5. Example for fundamental cut sets.

Each fundamental cut set contains a tree branch which is in no other cut set. Therefore, the KCL equations for the fundamental cut sets are linearly independent. Since there are $N_v - 1$ fundamental cut sets, there are at least $N_v - 1$ linearly independent KCL equations. Since there can't be any more, as we have seen, our main result is proved.

For example, the KCL equations for the fundamental cut sets of Fig. 5 are the following.

$$
\begin{array}{ccccccc}
3 & 4 & 5 & 6 & 1 & 2 & 7
\end{array}
$$

$$
\begin{array}{c}
3 \\ 4 \\ 5 \\ 6
\end{array}
\begin{bmatrix}
1 & 0 & 0 & 0 & -1 & 0 & 0 \\
0 & 1 & 0 & 0 & 1 & 0 & 1 \\
0 & 0 & 1 & 0 & 0 & 1 & 1 \\
0 & 0 & 0 & 1 & 0 & 1 & 0
\end{bmatrix}
\begin{bmatrix}
i_3(t) \\ i_4(t) \\ i_5(t) \\ i_6(t) \\ i_1(t) \\ i_2(t) \\ i_7(t)
\end{bmatrix}
=
\begin{bmatrix}
0 \\ 0 \\ 0 \\ 0
\end{bmatrix}
\qquad (67)
$$

We notice the 4×4 unit matrix here, showing that the rank of the coefficient matrix is four.

Since the matrix A_a has a rank $N_v - 1$, we generally delete one row (any one row) and denote the resulting matrix by A.

Next let us turn our attention to Kirchhoff's voltage law. KVL can be written in matrix notation as follows.

$$
\boldsymbol{B}_a \boldsymbol{v}_b(t) = \boldsymbol{0} \qquad (68)
$$

For example, for the network of Fig. 3, with the choice of loops given in Fig. 6, the KVL equations in matrix notation are as follows.

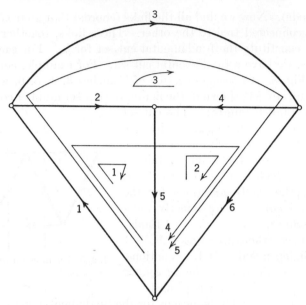

Fig. 6.   Choice of loops for KVL example.

$$
\begin{array}{c}
\begin{array}{cccccc} 1 & 2 & 3 & 4 & 5 & 6 \end{array} \\
\begin{array}{c} 1 \\ 2 \\ 3 \\ 4 \\ 5 \\ 6 \\ 7 \end{array}
\begin{bmatrix}
1 & 1 & 0 & 0 & 1 & 0 \\
0 & 0 & 0 & -1 & -1 & 1 \\
0 & -1 & 1 & 1 & 0 & 0 \\
1 & 1 & 0 & -1 & 0 & 1 \\
1 & 0 & 1 & 0 & 0 & 1 \\
0 & -1 & 1 & 0 & -1 & 1 \\
1 & 0 & 1 & 1 & 1 & 0
\end{bmatrix}
\begin{bmatrix}
v_1(t) \\ v_2(t) \\ v_3(t) \\ v_4(t) \\ v_5(t) \\ v_6(t)
\end{bmatrix}
=
\begin{bmatrix}
0 \\ 0 \\ 0 \\ 0 \\ 0 \\ 0 \\ 0
\end{bmatrix}
\end{array}
\qquad (69)
$$

(Loops 6 and 7 are not shown in the figure to avoid confusion.)   The matrix

$$\boldsymbol{B}_a = [b_{ij}]_{N_m, N_b}$$

is called the *circuit matrix* (or the circuit-edge incidence matrix) and has elements b_{ij} defined by Eq. (7) of Chapter 1.   Remembering our reference convention, we can replace the definition of b_{ij} by the following:

$b_{ij} = 1$ if branch j is in loop i and the branch reference agrees with the loop reference;

$b_{ij} = -1$ if branch j is in loop i and the branch reference is opposite to the loop reference;

$b_{ij} = 0$ if branch j is not in loop i.

We saw in Chapter 1 that there are at least $N_b - N_v + 1$ linearly independent KVL equations for a connected network. In other words the rank of $\boldsymbol{B}_a$ is greater than or equal to $N_b - N_v + 1$. It remains for us to show that this number is also an upper bound, so that the rank is exactly equal to $N_b - N_v + 1$. To prove this fact we make use of the following result, which is one of the fundamental theorems in network topology.

If the columns of the matrices $\boldsymbol{A}_a$ and $\boldsymbol{B}_a$ are arranged in the same branch order, then

$$\boldsymbol{A}_a\boldsymbol{B}_a' = 0; \qquad \boldsymbol{B}_a\boldsymbol{A}_a' = 0$$

The proof of this important result is very simple. Each row of $\boldsymbol{A}_a$ corresponds to a node and each column of $\boldsymbol{B}_a'$ corresponds to a loop. Consider the rth row of $\boldsymbol{A}_a$ and the jth column of $\boldsymbol{B}_a'$. The product of these two is the (r,j) element of the product $\boldsymbol{A}_a\boldsymbol{B}_a'$. If loop j does not contain node r, loop j does not contain any of the branches at node r. Thus when an element in row r of $\boldsymbol{A}_a$ is nonzero, the corresponding element in column j of $\boldsymbol{B}_a'$ is zero and vice versa. Thus the product is zero. If loop j contains node r, then it contains exactly two of the branches at node r. The possible orientations of the loop j and the branches at node r which are in this loop are the four shown in Fig. 7, and four others obtained by reversing the loop reference.

Fig. 7.   Orientations of the loop and branches.

These two elements contribute the only nonzero products. It is quite obvious by inspection that the two products are 1 and -1, adding to zero. Thus the result is proved.

This result, along with a result known as Sylvester's law of nullity, actually sets $N_b - N_v + 1$ as the upper bound for the rank of the circuit matrix of a connected graph. Since we don't know Sylvester's law, we shall establish this result directly.

As we have just proved,

$$\boldsymbol{B}_a\boldsymbol{A}' = 0 \tag{70}$$

where one row of $\boldsymbol{A}_a$ has been deleted. Let the matrix $\boldsymbol{A}$ be arranged so that the first $N_v - 1$ columns constitute a nonsingular matrix, and let $\boldsymbol{B}_a$ be rearranged correspondingly. Partitioning the matrices

B_a and A' conformally after the first $N_v - 1$ columns and rows respectively, we get:

$$[B_{11} \quad B_{12}] \begin{bmatrix} A_{11}' \\ A_{12}' \end{bmatrix} = 0 \tag{71}$$

where A_{11}, and so A_{11}', is nonsingular. Equation (71) may be solved for B_{11} to give

$$B_{11} = -B_{12}A_{12}'A_{11}^{-1'} \tag{72}$$

In other words the first $N_v - 1$ columns of B_a are expressible as linear combinations of the last $(N_b - N_v + 1)$ columns. It is now obvious that B_a cannot contain a nonsingular submatrix of order greater than $N_b - N_v + 1$. Thus

$$\text{Rank of } B_a \leq N_b - N_v + 1$$

Since we know from Chapter 1 that there are at least $N_b - N_v + 1$ linearly independent KVL equations (for the fundamental loops), and we have now shown that there are no more than this number, then

$$\text{Rank of } B_a \text{ is } = N_b - N_v + 1$$

for a connected network.

PROBLEMS

3.1 Find the indicated sums.

(a) $\begin{bmatrix} 4 & 7 \\ 2 & 3 \end{bmatrix} + \begin{bmatrix} 3 & 2 \\ 4 & 5 \end{bmatrix}$ (b) $\begin{bmatrix} 4 & j \\ -j & 0 \end{bmatrix} + \begin{bmatrix} j & 1+j \\ 1+j & 1 \end{bmatrix}$

(c) $\begin{bmatrix} s & 2s \\ 2s & 1 \end{bmatrix} + \begin{bmatrix} \frac{1}{s} & \frac{2}{s} \\ \frac{2}{s} & s \end{bmatrix}$ (d) $\begin{bmatrix} s^2 + 2s & 2s & 1 \\ 2s & 3 & 0 \\ 1 & 0 & 4 \end{bmatrix} + \begin{bmatrix} 2s & s & 1 \\ s & s^2 & -s \\ 1 & -s & 1 \end{bmatrix}$

3.2 Find the conformable products that can be made from the following matrices and evaluate them.

$$A = \begin{bmatrix} 1 & 2 & -3 \\ 2 & 1 & -6 \end{bmatrix} \qquad D = \begin{bmatrix} 2 \\ 4 \\ 6 \end{bmatrix}$$

$$B = [1 \quad -2]$$

$$E = \begin{bmatrix} 4 \\ 3 \end{bmatrix}$$

$$C = \begin{bmatrix} 1 & 4 \\ 0 & 2 \\ -3 & 7 \end{bmatrix}$$

3.3 *Prove:* If AB and BC are defined (i.e., conformable),

$$A(BC) = (AB)C$$

3.4 *Prove:* Under suitable hypotheses about orders (state these)

$$A(B + C) = AB + AC$$

$$(A + B)C = AC + BC$$

3.5 Is $(A + B)^2 = A^2 + 2AB + B^2$ in matrix algebra? Give the correct formula.

3.6 Check whether any of the following matrices are nonsingular. Find the inverses of the nonsingular matrices.

$$A = [2 \quad 3]$$

$$B = \begin{bmatrix} 1 & 0 & 5 & 2 \\ 0 & 1 & 4 & 6 \\ 0 & 0 & 1 & 3 \\ 0 & 0 & 0 & 1 \end{bmatrix}$$

$$C = \begin{bmatrix} 1 & 0 & 0 & 0 \\ 2 & 2 & 0 & 0 \\ 3 & 0 & 4 & 0 \\ 2 & 1 & 3 & 1 \end{bmatrix}$$

$$D = \begin{bmatrix} 1 & 0 & 3 \\ 0 & 2 & 1 \\ 3 & 1 & 2 \end{bmatrix}$$

$$E = \begin{bmatrix} 1 & 0 & 1 \\ -1 & 1 & 0 \\ 0 & -1 & -1 \end{bmatrix}$$

3.7 Show that under the definition of A^{-1} (Eq. 28), $A^{-1}A = AA^{-1} = U$.

3.8 Find the condition that $\begin{bmatrix} a_{11} & a_{12} \\ a_{21} & a_{22} \end{bmatrix}$ be nonsingular. What is the inverse?

3.9 *Prove:* The inverse of a symmetric matrix is symmetric.

3.10 *Prove:* If A is nonsingular, so is A^{-1}.

3.11 *Prove:* $(A^{-1})' = (A')^{-1}$

3.12 *Prove:* $(AB)' = B'A'; (AB)^{-1} = B^{-1}A^{-1}$, where A and B are nonsingular.

3.13 *Prove:* If Z is symmetric, so is (BZB').

3.14 Let

$$A = \begin{bmatrix} 1 & 0 & -1 \\ 0 & 1 & 2 \end{bmatrix}, \ B = \begin{bmatrix} 4 & 2 \\ 1 & 2 \\ 2 & 1 \end{bmatrix}, \ C = \begin{bmatrix} 2 & 5 \\ 5 & -4 \\ 0 & 4 \end{bmatrix}$$

Compute AB and AC and compare them. What law of ordinary algebra fails to hold for matrices?

3.15 Under what conditions can we conclude $B = C$ from $AB = AC$?

3.16 Let

$$A = \begin{bmatrix} 1 & -1 \\ -1 & 1 \end{bmatrix} \text{ and } B = \begin{bmatrix} 1 & -1 \\ 1 & -1 \end{bmatrix}$$

Compute AB. What theorem of ordinary algebra is not true for matrices?

3.17 If $AB = 0$, what can we say about A and B?

3.18 Solve the following equations.

$$2x_1 - 3x_2 + x_3 = 0$$

$$x_1 + x_2 - x_3 = 0$$

3.19 Solve the system of equations.

$$x_1 + x_2 - x_3 = 2$$
$$2x_1 - x_2 + x_3 = 7$$
$$x_1 + 4x_2 - 4x_3 = -1$$

3.20 The following three operations are known as *elementary operations:*
(i) Multiplication of a row (or column) by a nonzero constant.
(ii) Addition to any row (or column) of any multiple of another row (or column).
(iii) Interchange of rows (or columns).
Show that the rank of a matrix remains unaltered under these three operations.
How can we use this fact to find the rank of a matrix?

3.21 (Structure of the incidence matrix.) Prove the following statements in order. The last statement needs the others for proof.
(i) If from the incidence matrix A of a connected network, we select the columns corresponding to the branches of a tree, these columns constitute a nonsingular submatrix. (*Hint:* Construct the incidence matrix of the tree and use the fact that the tree is connected.) A is A_a with one row deleted.
(ii) If any set of branches of the network contains a loop, the corresponding columns of A are linearly dependent. (*Hint:* $B_a A_a' = 0$.)
(iii) Any set of $N_v - 1$ branches which does not contain a loop is a tree of the network.
(iv) A square submatrix of order $N_v - 1$ of the incidence matrix A of a connected graph is nonsingular if and only if the columns of this submatrix correspond to the branches of a tree.

3.22 (Structure of the circuit matrix.) State and prove the duals of the statements of Problem 3.21, for the circuit matrix B, ending up with the statement:

> Let B be the circuit matrix of a connected network, with $N_b - N_v + 1$ rows and rank $N_b - N_v + 1$. Then a square submatrix of B of order $N_b - N_v + 1$ is nonsingular if and only if the columns of this submatrix correspond to a set of links for a tree of the network.

(*Hint:* The dual of a loop is a cut set.)

3.23 A cut set matrix is defined as a matrix Q_a with elements 1, -1, or 0 depending upon the relative orientations of the cut sets and branches. Prove that Q_a has a rank $N_v - 1$. Further if Q is a cut set matrix of $N_v - 1$ rows and rank $N_v - 1$, show that Q has all the properties of A except that each column of Q may contain more than one 1 and one -1. (For example, $BQ' = 0$, the statements of Problem 3.21 hold for Q, etc.)

3.24 Choosing branch orientations for the networks of Problem 2.1, construct the matrices A, B, and Q for these networks.

3.25 In the network of Problem 2.3, let each R and L be a branch, and let v_g be a branch. Construct the matrices A and B for this network. Find all the nonsingular submatrices of maximum order in these two matrices, thus verifying the final statements of Problems 3.21 and 3.22.

4 · GENERAL NETWORK ANALYSIS

In the second chapter we saw how the fundamental equations of an electrical network can be combined to reduce the number of simultaneous equations that have to be solved. In the present chapter we will formalize the development of Chapter 2 in matrix notation, in addition to considering certain special cases and the question of duality.

Before we begin the formal discussion of loop and node systems of equations, the philosophical question of the value of formal procedures needs to be considered. Formal procedures are not always the simplest methods for all problems. In many common problems, inspection and short cuts may provide answers much more easily than solving the loop or node systems of equations. In some networks (especially active networks) "mixed variable" equations—that is, equations in which both currents and voltages appear as unknowns—are more useful than either the loop or the node systems of equations.

The real value of loop and node equations lies in their generality. They can *always* be used for any lumped network. (We can solve them in general only for linear, time-invariant systems.) As such they have two principal uses. First, they are very useful as bases for the development of network theory—active, passive, linear, or nonlinear. Secondly, whenever there is disagreement as to the "right answer," one can always solve the loop or the node systems of equations to find the right answer.

The present discussion should not be construed to mean that no one uses loop or node equations to solve practical problems. On the contrary they are widely used in practice: to check the designs of filter networks, for example. We would merely like to caution you not to start "turning the crank" on every problem. You should learn to look at the problem first and decide on the best method of attack—and the best method for a problem is not always the most general one.

4.1   Loop Currents and General Loop Equations *

Since we are going to be concerned only with lumped linear networks and are using Laplace transforms to solve them, we will begin our discussion with all the fundamental equations in Laplace transforms.

Kirchhoff's current law was written in Eq. (2), Chapter 1 as

$$\sum_{j=1}^{N_b} a_{kj} i_j(t) = 0 \qquad k = 1, 2, \cdots, N_v \tag{1}$$

where $a_{kj} = \pm 1$ or 0, depending on the branch reference. Using our knowledge of matrix methods from the last chapter, we can rewrite this equation in matrix notation. If we simultaneously transform the currents, the result will be

$$A_a I_b(s) = 0 \tag{2}$$

where

$$A_a = [a_{kj}] \tag{3}$$

is of order (N_v, N_b) and a_{kj} is as defined in Eq. (2), Chapter 1. $I_b(s)$ is the column matrix of N_b rows, consisting of the transformed branch currents.

Since we know that exactly $N_v - 1$ of the equations in (1) are linearly independent for a connected network, we know immediately that the rank of the matrix A_a is $N_v - 1$. Therefore we may delete one row (*any* row) of A_a and write KCL as

$$A I_b(s) = 0 \tag{4}$$

where the matrix A has $N_v - 1$ rows and N_b columns.

As an example, consider the network shown in Fig. 1. This is the same example that we considered in Fig. 4 of Chapter 1. For this

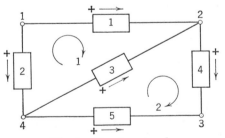

Fig. 1.   Simple network.

---

* Some duplication between section 3.3 and this section will be found. This is intentional, to allow for the omission of section 3.3 if desired.

example Eq. (2), including all the nodes, becomes

$$
\begin{array}{c} 1 \\ 2 \\ 3 \\ 4 \end{array}
\begin{bmatrix}
1 & 1 & 0 & 0 & 0 \\
-1 & 0 & -1 & 1 & 0 \\
0 & 0 & 0 & -1 & -1 \\
0 & -1 & 1 & 0 & 1
\end{bmatrix}
\begin{bmatrix}
I_{b1}(s) \\
I_{b2}(s) \\
I_{b3}(s) \\
I_{b4}(s) \\
I_{b5}(s)
\end{bmatrix}
=
\begin{bmatrix}
0 \\
0 \\
0 \\
0
\end{bmatrix}
\tag{5}
$$

(Since we have to deal with loop currents shortly, the double subscript notation for branch currents has been used.) If we omit any one of the equations, the remaining set will be independent. Omitting the third equation, we will get

$$
\begin{array}{c} 1 \\ 2 \\ 4 \end{array}
\begin{bmatrix}
1 & 1 & 0 & 0 & 0 \\
-1 & 0 & -1 & 1 & 0 \\
0 & -1 & 1 & 0 & 1
\end{bmatrix}
\begin{bmatrix}
I_{b1}(s) \\
I_{b2}(s) \\
I_{b3}(s) \\
I_{b4}(s) \\
I_{b5}(s)
\end{bmatrix}
=
\begin{bmatrix}
0 \\
0 \\
0
\end{bmatrix}
\tag{6}
$$

This corresponds to Eq. (4) for the example.

Turning next to Kirchhoff's voltage law, let us repeat Eq. (7) of Chapter 1 for convenience.

$$
\sum_{j=1}^{N_b} b_{kj} v_j(t) = 0 \qquad k = 1, 2, \cdots, N_m \tag{7}
$$

We can write this in matrix notation with transformed voltages as

$$
\boldsymbol{B}_a \boldsymbol{V}_b(s) = \boldsymbol{0} \tag{8}
$$

where

$$
\boldsymbol{B}_a = [b_{kj}] \tag{9}
$$

is of order (N_m, N_b) and b_{kj}'s are as defined in Eq. (7) of Chapter 1.

If instead of writing all possible equations, we write only the independent ones, which will be $N_b - N_v + 1$ in number for a connected network, we get

$$
\boldsymbol{B} \boldsymbol{V}_b(s) = \boldsymbol{0} \tag{10}
$$

For the example of Fig. 1, there are two independent KVL equations. Choosing loops 1 and 2 in writing the KVL equations, as shown in the figure, Eq. (10) becomes

$$
\begin{matrix} 1 \\ 2 \end{matrix}
\begin{bmatrix} 1 & -1 & -1 & 0 & 0 \\ 0 & 0 & 1 & 1 & -1 \end{bmatrix}
\begin{bmatrix} V_1(s) \\ V_2(s) \\ V_3(s) \\ V_4(s) \\ V_5(s) \end{bmatrix}
= \begin{bmatrix} 0 \\ 0 \end{bmatrix} \tag{11}
$$

Suppose we now choose the same two loops to define the two loop currents $I_1(s)$ and $I_2(s)$. (As we noted in Chapter 2, this is not necessary. We might choose some other two loops for loop currents.) Then, as in Chapter 2, we can express all branch currents in terms of these loop currents. Let us write this mesh transformation in matrix notation. The result is

$$
\begin{bmatrix} I_{b1}(s) \\ I_{b2}(s) \\ I_{b3}(s) \\ I_{b4}(s) \\ I_{b5}(s) \end{bmatrix}
= \begin{bmatrix} 1 & 0 \\ -1 & 0 \\ -1 & 1 \\ 0 & 1 \\ 0 & -1 \end{bmatrix}
\begin{bmatrix} I_1(s) \\ I_2(s) \end{bmatrix} \tag{12}
$$

Comparing Eq. (11) and (12), we see that the matrix of the transformation in Eq. (12) is the transpose of the coefficient matrix of KVL equations.

A little reflection will show that this observation is perfectly general, as long as the reference plus for the branch voltage is at the tail of the reference arrow for the branch current for all branches. In the general case, if Kirchhoff's voltage law is written as

$$
BV_b(s) = 0 \tag{13}
$$

then the mesh transformation is

$$
I_b(s) = B'I_m(s) \tag{14}
$$

where $I_m(s)$ is the column matrix of loop currents. The proof of this statement is left as a problem.

Let us now return to the example and substitute the mesh transformation for the branch currents given by Eq. (12) into the KCL equations given by Eq. (6). This leads to

$$
\begin{bmatrix} 1 & 1 & 0 & 0 & 0 \\ -1 & 0 & -1 & 1 & 0 \\ 0 & -1 & 1 & 0 & 1 \end{bmatrix}
\begin{bmatrix} 1 & 0 \\ -1 & 0 \\ -1 & 1 \\ 0 & 1 \\ 0 & -1 \end{bmatrix}
\begin{bmatrix} I_1(s) \\ I_2(s) \end{bmatrix}
= \begin{bmatrix} 0 & 0 \\ 0 & 0 \\ 0 & 0 \end{bmatrix}
\begin{bmatrix} I_1(s) \\ I_2(s) \end{bmatrix} \equiv 0 \tag{15}
$$

Thus, when the branch currents are expressed in terms of loop currents, KCL is identically satisfied no matter what the loop currents may be.

This statement is again perfectly general. For the general case, if we substitute the mesh transformation of Eq. (14) into the KCL equation in Eq. (4), we will get

$$AB'I_m(s) = 0 \tag{16}$$

If KCL is to be satisfied independent of the values of the loop currents, this expression must be an identity, which requires

$$AB' = 0 \tag{17}$$

It is easy to show that the last expression is valid as long as the reference convention is used.* To do this note that A and B' have the following forms.

Focus attention on any one of the columns of B', say column 1 and on any one of the rows of A, say row 1. That is, focus attention on a loop and a node of the network. Either the loop "goes through" the node or not. If it does not, then none of the branches on the loop can be connected at the node. This means that corresponding to any nonzero entry in column 1 of B', there will be a zero entry in row 1 of A. In case the loop goes through the node, exactly two of the branches connected at the node will lie on the loop. If these two branches are similarly oriented with respect to the node (both current references away from the node or both toward the node), they are oppositely oriented with respect to the loop, and vice versa. This means that in row 1 of A, if the entries corresponding to the two branches are both $+1$ or -1, the corresponding two entries in column 1 of B' will be of opposite sign, and vice versa. Following these thoughts through shows that all the entries in the product AB' will be zero.

Before proceeding with the development of loop equations, let us relate the preceding observations to our discussion of linear equations

---

* Knowledge of section **3.3** is not assumed here.

in Chapter 3. Kirchhoff's current law

$$AI_b(s) = 0 \tag{18}$$

is a system of homogeneous linear algebraic equations. There are $N_v - 1$ linearly independent equations—this being the *rank* of A—in N_b unknowns. Therefore, the complete solution of Eq. (18) should contain $N_b - (N_v - 1)$ arbitrary constants.

The mesh transformation

$$I_b(s) = B'I_m(s) \tag{19}$$

which has been seen to be a solution of (18) *does* contain $N_b - (N_v - 1)$ "arbitrary constants," namely the loop currents, provided B' has a rank of $N_b - (N_v - 1)$. Thus, in fact, the mesh transformation can be looked upon as a *complete solution* of Kirchhoff's current law—a complete solution that we can write down by inspection from the network. Another point of view which is equally valid is to consider the mesh transformation as being *equivalent* to Kirchhoff's current law, equivalent in the sense that either one implies the other.

Let us proceed with our derivation of loop equations. To begin with, let us draw a chart showing the development of loop equations and node equations because charts are much more descriptive.

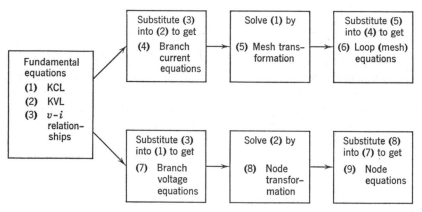

The three basic relationships are KCL, KVL, and the branch v-i relationships. We haven't yet formulated the branch voltage–current relationships in matrix notation, and so let us rectify this omission. The relation between branch voltage and current transforms can be expressed in matrix notation as

$$V_b(s) =$$
$$V_g(s) + R_b I_b(s) + s L_b I_b(s) - L_b i_L(0+) + \frac{1}{s} D_b I_b(s) + \frac{1}{s} v_C(0+) \tag{20}$$

where $V_g(s)$ is the matrix of generators; R_b, L_b, and D_b are the matrices of branch resistances, inductances, and reciprocal capacitances, with L_b containing mutual inductance as well. We are taking the most general branch to consist of a series connection of a source, a resistance, a capacitance, and an inductance. The form of Eq. (20) is unaltered by the presence of dependent generators. When no dependent generators are present, the matrices R_b and D_b are diagonal (with all off-diagonal elements zero), and L_b is symmetric. But when dependent generators are present, the matrices R_b, D_b and L_b *may not* be symmetric.

Equation (20) may be written more concisely as

$$V_b(s) = V_g(s) + Z_b(s)I_b(s) + \frac{1}{s}v_C(0) - L_b i_L(0) \qquad (21)$$

where $Z_b(s) = R_b + sL_b + (D_b/s)$ is symmetric in the absence of dependent generators. As in Eq. (20), $v_C(0)$ and $i_L(0)$ are the initial (time) value matrices of capacitance voltages and inductance currents.

Let us now see by means of examples that the Eqs. (20) and (21) state the usual relationships between voltage and current.

In the network of Fig. 2, if we consider R_2L_2 as one branch, $R_3L_3C_3$ as

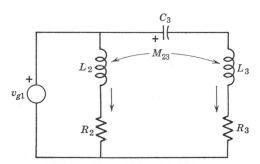

Fig. 2.   Example for *v-i* relations.

one branch, and let all the branch voltage reference $+$'s be at the tails of the branch current references, the transformed *v-i* relationships are

$$V_1(s) = V_{g1}(s) \qquad (a)$$

$$V_2(s) = (R_2 + sL_2)I_2(s) + sM_{23}I_3(s) - L_2 i_2(0) - M_{23}i_3(0) \quad (b) \qquad (22)$$

$$V_3(s) = \left(R_3 + sL_3 + \frac{1}{sC_3}\right)I_3(s) + \frac{1}{s}v_{C_3}(0) + sM_{23}I_2(s)$$

$$-L_3 i_3(0) - M_{23}i_2(0) \qquad (c)$$

Collecting these equations in matrix notation, we have

$$
\begin{bmatrix} V_1(s) \\ V_2(s) \\ V_3(s) \end{bmatrix} = \begin{bmatrix} V_{g1}(s) \\ 0 \\ 0 \end{bmatrix} + \begin{bmatrix} 0 & 0 & 0 \\ 0 & R_2 & 0 \\ 0 & 0 & R_3 \end{bmatrix} \begin{bmatrix} I_1(s) \\ I_2(s) \\ I_3(s) \end{bmatrix}
$$

$$
+ s \begin{bmatrix} 0 & 0 & 0 \\ 0 & L_2 & M_{23} \\ 0 & M_{23} & L_3 \end{bmatrix} \begin{bmatrix} I_1(s) \\ I_2(s) \\ I_3(s) \end{bmatrix} + \frac{1}{s} \begin{bmatrix} 0 & 0 & 0 \\ 0 & 0 & 0 \\ 0 & 0 & \dfrac{1}{C_3} \end{bmatrix} \begin{bmatrix} I_1(s) \\ I_2(s) \\ I_3(s) \end{bmatrix}
$$

$$
+ \frac{1}{s} \begin{bmatrix} 0 \\ 0 \\ v_{C_3}(0) \end{bmatrix} - \begin{bmatrix} 0 & 0 & 0 \\ 0 & L_2 & M_{23} \\ 0 & M_{23} & L_3 \end{bmatrix} \begin{bmatrix} 0 \\ i_2(0) \\ i_3(0) \end{bmatrix} \quad (23)
$$

corresponding to Eq. (20); or adding the parameter matrices together, we get

$$
\begin{bmatrix} V_1(s) \\ V_2(s) \\ V_3(s) \end{bmatrix} = \begin{bmatrix} V_{g1}(s) \\ 0 \\ 0 \end{bmatrix} + \begin{bmatrix} 0 & 0 & 0 \\ 0 & R_2 + sL_2 & sM_{23} \\ 0 & sM_{23} & R_3 + sL_3 + \dfrac{1}{sC_3} \end{bmatrix} \begin{bmatrix} I_1(s) \\ I_2(s) \\ I_3(s) \end{bmatrix}
$$

$$
- \begin{bmatrix} 0 & 0 & 0 \\ 0 & L_2 & M_{23} \\ 0 & M_{23} & L_3 \end{bmatrix} \begin{bmatrix} i_1(0) \\ i_2(0) \\ i_3(0) \end{bmatrix} + \frac{1}{s} \begin{bmatrix} 0 \\ 0 \\ v_{C_3}(0) \end{bmatrix} \quad (24)
$$

corresponding to Eq. (21).

As another example, consider the network of Fig. 3, which contains

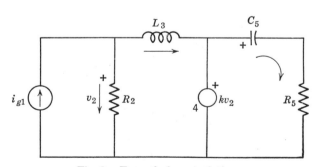

Fig. 3. Example for v-i relations.

a dependent generator as well as a current generator. The branch relations for this network are:

$$V_1(s) = V_{g1}(s) \quad \text{(Generator)} \qquad (a)$$

$$V_2(s) = R_2 I_2(s) \qquad (b)$$

$$V_3(s) = sL_3 I_3(s) - L_3 i_3(0) \qquad (c) \qquad (25)$$

$$V_4(s) = kV_2(s) = kR_2 I_2(s) \qquad (d)$$

$$V_5(s) = \left(R_5 + \frac{1}{sC_5} \right) I_5(s) + v_{C_5}(0) \qquad (e)$$

Collecting these equations together in matrix notation, we get

$$
\begin{bmatrix} V_1(s) \\ V_2(s) \\ V_3(s) \\ V_4(s) \\ V_5(s) \end{bmatrix}
=
\begin{bmatrix} V_{g1}(s) \\ 0 \\ 0 \\ 0 \\ 0 \end{bmatrix}
+
\begin{bmatrix}
0 & 0 & 0 & 0 & 0 \\
0 & R_2 & 0 & 0 & 0 \\
0 & 0 & sL_3 & 0 & 0 \\
0 & kR_2 & 0 & 0 & 0 \\
0 & 0 & 0 & 0 & R_5 + \dfrac{1}{sC_5}
\end{bmatrix}
\begin{bmatrix} I_{g1}(s) \\ I_2(s) \\ I_3(s) \\ I_4(s) \\ I_5(s) \end{bmatrix}
$$

$$
- \begin{bmatrix} 0 \\ 0 \\ L_3 i_3(0) \\ 0 \\ 0 \end{bmatrix}
+ \frac{1}{s} \begin{bmatrix} 0 \\ 0 \\ 0 \\ 0 \\ v_{C_5}(0) \end{bmatrix} \qquad (26)
$$

We notice that the branch impedance matrix $\mathbf{Z}_b(s)$ is symmetric in the first example—Eq. (24)—and unsymmetric in the second example—Eq. (26).

Let us now follow the top row of the chart carefully observing the number of equations and the number of unknowns at each step. The basic equations are:

(1)   KCL: $\mathbf{A}\mathbf{I}_b(s) = \mathbf{0}$ $N_v - 1$ equations

(2)   KVL: $\mathbf{B}\mathbf{V}_b(s) = \mathbf{0}$ $N_b - N_v + 1$ equations

There are N_b equations in $2N_b$ quantities. Therefore we need N_b more specifications, one for each branch, before the system can be solved. In the case of some of the branches this additional specification takes the form of a *v-i* relationship. In the case of branches consisting of independent generators, this additional specification is the branch voltage or current. In the case of dependent generators, the specification is the dependence of the generator current or voltage on the other variables. We collect all of these as the third set of equations.

$$(3)\quad V_b(s) = V_g(s) + Z_b(s)I_b(s) + \frac{1}{s}v_C(0+) - L_b i_L(0+)$$

We now have $2N_b$ equations (some of which in set 3 may be trivial—those for the independent generators) which can be solved for the $2N_b$ unknowns. $2N_b$ is a rather large number, even for a very simple network. For the simple network of Fig. 1, we would need to solve ten simultaneous equations. The loop and node systems are, as we stated in Chapter 2, organized procedures to avoid solving $2N_b$ simultaneous equations. Nevertheless our basic objective is to solve these three systems of equations.

Following our chart, if we substitute set (3) into KVL, we get

$$BZ_b(s)I_b(s) = -B\left\{V_g(s) + \frac{1}{s}v_C(0+) - L_b i_L(0+)\right\}\qquad(27)$$

This expression, together with Kirchhoff's current law, is known as the system of branch current equations and is of historical importance. Early writers, including Kirchhoff himself, used branch current equations in their work. The branch current system is a set of N_b equations in the N_b branch currents.

The next step is to substitute the mesh transformation of Eq. (19) into Eq. (27). The result, the loop equations, can be written

$$BZ_b B' I_m(s) = -B\left\{V_g(s) + \frac{1}{s}v_C(0+) - L_b i_L(0+)\right\}\qquad(28)$$

We notice, using Problem 13, Chapter 3, that for a network without dependent generators the coefficient matrix of loop equations, which is

$$Z_m(s) = BZ_b B'\qquad(29)$$

is symmetric, if the same set of loops is used for both KVL and the mesh transformation. We refer to Z_m as the *loop impedance matrix*.

Equation (28) represents a system of $N_b - N_v + 1$ loop equations in as many loop currents. Referring back to the chart we notice that we can, if we like, reverse the order of the middle two blocks without any harm. The final result will be the same. This equation may be written more concisely as follows

$$Z_m(s)I_m(s) = V_m(s) + v_\lambda(0+) + \frac{1}{s} v_C(0+) \tag{30}$$

where the meanings of the various quantities are obvious.

Naturally, we would not go through the matrix multiplications of Eq. (28) to get the loop equations of a given network. From our earlier experience, we know how to write down the final result directly, almost by inspection, in all but the most complicated nonplanar networks. Since we have seen much of this already in Chapter 2, we need only remark on a few points and give one or two examples to illustrate Eq. (30).

Equation (30) can be solved for $I_m(s)$ provided $Z_m(s)$ is nonsingular, i.e., provided

$$\det Z_m(s) \neq 0 \quad \text{(in } s) \tag{31}$$

The solution will be

$$I_m(s) = Z_m^{-1}(s) \left\{ V_m(s) + v_\lambda(0+) + \frac{1}{s} v_C(0+) \right\} \tag{32}$$

This gives us the loop currents. Knowing the loop currents we can find the branch currents from the mesh transformation of Eq. (19). Finally Eq. (21) can be used to find the branch voltages. This completes the formal solution for the transforms. The time functions are found by inversion of the transforms.

Let us next consider the question of choosing an appropriate set of loops for loop equations. There are several methods known, which we shall list.

1. Choose a tree and take the fundamental system of loops. This method is completely general and will always "work." But generally speaking, the loop equations for a fundamental system of loops will always be more "complicated," in the sense that the loop impedance matrix $Z_m(s)$ will contain fewer off-diagonal zeros than the matrices obtained by other procedures.

2. Choose loops in order, such that each succeeding loop contains at least one new branch not contained in any of the previous loops. This method is also valid but care must be exercised to get $N_b - N_v + 1$ loops, since it is quite possible to exhaust all the branches of the network with fewer than $N_b - N_v + 1$ loops.

3. The dual procedure of arranging the loops such that at least one branch is "eliminated" at each step is also valid and is subject to the same conditions as procedure 2.

4. For planar networks the regions bounded by branches—the "windows" or meshes—may be chosen.

The justification of procedure 1 is obvious. We leave the justification of procedures 2 and 3 as problems. We will take up the justification of 4 in section 4.6.

Meanwhile let us answer a related question. Suppose we choose a completely arbitrary set of loops. How can we find out whether this set of loops is suitable for writing loop equations. We can answer this question very easily if we look back to our development of loop equations. The loops must satisfy two conditions. One, the KVL equations written for these loops must be independent, and the KVL equation for any other loop must be dependent on these. Two, for any set of branch currents satisfying KCL there must be a set of loop currents such that the mesh transformation holds. For both of these conditions, it is necessary and sufficient that the circuit matrix of these loops—the matrix $\boldsymbol{B}$ of KVL—have $N_b - N_v + 1$ rows and have a rank of $N_b - N_v + 1$.

When the network contains current generators, loop equations can still be used, as we saw in Chapter 2. In fact the presence of current generators simplifies life, since some of the loop currents become known and fewer equations need to be solved simultaneously. The loops are chosen in such a fashion that each current generator is in exactly one loop. It is always possible to do so in any solvable problem.

Let us consider a few examples to illustrate the effect of dependent generators and the use of judicious choice of loops in reducing computational effort. As a first example consider the amplifier network of Fig. 4.

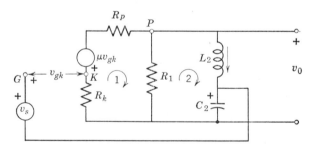

Fig. 4.   Example for writing loop equations.

The voltage of the dependent source is μv_{gk} which must be expressed in terms of the branch voltages and currents. From the figure, we can write

$$\mu V_{gk} = \mu[V_s + V_{C_2} - V_{R_k}] \tag{33}$$

Let us first write loop equations for the two loops leaving μV_{gk} as in Eq. (33) before expressing it in terms of loop currents. From Fig. 4, by inspection, the loop equations are

$$
\begin{bmatrix} R_p + R_k + R_1 & -R_1 \\[2mm] -R_1 & R_1 + sL_2 + \dfrac{1}{sC_2} \end{bmatrix}
\begin{bmatrix} I_1(s) \\[2mm] I_2(s) \end{bmatrix}
$$

$$
= \begin{bmatrix} -\mu V_{gk} \\[2mm] 0 \end{bmatrix}
+ \begin{bmatrix} 0 \\[2mm] L_2 i_L(0) - \dfrac{v_{C_2}(0)}{s} \end{bmatrix} \tag{34}
$$

Now insert the dependence of V_{gk} on I_1 and I_2. From Eq. (33) this is

$$
V_{gk} = \mu\{V_s + \frac{1}{sC_2} I_2(s) + \frac{v_{C_2}(0)}{s} + R_k I_1(s)\} \tag{35}
$$

Since I_1 and I_2 are unknown, we transpose them to the left after inserting this expression into Eq. (34).

$$
\begin{bmatrix} R_p + R_k + R_1 + \mu R_k & -R_1 + \dfrac{\mu}{sC_2} \\[2mm] -R_1 & R_1 + sL_2 + \dfrac{1}{sC_2} \end{bmatrix}
\begin{bmatrix} I_1(s) \\[2mm] I_2(s) \end{bmatrix}
$$

$$
= \begin{bmatrix} -\mu V_s \\[2mm] 0 \end{bmatrix}
+ \begin{bmatrix} \dfrac{-\mu v_{C_2}(0)}{s} \\[2mm] L_2 i_L(0) - \dfrac{v_{C_2}(0)}{s} \end{bmatrix} \tag{36}
$$

We notice that the coefficient matrix of Eq. (36) is *not* symmetric, as often happens with dependent generators. We can also note exactly where the parameter μ enters the coefficient matrix. It comes only in the first row since the dependent generator is in the first loop only. The parameter μ appears in both columns 1 and 2, since the dependent generator depends on both I_1 and I_2.

We may now solve these loop equations for any quantity of interest. We may, for example be interested in the voltage gain of the amplifier stage, defined as

$$
G(s) = \frac{V_0(s)}{V_s(s)}, \text{ with } v_{C_2}(0) = i_L(0) = 0 \tag{37}
$$

Since the initial conditions are taken as zero, we evidently have

$$
V_0(s) = \left(sL_2 + \frac{1}{sC_2}\right) I_2(s) \tag{38}
$$

From Eq. (36), since the second matrix on the right is zero, we get

$$I_2(s) = \frac{\Delta_{12}}{\Delta}(-\mu V_s) \qquad (39)$$

with the usual notation. Thus only one element of the inverse matrix is required. Performing the indicated operations, we get finally

$$G(s) = \frac{V_0(s)}{V_s(s)}$$

$$= \frac{-\left(sL_2 + \dfrac{1}{sC_2}\right)\mu R_1}{[R_p + R_k(1+\mu)]\left(sL_2 + \dfrac{1}{sC_2}\right) + R_1\left[R_p + R_k(1+\mu) + sL_2 + \dfrac{1+\mu}{sC_2}\right]} \qquad (40)$$

As a second example consider the network shown in Fig. 5. Suppose we are interested in computing V_4, the voltage across R_4, with zero

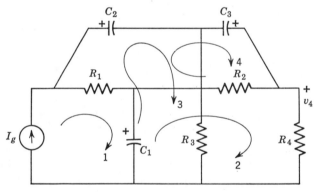

Fig. 5.   Another example.

initial voltages. Since we have a current generator, we will make loop 1 contain the current generator and make

$$I_1 = I_g \qquad (41)$$

by choosing loops as shown. Since we want to compute V_4, we have to compute the branch current in R_4. So if we arrange the loops such that branch R_4 is in only one loop, we need compute only one loop current.

The choice of loops shown in Fig. 3 satisfies this condition. However we see from Fig. 3 that loop 1 is coupled to (i.e., has branches in common with) all other loops. Thus to compute I_2, we would have to compute three cofactors and one determinant. (Write the form of the equations and the inverse to see this.) A slightly different choice which reduces the computation to two cofactors and one determinant is shown in Fig. 6.

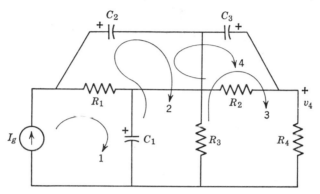

Fig. 6.　Alternative choice of loops.

The loop equations for this network are

$$
\begin{bmatrix}
R_1+\dfrac{1}{sC_1} & -\left(R_1+\dfrac{1}{sC_1}\right) & 0 & -R_1 \\[2ex]
-\left(R_1+\dfrac{1}{sC_1}\right) & \left(R_1+R_3+\dfrac{1}{sC_1}+\dfrac{1}{sC_2}\right) & -R_3 & R_1+\dfrac{1}{sC_2} \\[2ex]
0 & -R_3 & R_3+R_4+\dfrac{1}{sC_3} & \dfrac{1}{sC_3} \\[2ex]
-R_1 & R_1+\dfrac{1}{sC_2} & \dfrac{1}{sC_3} & R_1+R_2+\dfrac{1}{sC_2}+\dfrac{1}{sC_3}
\end{bmatrix}
\begin{bmatrix}
I_1(s) \\[2ex] I_2(s) \\[2ex] I_3(s) \\[2ex] I_4(s)
\end{bmatrix}
$$

$$
=
\begin{bmatrix}
V_g(s) \\[2ex] 0 \\[2ex] 0 \\[2ex] 0
\end{bmatrix}
+
\begin{bmatrix}
-\dfrac{1}{s}v_{C_1}(0) \\[2ex]
\dfrac{1}{s}v_{C_1}(0) - \dfrac{1}{s}v_{C_2}(0) \\[2ex]
\dfrac{1}{s}v_{C_3}(0) \\[2ex]
-\dfrac{1}{s}v_{C_2}(0) + \dfrac{1}{s}v_{C_3}(0)
\end{bmatrix}
\tag{42}
$$

Since $V_g(s)$ appears only in the first equation and is unknown, we leave the first equation alone. In the others we transpose $I_1(s) = I_g(s)$ to the right side, as in Chapter 2, to get

$$
\begin{bmatrix}
\left(R_1 + R_3 + \dfrac{1}{sC_1} + \dfrac{1}{sC_2}\right) & -R_3 & \left(R_1 + \dfrac{1}{sC_2}\right) \\[2ex]
-R_3 & \left(R_3 + R_4 + \dfrac{1}{sC_3}\right) & \dfrac{1}{sC_3} \\[2ex]
\left(R_1 + \dfrac{1}{sC_2}\right) & \dfrac{1}{sC_3} & R_1 + R_2 + \dfrac{1}{sC_2} + \dfrac{1}{sC_3}
\end{bmatrix}
\begin{bmatrix}
I_2(s) \\[2ex]
I_3(s) \\[2ex]
I_4(s)
\end{bmatrix}
$$

$$
=
\begin{bmatrix}
\left(R_1 + \dfrac{1}{sC_1}\right) I_g(s) \\[2ex]
0 \\[2ex]
R_1 I_g(s)
\end{bmatrix}
+
\begin{bmatrix}
\dfrac{1}{s} v_{C_1}(0) - \dfrac{1}{s} v_{C_2}(0) \\[2ex]
\dfrac{1}{s} v_{C_3}(0) \\[2ex]
\dfrac{1}{s} v_{C_2}(0) + \dfrac{1}{s} v_{C_3}(0)
\end{bmatrix}
\tag{43}
$$

If the initial capacitance voltages are nonzero, we can't save any effort. Three cofactors and a determinant have to be computed for I_3. If they are zero, only two cofactors and the determinant have to be computed. Under zero initial conditions we see from the inverse matrix that

$$
I_3(s) = \left[\frac{\Delta_{23}}{\Delta} \left(R_1 + \frac{1}{sC_1} \right) + \frac{\Delta_{43}}{\Delta} R_1 \right] I_g(s)
\tag{44}
$$

where subscripts on Δ correspond to those on I rather than on the position in the coefficient matrix of Eq. (43). The computation of Δ and its cofactors shall be left to you.

In both of these examples we wrote down the loop equations by inspection and did not go through the matrix multiplication of Eq. (28). It is quite possible to formulate explicit rules for writing the equations by inspection in the matrix notation. These rules are usually taught in undergraduate ac circuits courses. We will not include these rules here. If any difficulty is encountered, the simplest procedure is to write down Kirchhoff's voltage law in terms of loop currents before collecting coefficients for the standard form. We might remark however, that the initial inductance currents enter all equations like current generators and initial capacitance voltages enter all equations like voltage generators.

4.2   Node Voltages and General Node Equations

The node system of equations is exactly dual to the loop equations as we can see on the chart given at the beginning of section 4.1. Therefore, we can afford to keep the discussion of the general node equations somewhat shorter than the discussion of the last section. Just as we observed that the matrix of the mesh transformation is the transpose of the coefficient matrix of KVL equations, we find that the matrix of the node transformation is the transpose of the coefficient matrix of KCL equations. That is, if KCL is written as

$$AI_b(s) = 0 \qquad (45)$$

then the expression for branch voltages in terms of node voltages is

$$V_b(s) = A'V_n(s) \qquad (46)$$

There are two assumptions involved here that must be clearly stated. First, the reference (or datum) node for the node voltages is taken to be the same node as the one omitted in writing the independent KCL equations. Secondly, the reference convention (voltage plus at the tail of current reference arrow) has been adopted. Clearly, neither assumption needs to be made in a network; but they are both convenient for theoretical purposes.

The node transformation is a complete solution of the KVL equations. This statement is verified by noting that

$$BV_b(s) = BA'V_n(s) \equiv 0 \qquad (47)$$

The right hand side follows from the fact that

$$BA' = (AB')' = 0 \qquad (48)$$

which follows from Eq. (17). This result is also obvious from physical considerations. From an alternative viewpoint it is also possible to consider the node transformation as being equivalent to KVL. In any case, there is no need to consider KVL any further after the branch voltages are expressed in terms of the node voltages.

Let us consider an example to illustrate the relationship shown in Eqs. (45) and (46), leaving the proof as a problem. A network is shown in Fig. 7. Omitting the equation at node 4, the KCL equations

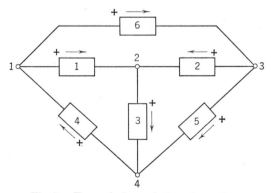

Fig. 7.   Example for node transformation.

at the other three nodes may be written in matrix notation as

$$
\begin{matrix} 1 \\ 2 \\ 3 \end{matrix}
\begin{bmatrix} 1 & 0 & 0 & -1 & 0 & 1 \\ -1 & -1 & 1 & 0 & 0 & 0 \\ 0 & 1 & 0 & 0 & 1 & -1 \end{bmatrix}
\begin{bmatrix} I_1(s) \\ I_2(s) \\ I_3(s) \\ I_4(s) \\ I_5(s) \\ I_6(s) \end{bmatrix}
= \begin{bmatrix} 0 \\ 0 \\ 0 \end{bmatrix}
\tag{49}
$$

We see by inspection that the relationship between the branch voltages and node voltages—with 4 as the reference node—is

$$
\begin{bmatrix} V_{b1}(s) \\ V_{b2}(s) \\ V_{b3}(s) \\ V_{b4}(s) \\ V_{b5}(s) \\ V_{b6}(s) \end{bmatrix}
= \begin{bmatrix} 1 & -1 & 0 \\ 0 & -1 & 1 \\ 0 & 1 & 0 \\ -1 & 0 & 0 \\ 0 & 0 & 1 \\ 1 & 0 & -1 \end{bmatrix}
\begin{bmatrix} V_1(s) \\ V_2(s) \\ V_3(s) \end{bmatrix}
\tag{50}
$$

It is evident by inspection that the matrix of the transformation (50) is the transpose of the coefficient matrix of Eq. (49).

Referring back to our chart we note that the first step in obtaining the node equations is to substitute the branch v-i relations into KCL. These relations are given in Eq. (21). In order to substitute this into KCL we evidently have to solve for the branch current matrix $I_b(s)$ first. We may run into some difficulty here because $Z_b(s)$ may have rows and columns of zeros corresponding to branches consisting of voltage or current sources and hence may be singular. Zero rows due to current generators do not matter. Let us write

$$
Z_b(s) = \begin{bmatrix} 0 & 0 \\ 0 & Z_{22}(s) \end{bmatrix}
\tag{51}
$$

where the current generators correspond to the first set of rows and columns. Let us now define

$$
Y_b(s) = \begin{bmatrix} 0 & 0 \\ 0 & Z_{22}{}^{-1}(s) \end{bmatrix}
\tag{52}
$$

Using this expression, the solution for $I_b(s)$ will be

$$I_b(s) = I_g(s) + Y_b(s)\left[V_b(s) - V_{g2}(s) + L_b i_L(0) - \frac{1}{s}v_C(0)\right] \quad (53)$$

where $V_{g2}(s)$ contains only the voltages of the voltage generators, and $I_g(s)$ contains only the currents of the current generators.

Let us illustrate this procedure by means of an example.   Consider

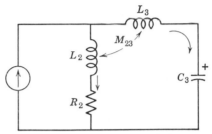

Fig. 8.   Example for *v-i* relations.

the network of Fig. 8.   The *v-i* relationships in matrix notation are

$$\begin{bmatrix} V_1(s) \\ V_2(s) \\ V_3(s) \end{bmatrix} = \begin{bmatrix} V_{g1}(s) \\ 0 \\ 0 \end{bmatrix} + \begin{bmatrix} 0 & 0 & 0 \\ 0 & R_2 + sL_2 & sM_{23} \\ 0 & sM_{23} & sL_3 + \dfrac{1}{sC_3} \end{bmatrix} \begin{bmatrix} I_1(s) \\ I_2(s) \\ I_3(s) \end{bmatrix}$$

$$+ \frac{1}{s}\begin{bmatrix} 0 \\ 0 \\ v_{C_3}(0) \end{bmatrix} - \begin{bmatrix} 0 \\ L_2 i_2(0) + M_{23} i_3(0) \\ L_3 i_3(0) + M_{23} i_2(0) \end{bmatrix} \quad (54)$$

(Note the row and column of zeros.)   Leaving the first equation alone, we get

$$\begin{bmatrix} V_2(s) \\ V_3(s) \end{bmatrix} = \begin{bmatrix} R_2 + sL_2 & sM_{23} \\ sM_{23} & sL_3 + \dfrac{1}{sC_3} \end{bmatrix} \begin{bmatrix} I_2(s) \\ I_3(s) \end{bmatrix}$$

$$+ \frac{1}{s}\begin{bmatrix} 0 \\ v_{C_3}(0) \end{bmatrix} - \begin{bmatrix} L_2 & M_{23} \\ M_{23} & L_3 \end{bmatrix}\begin{bmatrix} i_2(0) \\ i_3(0) \end{bmatrix} \quad (55)$$

We now solve this equation for the current transforms. The result will be

$$\begin{bmatrix} I_2(s) \\ I_3(s) \end{bmatrix} = \frac{1}{\Delta} \begin{bmatrix} sL_3 + \dfrac{1}{sC_3} & -sM_{23} \\ -sM_{23} & R_2 + sL_2 \end{bmatrix} \left\{ \begin{bmatrix} V_2(s) \\ V_3(s) \end{bmatrix} \right.$$

$$\left. + \begin{bmatrix} L_2 & M_{23} \\ M_{23} & L_3 \end{bmatrix} \begin{bmatrix} i_2(0) \\ i_3(0) \end{bmatrix} - \frac{1}{s} \begin{bmatrix} 0 \\ v_{C_3}(0) \end{bmatrix} \right\} \tag{56}$$

where $\qquad \Delta = R_2 \left(sL_3 + \dfrac{1}{sC_3} \right) + \dfrac{L_2}{C_3} + s^2(L_2L_3 - M_{23}{}^2) \tag{57}$

Finally, the matrix $\boldsymbol{I}_b(s)$ is given by

$$\begin{bmatrix} I_1(s) \\ I_2(s) \\ I_3(s) \end{bmatrix} = \begin{bmatrix} I_{g1}(s) \\ 0 \\ 0 \end{bmatrix} + \frac{1}{\Delta} \begin{bmatrix} 0 & 0 & 0 \\ 0 & sL_3 + \dfrac{1}{sC_3} & -sM_{23} \\ 0 & -sM_{23} & R_2 + sL_2 \end{bmatrix} \left\{ \begin{bmatrix} V_1(s) \\ V_2(s) \\ V_3(s) \end{bmatrix} \right.$$

$$\left. + \begin{bmatrix} 0 & 0 & 0 \\ 0 & L_2 & M_{23} \\ 0 & M_{23} & L_3 \end{bmatrix} \begin{bmatrix} i_1(0) \\ i_2(0) \\ i_3(0) \end{bmatrix} - \frac{1}{s} \begin{bmatrix} 0 \\ 0 \\ v_{C_3}(0) \end{bmatrix} \right\} \tag{58}$$

which should be compared with Eq. (53).

Let us now turn to zero rows and columns in $\boldsymbol{Z}_b(s)$ due to voltage generators. We shall be in some difficulty, since the currents of the generators will be unknown. This difficulty may be overcome in at least two general ways. One of these is to introduce *fundamental cut set* equations, exactly analogous to our treatment of current generators in the loop system. This we shall not do.* The second procedure is to introduce a transformation of the network that eliminates the zero rows and columns in $\boldsymbol{Z}_b(s)$, leaving some property unaltered. This procedure, known as the *Blakesley transformation* or the *e-shift*, will be considered next.

It is clear that we need such transformations only if there is no network element in series with the voltage generator. Otherwise the series element, together with the voltage driver, might be considered as a branch, thus eliminating the zero row and column in $\boldsymbol{Z}_b(s)$. Therefore, suppose there are two or more other branches connected to both ends of the voltage generator. Let the voltage generator be in branch j between nodes k and n as in Fig. 9. If now the voltage generator is

---

* We are not assuming the discussion of section 3.3.

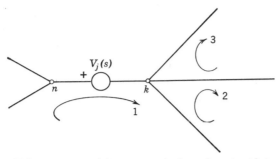

Fig. 9.   Voltage source with two or more branches at each terminal.

"shifted" through one of the two nodes (k or n) into each of the other elements connected to the node, preserving its reference orientation as in Fig. 10, the branch currents before and after the transformation will

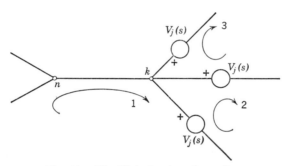

Fig. 10.   The Blakesley transformation.

be the same.   In other words the Blakesely step is a *current invariant* transformation.   We observe the validity of the result by examining the loop equations of the network before and after the change.   The loop equations remain unaltered.

After the generator is shifted, nodes k and n become the same node. Thus, the voltage generator reduces the number of node equations to be solved simultaneously.

Another method of attack is possible if all the voltage generators in the network have a common node.   This common node can be taken as the datum and then some of the node voltages become known.   We need only solve for the others.   Thus voltage generators always simplify the node system of equations.   We conclude that Eq. (21) can always be solved for $I_b(s)$ either in the original network or in the transformed network, leading to Eq. (53).

Referring back to our chart we see that the solution for the branch currents is to be substituted into KCL. If we do this, we will get

$$AY_b(s)V_b(s) = -AI_g(s) + AY_bV_{g2}(s) - AY_b\left\{L_bi_L(0) - \frac{1}{s}v_C(0)\right\}$$

(59)

This expression, together with KVL, is known as the system of branch voltage equations. The branch voltage system is also of historical importance. The system consists of N_b equations in the N_b branch voltage variables.

The next step is to solve the KVL equations by means of the node transformation given in Eq. (46). When this solution is substituted in Eq. (59), the result is the node system of equations. Thus,

$$AY_b(s)A'V_n(s)$$
$$= -AI_g(s) + AY_bV_{g2}(s) - AY_b(s)\left\{L_bi_L(0) - \frac{1}{s}v_C(0)\right\}$$

(60)

Similar to the loop impedance matrix given by Eq. (29), we define the node admittance matrix as

$$Y_n = AY_bA'$$

(61)

If the network contains no dependent sources, then Y_n will be symmetric in the standard node system.

The node equations can be written more simply as

$$Y_n(s)V_n(s) = I_n(s) + \frac{1}{s}i_L(0) + q_C(0)$$

(62)

The meanings of the terms on the right are found by comparing this expression with Eq. (60). If the node admittance matrix is nonsingular, this equation can be solved to give

$$V_n(s) = Y_n^{-1}\left\{I_n(s) + \frac{1}{s}i_L(0) + q_C(0)\right\}$$

(63)

With the node voltages determined, we now find the branch voltages from the node transformation. Finally, the branch currents are found from the v-i relationships.

In many practical problems there is a single source and we are interested in only one or two currents or voltages, not all of them. In such a case, we choose the datum node to be the common node of the source and the branch of interest, if they have a common node. If they do not, we choose one end of either the source or the load as datum node. This reduces the amount of computation required.

Once again, this matrix formulation of node equations is mainly for theoretical convenience. We would not normally perform these matrix multiplications to get the node equations of a network, preferring to write them down by inspection. The method of writing down the node equations by inspection is familiar and needs no comment. We can, however, say one or two things about the matrix formulation that might otherwise go unnoticed. First, we have no exceptional networks to which node equations cannot be applied. Mutual inductance is freely admitted. (See example of Fig. 8.) Secondly a branch may be taken to be either a simple R, L, or C or a series combination of elements and generators, as we choose. Neither of these remarks applies to the procedure of writing equations by inspection. Mutual inductance cannot be admitted easily (see Chapter 2 where the equivalent of the matrix inversion Z_{22}^{-1} of Eq. (52) is done in scalar notation). If we choose a series combination of elements as a branch, we must be very careful with initial conditions.

To illustrate the latter remark let us consider the branch consisting of a series combination of R and C as shown in Fig. 11a. For this branch, the transformed voltage-current relationship is

$$V(s) = \left(R + \frac{1}{sC}\right)I(s) + \frac{v_C(0)}{s} \tag{64}$$

or

$$I(s) = \frac{V(s)}{\left(R + \dfrac{1}{sC}\right)} - \frac{v_C(0)/s}{\left(R + \dfrac{1}{sC}\right)} \tag{65}$$

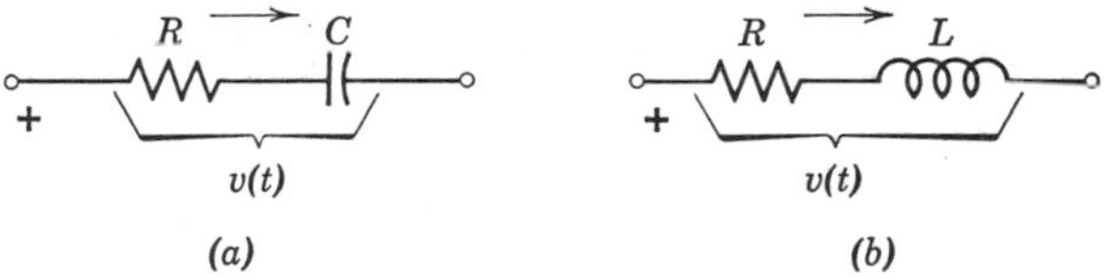

(a)   (b)

Fig. 11.   Network branches.

Thus, the initial capacitance voltage does not appear very simply. For the series RL branch of Fig. 11b, the transformed voltage-current relationship is

$$V(s) = (R + sL)I(s) - Li(0) \tag{66}$$

or

$$I(s) = \frac{V(s)}{R + sL} + \frac{Li(0)}{R + sL} \tag{67}$$

which is just as complicated. (Equations (65) and (67) are quite reasonable, and easily remembered, if you think of the initial values as drivers.)

In practice it is much simpler to choose each R, L, and C (in series with voltage generators if any) as a branch, while writing node equations by inspection. If any doubt should arise, the easiest procedure is to write KCL in terms of branch voltages and then substitute the node transformation, before rewriting them in standard form.

As an example consider the network shown in Fig. 12. The conven-

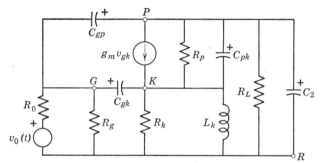

Fig. 12. Example for writing node equations.

tional notation of vacuum tube circuitry is used here. (Drawing L_k in parallel with R_k is not too realistic but is done to simplify the example.) Again only the minimum of references have been shown. This is a good example for node equations as there are eight loops to be considered whereas only three node equations are required. Choosing R as the reference node, the node equations are

$$
\begin{array}{l}
\begin{array}{c}
P \\ \\ \\ G \\ \\ \\ K
\end{array}
\left[
\begin{array}{ccc}
\left[\left(sC_{gp}+\dfrac{1}{R_p}+sC_{pk}\right) \atop +\dfrac{1}{R_L}+sC_2\right) & (-sC_{gp}+g_m) & \left(\dfrac{1}{R_p}-sC_{pk}-g_m\right) \\[3ex]
-sC_{gp} & \left(\dfrac{1}{R_0}+\dfrac{1}{R_g}+sC_{gp}+sC_{gk}\right) & -sC_{gk} \\[3ex]
-\dfrac{1}{R_p}-sC_{pk} & (-sC_{gk}-g_m) & \left(\left(\dfrac{1}{R_k}+\dfrac{1}{R_p}+sC_{gk}+sC_{pk}\right) \atop +\dfrac{1}{sL_k}+g_m\right)
\end{array}
\right]
\left[
\begin{array}{c}
V_p \\ V_g \\ V_k
\end{array}
\right]
\end{array}
$$

$$
=\left[\begin{array}{c} 0 \\ \dfrac{V_0(s)}{R_0} \\ 0 \end{array}\right]+\left[\begin{array}{c} 0 \\ 0 \\ -\dfrac{i_{Lk}(0+)}{s} \end{array}\right]+\left[\begin{array}{c} C_{gp}v_{pg}(0+)+C_{pk}v_{pk}(0+)+C_{pk}v_{pk}(0+) \\ -C_{gp}v_{pg}(0+)+C_{gk}v_{gk}(0+) \\ -C_{gk}v_{gk}(0+)-C_{pk}v_{pk}(0+) \end{array}\right] \qquad (68)
$$

The terms of the coefficient matrix other than the g_m's are easily obtained. On the main diagonal we simply have the sum of the admittances connected to the node. In the off-diagonal position, say $(1, 2)$, we have the negative sum of the admittances between nodes P and G.

In terms of node voltages, we see immediately that

$$V_{gk}(s) = V_g(s) - V_k(s) \tag{69}$$

so that the current of the dependent source is simply

$$g_m V_{gk} = g_m[V_g(s) - V_k(s)] \tag{70}$$

This term enters the equations at nodes P and K. When we transpose this term to the left side we get the four g_m's in the coefficient matrix. The independent driver $v_0(t)$ enters the equation for node G. Since it is on the right side, the term $[V_0(s)$ times series admittance] enters the equation at G with a plus sign, as the reference plus is nearer node G.

The arguments for initial conditions are similar to those in loop equations. In general, the initial inductance currents enter the equations as current sources would and the initial capacitance voltages enter as voltage sources would. In the next section we will discuss this statement more fully.

4.3 Initial Conditions

In deriving the equations for a network up to this point we have taken the mathematician's point of view on initial conditions, namely that these were "somehow" specified. However, as engineers it is our business to find these initial conditions. The only initial conditions we need are the initial capacitance voltages and the initial inductance currents. We need these as right hand limits as t approaches zero (the time zero being some reference time chosen conveniently), as denoted by $v_C(0+)$ and $i_L(0+)$. These currents and voltages are branch variables, not loop or node variables.

The conditions that we are looking for are the initial values of the solutions of the integrodifferential equations. Since they are initial conditions, they can be (intuitively) expected to depend upon the past history of the system. As they are right hand limits ($0+$ values), they will also be functions of the state of the system after $t = 0$. Thus we should expect to make use of both the past history of the system and the configuration for $t > 0$, in computing $i_L(0+)$ and $v_C(0+)$. In general they cannot be computed knowing the past history alone or knowing the configuration of the network for $t > 0$ alone.

Let us elaborate on this point just a little more. The system of differential equations written for the network for $t > 0$ cannot possibly tell us what the value of the solution is at $t = 0$. The specification of initial conditions is unrelated to the system of differential equations. There is no standard procedure in mathematics that we can use for computing the initial conditions for any physical system. The computation of initial conditions requires additional knowledge of the physical system over and above the differential equations. To put it another way, we normally choose $t = 0$ as the time when some change takes place in the system; either some switch is closed, or some generator voltage or current is discontinuous, etc. Under these conditions we cannot expect that the derivatives will exist at $t = 0$. In other words the differential equations are meaningless at such points in time; no information can be expected from the differential equations about what happens across discontinuities. Something else is needed, something that we have not introduced up to this point.

A question may be asked at this point from a purely physical point of view. Why do we have to "compute" $i_L(0+)$ and $v_C(0+)$ when we "know" that in any physical system the inductance currents and capacitance voltages are always continuous. The answer to this question is simple: the reason is *idealization*. The networks that we deal with and analyze are *models*. An inductance should not be thought of as a coil of wire. The current in a physical coil of wire will be continuous because the model for a coil needs series and/or shunt resistance (and even capacitance), in addition to inductance, for its complete representation. Similar statements are true for any physical component. If we are willing to say that our generators, inductances, and capacitances will always come with series and shunt resistances connected as shown in Fig. 13, and that we won't *admit* any single elements in the network

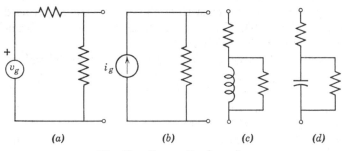

Fig. 13.   Composite elements.

but will consider these composite devices as units, then all currents and voltages of the inductances and capacitances in these units will be continuous and the present section will be unnecessary.

Although such a procedure is physically justifiable, it is extremely inconvenient from a theoretical point of view. If this procedure is used, the equations of a network consisting of even a few of these composite units will become very complicated. All of the techniques of network synthesis that have been developed will be useless. A great many practical networks—filters, interstage networks, wave shaping networks etc.—are designed on the idealized basis, and nobody is going to give them up merely to avoid discontinuous currents in inductances and discontinuous voltages in capacitances.

A different question may be asked by those mathematically inclined and familiar with the classical theory of differential equations. Most existence theorems and classical procedures are based on the concept that initial conditions are "arbitrary." In a system of differential equations that has the maximum order which it can possibly have, this is true. The system of equations associated with a network will have the maximum possible order, if the branches are as shown in Fig. 13. Under these conditions therefore we may set $i_L(0-) = i_L(0+)$, $v_C(0-) = v_C(0+)$ and expect normal solutions. If idealized R, L, and C branches, voltage generators, and current generators are arbitrarily connected together, the system may not have the maximum possible order. It is only when such degeneracies are present that discontinuities in inductance currents and capacitance voltages are encountered. No existence theorems have been proved by mathematicians for these cases without making assumptions about the existence of derivatives higher than those required by the differential equations.

Having disposed of these questions let us ask some practical questions from the point of view of the network analyst. How can we recognize situations in which discontinuities in inductance currents and capacitance voltages are likely to occur? What physical principles are involved? Finally, what can we do about them?

The situations in which these functions may be discontinuous are those that demand discontinuities for the satisfaction of Kirchhoff's current and voltage laws. In the case of capacitance voltages, loops consisting exclusively of capacitances, or capacitances and voltage generators *may* lead to discontinuous capacitance voltages. Two situations are possible. Either we may suddenly establish the loop in question (by closing a switch) or the voltage of the generator in the loop may be a discontinuous function. In the first case we demand the satisfaction of Kirchhoff's voltage law after the closure of the switch, whereas the voltages before closure are completely arbitrary. In the second case, we demand that the sum of the voltages across the capacitances in the loop be discontinuous. Obviously, something has to "give" if we are to have a consistent system.

Analogously, it may be expected that inductance currents will be discontinuous when there are junctions or effective junctions * at which only inductances and current generators are present.   Here again Kirchhoff's current law may demand a discontinuity if we suddenly establish the junction by closing or opening a switch, or if the current of the generator is discontinuous.   Thus, it is quite easy to recognize these degenerate situations.   (Figure 14 gives a few examples of such net-

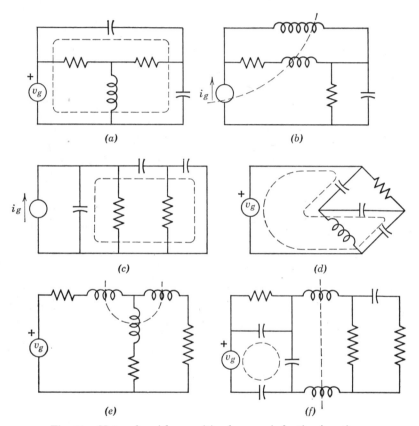

Fig. 14.   Networks with capacitive loops or inductive junctions.

works.   The dotted lines indicate the degeneracy.)   In all other cases the functions $i_L(t)$ and $v_C(t)$ are continuous and we may let

---

* By an *effective junction* of inductances and current generators we mean a junction at which only inductances and current generators would meet if we suitably interchanged series connected two terminal subnetworks or shorted some branches. Thus, an effective junction is the same as a *cut set*.

$$i_L(0+) = i_L(0-)$$
$$v_C(0+) = v_C(0-)$$
(71)

Now for the next question. The physical principles involved are those which are one step up in the hierarchy from Kirchhoff's laws—namely, conservation of charge and conservation of flux linkages. The *principle of conservation of charge* applied to a network states that the total charge transferred into a junction or out of a junction at any time is zero. The *principle of conservation of flux linkages* states that $\Sigma L_j i_j(t)$ summed over any closed loop is continuous. These two principles *cannot* be derived from Kirchhoff's laws. If they could, we wouldn't need to introduce them at all; we could derive everything from Kirchhoff's laws.

Finally, what can we do about these discontinuities? There are two avenues open to us, conventional mathematics or unconventional computations. If we wish to follow conventional mathematics, getting well-behaved (ordinary) functions for our currents and voltages, we have to compute the discontinuities using the required physical principles and put in the $(0+)$ values in the loop and node equations. Or, we may disregard mathematical rules and substitute the $(0-)$ values where the loop or node equations ask for $(0+)$ values. Now the solutions will not be ordinary functions, but will contain the so-called *impulse function*. We shall consider both of these procedures.

Let us first consider the procedure within the framework of conventional mathematics. We have seen that the only time a capacitance voltage needs to be discontinuous is when the network contains loops consisting of capacitances only or capacitances and voltage generators. In such cases only the voltages of the capacitances within the loop are discontinuous. Since we wish to compute these discontinuities only (at present), we might as well remove all other branches from the network. That is, we can first remove all the resistances, inductances, and current generators. If there are any capacitances that are not in a loop, we remove them too, since their voltages will be continuous. Now, we are left with a subnetwork consisting only of capacitances and voltage generators. To this network we apply Kirchhoff's voltage law and the equations of conservation of charge. The charge that we are concerned with is the charge that is instantaneously transferred, at the time of the discontinuity. The equation of conservation of charge says that the total charge transferred out of a junction must be zero. This result has the same form as Kirchhoff's current law. Therefore, we can use the *loop charge* variables and adopt a method of solution analogous to loop equations. Let us illustrate these remarks with an example.

Consider the network shown in Fig. 15. Since all voltages in this network would be expected to remain finite [assuming $v_g(t)$ is finite],

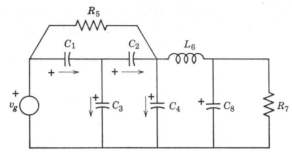

Fig. 15.   Network with discontinuous capacitance voltages.

no charge can be instantaneously transferred through R_5, L_6, or R_7, and therefore also through C_8. Hence, for the purpose of computing instantaneous charge transfer we may delete these branches and consider only the remaining subnetwork, as shown in Fig. 16. In a network of this

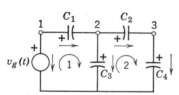

Fig. 16.   Simplified network.

type the capacitance voltage may be discontinuous either because the network is suddenly established by closing a switch or because the voltage $v_g(t)$ is a discontinuous function.

Let $v_k(0-)$ be the voltage of capacitance k before the discontinuity. Let q_k be the instantaneous charge moved into branch k in the direction of the reference arrow. Then the voltage on capacitance k after the charge transfer is obviously

$$v_k(0+) = v_k(0-) + q_k/C_k \qquad (72)$$

This expression will take the place of the v-i relations of a capacitance at $t = 0$, as it should. The equations of conservation of charge transfer are

$$q_g + q_1 = 0 \quad \text{(node 1)}$$

$$-q_1 + q_2 + q_3 = 0 \quad \text{(node 2)} \qquad (73)$$

$$-q_2 + q_4 = 0 \quad \text{(node 3)}$$

omitting the last node.

These equations are solved by using the loop charges, which are defined in a manner analogous to the definition of loop currents. In the present case the loop charges are the same as q_1 and q_2. The branch charges expressed in terms of the loop charges (the mesh transformation) are

$$q_g = -q_1$$

$$q_3 = q_1 - q_2 \tag{74}$$

$$q_4 = q_2$$

Kirchhoff's voltage law, written for $(0+)$, demands that

$$v_g(0+) = v_1(0+) + v_3(0+)$$
$$0 = v_2(0+) - v_3(0+) + v_4(0+) \tag{75}$$

On inserting the q-v relation of Eq. (72) and the loop transformation in Eq. (74) into these KVL equations, we get

$$\begin{bmatrix} \dfrac{1}{C_1} + \dfrac{1}{C_3} & -\dfrac{1}{C_3} \\[2ex] -\dfrac{1}{C_3} & \dfrac{1}{C_2} + \dfrac{1}{C_3} + \dfrac{1}{C_4} \end{bmatrix} \begin{bmatrix} q_1 \\[1ex] q_2 \end{bmatrix} = \begin{bmatrix} v_g(0+) - v_1(0-) - v_3(0-) \\[1ex] v_3(0-) - v_2(0-) - v_4(0-) \end{bmatrix} \tag{76}$$

We could obviously have written down this equation by inspection (without going through the intermediate steps) by analogy with loop equations.

Solving Eq. (76) we find the loop charges q_1 and q_2.

$$\begin{bmatrix} q_1 \\[1ex] q_2 \end{bmatrix} = K \begin{bmatrix} \dfrac{1}{C_2} + \dfrac{1}{C_3} + \dfrac{1}{C_4} & \dfrac{1}{C_3} \\[2ex] \dfrac{1}{C_3} & \dfrac{1}{C_1} + \dfrac{1}{C_3} \end{bmatrix} \begin{bmatrix} v_g(0+) - v_1(0-) - v_3(0-) \\[1ex] v_3(0-) - v_2(0-) - v_4(0-) \end{bmatrix}$$

$$\tag{77}$$

where K is given by

$$K = \cfrac{1}{\dfrac{1}{C_1}\left(\dfrac{1}{C_2} + \dfrac{1}{C_4}\right) + \dfrac{1}{C_3}\left(\dfrac{1}{C_1} + \dfrac{1}{C_2} + \dfrac{1}{C_4}\right)}$$

These are the loop charges instantaneously transferred at the discontinuity. Going back to Eq. (74) we can find the charges transferred into the capacitances and finally from Eq. (72) we can find the capacitance voltages after the change. In this development we could just as well have used nodal analysis if we had liked.

We shall now proceed to an evaluation of initial inductance currents.

Let us first examine the principle of continuity of flux linkage as applied to an electrical network before formulating a computational procedure. Since flux is a magnetic field concept, we have to appeal to field theory in the present discussion. Momentarily, then, let us abandon our model and think of a physical network consisting of the interconnection of various physical components, including coils of wire. Focus attention on a closed path in this network formed by the conductors. (If there are capacitors on this path, assume the path is closed across the gap.) The surface which is bounded by the conductors forming this closed path is of particular interest. This surface is rather contorted because part of the contour of the surface is made up of coils of wire. There is a certain magnetic flux over this surface which is principally through the part of the surface enclosed by the turns of the coil. The principle of continuity of flux linkage demands that the total flux enclosed by the closed loop be continuous.

Let us again return to our model. In the model there is no flux straying around the closed loops. The flux is assumed to be completely within the confines of the inductance. The flux, or flux linkage, associated with any inductance L_j with a current i_j is defined as $L_j i_j$. Let us see the implications of the principle of continuity of flux linkage at a point of discontinuity of the current in an inductance. Let $t = 0$ be the time at which the discontinuity occurs and let the "flux transferred" be defined as

$$\lambda_j = L_j\{i_j(0+) - i_j(0-)\} \tag{78}$$

This can be rewritten as

$$i_j(0+) = i_j(0-) + \frac{\lambda_j}{L_j} \tag{79}$$

The reference direction of λ_j is the same as that of i_j. Compare the last expression with the corresponding one for capacitance voltage given in Eq. (72).

Now, if we sum λ_j's around a loop, taking the current references into account, we get the total instantaneous change in flux, which must be zero since the total flux must be continuous. Thus, λ_j's as defined by Eq. (78) satisfy the same equations as branch voltages. This is not surprising in view of Faraday's law of induction.

The three systems of equations that we shall use for the computation of $i_L(0+)$ are

1. Continuity of flux linkages,
2. λ-i relationships (Eq. 78),
3. KCL, which must be satisfied by $i_j(0+)$.

These equations have the same general structure as network equations themselves, and so we may use the loop or the node method of analysis.

Let us illustrate the node system with an example. The network is shown in Fig. 17. Due to the fact that two inductances and a current

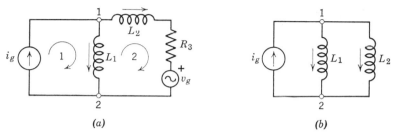

(a)   (b)

Fig. 17. Network with discontinuous inductance currents.

generator are the only branches tied to node 1, we may recognize this network as one in which the inductance currents might be discontinuous, either due to switching or due to the generator current being discontinuous. If the generator current is discontinuous, at least one of the inductance currents has to be discontinuous. Thus, the current generators have to be included somehow in our computations. Therefore, we shall associate a λ-variable with a current generator also. (That is, a current generator is also a "flux source.") The continuity of flux principle applied to the two loops of Fig. 17 will give

$$\lambda_g + \lambda_1 = 0$$
$$-\lambda_1 + \lambda_2 = 0$$

(80)

Since these equations have the same coefficient matrix as Kirchhoff's voltage law, the node transformation is valid and we may write

$$-\lambda_g = \lambda_1 = \lambda_2$$

(81)

In this special case the node transformation is seen to be a direct solution of Eqs. (80).

Kirchhoff's current law applied at junction 1, which is valid at (0+), requires

$$-i_g(0+) + i_1(0+) + i_2(0+) = 0$$

(82)

If we substitute the λ-i relations from Eq. (79), this becomes

$$\frac{\lambda_1}{L_1} + i_1(0-) + \frac{\lambda_2}{L_2} + i_2(0-) = i_g(0+)$$

(83)

Using the node transformation, we have finally,

$$\lambda_1 \left(\frac{1}{L_1} + \frac{1}{L_2} \right) = i_g(0+) - i_1(0-) - i_2(0-) \tag{84}$$

or

$$\lambda_1 = \lambda_2 = \frac{L_1 L_2}{L_1 + L_2} \{ i_g(0+) - i_1(0-) - i_2(0-) \} \tag{85}$$

With the λ's known, we can find $i_1(0+)$ and $i_2(0+)$, using Eq. (79).

The same procedure can be used if we have magnetic coupling in addition to inductance junctions. We merely have to modify the definition of λ. Instead of the scalar Eq. (78), we write the matrix equation

$$\Lambda_b = L_b \{ i_L(0+) - i_L(0-) \} \tag{86}$$

where

$$\Lambda_b = \begin{bmatrix} \lambda_1 \\ \lambda_2 \\ \cdot \\ \cdot \\ \cdot \\ \lambda_n \end{bmatrix} \tag{87}$$

Let us illustrate by means of a second example the use of loop analysis and the effect of mutual inductance in the computation of initial currents.

In the network of Fig. 18 we may expect discontinuities in inductance

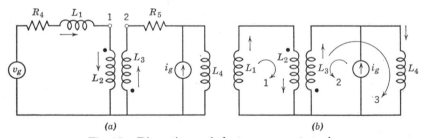

(a)   (b)

Fig. 18. Discontinuous inductance currents again.

currents due to the inductance junction 1 and the inductance-current generator junction 2. As before, the resistances, capacitances, and voltage generators make no contribution to the flux, and so for the purposes of the present computation the network of Fig. 18a may be replaced by that of Fig. 18b.

Since we wish to adopt loop analysis, we choose the loops in such a way that the current generator appears in only one loop. The loop initial currents are seen to be

Loop 1: $i_1(0+)$ (same as the initial current in L_2)
Loop 2: $i_g(0+)$ (same as the initial generator current)
Loop 3: $i_4(0+)$ (same as the initial current in L_4)

The continuity of flux linkage equations are

$$
\begin{bmatrix} 1 & 1 & 0 & 0 \\ 0 & 0 & -1 & 0 \\ 0 & 0 & 1 & 1 \end{bmatrix}
\begin{bmatrix} \lambda_1 \\ \lambda_2 \\ \lambda_3 \\ \lambda_4 \end{bmatrix}
=
\begin{bmatrix} 0 \\ \lambda_g \\ 0 \end{bmatrix}
\tag{88}
$$

As usual in loop analysis, we neglect the second of these equations since the loop current is known. In the others we insert the λ-i relations, which are given by

$$
\begin{bmatrix} \lambda_1 \\ \lambda_2 \\ \lambda_3 \\ \lambda_4 \end{bmatrix}
=
\begin{bmatrix} L_1 & 0 & 0 & 0 \\ 0 & L_2 & M_{23} & 0 \\ 0 & M_{23} & L_3 & 0 \\ 0 & 0 & 0 & L_4 \end{bmatrix}
\begin{bmatrix} i_1(0+) - i_1(0-) \\ i_2(0+) - i_2(0-) \\ i_3(0+) - i_3(0-) \\ i_4(0+) - i_4(0-) \end{bmatrix}
\tag{89}
$$

The result will be

$$
\begin{bmatrix} 1 & 1 & 0 & 0 \\ 0 & 0 & 1 & 1 \end{bmatrix}
\begin{bmatrix} L_1 & 0 & 0 & 0 \\ 0 & L_2 & M_{23} & 0 \\ 0 & M_{23} & L_3 & 0 \\ 0 & 0 & 0 & L_4 \end{bmatrix}
\begin{bmatrix} i_1(0+) \\ i_2(0+) \\ i_3(0+) \\ i_4(0+) \end{bmatrix}
$$

$$
=
\begin{bmatrix} 1 & 1 & 0 & 0 \\ 0 & 0 & 1 & 1 \end{bmatrix}
\begin{bmatrix} L_1 & 0 & 0 & 0 \\ 0 & L_2 & M_{23} & 0 \\ 0 & M_{23} & L_3 & 0 \\ 0 & 0 & 0 & L_4 \end{bmatrix}
\begin{bmatrix} i_1(0-) \\ i_2(0-) \\ i_3(0-) \\ i_4(0-) \end{bmatrix}
\tag{90}
$$

In this form the principle of conservation of flux linkage is certainly placed in evidence. In this network $M_{23} > 0$, because the two magnetic polarity marks (dots) are both at the tails of the branch current references.
The mesh transformation for this case is

$$
\begin{bmatrix} i_1(0+) \\ i_2(0+) \\ i_3(0+) \\ i_4(0+) \end{bmatrix}
=
\begin{bmatrix} i_1(0+) \\ i_1(0+) \\ -i_g(0+) + i_4(0+) \\ i_4(0+) \end{bmatrix}
\tag{91}
$$

Inserting this equation into Eq. (90), performing the indicated multiplications, and transposing the known $i_g(0+)$ to the right side, we get the final equations.

$$\begin{bmatrix} L_1 + L_2 & M_{23} \\ M_{23} & L_3 + L_4 \end{bmatrix} \begin{bmatrix} i_1(0+) \\ i_4(0+) \end{bmatrix}$$

$$= \begin{bmatrix} L_1 i_1(0-) + L_2 i_2(0-) + M_{23} i_3(0-) \\ M_{23} i_2(0-) + L_3 i_3(0-) + L_4 i_4(0-) \end{bmatrix} + \begin{bmatrix} M_{23} i_g(0+) \\ L_3 i_g(0+) \end{bmatrix} \quad (92)$$

The right side is written as the sum of two columns simply to place in evidence the effects of the $(0-)$ values and the current generator. On solving Eq. (92) we can find the initial values $i_1(0+)$ and $i_4(0+)$. These, together with the mesh transformation (91), give all the initial inductance currents.

In this development we could just as well have used node equations. The only additional step necessary would be to invert the λ-i relations (89) to find $\mathbf{i}_L(0+)$ in terms of $\mathbf{\Lambda}$ and $\mathbf{i}_L(0-)$.

The preceding discussion has demonstrated that it is a simple matter to determine when the capacitance voltages and inductance currents are likely to be discontinuous. In such cases, a method for computing the discontinuities has also been discussed. The techniques are essentially the same as the ones we have already learned—namely, loop and node analyses.

Now let us turn to the alternative scheme of using impulse functions. First of all we have to know what the impulse function is; so let us digress a little to introduce the impulse and the related step function, as well as to study their important properties. For ease of reference we shall include this discussion in a separate section.

4.4   The Impulse Function

The impulse function has been the center of a great deal of controversy spread over the last half century. On critically examining the arguments pro and con, we can make the following broad statements about the impulse function. First of all the impulse is widely used by engineers and no "wrong answers" have been obtained by its judicious use. Secondly, the properties attributed to the impulse function are not justifiable on the basis of conventional mathematics. Finally, if one is willing to go to some extra trouble, it is quite possible to avoid the impulse function completely in electrical network theory.

In this section we wish to collect together all the discussion that we shall need about the impulse function, point out the mathematical difficulties, and give one use of the impulse, namely in solving network equations. Another use of the impulse function will be introduced in Chapter 6.

Since the impulse is very closely related to the step function, let us begin by defining the unit step function. The unit step function was used so widely by Oliver Heaviside that it is also called the Heaviside unit function.

The *unit step function* is defined as

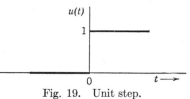

$$u(t) = 0 \qquad t < 0$$
$$u(t) = 1 \qquad t \geq 0 \tag{93}$$

Fig. 19. Unit step.

This is a perfectly well-defined, well-behaved mathematical function and is illustrated graphically in Fig. 19. The unit step as a driver is also easily interpretable. As a voltage driver it is simply a *d-c* source of 1 volt connected to the network at a specific time which we can call $t = 0$, the input to the network having been shorted up to that time. Figure 20 explains this equivalence. The position of the switch in Fig. 20*b* is changed at $t = 0$. We will also be interested in displaced unit step functions, i.e., functions which are zero up to $t = \tau$ and take on the value 1 for $t > \tau$. Such a function is obviously representable as

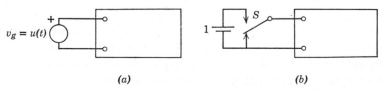

(a)   (b)

Fig. 20. Unit step voltage source applied to network.

$u(t - \tau)$. The unit step, as we can compute very easily, has the simple Laplace transform $1/s$.

$$L\{u(t)\} = \int_0^\infty \epsilon^{-st} u(t)\, dt = \frac{1}{s} \tag{94}$$

This fact, that the transform is a very simple function of s, makes the unit step useful in some applications. The delayed function $u(t - \tau)$ will have the transform $\epsilon^{-s\tau}/s$.

Let us now turn to the impulse function. The name impulse originated in mechanics. A force F acting on a body for a time Δt gives it an increase in momentum of $F\, \Delta t$. Frequently the time Δt is small enough so that no appreciable change in the motion of the body has taken place at the end of the interval Δt. The effect of the force at times later than Δt is fairly accurately predicted by considering that the increase in momentum—the impulse—has been given to the body at $t = 0$. Thus, an "impulsive force" is really an instantaneous change of momentum.

In a very similar manner, if a current i is applied to a capacitance for a time Δt, the charge deposited on one plate is $i\,\Delta t$. Again, if Δt is small enough so that very little effect is produced on voltages and currents in other parts of the network in which the capacitance is connected, the subsequent behavior of the network is fairly accurately described if we consider that the charge on the capacitance has been instantaneously changed by a nonzero amount. Thus, an "impulse of current" is nothing but a nonzero charge transferred instantaneously.

An analogous discussion applies to an impulse of voltage. This is simply a nonzero change of flux in zero time.

In all of the above situations, a nonzero change in some physical quantity takes place in a short but nonzero time. In many cases, this time is small enough so that other changes in the state of the system are small. The subsequent behavior of the system can be approximated quite closely by assuming that the change in the physical quantity occurs in zero time.

For purposes of discussion suppose we think of a short pulse of current which is applied to a network. In the idealized approximation, we wish to describe the current analytically in such a way that, even though it acts for zero time, the same amount of charge is transported into the network. There is no reason to believe that such a function exists. Nevertheless, the intuitive feeling is that the desired function must look like a very narrow, tall pulse. This desired function is the *impulse function*.

There are various "definitions" of the impulse function. One of these definitions goes as follows. Let $f_n(t)$ be a sequence of pulses defined by

$$
\begin{aligned}
f_n(t) &= 0 & t &< 0 \\[2mm]
&= n & 0 &\le t < \frac{1}{n} \\[2mm]
&= 0 & t &> \frac{1}{n}
\end{aligned}
\tag{95}
$$

For example the functions $f_1(t)$, $f_2(t)$, and $f_4(t)$ are shown in Fig. 21. Thus, each $f_n(t)$ is a pulse. As n increases, the pulse width becomes

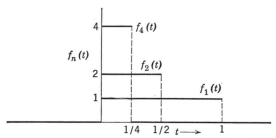

Fig. 21. Definition of impulse.

smaller and the height increases, both indefinitely. Also, for each n, the area under the pulse is unity. That is,

$$\int_0^\epsilon f_n(t) = 1 \qquad \text{if } \epsilon > \frac{1}{n} \tag{96}$$

Thus, if ϵ is any positive number ($\epsilon > 0$), then

$$\lim_{n \to \infty} \int_0^\epsilon f_n(t) = 1 \tag{97}$$

since $1/n$ becomes smaller than ϵ for all sufficiently large n. The impulse function $\delta_1(t)$ is now defined as

$$\delta_1(t) = \lim_{n \to \infty} f_n(t) \tag{98}$$

Quite obviously

$$\delta_1(t) = 0 \qquad \text{if } t \neq 0 \qquad (a)$$
$$\delta_1(0) = \infty \qquad\qquad\qquad (b) \tag{99}$$

It is usually formally written that

$$\delta_1(t) = \frac{d}{dt} u(t) \tag{100}$$

$$\int_{-\infty}^t \delta_1(x)\, dx = u(t) \tag{101}$$

Equation (100) is justifiable on the basis of Eq. (99). But, if $\delta_1(t)$ is interpreted as an ordinary point function, then Eq. (101) introduces a very fundamental inconsistency in our mathematics since the ordinary (Riemann) integral is a continuous function of the upper limit, whereas $u(t)$ is obviously discontinuous. It is not difficult to determine the source of the difficulty. Let us substitute the definition of the impulse function from Eq. (98) into the left hand side of the last equation. The result will be

$$\int_{-\infty}^{t} \delta_1(x) \, dx = \int_{-\infty}^{t} \{ \lim_{n \to \infty} f_n(x) \} \, dx \qquad (102)$$

On comparing this with Eq. (97) we see that Eq. (101) implies

$$\lim_{n \to \infty} \int_{-\infty}^{t} f_n(x) \, dx = \int_{-\infty}^{t} \{ \lim_{n \to \infty} f_n(x) \} \, dx \qquad (103)$$

This interchange of operations—the limit on n and the integral—is not justifiable because the convergence of the integral is not uniform. In fact, in the sense of an improper Riemann integral of a real function,

$$\int_{-\infty}^{t} \delta_1(x) \, dx \equiv 0 \qquad \text{all } t \qquad (104)$$

as can be verified directly.

There are other ways of defining the impulse function, some involving continuous and differentiable functions $f_n(t)$ but each of them will contain the same sort of interchange of operations which is not justifiable.

The functions $f_n(t)$ defined in Eq. (95) have the following Laplace transform.

$$\mathcal{L}\{f_n(t)\} = \frac{n}{s} \{ 1 - \epsilon^{-s/n} \} \qquad (105)$$

If we expand the exponential function as a power series, we can rewrite Eq. (105) as

$$\mathcal{L}\{f_n(t)\} = \frac{n}{s} \left\{ 1 - 1 + \frac{s}{n} - \sum_{k=2}^{\infty} \left(-\frac{s}{n} \right)^k \cdot \frac{1}{k!} \right\}$$

$$= 1 + \sum_{k=2}^{\infty} \frac{1}{k!} \left(-\frac{s}{n} \right)^{k-1} \qquad (106)$$

For any fixed s, the series in the last line of this expression approaches 0 as n approaches ∞.

Thus, as n increases, the transform of $f_n(t)$ gets closer and closer to 1. In other words

$$\lim_{n \to \infty} \mathcal{L}[f_n(t)] = 1 \qquad (107)$$

Let us now write the Laplace transform of the unit impulse from its definition in Eq. (98). If we again interchange the two operations of taking the Laplace integral and taking the limit (which is again not justifiable if $\delta_1(t)$ is interpreted as a point function), we get

$$\mathcal{L}[\delta_1(t)] = \mathcal{L}\left\{\lim_{n\to\infty} f_n(t)\right\}$$

$$\stackrel{?}{=} \lim_{n\to\infty} \mathcal{L}[f_n(t)] = 1 \tag{108}$$

Thus, we can make the claim that the Laplace transform of the impulse function is unity only if the interchange of operations is permissible.

Let us now view the situation from transform theory. From the theory of Laplace transforms of real functions, we know that for any transform function $F(s)$

$$\lim_{s\to\infty} F(s) = 0 \tag{109}$$

provided s approaches ∞ in the sector

$$|\arg s| \leq \pi/2 - \epsilon, \qquad \epsilon > 0 \tag{110}$$

The function $F(s) = 1$ certainly will not satisfy this condition. Therefore, *this function is not the transform of any ordinary real-valued (point) function $f(t)$.*

The fact that there is no ordinary point function with a transform 1 does not imply that there is no other entity with a transform 1. Such an entity has been invented by the French mathematician Laurent Schwarz and is known as a *distribution*. A distribution is not an ordinary point function but a "continuous linear functional," which is a very different kind of animal. Its domain of definition is an abstract space of functions and its range is another abstract space. The theory of distributions is far too complicated for us to give an elementary discussion of the subject with the mathematics assumed in this text.*

With the aid of this theory it is possible to justify the answers that have been obtained using the impulse functions. The "Dirac Distribution δ" has properties analogous to those attributed to the impulse function.

Because the impulse function is so widely used we shall continue to call it an impulse function in this text and talk about it as if it were an ordinary point function. None of these statements are mathematically meaningful unless we interpret the impulse function as a distribution. (There are certain philosophical questions to be answered if

---

* Interested readers are referred to the following sources:

(1) Laurent Schwarz, *Theorie des Distributions*, Hermann et Cie, Paris, 1950–51.

(2) Sir George Temple, *J. London Math. Soc.*, Vol. 28, 1953, pp. 134–148; *Proc. Roy Soc.* (A) Vol. 338, 1955, pp. 175–190.

(3) Halperin, *Introduction to the Theory of Distributions*, Canadian Math. Congress, University of Toronto Press, 1952.

(4) P. W. Ketchum and R. Aboudi, *Schwartz Distributions*, Second Midwest Symposium on Circuit Theory, 1956, pp. 5.1–5.17.

we wish to call a current or a voltage, a distribution. We shall not concern ourselves with these questions.)

None of the preceding discussion is affected if we multiply the unit impulse by a constant k. In the function $k\delta_1(t)$ the number k is called the *strength* of the impulse. The name *unit impulse* or *impulse of strength* 1 is given to $\delta_1(t)$.

There is one more property of the impulse function that is frequently useful. This is the so-called sampling property, defined by

$$\int_0^\infty g(t)\, \delta(t - \tau)\, dt = g(\tau) \tag{111}$$

for a function $g(t)$ which is continuous at τ. The result is "proved" by methods similar to the ones used earlier. For any continuous function $g(t)$, and using the function $f_n(t)$ as defined in Eq. (95), we get

$$\int_0^\infty g(t)f_n(t - \tau)\, dt = \int_\tau^{\tau+\frac{1}{n}} ng(t)\, dt \tag{112}$$

Now using the continuity of $g(t)$ at $t = \tau$, we can easily show that

$$\lim_{n \to \infty} \int_0^\infty g(t)f_n(t - \tau)\, dt = g(\tau) \tag{113}$$

Once again interchanging the limit and integral in Eq. (113), we get

$$\int_0^\infty g(t)\delta(t - \tau)dt = g(\tau) \tag{114}$$

Note that this interchange of limits is again not justifiable on the basis of conventional mathematics.

Since we have obtained the unit impulse by differentiating the unit step, there is no reason why we should not repeat this process and derive a new function $\delta_2(t)$, such that

$$\delta_2(t) = \frac{d}{dt}\, \delta_1(t) \tag{115}$$

and

$$\int_{-\infty}^t \delta_2(x)\, dx = \delta_1(t) \tag{116}$$

Such a function $\delta_2(t)$ is called a *doublet* or a *second order impulse*. It is even more peculiar than $\delta_1(t)$. The function $\delta_2(t)$ may be alternately defined as follows. Let $g_n(t)$ be a sequence of functions defined by

$$g_n(t) = \begin{cases} 0 & t < 0 \\ n^2 & 0 \le t < 1/n \\ -n^2 & 1/n \le t < 2/n \\ 0 & t > 2/n \end{cases} \tag{117}$$

The function $g_n(t)$ has the shape shown in Fig. 22. Then the second-

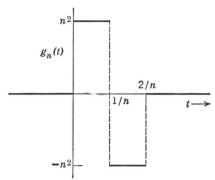

Fig. 22.   Definition of doublet.

order impulse is defined as

$$\delta_2(t) = \lim_{n \to \infty} g_n(t) \tag{118}$$

Thus

$$\delta_2(t) = 0 \quad \text{if } t \ne 0 \qquad (a)$$
$$\delta_2(0) = \infty \text{ and } -\infty \text{ } simultaneously \qquad (b) \tag{119}$$

The Laplace transform of $\delta_2(t)$ can now be "calculated" as

$$\mathcal{L}\{\delta_2(t)\} = s \tag{120}$$

It is clear how this same procedure may be repeated to give higher order impulses. For the nth *order impulse* we find

$$\mathcal{L}\{\delta_n(t)\} = s^{n-1} \tag{121}$$

As far as we are concerned, the following "rules of operation" with the impulse function $\delta_1(t)$ can be stated.

$$\int_{-\infty}^{t} k\delta_1(x) \, dx = ku(t) \qquad (k \text{ constant}) \tag{122}$$

$$\int_{-\infty}^{t} f(t)\delta_1(t - \tau) \, dt = f(\tau) \qquad (f \text{ continuous}) \tag{123}$$

$$\mathcal{L}\{\delta_1(t)\} = 1 \tag{124}$$

4.5 Impulse Functions and Initial Values

Let us now discuss the use of impulse functions in avoiding the computation of initial values whenever discontinuities in voltages and currents are likely to occur.

To begin with, let us interpret discontinuities in capacitance voltages and inductance currents as impulses. When a capacitance voltage is discontinuous, we say that some charge is instantaneously transferred from one plate of the capacitance to the other. Thus the charge on the capacitance is a step function. Since current is the time derivative of charge, we see from our discussion that the current in the capacitance contains an impulse occurring at the time of the discontinuity. The strength of the current impulse is exactly that which is required to transfer the charge. Quantitatively, the current through the capacitance is

$$i_C(t) = C[v_C(\tau+) - v_C(\tau-)]\delta(t - \tau) \tag{125}$$

where the discontinuity occurs at τ.

Similarly, when an inductance current is discontinuous at $t = \tau$, we say that a voltage impulse occurs across the inductance, instantaneously changing the flux linkage associated with the inductance. Quantitatively, the voltage impulse is

$$v_L(t) = L[i_L(\tau+) - i_L(\tau-)]\delta(t - \tau) \tag{126}$$

Notice that under both of these conditions, the energy stored (in the capacitance and inductance) is also discontinuous.

Let us now return to the loop and node equations and determine how we can avoid calculating (0+) values in those singular networks which contain capacitance loops or inductance junctions. The process is very simple; we proceed as if all capacitance voltages and inductance currents are continuous and substitute (0−) values whenever (0+) values are called for. When we get the transforms of the loop currents or node voltages, we will find that these are not proper rational functions; that is, they do not go to zero when s approaches ∞. Hence, the solution will contain impulses at $t = 0$. Let us illustrate these remarks by means of an example.

Consider the network shown in Fig. 23. The source voltage and the elements are also given.

$$R_1 = R_2 = 1$$
$$C_1 = C_2 = \tfrac{1}{2}$$
$$C_3 = \tfrac{1}{3}$$
$$v_g(t) = u(t) \quad \text{(unit step)}$$

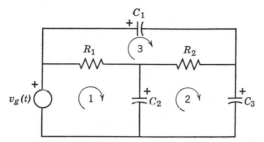

Fig. 23.   Network with impulsive currents.

Due to the loop v_g, C_1, C_3, we may expect discontinuities in the capac-itance voltages.   Writing loop equations for the network, we get

$$
\begin{bmatrix}
R_1 + \dfrac{1}{sC_2} & -\dfrac{1}{sC_2} & -R_1 \\[2mm]
-\dfrac{1}{sC_2} & R_2 + \dfrac{1}{sC_2} + \dfrac{1}{sC_3} & -R_2 \\[2mm]
-R_1 & -R_2 & R_1 + R_2 + \dfrac{1}{sC_1}
\end{bmatrix}
\begin{bmatrix}
I_1(s) \\[2mm]
I_2(s) \\[2mm]
I_3(s)
\end{bmatrix}
$$

$$
=
\begin{bmatrix}
Vg(s) - \dfrac{v_{C_2}(0+)}{s} \\[3mm]
\dfrac{v_{C_2}(0+)}{s} - \dfrac{v_{C_3}(0+)}{s} \\[3mm]
-\dfrac{v_{C_1}(0+)}{s}
\end{bmatrix}
\quad (127)
$$

It is here that we make the modification.   Whereas these equations call for $v_C(0+)$, we shall, instead, insert $v_C(0-)$.   Substituting the given numbers, the modified equations become

$$
\begin{bmatrix}
1 + \dfrac{2}{s} & -\dfrac{2}{s} & -1 \\[2mm]
-\dfrac{2}{s} & 1 + \dfrac{5}{s} & -1 \\[2mm]
-1 & -1 & 2 + \dfrac{2}{s}
\end{bmatrix}
\begin{bmatrix}
I_1(s) \\[2mm]
I_2(s) \\[2mm]
I_3(s)
\end{bmatrix}
=
\begin{bmatrix}
\dfrac{1}{s} - \dfrac{v_{C_2}^-(0-)}{s} \\[3mm]
\dfrac{v_{C_2}(0-)}{s} - \dfrac{v_{C_3}(0-)}{s} \\[3mm]
-\dfrac{v_{C_1}(0-)}{s}
\end{bmatrix}
\quad (128)
$$

Solving these equations, we get

$$
\begin{bmatrix} I_1(s) \\ I_2(s) \\ I_3(s) \end{bmatrix} = \begin{bmatrix} \dfrac{s^3 + 12s^2 + 10s}{5s^2 + 26s + 12} & \dfrac{s^3 + 4s^2 + 4s}{5s^2 + 26s + 12} & \dfrac{s^3 + 7s^2}{5s^2 + 26s + 12} \\[2ex] \dfrac{s^3 + 4s^2 + 4s}{5s^2 + 26s + 12} & \dfrac{s^3 + 6s^2 + 4s}{5s^2 + 26s + 12} & \dfrac{s^3 + 4s^2}{5s^2 + 26s + 12} \\[2ex] \dfrac{s^3 + 7s^2}{5s^2 + 26s + 12} & \dfrac{s^3 + 4s^2}{5s^2 + 26s + 12} & \dfrac{s^3 + 7s^2 + 6s}{5s^2 + 26s + 12} \end{bmatrix}
$$

$$
\times \begin{bmatrix} \dfrac{1}{s} - \dfrac{v_{C_2}(0-)}{s} \\[2ex] \dfrac{v_{C_2}(0-)}{s} - \dfrac{v_{C_3}(0-)}{s} \\[2ex] -\dfrac{v_{C_1}(0-)}{s} \end{bmatrix} \qquad (129)
$$

In expanded form, these become

$$
I_1(s) = \frac{as^2 + bs + c}{5s^2 + 26s + 12}
$$

$$
I_2(s) = \frac{as^2 + ds + e}{5s^2 + 26s + 12} \qquad (130)
$$

$$
I_3(s) = \frac{as^2 + fs + g}{5s^2 + 26s + 12}
$$

where

$$a = 1 - v_{C_1}(0-) - v_{C_3}(0-)$$

$$b = 12 - 7v_{C_1}(0-) - 8v_{C_2}(0-) - 4v_{C_3}(0-)$$

$$c = 10 - 6v_{C_2}(0-) - 4v_{C_3}(0-)$$

$$d = 4 - 4v_{C_1}(0-) + 2v_{C_2}(0-) - 6v_{C_3}(0-)$$

$$e = 4 - 4v_{C_3}(0-)$$

$$f = 1 - 7v_{C_1}(0-) - 3v_{C_2}(0-) - 4v_{C_3}(0-)$$

$$g = -6v_{C_1}(0-)$$

Note that the coefficient of s^2 in all three numerators is the same. We can learn a great deal by examining these solutions. First of all, none of these functions is the Laplace transform of an ordinary function. They all have the same non-zero value at $s = \infty$, this value being

$$I_1(\infty) = I_2(\infty) = I_3(\infty) = \frac{1 - v_{C_1}(0-) - v_{C_3}(0-)}{5} \tag{131}$$

Notice that the numerator of this expression is simply the amount by which Kirchhoff's voltage law is not satisfied by the capacitance–voltage generator loop at $t = 0$, and the denominator is the sum of inverse capacitances in this loop. Thus the quantity on the right of Eq. (131) is simply the amount of charge that will be transferred into C_1 and C_3 at $t = 0$.

It is thus evident that each loop current contains an impulse, the strength of the impulse being exactly the amount required to satisfy Kirchhoff's voltage law for $t > 0$.

On examining Fig. 23, we may also note that the only *branch* currents that contain this impulse are those in the V_g, C_1, and C_3 branches. Thus, although we did not choose this capacitance–voltage generator loop as one of our loops, the solution gives us an impulse of current in only these branches. Actually by choosing loop currents differently we would be able to get loop currents only one of which has an impulse.

We can heuristically generalize from this example, even though the formal generalization is rather involved. (For the formal generalization, we have to find the degrees of the numerator and denominator in each transform, as well as the coefficients of the highest powers, by using network topology.) Whenever there is a capacitance loop or a capacitance–voltage generator loop in the network, the solution for the branch or loop currents *may* contain impulses. Since we use Kirchhoff's voltage law in obtaining the loop equations, the solutions for branch voltages will satisfy Kirchhoff's voltage law. Since a loop current impulse of strength k carries a charge k around the loop, conservation of charge transfer is automatically satisfied. Thus the impulse technique is merely a *combination* of the two steps: initial value computation and loop solution.

By analogy we should expect that the branch voltages in a network containing inductance junctions will contain impulses and we can find these if we put $i_L(0-)$ in the equations instead of $i_L(0+)$. This shall be illustrated with an example in which the node voltage solution contains impulses.

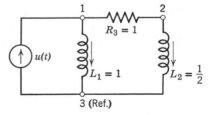

Fig. 24. Network with impulsive voltages.

In the network of Fig. 24, the inductance junction is not apparent, but it is placed in evidence by interchanging R_3 and L_2. Writing node equations and inserting $i_L(0-)$ in the equations in the place of $i_L(0+)$, we get

$$\begin{bmatrix} \dfrac{1}{R_3} + \dfrac{1}{sL_1} & -\dfrac{1}{R_3} \\[3mm] -\dfrac{1}{R_3} & \dfrac{1}{R_3} + \dfrac{1}{sL_2} \end{bmatrix} \begin{bmatrix} V_1(s) \\[3mm] V_2(s) \end{bmatrix} = \begin{bmatrix} I_g(s) - \dfrac{i_{L_1}(0-)}{s} \\[3mm] -\dfrac{i_{L_2}(0-)}{s} \end{bmatrix} \tag{132}$$

If we insert the given numerical values and solve for $V_1(s)$ and $V_2(s)$, the result will be

$$V_1(s) = \frac{[1 - i_{L_1}(0-) - i_{L_2}(0-)]s + [1 - i_{L_1}(0-)]}{3s + 2}$$

$$\tag{133}$$

$$V_2(s) = \frac{[1 - i_{L_1}(0-) - i_{L_2}(0-)]s - i_{L_2}(0-)}{3s + 2}$$

Here, again, the functions do not approach 0 as s approaches ∞ and so the node voltages will contain impulses. Both of these impulses have the same strength, whose value is given by

$$V_1(\infty) = V_2(\infty) = \frac{1 - i_{L_1}(0-) - i_{L_2}(0-)}{3} \tag{134}$$

We notice here too that the strength of each impulse is proportional to the amount by which the $(0-)$ values fail to satisfy Kirchhoff's current law. And the strength is exactly enough to transfer the required flux into L_1 and L_2 so that the $(0+)$ values will satisfy Kirchhoff's current law. As we can observe, there is no impulse of voltage across R_3.

Since the impulses are in the node voltages, Kirchhoff's voltage law is automatically satisfied and so is the continuity of flux linkage. Since node equations explicitly contain Kirchhoff's current law, the solutions of the node equations will also satisfy Kirchhoff's current law as $t \rightarrow 0+$. Thus the use of the impulse here, is equivalent to computing $i_L(0+)$ as we did earlier.

4.6 Duality

A striking parallelism is apparent in sections 4.1 and 4.2 between the developments of the loop and the node systems of equations. This observation raises the following interesting question. Is it possible to find two networks such that the loop equations for one network are the same as the node equations of the other network, except for the symbolism? In other words we would like to know whether the loop equations for one network can become the node equations for the other if we interchange the symbols v and i throughout. Looking back over our chart in section 4.1, p. 82, we see a possible way in which this might happen. If the following two conditions are satisfied, then the node equations of network 1 will become the loop equations of network 2, on interchanging the symbols v and i.

1. The Kirchhoff current law equations of network 1 are a suitable set of Kirchhoff voltage law equations of network 2 on substituting v_j for i_j.

2. The expression for branch voltage v_j of network 2 in terms of branch currents i_j becomes the expression for branch current i_j of network 1 in terms of branch voltages, on interchanging i_j and v_j.

Networks N_1 and N_2 which satisfy conditions 1 and 2 above are called *dual networks*. Strictly speaking we should call N_2 the dual of N_1. But it can be shown that if conditions 1 and 2 are satisfied, then we can interchange N_1 and N_2 and conditions 1 and 2 will still be satisfied. That is, if N_2 is the dual of N_1, then N_1 is the dual of N_2.

Condition 1 may be restated in terms of matrix notation as follows. Construct the matrix $A_1 = [a_{kj}]$ where the a_{kj}'s are defined by the Kirchhoff current law equations for network N_1. Then,

$$A_1 = B_2 = [b_{kj}] \tag{135}$$

where the b_{kj}'s are obtained from the Kirchhoff voltage law equations of network N_2. This statement obviously implies that the number of branches of the two networks must be equal, and that the number of independent KCL equations of one must be equal to the number of independent KVL equations of the other. That is,

$$N_{b1} = N_{b2} \tag{136}$$

$$N_{v1} - 1 = N_{b2} - N_{v2} + 1 \tag{137}$$

where the numerical subscripts refer to the networks and N_b, N_v are numbers of branches and junctions, respectively. Evidently this is a condition on the structure of the network. We are asking for two things. First, there must be a correspondence between the branches of the two networks, as defined by the ordering of columns in the matrices A_1 and B_2 to satisfy Eq. (135). Secondly, there must be a correspondence between the junctions of N_1 (rows of A_1) and loops of N_2 (rows of B_2).

Two structures which are related by Eq. (135) are known as *dual graphs*. The detailed study of the existence and characteristics of dual graphs would take us on a long excursion into topology which we have to pass up in this text.*

We can, however, say the following. If the two networks can be superimposed such that each junction of N_1 at which a current equation is written is inside a loop of N_2, and the references of corresponding elements are lined up suitably, then the row of A_1 and the row of B_2 will be identical. Such a node and loop are shown in Fig. 25. The branches

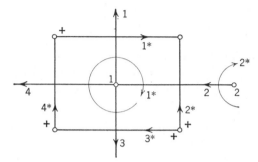

Fig. 25.   Dual loop and node.

of N_1 are numbered 1, 2, 3 and the branches of N_2 are numbered 1*, 2*, 3*, where 1 corresponds to 1*, etc. Junction 1 corresponds to loop 1*. It is left for you to verify that the equation at junction 1 and the equation for loop 1* have the same coefficients. At junction 2 we will have $+1$ as the coefficient of $i_2(t)$ in Kirchhoff's current law. To make $+1$ the coefficient of $v_2*(t)$ we see that loop 2* must be oriented as shown. By following through it can be seen that all the loops in N_2 must be oriented clockwise (or all counterclockwise with branch references reversed).

If windows are chosen for loops and all loops oriented clockwise (or all counterclockwise) then we can also observe that the off diagonal terms in loop equations all carry negative signs just as they do in node equations. In node equations the off diagonal terms all carry negative signs because we choose the conventions of writing Kirchhoff's current law as "away from the node" and the node voltages as having $+$ reference away from the reference node.

It is time for us to state the answer to the basic question of existence of dual structures. A network will have a geometrical (structural) dual if and only if it can be drawn on paper without cross-overs, i.e., only if

---

* Detailed discussions of the subject may be found in the following two papers.

(1) Whitney, H., "Non-Separable and Planar Graphs," *Trans-American Math. Society*, vol. 34, No. 2, pp. 339–362, 1932.

(2) Kuratowski, C., "Sur le Problem des Courbes Gauches en Topologie," *Fundamenta Matematicae*, vol. 15, pp. 271–283, 1930.

it is planar. For a planar network the dual is constructed exactly as in Fig. 25. Inside each region of the given network N_1 we place a node of the dual N_2. In addition we have a node outside N_1 (the reference node). Crossing each branch of N_1 we have a branch of N_2. These two are "corresponding" branches for the rest of the discussion. The references are next chosen such that the matrix of the Kirchhoff voltage law equations for N_1 (with all loops oriented clockwise) will be the same as the matrix of the Kirchhoff current law equations of N_2. (All the voltage references may be taken at the tail of the current reference for convenience.)

Condition 2 is relatively easy to satisfy. We have the dual pairs of v-i relationships as given in Fig. 26. The only element with no dual

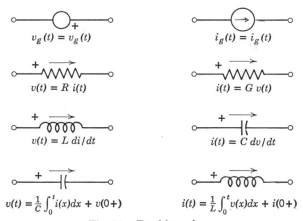

$$v_g(t) = v_g(t) \qquad\qquad i_g(t) = i_g(t)$$

$$v(t) = R\ i(t) \qquad\qquad i(t) = G\ v(t)$$

$$v(t) = L\ di/dt \qquad\qquad i(t) = C\ dv/dt$$

$$v(t) = \frac{1}{C}\int_0^t i(x)dx + v(0+) \qquad i(t) = \frac{1}{L}\int_0^t v(x)dx + i(0+)$$

Fig. 26. Dual branches.

relationship is a mutual inductance. Thus, by our definition of duality, only planar networks without mutual inductances have duals.

The construction of the dual of a given planar network is now evident. We first construct the structural dual as in Fig. 25. Then we make corresponding elements duals as in Fig. 26. The node equations of either network will be a suitable set of loop equations for the other. In terms of the coefficient matrices of the loop and node equations for N_1 and N_2,

$$Y_{n1} = Z_{m2} \tag{138}$$

$$Z_{m1} = Y_{n2} \tag{139}$$

Since the matrices are equal, their determinants, cofactors, etc., will all be equal. This fact is used to construct so-called inverse networks as we shall discuss later.

We will now illustrate the construction of a dual network by means of an example. Consider the diagrams in Fig. 27. The original network is the one in Fig. 27a. The geometrical construction of the dual is shown in Fig. 27b and the final network, with the branches properly chosen, is given in Fig. 27c. The current of the source, $i_g{}^*$, must be the same function of t as the voltage of the dual source, $v_g{}^*$.

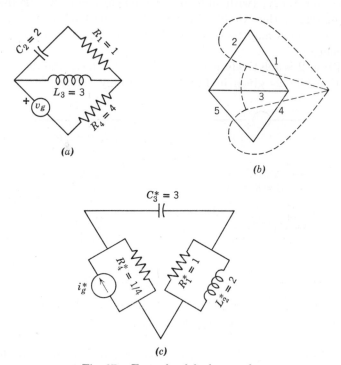

(a)
(b)
(c)

Fig. 27.   Example of dual networks.

We can now see the justification of procedure 4 in section 2 for choosing loops; namely, for a planar network, we choose the windows of the network for the loops. This is one of the first methods of writing loop equations that undergraduate students learn. To justify the procedure, we have to consider the dual network. Let the original network be N_1 and the dual N_2. We have constructed a matrix $\mathbf{B}_1$ of the network N_1 by choosing the windows for loops. By our discussion, this matrix is also equal to the coefficient matrix of KCL equations for network N_2. Therefore, it has the rank $N_{v2} - 1$, which by Eq. (137) with the subscripts interchanged, is equal to $N_{b1} - N_{v1} + 1$, thus making $\mathbf{B}_1$ an appropriate matrix for KVL and the mesh transformation of N_1.

4.7   Network Functions, Driving Point and Transfer

In this text, we have been studying lumped linear networks entirely from the Laplace transform point of view. So far we have used Laplace transforms mainly as a tool, to compute the complete response of a given network to a specified excitation. But the real value of Laplace transforms in lumped network theory is that it allows us to associate analytic functions with networks, and thus enables us to use all the knowledge we have about analytic functions in our study of networks. Networks are most usefully characterized by their external behavior. This external behavior is most conveniently described by an analytic function or a set of analytic functions. It is our purpose, in this section to define these analytic functions describing a network, and to show how we can compute them using the loop and node systems of equations. You have probably met all of the concepts that we shall introduce in this section in steady-state circuit analysis. But in steady-state circuit analysis, these concepts are introduced as *complex numbers*, whereas we are going to define them as *analytic functions* of the complex variable s. We shall show in the next chapter how these analytic functions are related to the corresponding steady-state concepts.

By a *one terminal-pair network* or *one-port* we mean a network with two nodes specially designated as *input terminals.*

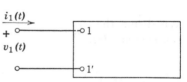

Fig. 28.   One-port network.

The "black box" description of a one terminal pair network with the conventional notation for the terminal nodes is shown in Fig. 28. The voltage across the terminals (1, 1') is designated as $v_1(t)$, with the reference $+$ at the terminal 1, and the current at these terminals is $i_1(t)$, with the voltage reference plus being at the tail of the current reference arrow. Network functions can be (meaningfully) defined only when the black boxes (such as Fig. 28) do *not* contain any *independent* generators. For the present we will make only this assumption (in addition to lumped, linear, time-invariant, components). The one terminal-pair network may contain *dependent* generators in addition to R, L, C, M parameters.

By the *driving point impedance* Z(s) of a one terminal-pair network, we mean

$$Z(s) = \frac{V_1(s)}{I_1(s)}, \qquad \text{with all initial conditions equal to zero} \quad (140)$$

where $V_1(s)$ and $I_1(s)$ are the transforms of the input voltage and current, with references as shown in Fig. 28.

The *driving-point admittance* $Y(s)$ is defined simply as the reciprocal of the driving-point impedance.

$$Y(s) = \frac{1}{Z(s)} = \frac{I_1(s)}{V_1(s)}, \quad \text{with all initial conditions equal to zero} \quad (141)$$

Let us examine these definitions for a moment before getting involved in formulas. First let us compare this definition with the a-c steady-state definition even though we won't relate them until we get to the next chapter. In a-c steady-state analysis, we assume that all the currents and voltages are sinusoidal functions of time. In particular the functions $v_1(t)$ and $i_1(t)$ of Fig. 28 may be written as

$$v_1(t) = |U_1| \sin (\omega_1 t + \theta_1)$$
$$i_1(t) = |J_1| \sin (\omega_1 t + \theta_2) \tag{142}$$

where the subscript 1 on ω is used merely to emphasize the fact that the angular frequency is a constant. Then we construct the complex numbers U_1 and J_1 by writing

$$U_1 = |U_1| \epsilon^{j\theta_1} \qquad (a)$$
$$J_1 = |J_1| \epsilon^{j\theta_2} \qquad (b) \tag{143}$$

We define the driving-point impedance Z_s as the ratio of these two *complex numbers*.

$$Z_s = \frac{U_1}{J_1} \tag{144}$$

and the driving-point admittance as the reciprocal. (The subscript is to remind us of sinusoids.) By comparison, the general definitions (140) and (141) are more natural. We shall show in the next chapter that our definition is a generalization of the a-c steady-state definition.

These definitions imply something else that is more important. In definitions (140) and (141), we did not say anything about the external circuitry connected to the terminals 1 and 1'. The implication is that it makes no difference. We may, if we like, connect a voltage generator or a current generator, or embed the black box of Fig. 28 in any complicated network. As long as we make external connections only at the terminals 1 and 1' (i.e., as long as we don't make any connection to one of the internal nodes inside the black box), the ratio $V_1(s)/I_1(s)$ remains fixed. This fact requires proof, but we will consider it as intuitively obvious. A formal proof would have to appeal to Thévenin's theorem. It is here that we need the assumption that there are no independent generators inside the one terminal-pair network. If it contains any independent generators, the ratio $V_1(s)/I_1(s)$ will depend on the external circuitry and thus will not be a characteristic of the one terminal-pair itself.

Another factor that should be noticed is that we have made no assumption as to the nature of the time functions $v_1(t)$, $i_1(t)$. The network may be excited by a battery for all the difference it makes. However we have made the assumption that, if $v_1(t)$ is the excitation, then $i_1(t)$ is the complete response—not just steady state. (Of course, the roles of i_1 and v_1 can be interchanged.) This is implied in the definition of the Laplace transforms $V_1(s)$ and $I_1(s)$.

These comments will apply to all the network function that we shall define and so will not be repeated.

Now let us turn to the computation of the driving-point functions from loop and node systems of equations. Let us begin with the warning that the important things to understand are the definitions. Memorization of formulas that may be derived from the definitions is a poor and misleading substitute.

Let us first consider the case in which the network contains no dependent sources. Let us excite the network with a voltage source and write loop equations, choosing the loops in such a way that the voltage source appears in only one loop (we label this loop

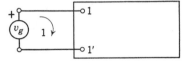

Fig. 29. Calculation of driving-point functions.

1) as illustrated in Fig. 29. The loop equations take the form

$$
\begin{bmatrix} c_{11} & c_{12} & \cdots & c_{1n} \\ c_{21} & c_{22} & \cdots & c_{2n} \\ \cdot & \cdot & \cdots & \cdot \\ c_{n1} & c_{n2} & \cdots & c_{nn} \end{bmatrix}
\begin{bmatrix} I_1(s) \\ I_2(s) \\ \cdot \\ \cdot \\ I_n(s) \end{bmatrix}
=
\begin{bmatrix} V_g(s) \\ 0 \\ \cdot \\ \cdot \\ 0 \end{bmatrix}
\tag{145}
$$

It is now a simple matter to solve for $I_1(s)$ and then take the ratio of $V_g(s)$ (which is equal to V_1) to $I_1(s)$. The result is

$$
Z(s) = \left. \frac{\Delta(s)}{\Delta_{11}(s)} \right|_z
\tag{146}
$$

The notation z is used to emphasize that the determinant and cofactor are those associated with the loop equations.

We can, quite evidently, write a dual formula in terms of node equations, by considering that the network is excited by a current source. Still assuming that there are no dependent sources and choosing one of the input terminals as the datum node (say $1'$), the driving-point admittance will be given by

$$Y = \frac{\Delta(s)}{\Delta_{11}(s)}\bigg|_y \qquad (147)$$

The notation y implies that the determinant and cofactor are those associated with the node equations.

The conditions under which these formulas for the driving point functions are valid should always be borne in mind. Only one cofactor is involved because the voltage source appears in only one loop, in the first case, and the current source is connected at only one node (and the datum), in the second case.

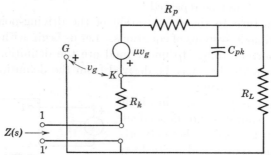

Fig. 30.   Example for computing driving-point impedance.

Let us now illustrate by means of an example that these formulas do not apply when dependent sources are present in the network. Suppose we wish to compute the driving point impedance between cathode and

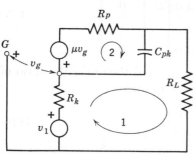

Fig. 31.   Example of Fig. 30, cont'd.

ground of a grounded grid amplifier, taking the plate-cathode capacitance into account. The appropriate network is shown in Fig. 30. Since the input impedance is independent of the method of excitation, we may elect to connect a voltage source between the terminals 1 and 1′ and use loop equations to find the input current. A suitable choice of loops is shown in Fig. 31.

Since we have chosen only one loop through the source v_1, the input current is the same as loop current 1. By inspection we notice that

$$v_g(t) = R_k i_1(t) - v_1(t) \qquad (148)$$

Using this expression and setting initial conditions equal to zero as required by the definition, the transformed loop equations are given by

$$\begin{bmatrix} R_k + R_L + \dfrac{1}{sC_{pk}} & -\dfrac{1}{sC_{pk}} \\ -\dfrac{1}{sC_{pk}} + \mu R_k & R_p + \dfrac{1}{sC_{pk}} \end{bmatrix} \begin{bmatrix} I_1(s) \\ I_2(s) \end{bmatrix} = \begin{bmatrix} V_1(s) \\ \mu V_1(s) \end{bmatrix} \tag{149}$$

Solving for $I_1(s)$, we get

$$I_1(s) = \left(\frac{\Delta_{11}}{\Delta} + \frac{\mu \Delta_{21}}{\Delta} \right) V_1(s) \tag{150}$$

and

$$Z(s) = \frac{\Delta}{\Delta_{11} + \mu \Delta_{21}} \tag{151}$$

where the usual notation for determinant and cofactors has been used. Inserting the values of Δ and the cofactors into this expression, we find

$$Z(s) = \frac{(R_k + R_L)R_p + \dfrac{1}{sC_{pk}}(R_k + \mu R_k + R_p + R_L)}{R_p + \dfrac{1 + \mu}{sC_{pk}}} \tag{152}$$

Notice that although we were very careful to choose only one loop through the generator, $V_1(s)$ appears in two places on the right side of Eq. (149), and no choice of loops can avoid this circumstance. The reason for this is traceable directly to the dependent generator.

The driving-point functions express a relationship between the current and voltage transforms at a single pair of terminals. We are frequently interested in such a ratio of current or voltage transforms when the two functions are not taken at the same pair of terminals. We refer to such functions as *transfer functions*. In the case of driving-point functions the analytic properties of the function and its reciprocal are the same, as we shall see in Chapter 9. But in the case of transfer functions this is not the case. Therefore to avoid endless confusion, we shall make a convention in the definition of transfer functions. The convention we adopt will agree with modern usage in network theory. Whenever we define a transfer function as the quotient of two transforms, we shall always write the response transform (or output transform) in the numerator and the excitation transform (or input transform) in the denominator.

For instance, suppose we single out for our attention the voltage or current in one of the branches of a network. Let us draw it outside the black box, as shown in Fig. 32. We shall make the assumption, as before, that the network N contains no *independent generators* but may

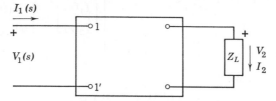

Fig. 32.   Network relevant to the definition of transfer functions.

contain dependent generators. We can define four different transfer functions (using our convention) as follows.

$$G_{21}(s) = \frac{V_2(s)}{V_1(s)} \tag{153}$$

$$\alpha_{21}(s) = \frac{I_2(s)}{I_1(s)} \tag{154}$$

$$Z_{21}(s) = \frac{V_2(s)}{I_1(s)} \tag{155}$$

$$Y_{21}(s) = \frac{I_2(s)}{V_1(s)} \tag{156}$$

all of them under the condition that all initial conditions are zero. The names associated with these four functions are:

$G_{21}(s)$: voltage gain or voltage ratio transfer function,
$\alpha_{21}(s)$: current gain or current ratio transfer function,
$Z_{21}(s)$: transfer impedance,
$Y_{21}(s)$: transfer admittance.

We should here emphasize several points about the transfer functions. First, the ordering of the subscripts in these functions is quite important (the first subscript refers to the output and the second to the input). Secondly, the references for the currents or voltages appearing in a function must be specified, since changing one of the references will change the function. Thirdly, $G_{21}(s)$ and $\alpha_{21}(s)$ are unrelated. Finally, $Z_{21}(s)$ is *not* the reciprocal of $Y_{21}(s)$.

The method by which the network is excited is not specified in these definitions, and so, by implication, the functions are independent of the excitation.   In computing these functions, we may choose a current source or a voltage source as the excitation, whichever happens to be convenient.

As in the case of driving-point functions, it is possible to obtain formulas for the transfer functions when the network does not contain any dependent sources.   (These same formulas may be valid under some conditions even with dependent sources.)   Formulas using loop equations can be derived by assuming a voltage generator at the input. Alternative formulas can also be derived starting with node equations and exciting the network with a current generator.   The choice of loops and the datum node are shown in Fig. 33.   Remember that, for the

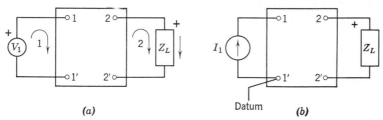

(a)   Datum   *(b)*

Fig. 33.   Calculation of transfer functions.

immediately following development, N contains *no dependent generators*. For Fig. 33a the loop equations are

$$\begin{bmatrix} c_{11} & c_{12} & \cdots & c_{1n} \\ c_{21} & c_{22} & \cdots & c_{2n} \\ \cdot & \cdot & \cdot & \cdot \\ c_{n1} & c_{n2} & \cdots & c_{nn} \end{bmatrix} \begin{bmatrix} I_1(s) \\ I_2(s) \\ \cdots \\ I_n(s) \end{bmatrix} = \begin{bmatrix} V_1(s) \\ 0 \\ \cdot \\ 0 \end{bmatrix} \qquad (157)$$

since the initial conditions are zero and no dependent generators are present.   Similarly the node equations for Fig. 33b are:

$$\begin{bmatrix} d_{11} & d_{12} & d_{12'} & \cdots & d_{1n} \\ d_{21} & d_{22} & d_{22'} & \cdots & d_{2n} \\ d_{2'1} & d_{2'2} & d_{2'2'} & \cdots & d_{2'n} \\ \cdot & \cdot & \cdot & \cdot & \cdot \\ d_{n1} & d_{n2} & d_{n2'} & \cdots & d_{nn} \end{bmatrix} \begin{bmatrix} V_1 \\ V_2 \\ V_{2'} \\ \cdot \\ V_n \end{bmatrix} = \begin{bmatrix} I_1 \\ 0 \\ 0 \\ \cdot \\ 0 \end{bmatrix} \qquad (158)$$

From these equations we can write down the desired formulas for the transfer functions by inspection.   These formulas are given below, using z to indicate that the determinants and cofactors are from the loop equations and y to indicate that they are from the node equations.

$$G_{21}(s) = \frac{V_2(s)}{V_1(s)} = Z_L \frac{\Delta_{12}}{\Delta}\bigg|_z = \frac{\Delta_{12} - \Delta_{12'}}{\Delta_{11}}\bigg|_y \qquad (159)$$

$$\alpha_{21}(s) = \frac{I_2(s)}{I_1(s)} = \frac{\Delta_{12}}{\Delta_{11}}\bigg|_z = \frac{1}{Z_L}\frac{\Delta_{12} - \Delta_{12'}}{\Delta}\bigg|_y \qquad (160)$$

$$Y_{21}(s) = \frac{I_2(s)}{V_1(s)} = \frac{\Delta_{12}}{\Delta}\bigg|_z = \frac{1}{Z_L}\frac{\Delta_{12} - \Delta_{12'}}{\Delta_{11}}\bigg|_y \qquad (161)$$

$$Z_{21}(s) = \frac{V_2(s)}{I_1(s)} = Z_L \frac{\Delta_{12}}{\Delta_{11}}\bigg|_z = \frac{\Delta_{12} - \Delta_{12'}}{\Delta}\bigg|_y \qquad (162)$$

The loop and the node formulas become dual only when 1' and 2' are the same node.

Let us repeat the statement that the definitions are more fundamental than the special formulas for passive networks. You should be able to derive the formulas any time you need them and so you should not memorize them.

Before concluding the section, a few examples of computation of network functions shall be given, simultaneously illustrating the remarks at the beginning of the chapter. That is, we will *not* use the formal procedures of loop and node equations but, instead, will use some of the short-cut techniques which are helpful in special cases.

When all the initial conditions are zero, the transformed equations (KCL, KVL, and v-i) are of the same form as the a-c steady-state equations, except that s replaces $j\omega$. It follows therefore, that we can use all the a-c steady-state simplifications in this case; in particular we have the familiar rules for series and parallel combinations of impedances and admittances, voltage and current divisions for series and parallel connections, etc. (In fact even when initial conditions are not zero, we can use such simplifications, provided we treat initial conditions as sources.) For a first example, let us find the driving point impedance of the *ladder* network of Fig. 34.

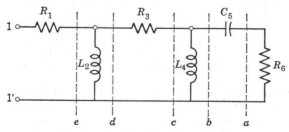

Fig. 34.   Ladder network example.

To find the driving point impedance we start from the far end, away from the input terminals.   Looking right from the dotted line a we have a resistance R_6.   Coming back to b (and still looking right), we have a capacitance C_5 in series with R_6, so that the impedance here is

$$Z_b = Z_a + \frac{1}{sC_5} = R_6 + \frac{1}{sC_5} \tag{163}$$

Coming back to c and still looking right, this impedance Z_b is in parallel with L_4, giving us

$$Z_c = \cfrac{1}{\cfrac{1}{sL_4} + \cfrac{1}{R_6 + (1/sC_5)}} \tag{164}$$

At the next step R_3 is in series with Z_c so that

$$Z_d = R_3 + Z_c = R_3 + \cfrac{1}{\cfrac{1}{sL_4} + \cfrac{1}{R_6 + (1/sC_5)}} \tag{165}$$

Next, L_2 is in parallel with Z_d so that

$$Z_e = \frac{1}{(1/sL_2) + (1/Z_d)}$$

$$= \cfrac{1}{\cfrac{1}{sL_2} + \cfrac{1}{R_3 + \cfrac{1}{\cfrac{1}{sL_4} + \cfrac{1}{R_6 + (1/sC_5)}}}} \tag{166}$$

Finally, coming back to the input terminals, R_1 is in series with Z_e, giving us the required driving point impedance as

$$Z = R_1 + \cfrac{1}{\cfrac{1}{sL_2} + \cfrac{1}{R_3 + \cfrac{1}{\cfrac{1}{sL_4} + \cfrac{1}{R_6 + (1/sC_5)}}}} \tag{167}$$

An expression like this is known as a *continued fraction* and is quite characteristic of ladder networks.   We can, of course, write Z as a rational fraction by clearing the other fractions suitably.

The same result is obtained if we start from the input end. Here the impedance is written as R_1 plus the impedance looking toward the right at e. This impedance is the reciprocal of $1/sL_2$ plus the admittance looking to the right at d. If we continue in this manner, Eq. (167) will again result.

From the method of obtaining the continued fraction, we see that this result does not depend on the constituents of the branches of the ladder network. It is possible for each branch to be any arbitrary passive one-port, so long as there is no magnetic coupling between branches. The impedance can always be written as a continued fraction.

As another example where series-parallel manipulations are handy, let us find the voltage ratio transfer function of the network of Fig. 35.

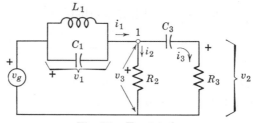

Fig. 35.   T network.

This is again a ladder network. In this case, the transmission network—between the generator v_g and the load R_3—is called a Tee network (since it looks like a T).

Starting from the load, let $V_2(s)$ be the transform of the load voltage. Since the current transform is then $V_2(s)/R_3$, and this is also the current in C_3, the voltage transform V_3 across the series combination of C_3 and R_3 is:

$$V_3(s) = \frac{R_3 + (1/sC_3)}{R_3} V_2(s) \tag{168}$$

This is also the transform of the voltage across R_2. Therefore I_2 is given by

$$I_2(s) = \frac{R_3 + (1/sC_3)}{R_2 R_3} V_2(s) \tag{169}$$

Using KCL at junction 1, the current transform I_1 is

$$I_1(s) = I_2(s) + I_3(s)$$

$$= \left(\frac{R_3 + (1/sC_3)}{R_2 R_3} + \frac{1}{R_3}\right) V_2(s) \tag{170}$$

Since the impedance of the parallel $L_1 C_1$ combination is

$$Z_1(s) = \frac{sL_1}{s^2 L_1 C_1 + 1} \tag{171}$$

the transform of $v_1(t)$ across $L_1 C_1$ will be

$$V_1(s) = Z_1(s) \cdot I_1(s)$$

$$= \frac{sL_1}{s^2 L_1 C_1 + 1} \left(\frac{R_3 + (1/sC_3)}{R_2 R_3} + \frac{1}{R_3} \right) V_2(s) \tag{172}$$

Finally, using KVL for the first window, we get

$$V_g(s) = V_1(s) + V_3(s)$$

$$= \left\{ \frac{sL_1}{s^2 L_1 C_1 + 1} \left(\frac{R_3 + (1/sC_3)}{R_2 R_3} + \frac{1}{R_3} \right) + \frac{R_3 + (1/sC_3)}{R_3} \right\} V_2(s) \tag{173}$$

On solving this equation for $V_2(s)/V_g(s)$, we get the desired function.

$$\frac{V_2(s)}{V_g(s)} = \frac{1}{\left(\dfrac{sL_1}{s^2 L_1 C_1 + 1} \right) \left(\dfrac{R_3 + (1/sC_3)}{R_2 R_3} + \dfrac{1}{R_3} \right) + \dfrac{R_3 + (1/sC_3)}{R_3}} \tag{174}$$

Notice how we switched between current and voltage in this problem, and used the fundamental equations—KCL, KVL and the v-i relationships—directly, without using loop or node variables. You should look through the argument carefully and see that we actually used all the information in the fundamental equations (12 of them in this problem) except that the initial conditions were zero.

As another example where mixed variable equations are more useful than loop or node equations, consider the network of Fig. 36. This is

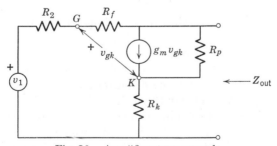

Fig. 36. Amplifier stage example.

the "midband linear equivalent" of an amplifier with potentiometer feedback and an unbypassed cathode. (The coupling capacitor is not included.) We wish to find the output impedance of this amplifier. So we short $v_1(t)$ and connect a generator at the output terminals, getting the network of Fig. 37. This network has three nodes and five branches

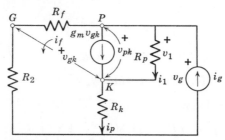

Fig. 37.   Output impedance computation.

(counting $R_2 R_f$ as one branch). Therefore there are two KCL equations which, if solved, would leave three branch current variables. Since i_g, R_p, and $g_m v_{gk}$ constitute a chord set, let us express the other two currents in terms of these by mentally solving KCL. The result is

$$i_f = -g_m v_{gk} - i_1 + i_g \qquad (a)$$
$$i_p = g_m v_{gk} + i_1 \qquad (b)$$

(175)

On the other hand, using the fundamental loops for this tree consisting of branches R_k and $R_2 R_f$, we can express the branch voltages of the other three branches in terms of tree branch voltages as

$$v_1 = v_f - v_{R_k} \qquad (a)$$
$$v_{pk} = v_f - v_{R_k} \qquad (b)$$
$$v_g = v_f \qquad (c)$$

(176)

(The reference for v_g is chosen according to the definition of impedance.)

Now we do not need to know v_{pk}, so we leave Eq. (176b) alone. v_g and i_g are unrelated, so we leave Eq. (176c) to the end, when we will use it to find v_g. In the other three equations, we have more than three variables, in fact eight. One of these, i_g, is the generator. We can now use the v-i relationships to eliminate four other variables, leaving us three equations in three unknowns. The variables we keep are chord currents and branch voltages, in this case i_1, i_g, v_f, v_{R_k}. One of the chord currents,

$g_m v_{gk}$, is to be eliminated since it is dependent. Elimination of i_f, i_p, and v_1, is obvious. For v_{gk} we have

$$v_{gk} = \frac{R_2}{R_2 + R_5} v_f - v_{R_k} \tag{177}$$

Then Eqs. (175a), (175b), (176a) become, respectively,

$$\frac{v_f}{R_2 + R_5} + g_m \left(\frac{R_2}{R_2 + R_5} v_f - v_{R_k} \right) + i_1 = i_g \quad (a)$$

$$\frac{v_{R_k}}{R_k} - g_m \left(\frac{R_2}{R_2 + R_5} v_f - v_{R_k} \right) - i_1 = 0 \quad (b) \tag{178}$$

$$R_p i_1 - v_f + v_{R_k} = 0 \quad (c)$$

Or, more clearly, in matrix notation

$$\begin{bmatrix} \dfrac{1 + g_m R_2}{R_2 + R_5} & -g_m & 1 \\[2mm] -\dfrac{g_m R_2}{R_2 + R_5} & g_m + \dfrac{1}{R_k} & -1 \\[2mm] -1 & 1 & R_p \end{bmatrix} \begin{bmatrix} v_f \\ v_{R_k} \\ i_1 \end{bmatrix} = \begin{bmatrix} i_g \\ 0 \\ 0 \end{bmatrix} \tag{179}$$

Since there are no derivatives or integrals involved, no Laplace transform is needed, and we can find the output impedance (in this case, a resistance) directly. Since we need v_f (see Eq. (176c)), we need find only Δ and Δ_{11}. Then,

$$v_f = (\Delta_{11}/\Delta) i_g = v_g \tag{180}$$

Hence, the driving-point impedance is given by

$$Z = \frac{V_g}{I_g} = \frac{v_g}{i_g} = \frac{\Delta_{11}}{\Delta} \tag{181}$$

Finally, computing Δ and Δ_{11},

$$Z = \frac{(R_2 + R_5)(g_m R_p R_k + R_p + R_k)}{g_m R_p (R_k + R_2) + R_k + R_p + R_2 + R_5} \tag{182}$$

In this example we used a mixed variable system of equations. For this type of a network, mixed variable systems are extremely useful. In fact, in the so-called "signal-flow graph" method which we shall see in Chapter 10, exactly the procedure followed above is used.

4.8 Summary

In this chapter we have seen some of the general concepts about networks, making very few assumptions about the components—other than the lumped, linear, and time invariant ones. We have seen two general methods that can be used for analyzing *any* network satisfying these conditions, namely loop and node analyses, and we have seen how they arise out of the fundamental equations of the network as postulated in Chapter 1.

We considered certain "singular" problems in which the inductance currents and capacitance voltages may be discontinuous. In such cases, we saw that we can handle the problem either by means of conventional methods or by using singular functions (impulse functions). We considered only impulses in the solution, postponing the discussion of impulse drivers to Chapter 6.

Another general concept that we considered (in as much detail as is possible at this stage) was that of duality.

Finally, we defined certain network functions in order to have the terminology available for later chapters.

PROBLEMS

4.1 For the network of Fig. P4.1 write down, in matrix notation,
(1) Kirchhoff's current law equations (independent ones)
(2) Kirchoff's voltage law equations (independent ones)
(3) Mesh transformation
(4) Node transformation

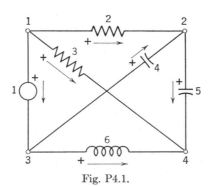

Fig. P4.1.

4.2 Write down by inspection the transformed loop and node equations for the networks in Fig. P4.2 and change into matrix notation.

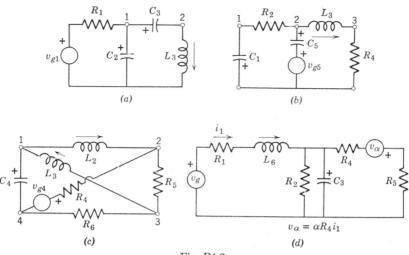

(a) (b)

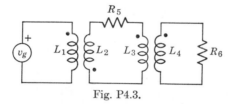

(c) (d)

$$v_\alpha = \alpha R_4 i_1$$

Fig. P4.2.

4.3 Write down by inspection the loop equations in transforms for the network of Fig. P4.3. Change into a matrix equation.

Fig. P4.3.

4.4 Write down by inspection a suitable (linearly independent) set of transformed loop equations for the network shown in Fig. P4.4.

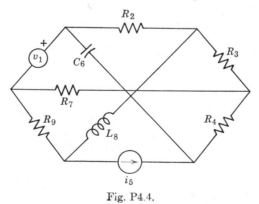

Fig. P4.4.

4.5 Find the solution for the branch current $i_3(t)$ for $t > 0$ in the network of Fig. P4.5.

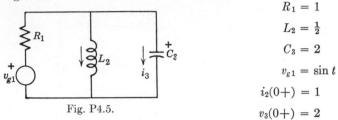

Fig. P4.5.

$$R_1 = 1$$
$$L_2 = \tfrac{1}{2}$$
$$C_3 = 2$$
$$v_{g1} = \sin t$$
$$i_2(0+) = 1$$
$$v_3(0+) = 2$$

4.6 In the network of Fig. P4.6 find the solution for $v_4(t)$, the voltage across R_4, for $t > 0$. All initial currents and voltages are zero.

$$L_1 = L_2 = 2$$
$$M = 1$$
$$C_3 = \tfrac{1}{2}$$
$$R_4 = 10$$
$$v_{g1}(t) = 1, \quad t > 0$$
$$= 0, \quad t < 0$$

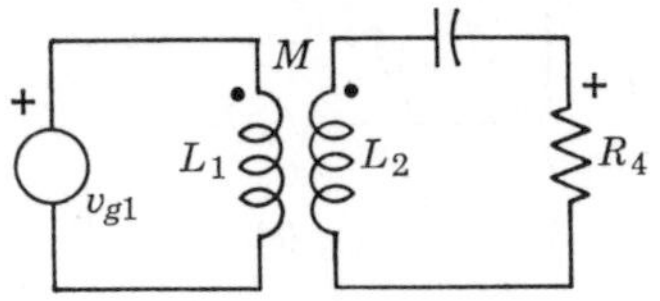

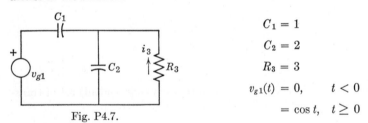

Fig. P4.6.

4.7 In the network of Fig. P4.7 find $i_3(t)$ for $t > 0$, using both techniques for initial conditions and both loop and node equations. Comment on any peculiarities in the solution.

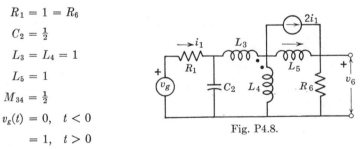

Fig. P4.7.

$$C_1 = 1$$
$$C_2 = 2$$
$$R_3 = 3$$
$$v_{g1}(t) = 0, \qquad t < 0$$
$$= \cos t, \quad t \ge 0$$

(This condition implies that C_1 and C_2 are discharged up to $t = 0$.)

4.8 In the network of Fig. P4.8, find $v_6(t)$, using both techniques for initial conditions. Comment on any peculiarities in the solution.

$$R_1 = 1 = R_6$$
$$C_2 = \tfrac{1}{2}$$
$$L_3 = L_4 = 1$$
$$L_5 = 1$$
$$M_{34} = \tfrac{1}{2}$$
$$v_g(t) = 0, \quad t < 0$$
$$= 1, \quad t > 0$$

Fig. P4.8.

4.9 In the network of Fig. P4.9, the source $v_g(t)$ is a dc source,

$$v_g(t) = 2$$

With the switch in the position shown, the network is allowed to reach a steady state. Then the switch is moved to the other position. Find $v_4(t)$ after the switch is moved.

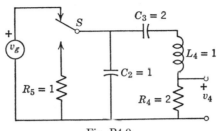

Fig. P4.9.

4.10 Using the matrix expressions for loop and node equations and the initial value theorem of Laplace transform theory, find the conditions that the solutions of the loop or node equations contain no impulses, neither current nor voltage.

4.11 In the network of Fig. P4.11

$$v_g = \begin{cases} 0, & t < 0 \\ 1, & 0 \le t < 1 \\ 0, & t \ge 1 \end{cases}$$

$$R_1 = R_2 = 1$$

$$L_3 = 2, \quad L_4 = 1$$

$$C_5 = 1, \quad C_6 = \tfrac{1}{2}$$

$$v_{C_5}(0-) = v_{C_6}(0-) = 0$$

$$i_{L_3}(0-) = i_{L_4}(0-) = 0$$

Find $v_6(t)$ using (a) conventional mathematics and (b) impulse techniques. Explain any difficulties you meet in solving the problem. Change R_2 to 2 and repeat.

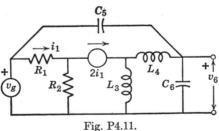

Fig. P4.11.

4.12 Find the pulse response of the transformer-coupled amplifier of Fig. P4.12.

$$R_k = 100 \text{ ohms} \qquad L_1 = 2 \text{ mh} \qquad C_2 = 100 \ \mu\mu\text{f}$$

$$\mu = 100 \qquad L_2 = 2 \text{ mh} \qquad R_2 = 10,000 \text{ ohms}$$

$$M = 1 \text{ mh} \qquad R_p = 100,000 \text{ ohms}$$

$$v_s(t) = \begin{cases} 0, & t < 0 \\ 1, & 0 \le t < 1 \\ 0, & 0 \le t \end{cases}$$

All initial conditions are zero.

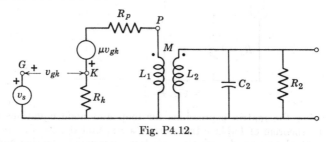

Fig. P4.12.

4.13 Find the duals of the elementary structures shown in Fig. P4.13a.

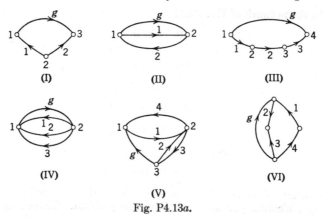

Fig. P4.13a.

What general conclusions can you draw from these examples. (Interpret g as a generator and consider series and parallel connections.) Using this principle construct the duals of the networks shown in Fig. P4.13b.

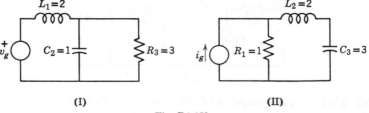

Fig. P4.13b.

4.14 Construct the dual of each of the networks shown in Fig. P4.14.

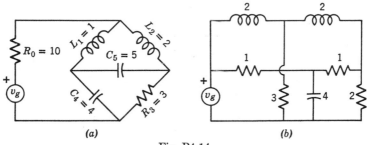

(a)   (b)

Fig. P4.14.

4.15 Find the output impedance Z of the cathode follower amplifier of P4.15.

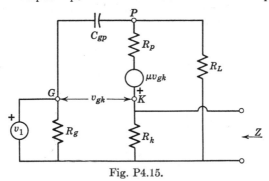

Fig. P4.15.

4.16 Find the output impedance of the network of Fig. P4.16.

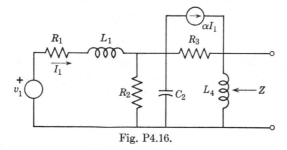

Fig. P4.16.

4.17 Find the gain or the voltage ratio transfer function $G(s) = V_2(s)/V_1(s)$ of the network of Fig. P4.17.

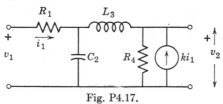

Fig. P4.17.

4.18 Find the transfer impedance $Z_{21}(s)$ of the network of Fig. P4.18.

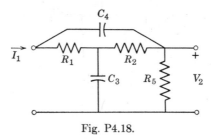

Fig. P4.18.

4.19 Find the transfer admittance $Y_{21}(s)$ of the network of Fig. P4.19. Find the zeros and poles of $Y_{21}(s)$. $R_1 = 1$, $R_2 = 2$, $C_1 = 1$, $C_2 = \frac{1}{2}$, $R_3 = 1$.

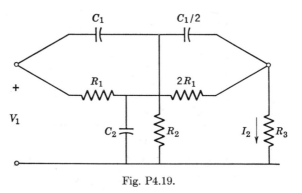

Fig. P4.19.

4.20 Find the driving point impedance of the networks of Fig. P4.20. Find the poles and zeros of $Z(s)$ and comment on any special properties that you observe. Find the residues of $Z(s)$ at all its poles. What can you say about them?

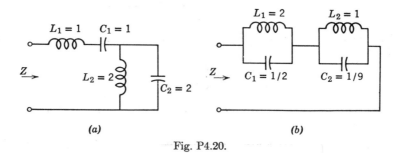

Fig. P4.20.

4.21 Repeat Problem 4.20 for the networks of Fig. P4.21.

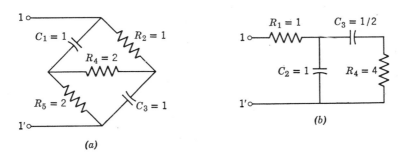

(a)

(b)

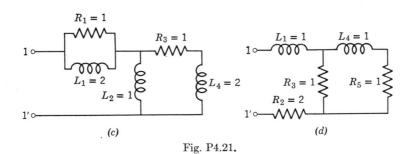

(c)

(d)

Fig. P4.21.

4.22 Find the current ratio transfer function $\alpha_{21}(s) = I_2(s)/I_1(s)$ for the network of Fig. P4.22. Find the poles and zeros of $\alpha_{21}(s)$.

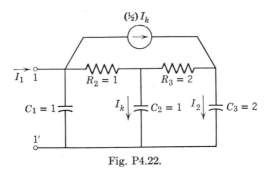

Fig. P4.22.

4.23 The bridged-Tee network shown in Fig. P4.23 is used very often in networks designed for low frequency operation. Find the transfer impedance

$$Z_{21}(s) = \frac{V_2(s)}{I_1(s)}$$

Plot the location of poles and zeros of $Z_{21}(s)$ in the complex plane. Find $v_2(t)$ if $i_1(t)$ is a unit step and all initial conditions are zero.

$$C_1 = C_2 = \tfrac{1}{2}$$

$$C_3 = \tfrac{3}{4}$$

$$G_4 = G_5 = \frac{1}{2\sqrt{3}}$$

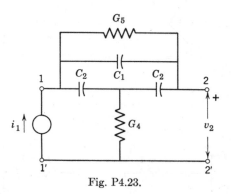

Fig. P4.23.

4.24 In the network of Fig. P4.24, find the voltage ratio transfer function

$$G_{21}(s) = \frac{V_2(s)}{V_1(s)}$$

Find $v_2(t)$ if the network is initially relaxed and if

$$v_1(t) = \sin t$$

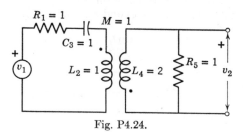

Fig. P4.24.

4.25 Compute the voltage ratio $G_{21} = V_2/V_1$ of the ladder network of Fig. P4.25.

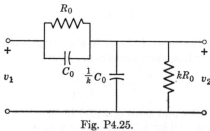

Fig. P4.25.

4.26 Power is defined in terms of current and voltage as $p_j(t) = v_j(t)\, i_j(t)$ for branch j, with the voltage $+$ at the tail of the current reference arrow. For any electrical network satisfying Kirchhoff's current and voltage laws, show that

$$\sum_j p_j(t) = 0$$

where the summation is over all the branches. Show that Kirchhoff's laws imply conservation of energy if energy is the integral of power.

4.27 The network in Fig. P4.27 is a low-pass filter. Find the voltage ratio function V_2/V_1, using both a formal approach and a continued fraction expansion.

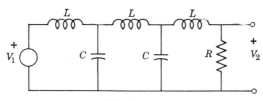

Fig. P4.27.

4.28 In Fig. P4.28 the network inside the rectangle is linear, lumped, passive, and time-invariant. A capacitance inside the box is charged and then discharged. This is repeated twice, once with the terminals of the box shorted and once with them open, as indicated in the figure. The first time the current is measured, whereas the second time the voltage is measured. These are found to be

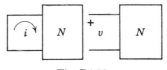

Fig. P4.28.

$$i(t) = A_1\epsilon^{-2t} \cos(2t + \phi_1)$$

$$v(t) = A_2\epsilon^{-t} \cos(3t + \phi_2) + A_3\epsilon^{-2t}$$

Determine the driving-point impedance function at the terminals of the box.

4.29 In the network of Fig. P4.29 all initial conditions are zero. Find the solution for $v_2(t)$.

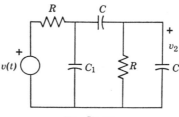

Fig. P4.29.

4.30 In the network of Fig. P4.30 the switch has been closed for a long time and is suddenly opened at $t = 0$.

(a) Find the currents in L_1 and L_2 immediately after the switch is opened.

(b) Find the voltage across the switch as a function of time.

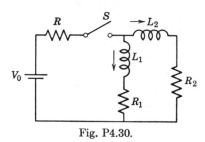

Fig. P4.30.

5 · NETWORK THEOREMS
AND STEADY-STATE RESPONSE

In the previous chapters we have discussed procedures for finding the complete solution for all the branch voltages and currents in any electrical network in response to any ($\mathcal{L}$-transformable) driving functions. However, frequently the complete solution is not required; only the steady-state response to periodic functions is needed. Similarly, the solution for all voltages and currents is often not required, only the current or voltage in one part of the network. In such a case it would be useful to be able to replace the part of the network which is not of interest by a simpler equivalent.

In this chapter we will discuss some of the major network theorems that are useful both in simplifying computations and in theoretical developments. We will also discuss the steady-state response of networks to sinusoids and to other periodic functions.

5.1 The Principle of Superposition

The Superposition Principle is usually stated as follows: *the response of a linear network to a number of excitations applied simultaneously is equal to the sum of the responses of the network when each excitation is applied individually.* This is a very general statement. It will be valid only if we consider the initial capacitance voltages and inductance currents themselves to be separate excitations and if we do not consider dependent sources as separate excitations.

To illustrate the remark concerning initial values, consider the simple arrangement of Fig. 1. The capacitance is initially charged to a voltage $v_C(0+) = V_0$ and the switch is closed at $t = 0$. The solution for the current when both batteries are present is easily obtained. The following steps are self-explanatory.

$$\left(R + \frac{1}{sC}\right) I(s) = \frac{2V_0}{s} - \frac{v_C(0+)}{s} = \frac{V_0}{s} \qquad (a)$$

$$I(s) = \frac{V_0}{R[s + (1/RC)]} \qquad (b) \qquad (1)$$

$$i(t) = \frac{V_0}{R} \epsilon^{-t/RC} \qquad (c)$$

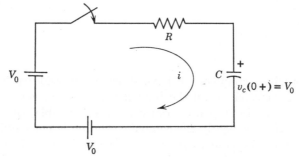

Fig. 1.   Illustration of the principle of superposition.

Now if we apply either one of the two batteries alone, the resulting current will be zero; adding the two zero responses we will get zero, which is certainly not the same as the last equation. What we have overlooked, of course, is the initial charge. The trouble is, the initial charge appeared twice, once with each battery, when they were applied separately, but only once when both were applied simultaneously. If we consider the initial capacitance voltage as an excitation, and treat it like the other excitations, then the correct result will be obtained.

The validity of the superposition principle is readily established by considering the expression for the general response in an arbitrary network as given by Eq. (32) in Chapter 4. Let us repeat this equation here for convenience.

$$\boldsymbol{I}_m(s) = \boldsymbol{Z}_m^{-1}(s) \left\{ \boldsymbol{V}_m(s) + \boldsymbol{v}_\lambda(0+) + \frac{1}{s} \boldsymbol{v}_C(0+) \right\} \qquad (2)$$

Applying the excitations one at a time and adding the partial responses so obtained is equivalent to writing

$$\boldsymbol{V}_m(s) = \sum_j \boldsymbol{V}_{mj}(s) \qquad (a)$$

$$\boldsymbol{v}_\lambda(0+) = \sum_j \boldsymbol{v}_{\lambda j}(0+) \qquad (b) \qquad (3)$$

$$\boldsymbol{v}_C(0+) = \sum_j \boldsymbol{v}_{Cj}(0+) \qquad (c)$$

and

$$I_m(s) = \sum_j Z_m{}^{-1}(s) \cdot V_{mj}(s) + \sum_j Z_m{}^{-1}(s) \cdot v_{\lambda j}(0+)$$

$$+ \frac{1}{s} \sum_j Z_m{}^{-1}(s) \cdot v_{Cj}(0+) \tag{4}$$

where the summations extend over all of the excitations. Equation (4) evidently follows from Eqs. (2) and (3).

But is it really necessary to thus "prove" the superposition principle? A little thought will show that what we outlined in the last paragraph is a consequence of our definitions of the R, L, and C elements and the fact that multiplication is distributive in our number system.

It is clear, then, that the superposition principle is intimately tied up with the idea of linearity; we can not have one without the other. We can say that linearity is necessary and sufficient for the validity of the principle of Superposition.

5.2   The Thévenin and Norton Theorems

Frequently in network problems we are interested not in the solution for all currents and voltages but in the current or voltage of a small part of the network. It would be computationally convenient to curtail our elaborate schemes for solution and concentrate on replacing the entire network, exclusive of the part in question, by a simple equivalent. Consider Fig. 2a which shows two parts of a network, the part on the right consisting of passive elements only. The two networks are connected only at the points shown and there is no magnetic coupling between them. We will initially assume that there are no dependent sources in the left hand network. A current whose transform is $I(s)$ flows between the two parts of the network. In part (b) of the figure a voltage source whose transform is $V(s)$ is added. By the principle of superposition the total current will be the sum of the original current $I(s)$ plus the current due to $V(s)$ alone with the other sources (including initial values) removed. Let this current be $I_1(s)$ with reference the same as that of $I(s)$.

Let us assume that it is possible to choose $V(s)$ (whose value we must still find) such that $I_1(s) = -I(s)$ and the total current transform is zero. Let the driving-point impedance of the network on the right be $Z(s)$. Since no current flows into the right hand network under the new conditions, the voltage at its terminals will be zero, and it may be disconnected from the other part without affecting conditions to the left. After the two parts are disconnected, the voltage at the open terminals will still be zero. But from Fig. 2c this voltage is $V_0(s) - V(s)$, where

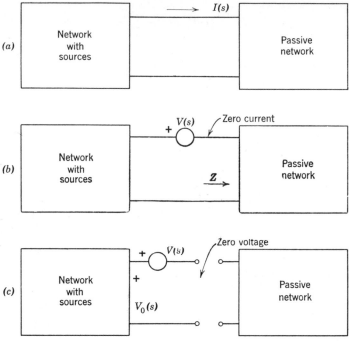

Fig. 2.   Development of Thévenin's theorem.

$V_0(s)$ is the value of the voltage transform at the terminals of the left hand network when these terminals are open-circuited.   This gives us the value of $V(s)$ as

$$V(s) = V_0(s) \qquad (5)$$

So far we have established that if we place, in the position and with the reference polarity shown in Fig. 2, a voltage source with transform $V(s) = V_0(s)$ and remove all other sources from the left (this includes reducing all initial conditions to zero), we will get a current transform $I_1(s) = -I(s)$.   Suppose we reverse the polarity of $V(s)$; then we will get $I_1(s) = I(s)$, which is the same current as before.   As far as the right hand network is concerned, the network on the left in Fig. 3 is com-

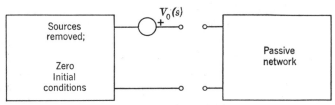

Fig. 3.   Thévenin equivalent.

pletely equivalent to the original. This consists of the original network with all sources removed and all initial conditions reduced to zero, in series with a voltage source (with the reference polarity shown in the figure) whose voltage transform is the open circuit voltage transform of the left hand network. Of course, this voltage will be a function of the initial conditions as well as the original sources.

We should say one word about removal of sources. We have made no stipulation as to the kind of source, current or voltage. Both kinds may be present. Sources are removed by setting their functions to zero. This is done for a voltage source by short-circuiting it and for a current source by open-circuiting it.

The equivalent circuit we have just developed was first stated by Thévenin in 1883 and is called *Thévenin's equivalent network*. The original network on the left with the sources removed can be represented by its driving point impedance $Z_0(s)$. This leads to Fig. 4a as the final

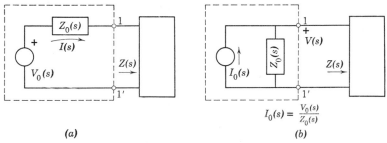

Fig. 4. Thévenin and Norton equivalent networks: (*a*) Thévenin equivalent; (*b*) Norton equivalent.

form of the Thévenin equivalent. The current $I(s)$ flowing into the network on the right is the same as in the original. It must be emphasized that the "equivalence" does not extend to any of the voltages or currents in the original left hand network.

Let us now assume that there is a dependent source in the left-hand network. When we now apply the superposition principle, this source is not removed. The remainder of the argument used in developing Thévenin's theorem will remain the same. Thus, Thévenin's theorem applies in the presence of dependent sources as well, but in determining Z_0 only the independent sources are removed.

As an example, consider the network shown in Fig. 5. This is the same as the network of Fig. 3 in Chapter 2. We will assume that the initial capacitance voltage is zero. Let us seek the Thévenin equivalent at the terminals a–b.

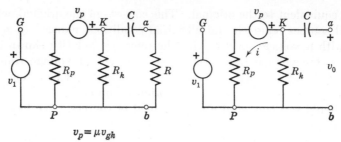

$$v_p = \mu v_{gk}$$

Fig. 5.   Illustration of Thévenin's theorem.

The voltage transform of the dependent source is

$$V_p(s) = \mu[V_1(s) + R_k I(s)] \tag{6}$$

It is a straight-forward matter to determine $V_0(s)$ from Fig. 5b.   It is

$$V_0(s) = -R_k I(s) = R_k \frac{V_p(s)}{r_p + R_k} = \frac{\mu R_k V_1}{r_p + (\mu + 1)R_k} \tag{7}$$

In obtaining the last step, Eq. (6) was used replacing $-R_k I(s)$ by $V_0(s)$.

To determine $Z_0(s)$ we set $V_1(s)$ equal to zero.   We then assume that a source v_2 is applied at terminals a–b.   The situation is illustrated in Fig. 6.   The desired $Z_0(s)$ will be the ratio of $V_2(s)$ to $I_2(s)$.   The de-

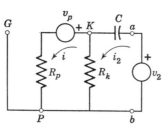

Fig. 6.   Determination of Z_0.

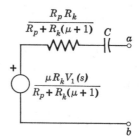

Fig. 7.   Thévenin equivalent of numerical example.

pendent source voltage transform is now

$$V_p(s) = -\mu R_k[I_2(s) - I(s)] \tag{8}$$

We can now write the loop equations of the network in Fig. 6 (with an obvious choice of loops), simultaneously transposing the terms involved in the dependent source.   The result is

$$[r_p + R_k(\mu + 1)]I(s) - R_k(\mu + 1)I_2(s) = 0$$

$$-R_k I(s) + \left(R_k + \frac{1}{Cs}\right)I_2(s) = V_2(s) \tag{9}$$

The solution of this set for $I_2(s)$ is

$$I_2(s) = \frac{[r_p + R_k(\mu + 1)]V_2(s)}{r_pR_k + [r_p + R_k(\mu + 1)]/Cs} \qquad (10)$$

Finally, for $Z_0(s)$ we get

$$Z_0(s) = \frac{V_2(s)}{I_2(s)} = \frac{1}{Cs} + \frac{r_pR_k}{r_p + R_k(\mu + 1)} \qquad (11)$$

The final result is shown in Fig. 7.

Half a century after Thévenin's theorem was stated, the dual theorem was given by E. L. Norton. A development of this can proceed in a dual manner to that already given. However, the following considerations will be sufficient to establish it.

Let us write the node equations at nodes 1 and 1' of Fig. 4a, considering V_0 in series with Z_0 as one branch and choosing the datum as a node inside the right hand network. The result will be

Node 1:

$$\frac{V_1 - V_{1'}}{Z_0} + \text{(contribution of network to the right)} = \frac{V_0(s)}{Z_0(s)} \qquad (a)$$

$$(12)$$

Node 1':

$$\frac{V_{1'} - V_1}{Z_0} + \text{(contribution of network to the right)} = -\frac{V_0(s)}{Z_0(s)} \qquad (b)$$

Suppose now, we replace the Thévenin equivalent network by the network within the dotted line of Fig. 4b. The network to the right is the same as before. Let us write the node equations for this combined network, at nodes 1 and 1'. We immediately see that the equations are the same as Eqs. (12). Since the network to the right is unaltered, the node equations at all other nodes remain unaltered. Thus the two networks of Fig. 4 have the same node equations, hence the same node voltages. Therefore the currents and voltages in the network to the right are the same.

In other words, the network within the dotted line of Fig. 4b is *equivalent* to the network within the dotted line of Fig. 4a. Since the latter is equivalent to the original network on the left of Fig. 2a, it follows that the network within the dotted lines of Fig. 4b is also equivalent to the original subnetwork. This is Norton's theorem. In the statement of Norton's theorem, $V_0(s)/Z_0(s)$, is referred to as the *short-circuit current*, which it obviously is (consider shorting the terminals of the Thévenin equivalent).

In discussing Thévenin's theorem we assumed that the network on the right was passive and was initially relaxed. As a matter of fact, the theorem is even more general than this and applies equally well if the right hand network contains sources. The only restriction is that the two networks not be magnetically coupled. It is possible to prove this statement but the length and complexity of the proof do not warrant its inclusion here. For the purpose of reference we will state these two theorems here.

A. Thévenin's Theorem: Any two terminal linear network, which is not magnetically coupled to an external network, is equivalent at the two terminals to the network shown in Fig. 4a. The impedance $Z_0(s)$ is the driving-point impedance at the two terminals when all independent sources in the network are removed; $V_0(s)$ is the voltage transform at the two terminals when these terminals are left open.

B. Norton's Theorem: Any two terminal linear network, which is not magnetically coupled to an external network, is equivalent at the two terminals to the network shown in Fig. 4b. The impedance $Z_0(s)$ is the same as in Thévenin's theorem, and $I_0(s)$ is the current between the two terminals when these terminals are short circuited.

5.3 The Reciprocity Theorem

A theorem which is useful in theoretical investigations is the theorem of reciprocity. Whereas linearity is the only condition for the previous theorems discussed, the reciprocity theorem applies to a more restricted class of networks. Consider the network shown in Fig. 8a. The network

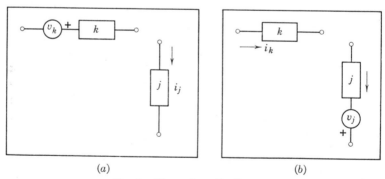

(a)   (b)

Fig. 8. The reciprocity theorem.

explicitly shows two branches only, both of which are assumed to be links for a particular choice of tree. One branch is a passive branch while the other contains a voltage source as well. We make the following assumptions about the network, which are central to reciprocity.

1. The network is initially relaxed. That is, all initial inductance currents and capacitance voltages are zero.

2. The source shown in Fig. 8 is the *only source* in the network.

3. The network contains only R, L, C, and M elements besides the single source.

The loop currents are chosen so that the jth loop current is identical with the branch current of the passive branch and the reference polarity of the voltage source is at the tip of the reference arrow of the kth loop current. If $\Delta(s)$ is the determinant of the mesh impedance matrix, we can write for $I_j(s)$

$$I_j(s) = \frac{\Delta_{kj}(s)}{\Delta(s)} V_k(s) \tag{13}$$

or

$$Y_{jk}(s) = \frac{I_j(s)}{V_k(s)} = \frac{\Delta_{kj}}{\Delta} \tag{14}$$

where $Y_{jk}(s)$ is the transfer admittance from loop k to loop j.

Now let us place the source in the same loop as the passive branch retaining the loop current references and insuring that the reference plus of the source is at the tip of the loop current reference. The transfer admittance from loop j to loop k will become:

$$Y_{kj}(s) = \frac{I_k(s)}{V_j(s)} = \frac{\Delta_{jk}(s)}{\Delta(s)} \tag{15}$$

Let us examine the cofactors Δ_{jk} and Δ_{kj}. If the network consists of bilateral elements only $(R, L, C, \text{and } M)$ then the mesh impedance matrix and its inverse are symmetric, leading to the result that these cofactors are equal.

We conclude that the transfer admittances in Eqs. (14) and (15) are equal. Another way of stating the reciprocity theorem is to say that *the ratio of the response transform to the excitation transform is invariant to an interchange of the position of the excitation and the response.*

Of course, the dual theorem, when the excitation is a current source and the response is a branch or node voltage, is also valid. This may be verified in a similar manner. Note the conditions of the theorem: there is only a single source and the network is initially relaxed. Furthermore, the network must not contain any dependent sources. We use this theorem as the basis of terminology. Networks for which the theorem is true are called *reciprocal* networks. Any elements which violate the reciprocity theorem are called *nonreciprocal elements.* Such elements may be either active or passive.

There are a number of additional theorems which are useful in particular cases. Some of these are simply modifications of the ones we have discussed. Others are so simple that they are not in the same class as the general theorems we have discussed. We will present some of these in the form of problems to be solved.

5.4   The Sinusoidal Steady State

Although in recent years expressions like "pulse circuits," "square wave testing," etc., are becoming more and more familiar, the sinusoidal function of time still holds an important place in network theory. Its importance is due to several factors. First of all the voltage or current waveforms of many actual generators are sinusoidal (at least approximately). For this reason alone we would be interested in finding solutions to network equations for sinusoidal driving functions. But even more important is the fact that any periodic function satisfying certain simple conditions (which are not important for the present discussion) can be represented by a (Fourier) series of sinusoidal functions with harmonic frequencies. The voltage or current waveforms of a large number of physical generators, if not sinusoidal, are at least periodic, so that a partial sum of the Fourier series can approximate these functions as closely as we desire. Since the networks we are dealing with are linear, the solution for a periodic driving function can be obtained as a summation of solutions for sinusoidal driving functions. Furthermore, the same idea can be extended to non-periodic functions (again satisfying certain conditions) by means of the Fourier integral formulation.

The sinusoidal function of time

$$g(t) = |G| \cos (\omega_0 t + \phi) \tag{16}$$

can be described in terms of three quantities; the *amplitude* $|G|$, the *angle* (or *phase*) ϕ, and the *angular frequency* ω_0 (this quantity is also called the *angular velocity*). The sinusoidal function can be written in terms of the exponential function in one of two ways.

$$|G| \cos (\omega_0 t + \phi) = \frac{|G| \epsilon^{j(\omega_0 t + \phi)} + |G| \epsilon^{-j(\omega_0 t + \phi)}}{2}$$

$$= \frac{G \epsilon^{j\omega_0 t} + G^* \epsilon^{-j\omega_0 t}}{2} \tag{17}$$

or

$$|G| \cos (\omega_0 t + \phi) = Re \, [|G| \, \epsilon^{j(\omega_0 t + \phi)}] = Re \, (G \epsilon^{j\omega_0 t}) \tag{18}$$

where

$$G = |G| \, \epsilon^{j\phi} \tag{19}$$

The complex number G gives the amplitude and angle information of the sinusoid. It is called a *phasor* or *sinor*. Thus, the function $Ge^{j\omega_0 t}$ completely describes a sinusoid by means of either Eq. (17) or Eq. (18).

Let us go one step further and consider the function $Ge^{s_0 t}$, where G is still a complex number given by Eq. (19), and $s_0 = \sigma_0 + j\omega_0$ is also a complex number. We can write

$$Ge^{s_0 t} = e^{\sigma_0 t}(|G|\,e^{j\phi}e^{j\omega_0 t})$$

$$= |G|\,e^{\sigma_0 t}[\cos(\omega_0 t + \phi) + j\sin(\omega_0 t + \phi)] \quad (a)$$

$$Re(Ge^{s_0 t}) = |G|\,e^{\sigma_0 t}\cos(\omega_0 t + \phi) \quad\quad\quad (b) \quad\quad (20)$$

$$Im(Ge^{s_0 t}) = |G|\,e^{\sigma_0 t}\sin(\omega_0 t + \phi) \quad\quad\quad (c)$$

The function $Ge^{s_0 t}$ is a complex function of t. Both its real part and its imaginary part are sinusoids with amplitudes which are real exponential functions of time. The actual waveforms will depend on the values of σ_0 and ω_0. Figure 9 shows some typical variations. In the limiting case

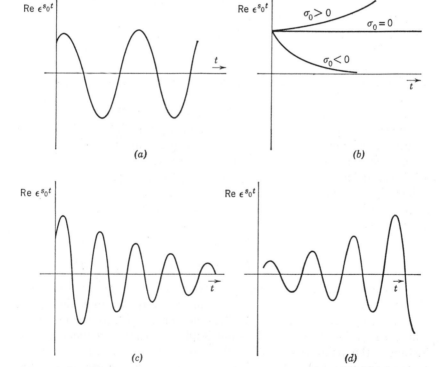

Fig. 9. Sketches of $Re\ e^{s_0 t}$ for various values of σ_0 and ω_0. (a) $s_0 = j\omega_0$; (b) $s_0 = \sigma_0$; (c) $s_0 = \sigma_0 + j\omega_0$, $\sigma_0 < 0$; (d) $s_0 = \sigma_0 + j\omega_0$, $\sigma_0 > 0$.

of $\sigma_0 = 0$, of course, we have a sinusoid. In the other extreme, $\omega_0 = 0$, we have increasing or decreasing exponentials, depending on the sign of σ_0. Of course, if σ_0 also is zero, there will be no variation with time. In the general case when neither σ_0 nor ω_0 is zero, the waveform is an exponentially modulated sinusoid, increasing or decreasing depending on the sign of σ_0.

The complex variable $s = \sigma + j\omega$, of which s_0 is a particular value, is often referred to as the complex frequency. This is unfortunate. With this designation, if we refer simply to frequency, it is not clear whether we mean s or ω. To emphasize the distinction people often say *real frequency* to mean ω. But ω is the *imaginary* part of s. Wouldn't it be more appropriate to call σ the real frequency? The question may arise, why give a name to s at all? Why not call it simply *the s variable?* This is a perfectly good procedure. However, there is a minor disadvantage; not everyone uses the symbol s for this variable. Other symbols in common use are p and λ.

There is another alternative and that is to coin a name for s, combining somehow the names for σ and ω. The disadvantage in a coined name is that on first appearance it sounds strange, and so is unacceptable to people. However, such coined words have found usefulness in science and mathematics in the past. Some day a name such as *frequement*, combining the words frequency and increment or decrement, may be acceptable for s. For the present we will use the term *complex frequency variable* for s.

Another question that crops up in this regard is: What is a negative frequency? From its basic definition, frequency is an inherently positive quantity. The number of times an alternating quantity passes through zero, in an increasing sense, per unit time is defined as its frequency. With this definition there can be no question of a negative frequency— a negative number of times the alternating quantity passes through zero. So what does it mean for ω to be negative? Consider the following expressions

$$\sin \omega t = \pm \sin|\omega|t \qquad (a)$$
$$\cos \omega t = \cos|\omega|t \qquad (b)$$

(21)

where ω may take on positive or negative values. The number of times either of the right hand sides passes through zero per unit time from negative to positive values is $|\omega|/2\pi$, whether ω is positive or negative. Thus, a negative value of ω does not imply a negative frequency. For instance, the point $\omega = -17$ radians per second corresponds to an angular frequency of $+17$ radians per second. *There are no negative frequencies, only negative values of ω.*

Let us now turn to a consideration of the solution of the loop or node equations of a network when the driving functions are exponentials. Let Fig. 10 represent an arbitrary network with an arbitrary number of voltage sources, of which one, v_{gk}, is shown explicitly. The sources are all exponential with the same exponent and are given by

$$v_{gk}(t) = U_{gk}\epsilon^{s_0 t}; \qquad Res_0 \geq 0 \qquad (22)$$

Our purpose is to find a solution of the loop equations. Of course we have already done this for the general case in Eq. (32) of the last chapter. The solution can be effected if the mesh impedance matrix is nonsingular, which requires its determinant to be nonzero. The roots of the equation $\Delta(s) = 0$ lie in the closed left half s-plane (i.e., in the left half plane or on the j-axis), since it is assumed that the network is stable. Since $Res_0 \geq 0$, the determinant will not be made to vanish unless s_0 is

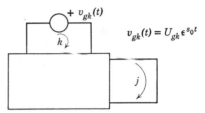

Fig. 10. Arbitrary network with exponential excitation.

purely imaginary ($s_0 = j\omega_0$), and this is a natural mode of the network. *Let us assume that this condition is avoided.*

Let us now find the transform of the jth loop current. In matrix notation the complete solution is given by

$$\boldsymbol{I}_m = \boldsymbol{Z}_m^{-1}\left(\boldsymbol{V}_g(s) + \boldsymbol{v}_\lambda(0) + \frac{\boldsymbol{v}_C(0)}{s}\right) \qquad (23)$$

which is Eq. (32) of Chapter 4. $\boldsymbol{Z}_m$ is the mesh impedance matrix, $\boldsymbol{V}_g(s)$ is the source transform matrix, while $\boldsymbol{v}_\lambda(0)$ and $\boldsymbol{v}_C(0)$ are the initial value matrices. If we expand this equation and solve for $I_j(s)$, we will get a complicated expression which consists of the sum of a number of terms. Each term will have $\Delta(s)$ in the denominator, and in the numerator there will be the product of a cofactor of Δ and the corresponding source voltage transform, plus initial values. The poles of $I_j(s)$ will consist of the zeros of $\Delta(s)$ and the poles of the source voltage transforms. In the present case, the source voltage transforms have only a single pole at $s = s_0$. Thus, if we write the partial fraction expansion of $I_j(s)$ we will get

$$I_j(s) = \frac{1}{(s - s_0)}\sum_{k=1}^{n}\frac{U_{gk}\Delta_{kj}(s_0)}{\Delta(s_0)} + \sum_{k=1}^{m}\frac{a_j^{(k)}}{s - s_k}; \qquad = 1, 2, \cdots n \qquad (24)$$

In writing this expression we have taken the number of loop equations to be n and the number of natural modes to be m. (For simplicity we have assumed that all the natural modes are simple.)

In Eq. (24) the terms in the first summation correspond to the forced response, and the terms in the second summation correspond to the natural response. *Let us assume that none of the zeros of* $\Delta(s)$ *lie on the* $j\omega$ *axis.* Then the terms in the second summation will also correspond to the transient solution.

Let us now look at the transform of the forced response. This has the form

$$I_j(s)\,|_{\text{forced}} = \frac{J_j}{s - s_0} \tag{25}$$

where

$$J_j = \sum_{k=1}^{n} U_{gk} \frac{\Delta_{kj}(s_0)}{\Delta(s_0)} \tag{26}$$

Note that J_j is a complex number, a phasor.

Suppose now that the source voltages v_{gk} are the conjugates of those given in Eq. (22). Then, the forced loop current transform in the jth loop will just be the conjugate of Eq. (25). Finally, if the source voltages are sinusoidal, then the forced loop current transform in the jth loop, which will also be the steady-state response, will be obtained in terms of Eq. (25) and the phasor J_j by the use of Eqs. (17) or (18) for the condition $s_0 = j\omega_0$. It is clear, then, that to find the steady-state response to sinusoidal driving functions, it is sufficient to find the forced response to exponential drivers like Eq. (22).

Let us now digress for a moment and review the procedure used in a-c steady-state anslysis, so that we may compare it with the present discussion. In a-c steady state we consider the source voltages to be sinusoidal functions of time, of the type $|U_{jk}| \cos(\omega_0 t + \phi_k)$, where the angular frequency ω_0 is a fixed real number. Then we express this sinusoidal function in terms of the exponential functions $\epsilon^{j\omega_0 t}$ and $\epsilon^{-j\omega_0 t}$ as in Eq. (17). By the principle of superposition, the solution to the sinusoid can be expressed as the sum of the solutions to the two exponential drivers considered separately. Now since the two drivers are conjugates and the network parameters are all real, the solutions to conjugate drivers will be conjugates. Therefore in a-c steady-state analysis we find *only one* of the two solutions. Also, instead of going through the Laplace transform as we did here, we use Eq. (26) directly. Since we would eventually replace s by $s_0 = j\omega_0$, we begin in a-c steady-state analysis with $s_0 = j\omega_0$. Thus we consider the voltage-current relationships of resistance, inductance, and capacitance elements to be

$$U_R = RJ \qquad\qquad (a)$$

$$U_L = j\omega_0 L J \qquad\qquad (b) \qquad (27)$$

$$U_C = \frac{1}{j\omega_0 C} J \qquad\qquad (c)$$

The equations that we write are essentially the same as the ones we would write in Laplace transforms, except that $j\omega_0$ replaces s, no initial conditions appear, and we write phasors U and J instead of transforms $V(s)$ and $I(s)$. It is clear now that the solution obtained for the phasor current J_j will be the same as Eq. (26). To find the current $i_j(t)$ we use the superposition principle as follows:

$$i_j(t) = \tfrac{1}{2}[J_j \epsilon^{j\omega_0 t} + J_j{}^* \epsilon^{-j\omega_0 t}] = Re[J_j \epsilon^{j\omega_0 t}] \qquad (28)$$

Unfortunately, we very rarely compute the real current $i_j(t)$ in a-c steady-state analysis, which leads to a lot of confusion. We think we are working with real currents and voltages, whereas we are really working with phasors. This leads to conceptions like $\cos \omega t = j \sin \omega t$, $Z = v(t)/i(t)$, etc., which are completely meaningless.

The a-c steady-state impedance is another quantity we should consider briefly, in order to relate it to our generalized concept of impedance as defined in Chapter 4. The a-c steady-state impedance is again defined in terms of phasor quantities. Given a one terminal-pair network, if the sinusoidal steady-state current and voltage are given by

$$v(t) = Re(U\epsilon^{j\omega_0 t}) \qquad\qquad (a)$$

$$i(t) = Re(J\epsilon^{j\omega_0 t}) \qquad\qquad (b) \qquad (29)$$

then we define the steady-state impedance as the *complex number*

$$Z_s = \frac{U}{J} \qquad (30)$$

(which is very different from $v(t)/i(t)$). Referring back to Eq. (26) and the definition of the driving-point impedance function in Chapter 4, we see that the steady-state impedance is the *value* of the driving point impedance *function* $Z(s)$ at $s = j\omega_0$. That is

$$Z(j\omega_0) = Z_s \qquad (31)$$

The same remark applies to all the other network functions.

Thus the concepts that are being developed in this text are true generalizations of those we know from steady-state analysis; and in fact, by considering the general method, we are able to justify the method of procedure used in a-c steady-state analysis.

Another important conclusion can also be drawn from this discussion. Suppose that the voltage sources are arbitrary instead of being exponential, and suppose that the network is initially relaxed. Eq. (23) still applies but v_λ and v_C are now zero. If we now expand Eq. (23) for the jth loop-current transform we will get

$$I_j(s) = \sum_{k=1}^{n} V_{gk}(s) \frac{\Delta_{kj}(s)}{\Delta(s)} \tag{32}$$

Comparison of this expression with Eq. (26) shows a striking resemblance. In the present case $I_j(s)$ and $V_{gk}(s)$ are Laplace transforms and the determinants are functions of s, whereas in Eq. (26) the variables J_j and U_{gk} are phasors, and the determinants are to be evaluated at s_0, which is a particular value of s. Thus, the expressions that relate a response transform and the transforms of the driving functions for arbitrary drivers are the same as the expressions that relate the response phasor to the driving function phasors in the case of sinusoidal driving functions, except that s replaces $j\omega_0$. This means that all the rules of simplification of networks, such as series and parallel connection of impedances, etc., which we have used in steady-state analysis, also apply in the general case, for an initially relaxed network (a fact that we have already used in section 4.7).

5.5   Steady-State Response to General Periodic Excitation

Besides the sinusoidal function, many other periodic functions commonly occur in the applications of electric networks. Of particular interest is the steady-state response to such functions. The results we are seeking do not depend on whether the driving function is a voltage or a current, and whether the response is a voltage or a current. Hence, we will use the symbols $e(t)$ to represent an excitation and $r(t)$ to represent the response.

Let the function $e(t)$ shown in Fig. 11 be a periodic function with period

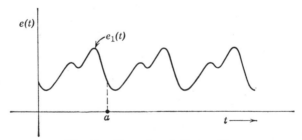

Fig. 11.   General periodic function.

a and let $e_1(t)$ be the first cycle of this function; that is

$$e_1(t) = e(t) \qquad 0 \leq t \leq a$$
$$e_1(t) = 0 \qquad t > a \tag{33}$$

Let us assume that $e_1(t)$ contains no impulses, has only a finite number of finite discontinuities and is absolutely integrable; that is, $\int_0^a |e_1(t)|\, dt$ is finite. These conditions permit the function to be representable in a Fourier series, and they are more than enough to make $e(t)$ £-transformable.

This function is to be applied to a network whose transfer function is $H(s)$, and it is desired to find the steady-state response of the network. * Recall that the steady-state response of a network to a periodic excitation is identical with the forced response. Furthermore it does not depend on the initial conditions.

One method of obtaining the desired response is to expand the periodic excitation function in a Fourier series. Knowing the transfer function, the steady-state response to each of the harmonic components can then be found. The complete steady-state response is then obtained by adding the responses to each of the harmonics. This will generally be an infinite series. Briefly, we write

$$e(t) = \sum_{n=-\infty}^{\infty} b_n \epsilon^{jn\omega_0 t} \tag{34}$$

where $\omega_0 = 2\pi/a$ and the b_n's are the Fourier coefficients, given by

$$b_n = \frac{1}{a} \int_0^a e(t) \epsilon^{-jn\omega_0 t}\, dt \tag{35}$$

The steady-state response is then given by

$$r_0(t) = \sum_{n=-\infty}^{\infty} b_n H(jn\omega_0) \epsilon^{jn\omega_0 t} \tag{36}$$

This procedure is at best tedious. It would be very useful to develop an alternate procedure which yields the desired steady-state response in closed form, possibly as the sum of just a few terms. We will now discuss such a procedure based on Laplace transforms.

The fundamental philosophy of the procedure to be described is very simple and intuitive. By contrast the mathematical intricacies that go into the proof of the validity of the method are far from obvious. For this reason, we shall first try to communicate the basic ideas by means

---

* Since we are not committing ourselves to voltage or current for the input and output, we are using a generic symbol $H(s)$ to represent the transfer function. It stands for any one of the transfer functions or driving point functions.

of intuitive arguments plus an example, before attempting mathematical precision.

We first make the assumption that the network function $H(s)$ has no poles on the $j\omega$ axis (*including* $s = \infty$), so that the transient response eventually dies out and only the forced response remains. Now, the excitation is periodic. Therefore, we would intuitively expect the forced response also to be periodic and of the same period as the driving function. That is, if $r_0(t)$ is the forced response,

$$r_0(t + a) = r_0(t) \tag{37}$$

This expression should also hold when $0 \leq t < a$, which is the first period. In other words, the forced response in the first period should be the same as the forced response in any period. Thus all we need to find is the forced response in the first period. That will be the steady-state response.

Now, it is very easy to find the complete response in the first period. For this we note (intuitively at present) that the complete response in the first period $0 \leq t < a$ cannot be affected by what $e(t)$ does at later times. To put it differently, if we replace $e(t)$ by $e_1(t)$, as defined in Eq. (33), the network will not know the difference until t becomes equal to a. Since $e_1(t)$ is a much simpler function to work with, we might as well use this fact. Thus the complete response in the first period is simply

$$r_1(t) = \mathcal{L}^{-1}[E_1(s)H(s)] \qquad 0 \leq t < a \tag{38}$$

(The initial conditions are neglected, since they affect only the transient.)

But this is the complete response. We don't want it. We want only that part of the complete response which corresponds to the steady state. The excess baggage we have collected is the transient. If we can somehow find the transient, and *subtract* it from $r_1(t)$, we'll be in business. Let us see how this may be done.

Since the function $e(t)$ can be described as the first period repeating itself periodically, it can be written in terms of $e_1(t)$ as

$$e(t) = \sum_{k=0}^{\infty} e_1(t - ka)u(t - ka) \tag{39}$$

where u is the unit step function. Transforming this expression, we get

$$E(s) = \mathcal{L}e(t) = \sum_{k=0}^{\infty} E_1(s)\epsilon^{-kas}$$

$$= E_1(s) \sum_{k=0}^{\infty} \epsilon^{-kas} \tag{40}$$

When $Re(s) > 0$, the last line is a convergent geometric series and so we can write:

$$E(s) = \frac{E_1(s)}{1 - \epsilon^{-as}} \qquad Re(s) > 0 \qquad (41)$$

The complete response for all t is therefore

$$r(t) = \mathcal{L}^{-1}[E(s)H(s)]$$

$$= \mathcal{L}^{-1}\left[\frac{E_1(s)}{1 - \epsilon^{-as}} H(s)\right] \qquad (42)$$

Let us examine this expression carefully and see whether we can find the steady state and the transient. As we shall show later, in the mathematical justification, the residue theorem is applicable to the inversion in Eq. (42); so we can concentrate our attention on the singular points of $R(s)$.

The singular points of the response transform $R(s)$ are those of $H(s)$ together with the singularities of $E(s)$. The singular points of $H(s)$ are poles in the open left half plane by our assumption, and so give rise to terms of the type

$$t^n \epsilon^{s_k t}$$

where $Re(s_k) < 0$. So, in the *complete* solution, the singular points of $H(s)$ contribute only transient terms. The singularities of $E(s)$ consist of the zeros of $1 - \epsilon^{-as}$ and the singular points of $E_1(s)$. Let us first look for the singularities of $E_1(s)$.

$$E_1(s) = \int_0^\infty e_1(t)\epsilon^{-st}\, dt = \int_0^a e_1(t)\epsilon^{-st}\, dt \qquad (43)$$

The last form follows from the fact that $e_1(t)$ is zero for $t > a$. Thus $E_1(s)$ has a representation as a finite integral. Furthermore, $e_1(t)$ is a bounded function. That is

$$|e_1(t)| \leq M \qquad (44)$$

for some real M. Therefore, $E_1(s)$ has a finite value for all s, and Leibnitz's rule for differentiation under the integral sign applies. That is,

$$\frac{d}{ds} E_1(s) = \int_0^a \frac{\partial}{\partial s}[e_1(t)\epsilon^{-st}]\, dt$$

$$= -\int_0^a te_1(t)\epsilon^{-st}\, dt \qquad (45)$$

which *exists for all finite values of s.* Thus, $E_1(s)$ is differentiable everywhere in the complex plane, and so is an entire function (no singularities except at infinity). Hence, the only singular points of $E(s)$ are the zeros of $1 - \epsilon^{-as}$.

The zeros of $1 - \epsilon^{-as}$ occur when

$$e^{-as} = 1 \qquad\qquad (a)$$

$$s = jk\omega_0 \ (k \text{ an integer}) \qquad\qquad (b)$$

$$(46)$$

where $\omega_0 = 2\pi/a$ is the fundamental frequency. Thus $E(s)$ has an infinite number of poles on the $j\omega$ axis, and, as you can verify, all of them are simple. Let us compute the residue at one of these poles. Residue of $R(s)\epsilon^{st}$ at $s = jk\omega_0$ is equal to

$$\lim_{s \to jk\omega_0} \left\{ (s - jk\omega_0) \frac{E_1(s)H(s)}{1 - \epsilon^{-as}} \epsilon^{st} \right\} = \frac{E_1(jk\omega_0)H(jk\omega_0)}{\dfrac{d}{ds}(1 - \epsilon^{-as}) \Big|_{s=jk\omega_0}} \epsilon^{jk\omega_0 t}$$

$$= \frac{1}{a} E_1(jk\omega_0)H(jk\omega_0)\epsilon^{jk\omega_0 t} \qquad (47)$$

Therefore the partial response due to the poles of $E(s)$ is

$$r_0(t) = \sum_{k=-\infty}^{\infty} \frac{1}{a} E_1(jk\omega_0)H(jk\omega_0)\epsilon^{jk\omega_0 t} \qquad (48)$$

We recognize this expression to be a Fourier series. (We will worry about its convergence later, along with all the other mathematical worries.) In fact, it is the same Fourier series as given in Eq. (36). To see this, let us compute $E_1(jk\omega_0)$ from Eq. (43).

$$E_1(jk\omega_0) = \int_0^a \epsilon^{-jk\omega_0 t} e_1(t)\, dt \qquad (49)$$

Comparing with Eq. (35) for the Fourier coefficients, we see immediately that

$$E_1(jk\omega_0) = ab_k \qquad (50)$$

which shows that Eqs. (48) and (36) represent the same function.

Thus in the complete response for all t, the residues of $R\epsilon^{st}$ at the singular points of $E(s)$ constitute the steady state and those at the singular points of $H(s)$ constitute the transient. This transient solution can therefore be written

$$r_t(t) = \Sigma \text{ residues of } \frac{E_1(s)}{1 - \epsilon^{-as}} H(s)\epsilon^{st} \text{ at poles of } H(s) \qquad (51)$$

This expression is valid for all values of t, but we are going to use it only for $0 \leq t < a$.

Now we have completed our job. All we need to do is to subtract this transient from the complete solution for the first period. The result will be the steady state solution. Using Eqs. (51), it will be

$$r_0(t) = r_1(t) - r_t(t)$$

$$= \mathcal{L}^{-1}[E_1(s)H(s)] - \text{residues of } \frac{E_1(s)H(s)}{1 - \epsilon^{-as}} \epsilon^{st} \text{ at poles of } H(s),$$

$$(0 \leq t < a) \tag{52}$$

Let us make a few comments on this equation before giving an example. We notice that both quantities on the right side have contributions only from the singular points of $H(s)$, which are usually associated with the transient. For this reason the steady-state response to periodic functions is sometimes referred to as the "recurrent transient response."

A more important point to be noted, one which makes this whole discussion valuable, is that only *finite operations* are involved. Being rational, $H(s)$ has only a finite number of poles, so we do not compute an infinite number of residues. The expression for $r_0(t)$ is in closed form, as the sum of a finite number of functions.

Now let us try an example. Let the saw-tooth voltage wave of Fig. 12a be applied to the network of Fig. 12b. Let it be required to find the

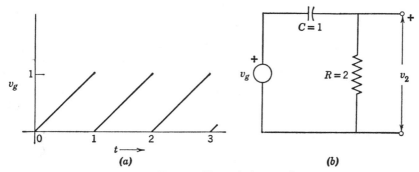

Fig. 12. Numerical example.

steady-state voltage output. For this simple network the voltage ratio function can be written down immediately using the voltage divider equation.

$$\frac{V_2(s)}{V_g(s)} = H(s) = \frac{R}{R + (1/sC)} = \frac{s}{s + \frac{1}{2}} \tag{53}$$

The network function $H(s)$ has one simple pole at $s = -\frac{1}{2}$. Using the notation introduced earlier,

$$e_1(t) = t \qquad 0 \le t < 1$$
$$= 0 \qquad 1 \le t \tag{54}$$

To find the Laplace transform easily, we may write this as

$$e_1(t) = t[u(t) - u(t - 1)]$$
$$= tu(t) - (t - 1)u(t - 1) - u(t - 1) \tag{55}$$

The transform of this expression is

$$E_1(s) = \frac{1}{s^2}(1 - \epsilon^{-s}) - \frac{1}{s}\epsilon^{-s} \tag{56}$$

(Verify that this function is regular at $s = 0$.) The complete response for the first period is therefore

$$r_1(t) = \mathcal{L}^{-1}[E_1(s)H(s)]$$
$$= \mathcal{L}^{-1}\left\{ \frac{1}{s(s + \frac{1}{2})} - \left[\frac{1}{s(s + \frac{1}{2})} + \frac{1}{s + \frac{1}{2}} \right]\epsilon^{-s} \right\} \tag{57}$$

We cannot simply write this as

$$r_1(t) = \Sigma \text{ residues of } E_1(s)H(s)\epsilon^{st} \text{ at poles of } H(s) \tag{58}$$

since the residue theorem does not apply directly in this case (why?). However we can find the inverse transform by using the translation theorem for the term multiplied by ϵ^{-s}. Then we get

$$r_1(t) = \mathcal{L}^{-1}\left[\frac{1}{s(s + \frac{1}{2})} \right] - \mathcal{L}^{-1}\left\{ \left[\frac{1}{s(s + \frac{1}{2})} + \frac{1}{s + \frac{1}{2}} \right]\epsilon^{-s} \right\}$$
$$= (2 - 2\epsilon^{-t/2}) - [2 - \epsilon^{-(t-1)/2}]u(t - 1) \tag{59}$$

We notice that the second term is multiplied by $u(t - 1)$. Therefore it contributes nothing to the first period. The reason is not far to seek. This is the term that we inserted in $e_1(t)$ in Eq. (56) to make it zero for $t > 1$. As far as the response in the first period is concerned, the network does not know whether the excitation is $e_1(t)$ as we have defined it in Eq. (54) or merely $e(t) = t$ for all t. We can use this fact, if we like, to find the complete solution for the first period. If we follow this procedure, however, we have to be very careful to use the proper expression, and not the simplified one, for $E_1(s)$ when finding the transient in the next step.

The transient response for this example is

$$r_t(t) = \Sigma \text{ residues of } E(s)H(s)\epsilon^{st} \text{ at poles of } H(s)$$

$$= \text{residue of } \frac{E_1(s)}{1 - \epsilon^{-s}} H(s)\epsilon^{st} \text{ at } s = -\tfrac{1}{2} \tag{60}$$

Using the expressions for $E_1(s)$ and $H(s)$ from Eqs. (56) and (53), we get

$$r_t(t) = -2\epsilon^{-t/2} + \frac{\epsilon^{-t/2}}{1 - \epsilon^{-\frac{1}{2}}} \tag{61}$$

The steady-state response in the first period is found by subtracting this expression from Eq. (59)

$$r_0(t) = r_1(t) - r_t(t)$$

$$= 2 - \frac{\epsilon^{-t/2}}{1 - \epsilon^{-\frac{1}{2}}} \tag{62}$$

For all other periods

$$r_0(t + k) = r_0(t) \tag{63}$$

Since this is the first example that we are working by a new procedure, let us verify that this is indeed the correct answer. The correct answer to the problem must satisfy the differential equation and the boundary conditions. In the present case the response r stands for voltage v_2. The differential equation to be satisfied by $r_0(t) = v_{20}(t)$ is the node equation at node 2 within any one period.

$$C\frac{d}{dt}[v_{20}(t + k) - v_g(t + k)] + \frac{v_{20}(t + k)}{R} = 0, \quad k \leq t < k + 1 \tag{64}$$

where node 3 is taken as the reference. The boundary condition to be satisfied is that the capacitance voltage be continuous for all t (since there is no current impulse). This condition can evidently be written as

$$\frac{1}{C}\int_k^{k+1} \frac{v_{20}(t + k)}{R} \, dt = 0 \tag{65}$$

Substituting the values of C and R and the expressions for $v_g(t)$ and $v_{20}(t)$, the left side of Eq. (64) becomes

$$\frac{d}{dt}\left[2 - \frac{\epsilon^{-(t+k)/2}}{1 - \epsilon^{-\frac{1}{2}}}\right] - \frac{d}{dt}(t - k) + \frac{1}{2}\left(2 - \frac{\epsilon^{-(t+k)/2}}{1 - \epsilon^{-\frac{1}{2}}}\right)$$

$$= \frac{1}{2}\frac{\epsilon^{-(t+k)/2}}{1 - \epsilon^{-\frac{1}{2}}} - 1 + 1 - \frac{1}{2}\frac{\epsilon^{-(t+k)/2}}{1 - \epsilon^{-\frac{1}{2}}} = 0 \tag{66}$$

Similarly, substituting into Eq. (65), the left side becomes

$$\frac{1}{2} \int_k^{k+1} \left(2 - \frac{\epsilon^{-(t+k)/2}}{1 - \epsilon^{-\frac{1}{2}}} \right) dt = 0 \qquad (67)$$

Thus, both conditions are satisfied and we indeed have the correct solution.

As we can observe, the procedure we have just described is both simple and intuitive. Let us next plunge into the intricacies of the mathematical justification which cannot qualify for either attribute.

Theorem. Let $e(t)$ be a periodic function of period a. Let $e(t)$ be of bounded variation and absolutely integrable within the period. Let $e(t)$ be the excitation for a stable network and $r(t)$ the response. Let the network function $H(s)$ be regular on the imaginary axis, including $s = \infty$. Then $r(t)$ is asymptotic to a periodic function $r_0(t)$ for large t. The function $r_0(t)$ is independent of the initial conditions and is given by

$$r_0(t) = \mathcal{L}^{-1}[E_1(s)H(s)] - \sum_{\substack{\text{poles} \\ \text{of } H(s)}} \text{residues of } \frac{E_1(s)H(s)}{1 - \epsilon^{-as}} \epsilon^{st} \quad (a)$$

$$0 \le t < a \qquad (68)$$

$$r_0(t + ka) = r_0(t) \qquad ka \le t < (k+1)a \quad (b)$$

where

$$E_1(s) = \int_0^a e(t)\epsilon^{-st} dt \qquad (69)$$

By assumption, $H(s)$ is a rational function, regular at ∞. If $H(\infty) \ne 0$, we can write

$$H(s) = H(\infty) + H_1(s) \qquad (70)$$

where $H_1(s)$ has a zero at ∞. Such a constant term will contribute $H(\infty)e(t)$ to the periodic solution. It will contribute nothing to the sum of the residues in Eq. (68). Such a contribution is therefore included in Eq. (68), and so we may assume without loss of generality that $H(s)$ has a zero at $s = \infty$ (of at least order one).

It is also clear that the initial conditions contribute nothing to the asymptotic solution for large t (since $H(s)$ has no poles on the $j\omega$ axis and certainly none in the right half plane).* Hence we can assume the network to be initially relaxed.

---

* In certain trivial cases the initial conditions may contribute a constant term to the asymptotic solution for large t, which is neglected in this theorem. Such a constant is not included in the Fourier analysis either.

As we computed earlier

$$\mathcal{L}e(t) = \frac{E_1(s)}{1 - \epsilon^{-as}} ; \qquad Re(s) > 0 \tag{71}$$

Hence the complete solution for all t is given by

$$r(t) = \mathcal{L}^{-1}[R(s)] = \mathcal{L}^{-1}\left[\frac{E_1(s)H(s)}{1 - \epsilon^{-as}}\right] \tag{72}$$

which can also be written as the complex inversion integral

$$r(t) = \frac{1}{2\pi j} \int_{\sigma_1-j\infty}^{\sigma_1+j\infty} \frac{E_1(s)H(s)}{1 - \epsilon^{-as}} \epsilon^{st}\, ds; \qquad \sigma_1 > 0 \tag{73}$$

It is not obvious however that this integral can be evaluated by closing the path of integration to the left and using the theory of residues. There are two obstacles in our way. First of all, there are an infinite number of poles to be taken into account; secondly it is not evident that Jordan's lemma is satisfied. We have to examine these questions carefully.

Let us first observe that if we do find the sum of the residues of the integrand in Eq. (73), the infinite sum so obtained will converge. The assumption that $e(t)$ is of bounded variation guarantees the absolute convergence of the Fourier series for $e(t)$. This result follows from a standard result of Fourier series known as Percival's theorem.* We have already computed the residue of $R(s)\epsilon^{st}$ at $s = jk\omega_0$, where $\omega_0 = 2\pi/a$ in Eq. (47). From the absolute convergence of the Fourier series for $e(t)$ and the boundedness of $H(jk\omega_0)$, it follows that the infinite series of residues on the $j\omega$ axis given in Eq. (48) converges absolutely, and therefore also converges.

The other residues of $R(s)\epsilon^{st}$ arise from the poles of $H(s)$, of which there are only a finite number. Thus the sum

$$\sum_{\sigma<\sigma_1} \text{residues of } R(s)\,\epsilon^{st}$$

is meaningful. We have yet to establish that this sum is $r(t)$.

There are two possible proofs that we can give at this point. The simpler proof consists of expanding the integrand of Eq. (73) in an appropriate infinite series (the Mittag-Lefler expansion) and integrating term-by-term. We shall leave this proof as an exercise and give the more difficult "brute force" proof. We shall use parts of this direct

* See, for instance, E. C. Titchmarsh, *Theory of Functions*, Oxford University Press, 1939.

proof to establish another result—which is one reason for giving it. It will also give us an intuition into the behavior of $E_1(s)$.

We will now close the path of integration of the complex inversion integral in Eq. (73) to the left appropriately, and carefully estimate the contributions of the parts of the contour in the left half plane. The contour that we shall choose is shown in Fig. 13. It goes exactly midway

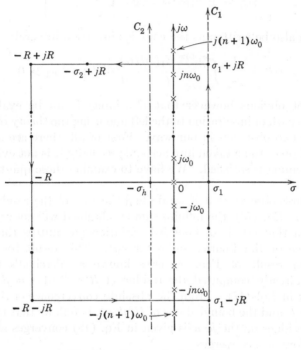

Fig. 13.   Contour for integration.

between the poles on the $j\omega$ axis and is a rectangle, rather than a semi-circle. (In dealing with exponential functions a rectangle is generally more convenient.) We shall take n so large that

$$R = (2n + 1)\frac{\omega_0}{2} \tag{74}$$

satisfies the following conditions.

(i)   All poles of $H(s)$ are included inside the contour so that $|H(s)|$ $\leq$ a constant K on the contour (and therefore also outside)

(ii) $R > \sigma_2 = \dfrac{1}{a}\log_\epsilon 2$. (The need for this condition arises in the development.)

These assumptions are clearly permissible, since we are going to take the limit as n goes to ∞. The number n is a positive integer, so that we have an infinite sequence of contours. Thus, R takes on discrete values rather than a continuous range of values, but this is clearly permissible.

Let us begin our estimates, starting with the vertical line to the left. On this line $\sigma = -R$. We have the bounds

$$|E_1(-R + j\omega)| = |\int_0^a \epsilon^{Rt} e_1(t)\epsilon^{-j\omega t}\, dt| \leq aM\epsilon^{aR} \quad (a)$$

where   (75)

$$M = \max |e_1(t)|, \quad \text{for } 0 \leq t < a \quad (b)$$

Also,

$$|1 - \epsilon^{-as}| = |\epsilon^{-as} - 1| \geq |\epsilon^{-as}| - 1$$
$$= \epsilon^{aR} - 1 \geq \epsilon^{aR} - \tfrac{1}{2}\epsilon^{aR}$$

or

$$|1 - \epsilon^{-as}| \geq \tfrac{1}{2}\epsilon^{aR} \quad (76)$$

The inequality (76) follows from assumption (ii) about R. Hence

$$\left|\int_{-R-jR}^{-R+jR} \frac{E_1(s)H(s)}{1 - \epsilon^{-as}} \epsilon^{st}\, ds\right| \leq \frac{aM\epsilon^{aR}K\epsilon^{-Rt}}{\tfrac{1}{2}\epsilon^{aR}} \cdot 2R = (4aMK)R\epsilon^{-Rt}$$

(77)

Thus

$$\lim_{R\to\infty} \int_{-R-jR}^{-R+jR} \frac{E_1(s)H(s)}{1 - \epsilon^{-as}} \epsilon^{st}\, ds = 0 \quad (78)$$

For the horizontal line from $\sigma_1 + jR$ to $-R + jR$, we split the contour into two parts, one from $\sigma_1 + jR$ to $-\sigma_2 + jR$ and the other from $-\sigma_2 + jR$ to $-R + jR$, where

$$\sigma_2 = \frac{1}{a}\log_\epsilon 2 \quad (79)$$

For the first integral

$$\int_{\sigma_1+jR}^{-\sigma_2+jR} \frac{E_1(s)H(s)}{1 - \epsilon^{-as}} \epsilon^{st}\, ds \quad (80)$$

we make the following observations. For each fixed σ,

$$E_1(\sigma + j\omega) = \int_0^a [\epsilon^{-\sigma t}e_1(t)]\epsilon^{-j\omega t}\, dt \quad (81)$$

which is of the form

$$\int_0^a f(t)\epsilon^{-j\omega t}\, dt$$

the same as one of the Fourier integrals. Therefore,

$$\lim_{\omega\to\infty} E_1(\sigma + j\omega) = \lim_{\omega\to\infty} \int_0^a [\epsilon^{-\sigma t}e_1(t)]\epsilon^{-j\omega t}\, dt = 0 \quad (82)$$

Thus for each fixed σ, $E_1(s)$ approaches 0 as ω approaches infinity. (The result that

$$\lim_{\omega \to \infty} \int_0^a f(t) \epsilon^{-j\omega t} \, dt = 0 \tag{83}$$

for any integrable function $f(t)$, is known as the Riemann-Lebesgue theorem, and is fundamental to the theories of Fourier series, Fourier transforms, and Laplace transforms.) If we restrict out attention to σ's on the closed interval

$$-\sigma_2 \leq \sigma \leq \sigma_1$$

the limit in Eq. (81) will also be approached uniformly with respect to σ. That is, for any given $\varepsilon > 0$, we can find an ω_1 such that

$$|E_1(\sigma + j\omega)| < \varepsilon \tag{84}$$

provided that $\omega > \omega_1$; the inequality holding for all σ in the range $-\sigma_2 \leq \sigma \leq \sigma_1$.

For the denominator of the integral in Eq. (80) we have an exact absolute value, since

$$R = (2n + 1)\frac{\omega_0}{2} = (2n + 1)\frac{\pi}{a} \tag{85}$$

$$|1 - \epsilon^{-as}|^2 = 1 + \epsilon^{-2a\sigma} - 2\epsilon^{-a\sigma} \cos aR$$

$$= (1 + \epsilon^{-a\sigma})^2$$

Hence,

$$|1 - \epsilon^{-as}| = 1 + \epsilon^{-a\sigma} \tag{86}$$

On the horizontal line from $\sigma_1 + jR$ to $-\sigma_2 + jR$, we have, therefore

$$\left| \int_{\sigma_1+jR}^{-\sigma_2+jR} \frac{E_1(s)H(s)}{1 - \epsilon^{-as}} \epsilon^{st} \, ds \right| < \frac{K\epsilon^{\sigma_1 t}}{1 + \epsilon^{-a\sigma_1}} (\sigma_1 + \sigma_2)\varepsilon \tag{87}$$

provided $(2n + 1)\omega_0/2 > \omega_1$. This follows from Eqs. (84) and (86), and from condition (i) on R. Therefore,

$$\lim_{n \to \infty} \int_{\sigma_1+jR}^{-\sigma_2+jR} \frac{E_1(s)H(s)}{1 - \epsilon^{-as}} \epsilon^{st} \, ds = 0 \tag{88}$$

Now let us look at the remainder of the line. From $-\sigma_2 + jR$ to $-R + jR$, we have

$$\left| \int_{-\sigma_2+jR}^{-R+jR} \frac{E_1(s)H(s)}{1 - \epsilon^{-as}} \epsilon^{st} \, ds \right| \leq \int_{-\sigma_2}^{-R} \frac{|E_1(s)| \, |H(s)| \, \epsilon^{\sigma t}}{\frac{1}{2}\epsilon^{-a\sigma}} \, |d\sigma| \tag{89}$$

Since $H(s)$ has a zero at infinity, we may assume R sufficiently large to make

$$|H(s)| \leq K_1 \frac{1}{|s|} \leq \frac{K_1}{R} \tag{90}$$

where K_1 is a constant.   Since $\sigma < 0$, we have, as in Eq. (75),

$$|E_1(s)| \leq aM\epsilon^{-a\sigma} \tag{91}$$

Inserting these bounds in inequality (89) and interchanging the limits of integration, we get

$$\left| \int_{-\sigma_2+jR}^{-R+jR} \frac{E_1(s)H(s)}{1 - \epsilon^{-as}} \epsilon^{st} \, ds \right| \leq \int_{-R}^{-\sigma_2} 2 \frac{K_1 aM\epsilon^{-\sigma a}\epsilon^{\sigma t}}{R\epsilon^{-\sigma a}} \, d\sigma$$

$$= (aK_1M) \frac{1}{Rt} (\epsilon^{-\sigma_2 t} - \epsilon^{-Rt}) \tag{92}$$

Therefore

$$\lim_{R \to \infty} \int_{-\sigma_2+jR}^{-R+jR} \frac{E_1(s)H(s)}{1 - \epsilon^{-as}} \epsilon^{st} \, ds = 0 \tag{93}$$

We have now shown that the contribution of the upper horizontal line to the complete integral around the contour in Fig. 13 is zero. Since the integrand is real on the real axis, the same limits, Eqs. (88) and (93), hold also for the lower horizontal line from $\sigma_1 - jR$ to $-R - jR$. So the lower horizontal line also contributes nothing to the closed contour integral.

Then, with all this trouble, we have proved that

$$r(t) = \frac{1}{2\pi j} \int_{\sigma_1-j\infty}^{\sigma_1+j\infty} \frac{E_1(s)H(s)}{1 - \epsilon^{-as}} \epsilon^{st} \, ds$$

$$= \sum_{\sigma < \sigma_1} \text{residues of } \frac{E_1(s)H(s)}{1 - \epsilon^{-as}} \epsilon^{st} \tag{94}$$

We can obviously rewrite this expression as follows.

$$r(t) = \Sigma \text{ residues of } \frac{E_1(s)H(s)}{1 - \epsilon^{-as}} \epsilon^{st} \text{ at poles of } H(s)$$

$$+ \frac{1}{a} \sum_{n=-\infty}^{\infty} H(jn\omega_0)E_1(jn\omega_0)\epsilon^{jn\omega_0 t} \tag{95}$$

from our earlier computation of the residues at poles on the $j\omega$ axis. The first sum in Eq. (95) contains exponential functions with negative real parts for the exponents and so goes to zero as t approaches infinity. The second sum, being a convergent Fourier series, represents a periodic function, of period a. Now our claim that the solution is asymptotic to a periodic function is established. If $H(\infty)$ is nonzero, this adds a constant multiple of $e(t)$ to the solution which does not destroy the periodicity. (The Fourier series expression of Eq. (95) remains valid even if $H(s)$ is nonzero at ∞.)

The periodic solution—the steady-state solution—is therefore given by

$$r_0(t) = \frac{1}{2\pi j} \int_{\sigma_1 - j\infty}^{\sigma_1 + j\infty} \frac{E_1(s)H(s)}{1 - \epsilon^{-as}} \epsilon^{st} \, ds$$

$$- \Sigma \text{ residues of } \frac{E_1(s)H(s)}{1 - \epsilon^{-as}} \epsilon^{st} \text{ at poles of } H(s) \qquad (96)$$

Using the same arguments that we used in proving that the integral from $\sigma_1 + jR$ to $-\sigma_2 + jR$ approaches zero as R approaches ∞, and, using a similar sequence of horizontal contours that avoid the poles, we can alternatively rewrite Eq. (96) as follows.

$$r_0(t) = \frac{1}{2\pi j} \int_{\sigma_1 - j\infty}^{\sigma_1 + j\infty} \frac{E_1(s)H(s)}{1 - \epsilon^{-as}} \epsilon^{st} \, ds - \frac{1}{2\pi j} \int_{\sigma_h - j\infty}^{\sigma_h + j\infty} \frac{E_1(s)H(s)}{1 - \epsilon^{-as}} \epsilon^{st} \, ds \quad (97)$$

where $\sigma_h < 0$ and all poles of $H(s)$ are to the left of the abscissa σ_h. (These two lines are shown as C_1 and C_2 in Fig. 13.) We are still dealing with expressions that are valid for all t. Since Eq. (97) is periodic, it suffices to compute the first period. Therefore we may assume that

$$0 \leq t < a \qquad (98)$$

For the first integral in Eq. (97), $Re(s) > 0$, and so $|\epsilon^{-as}| < 1$. Therefore we have

$$\frac{1}{1 - \epsilon^{-as}} = \sum_{n=0}^{\infty} \epsilon^{-ans} \qquad (99)$$

This series is uniformly convergent on the line $\sigma_1 - j\infty$ to $\sigma_1 + j\infty$. Therefore the integration may be performed term by term. The result is

$$\frac{1}{2\pi j} \int_{\sigma_1 - j\infty}^{\sigma_1 + j\infty} \frac{E_1(s)H(s)}{1 - \epsilon^{-as}} \epsilon^{st} \, ds = \frac{1}{2\pi j} \int_{\sigma_1 - j\infty}^{\sigma_1 + j\infty} E_1(s)H(s) \epsilon^{st} \, ds$$

$$+ \sum_{n=1}^{\infty} \frac{1}{2\pi j} \int_{\sigma_1 - j\infty}^{\sigma_1 + j\infty} E_1(s)H(s) \epsilon^{s(t-na)} \, ds \quad (100)$$

Since $E_1(s)$ is a Laplace transform and $H(s)$ is a rational function regular in the right half plane and at ∞, it follows that $E_1(s)H(s)$ is also a Laplace transform.   If we denote

$$\mathcal{L}^{-1}[E_1(s)H(s)] = r_1(t) \tag{101}$$

then we can write Eq. (100) using the translation theorem as

$$\frac{1}{2\pi j}\int_{\sigma_1-j\infty}^{\sigma_1+j\infty}\frac{E_1(s)H(s)}{1-\epsilon^{-as}}\epsilon^{st}\,ds = r_1(t) + \sum_{n=1}^{\infty}r_1(t-na)u(t-na) \tag{102}$$

Thus all the functions of the second sum are zero in the first period. This proves the theorem expressed in Eq. (68), and our job is done.

It is possible to express this result in other useful forms as well.   Using the last two equations, we can rewrite Eq. (97) as follows.

$$r_0(t) = \frac{1}{2\pi j}\int_{C_1}E_1(s)H(s)\epsilon^{st}\,ds - \frac{1}{2\pi j}\int_{C_2}\frac{E_1(s)H(s)}{1-\epsilon^{-as}}\epsilon^{st}\,ds \tag{103}$$

The paths C_1 and C_2 are the ones shown in Fig. 13.   The integrand in the first integral has no singularities to the right of the vertical path C_2.   Hence, the path may be moved to C_2 without modifying the result. We can therefore write

$$r_0(t) = \frac{1}{2\pi j}\int_{C_2}E_1(s)H(s)\left[1 - \frac{1}{1-\epsilon^{-as}}\right]\epsilon^{st}\,ds \tag{104}$$

Although this is a relatively compact form for the answer, evaluating it in any particular case involves the same steps.

Another form can be obtained by noting that only the poles of $H(s)$ contribute to the last integral in Eq. (103).   Suppose we expand the integrand in partial fractions and designate by $F_1(s)$ the principal parts at the poles of $H(s)$ and by $F_2(s)$ the remainder.   Then, we can write

$$\frac{E_1(s)H(s)}{1-\epsilon^{-as}} = F_1(s) + F_2(s) \tag{105}$$

Only $F_1(s)$ contributes to the integral.   Hence, Eq. (104) can be written

$$r_0(t) = \frac{1}{2\pi j}\int_{C_2}[E_1(s)H(s) - F_1(s)]\epsilon^{st}\,ds \tag{106}$$

Let us close the chapter with another example.   Consider the network shown in Fig. 14.   The triangular voltage v is applied to the network and it is required to find the steady-state output voltage v_2 (we are not using an additional subscript to indicate steady-state in order to avoid

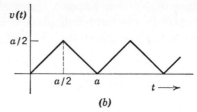

Fig. 14.   Illustrative example.

confusion).   The first period of the input voltage is given by

$$v_1(t) = tu(t) - 2(t - a/2)u(t - a/2) + (t - a)u(t - a) \quad (107)$$

$$V_1 = \frac{1}{s^2}(1 - 2\epsilon^{-as/2} + \epsilon^{-as}) \quad (108)$$

The transfer function of the network is

$$H(s) = \frac{V_2(s)}{V(s)} = \frac{1/sC}{sL + R + 1/sC} = \frac{2}{(s + 1)(s + 2)} \quad (109)$$

The desired response is obtained by substituting the last two equations into Eq. (103), keeping the differences in notation in mind.   Thus, we have

$$v_2(t) = \frac{1}{2\pi j} \int_{C_1} 2\frac{1 - 2\epsilon^{-as/2} + \epsilon^{-as}}{s^2(s + 1)(s + 2)} \epsilon^{st} \, ds$$

$$- \frac{1}{2\pi j} \int_{C_2} 2\frac{1 - 2\epsilon^{-as/2} + \epsilon^{-as}}{s^2(s + 1)(s + 2)(1 - \epsilon^{-as})} \epsilon^{st} \, ds$$

$$= v_{21}(t) + v_{22}(t) \quad (110)$$

with obvious definitions of v_{21} and v_{22}.   The integrand of the second integral satisfies Jordan's lemma, so that the path of integration can be closed on the left.   The value of $v_{22}(t)$ is simply the negative sum of the residues of the integrand at the poles of $H(s)$, which are $s = -1$ and $s = -2$.   Thus,

$$v_{22}(t) = -2\frac{(1 - 2\epsilon^{a/2} + \epsilon^a)\epsilon^{-t}}{1 - \epsilon^a} + 2\frac{(1 - 2\epsilon^a + \epsilon^{2a})}{4(1 - \epsilon^{2a})}\epsilon^{-2t} \quad (111)$$

$$= -2\frac{1 - \epsilon^{a/2}}{1 + \epsilon^{a/2}}\epsilon^{-t} + 2\frac{1 - \epsilon^a}{4(1 + \epsilon^a)}\epsilon^{-2t}$$

Let us now turn to the first integral in Eq. (110).   The exponentials in the numerator cause the integrand to diverge on the infinite arc to the left. Hence, we cannot simply add residues. Instead, let us write the integral as the sum of three integrals corresponding to the terms in the numerator of the integrand. Thus,

$$v_{21}(t) = A_1 + A_2 + A_3 \tag{112}$$

where

$$A_1 = \frac{1}{2\pi j} \int_{C_1} 2 \frac{\epsilon^{st}}{s^2(s+1)(s+2)} \, ds \qquad (a)$$

$$A_2 = \frac{1}{2\pi j} \int_{C_1} \frac{-4\epsilon^{s(t-a/2)}}{s^2(s+1)(s+2)} \, ds \qquad (b) \tag{113}$$

$$A_3 = \frac{1}{2\pi j} \int_{C_1} 2 \frac{\epsilon^{s(t-a)}}{s^2(s+1)(s+2)} \, ds \qquad (c)$$

The integrand of A_1 satisfies the condition of Jordan's lemma. Hence, A_1 can be evaluated by the Residue theorem. The result is

$$A_1 = \tfrac{1}{2}(2t - 3 + 4\epsilon^{-t} - \epsilon^{-2t}) \tag{114}$$

In the case of A_2 we see that the range $t < a/2$ must be handled differently from the range $t > a/2$. For $t < a/2$, we close the path to the right, which means there will be no poles inside the contour. For this range, then $A_2 = 0$. For $t > a/2$, we close the path to the left. The poles at $s = 0$, -1 and -2 will all be enclosed, and A_2 is found by adding residues; the result is

$$
\begin{aligned}
A_2 &= 0, & 0 \le t < a/2 \\
A_2 &= -(2t - a - 3 + 4\epsilon^{-(t-a/2)} - \epsilon^{-2(t-a/2)}), & t > a/2
\end{aligned}
\tag{115}
$$

(A_2 may also be found from A_1 using the shifting or translation theorem of Laplace transform theory.)

Finally, by the same reasoning, we find that $A_3 = 0$ in the interval $0 \le t < a$ and so it contributes nothing to the steady state.

The desired response is now obtained by adding Eqs. (111), (114), and (115). The result is

$$
\begin{aligned}
v_2(t) &= t - \frac{3}{2} + \frac{4\epsilon^{-(t-a/2)}}{1 + \epsilon^{a/2}} - \frac{\epsilon^{-2(t-a/2)}}{(1 + \epsilon^{a})}, & 0 \le t < \frac{a}{2} \\
v_2(t) &= -(t - a) + \frac{3}{2} - \frac{4\epsilon^{-(t-a)}}{1 + \epsilon^{a/2}} + \frac{\epsilon^{-2(t-a)}}{(1 + \epsilon^{a})}, & \frac{a}{2} \le t < a
\end{aligned}
\tag{116}
$$

A plot of this expression is shown in Fig. 15 for the value $a = 2$. As required by the periodicity of the response and the fact that the response is continuous, the value $v_2(0)$ is the same as $v_2(a)$.

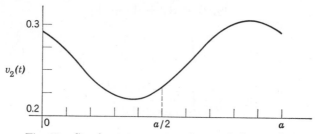

Fig. 15.   Steady-state response of numerical example.

PROBLEMS

5.1 Consider the network shown in Fig. P5.1. Show that the voltage is given by

$$V(s) = \frac{V_{g1}(s)Y_1(s) + \cdots + V_{gn}(s)Y_n(s)}{Y_1(s) + Y_2(s) + \cdots + Y_n(s)}$$

This is referred to as Millman's theorem.

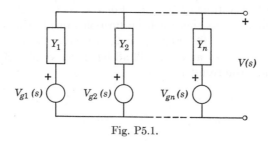

Fig. P5.1.

5.2 Because of the simple interchange permitted by Thévenin's and Norton's theorems between a voltage source in series with a branch and a current source in parallel with the same branch, it is often felt that it is simpler if current sources always appear in parallel with a branch.

Suppose there is a current source in a network which is not in parallel with a single branch. You have already seen that the number of loop equations that need to be satisfied simultaneously is reduced by one. Demonstrate this same fact in an alternate way as follows. Think in terms of the Blakesley step in which a node is eliminated, with an attendant reduction of the number of node equations by one, when a voltage source appears in a network with more than one branch connected at each of its terminals. In this procedure the number of voltage sources is increased. Show that a similar increase of the number of current sources can be made in the present case, permitting each of the sources to be placed in parallel with a branch. The use of Thévenin's theorem then

eliminates the loops formed by the current sources and these branches.   This
procedure may be referred to as the *i-shift*.

Illustrate this procedure on the networks shown in Fig. P5.2, in Fig. 2 of
Chapter 2, and in Fig. P4.22.

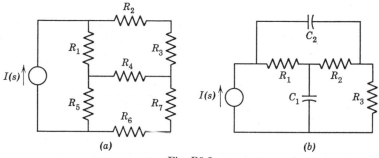

(a)   (b)

Fig. P5.2.

5.3   Obtain expressions for the output voltage transform in the networks of
Fig. P5.3 by judicious use of the *e-* and *i*-shifts and Thévenin's, Norton's, and
Millman's theorems.

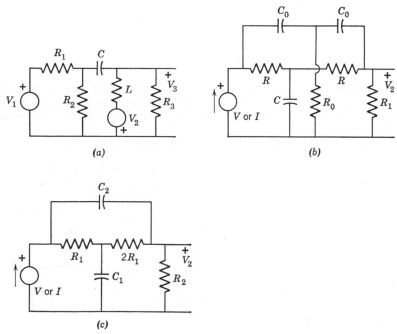

(a)   (b)

(c)

Fig P5.3.

5.4 The linear equivalent circuit of a vacuum tube network is shown in Fig. P5.4. Find the Norton equivalent network at the output terminals, assuming no initial voltage on C. Note that the network contains a dependent source.

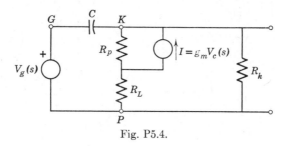

Fig. P5.4.

5.5 In a-c steady-state calculations, sinusoidal quantities are represented by phasors. Let $U = |U| \epsilon^{j\alpha}$ and $J = |J| \epsilon^{j\beta}$ be phasors representing a sinusoidal voltage and current as shown in Fig. P5.5. Let P_{av} be the average power entering the network. Show that $P_{av} = \frac{1}{2} Re\, (U^*J)$.

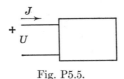

Fig. P5.5.

5.6 Figure P5.6 shows a network containing sinusoidal sources. Part (b) shows the Thévenin equivalent, where U_0 is the phasor representing the equivalent sinusoidal source. Let $Z(j\omega) = |Z| \epsilon^{j\theta}$ and $Z_0(j\omega) = |Z_0| \epsilon^{j\theta_0}$, and assume that $|Z|$ and θ can be independently varied.

(*a*) Suppose θ is held fixed. Show that the real power entering the branch Z will be a maximum if $|Z| = |Z_0|$.

(*b*) Now let $|Z|$ be fixed. Find the condition under which maximum power will be transferred. Show that the magnitude of θ, under the condition of maximum power transfer, will be largest when $|Z| = |Z_0|$.

(*c*) Assuming both $|Z|$ and θ may be varied, show that maximum power will be transferred under this condition when $Z = Z_0^*$.

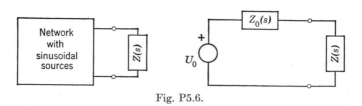

Fig. P5.6.

5.7 The periodic functions in Fig. P5.7(1) are the driving functions applied
to the networks shown in Fig. P5.7(2). Find the indicated steady-state response.

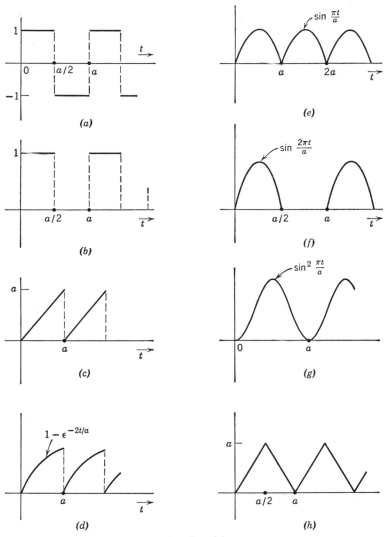

Fig. P5.7(1).

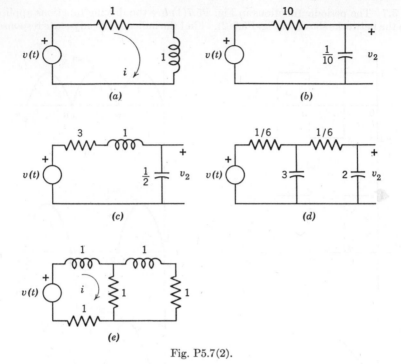

Fig. P5.7(2).

5.8 What will happen to the periodic solution if we relax the condition that $H(s)$ be regular at ∞. Verify your answer by trying to find the periodic solution for $v_2(t)$ of Fig. P5.8, when $v_1(t)$ is given by Fig. P5.7(1)a. First try by the method of Chapter 5 and then by the Fourier series method.

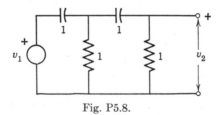

Fig. P5.8.

5.9 Repeat the second half of Problem 5.8 (both methods), this time letting v_1 be the squared sine wave of Fig. P5.7(1)f.

5.10 Quite often, Thévenin's theorem can be used to advantage, even when we are interested in currents and voltages in both subnetworks of Fig. 2, where there may be sources on both sides. The procedure is as follows. We find the Thévenin equivalent of each subnetwork, put them together as in Fig. P5.10(1)c, and find I_1. Then we disconnect the two subnetworks and replace the effect of the other network by a current generator I_1 as shown in Fig. P5.10(1)b. Now we solve the two pieces separately. The assumption of no magnetic coupling between the two halves is needed here also. (This is a simple case of G. Kron's tearing method.)

Use this procedure to find $i_1(t)$ and $i_2(t)$ in the network of Fig. P5.10(2) by breaking the network at the dotted line. (If you don't believe that the computation is simplified, try the problem directly, using loop analysis without tearing.)

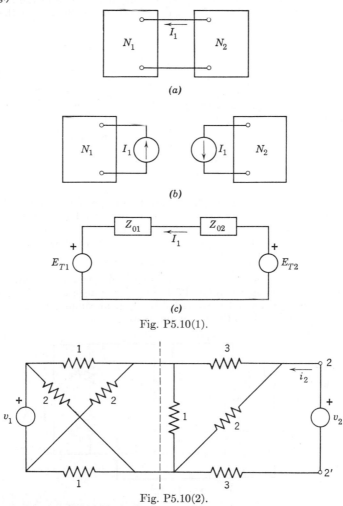

Fig. P5.10(1).

Fig. P5.10(2).

5.11 Using the solution obtained in Problem 5.10, find the Thévenin equivalent of the network of Fig. P5.10(2), at the terminals 2,2′, when the generator $v_2(t)$ is removed from the network. (*Hint:* Norton's theorem.)

5.12 Find explicit formulas for the voltage generator of the Thévenin equivalent and the current generator of the Norton equivalent in terms of loop and node determinants and cofactors.

5.13 Prove that the function $r(t)$ of Eq. (73) can be computed as

$$r(t) = \sum_{\sigma < \sigma_1} \text{residues of } \frac{E_1(s)H(s)}{1 - \epsilon^{-as}} \epsilon^{st}$$

by expanding the integrand as an infinite series as suggested in the text.

5.14 Find the Thévenin equivalent at the output terminals of the feedback amplifier shown in Fig. P5.14. Also find the Thévenin equivalent at the grids of the first and second stages.

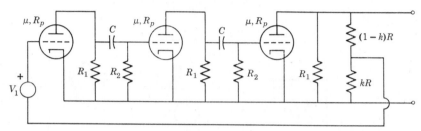

Fig. P5.14.

5.15 Prove the following generalization of the reciprocity theorem. Let the reciprocal network be initially relaxed. Let $V_{m1}(s)$ and $V_{m2}(s)$ be two values of the loop excitation matrix, corresponding to two sets of driving functions. Let $I_{m1}(s)$ and $I_{m2}(s)$ be the corresponding loop current matrices. Then:

$$V_{m1}'(s)I_{m2}(s) = V_{m2}'(s)I_{m1}(s)$$

Derive the reciprocity theorem as a special case of this general theorem.

5.16 In the network shown in Fig. P5.16 find the value of the load impedance Z_L which makes the power transferred into Z_L a maximum. Neglect interelectrode capacitances. Find this maximum power.

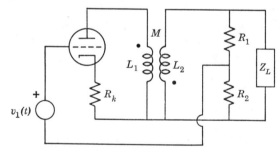

Fig. P5.16.

$$e_1(t) = 10 \sin 10^6 t \qquad\qquad R_1 = 1000 \text{ (ohms)}$$
$$L_1 = 0.1 \text{ (henry)} \qquad\qquad R_2 = 100 \text{ (ohms)}$$
$$L_2 = 0.05 \text{ (henry)} \qquad\qquad R_k = 100 \text{ (ohms)}$$
$$M_{12} = 0.04 \text{ (henry)} \qquad\qquad \mu = 20$$
$$r_p = 10,000 \text{ (ohms)}$$

5.17 The network of Fig. P5.17 is excited by the periodic function $v_g(t)$ also shown in the figure. Find the steady state (or recurrent transient) solution for $i_2(t)$.

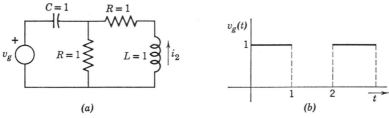

(a) *(b)*

Fig. P5.17.

5.18 In the network of Fig. P5.18 the capacitance is initially charged to a voltage of K volts with the polarity shown. The source voltage is $v_g(t) = V_m \cos \omega t$. The switch is closed at $t = 0$. Find the Thévenin equivalent at the open terminals. The element values satisfy the condition $R/L = 1/RC = a$.

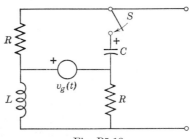

Fig. P5.18.

5.19 Find the Thévenin equivalent impedance of the network shown in Fig. P5.19 at the terminals (1,2).

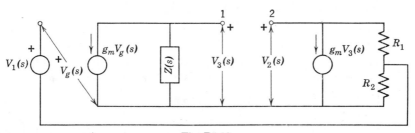

Fig. P5.19.

6 · INTEGRAL SOLUTIONS

We have now reached a state of accomplishment where given any network and arbitrary (transformable) excitations, the complete response can be readily obtained. When the network is initially relaxed, we have seen that it can be characterized by its appropriate transfer function. Hence, it is not even necessary that the network be given, as long as the transfer function is known.

In this chapter we will be concerned with the problem of determining the response of a network to an arbitrary driving function, not when the network is given, but when its response to some standard function is given. We know, for instance, that the steady-state response of a network to a periodic function can be obtained as a Fourier series when the steady-state response to a sinusoid is known. The standard functions we will consider will be the step and the impulse functions.

To achieve our purpose we will need a result from the theory of Laplace transforms. However, this result is probably less familiar than such standard things as partial-fraction expansions, etc. Hence, we will spend some time discussing it.

6.1 The Convolution Theorem

Suppose a driving function $e(t)$, which may be a voltage or a current, is applied to an initially relaxed network and it is desired to find a particular response $r(t)$. Let the pertinent transfer function be $H(s)$. Then the response transform will be given by

$$R(s) = H(s)E(s) \tag{1}$$

Our usual method of procedure to find $r(t)$ is to expand the right-hand side in partial fractions, or to employ the inversion integral. What we would like to do now is to express both $H(s)$ and $E(s)$ in terms of the time functions of which they are the transforms [assuming $H(s)$ is an ordinary transform function] by means of the definition of a Laplace transform. If we can, by subsequent manipulation, express the result in the form

$$R(s) = \int_0^\infty (\qquad) \epsilon^{-st} \, dt \qquad\qquad (2)$$

then, from the definition of the Laplace transform, we can conclude that whatever is in the parentheses is the desired response. What we plan to do does not depend on the interpretations of $H(s)$ as a transfer function and $E(s)$ as an excitation. Hence, we will use more general notation in developing this result.

Let $F_1(s)$ and $F_2(s)$ be two transform functions whose inverse transforms are $f_1(t)$ and $f_2(t)$, respectively. That is,

$$F_1(s) = \int_0^\infty f_1(u) \epsilon^{-su} \, du \qquad\qquad (a)$$

$$\qquad\qquad\qquad\qquad\qquad\qquad (3)$$

$$F_2(s) = \int_0^\infty f_2(y) \epsilon^{-sy} \, dy \qquad\qquad (b)$$

We have used dummy variables different from t in order to avoid confusion in the later development. Consider the product of these two functions

$$F(s) = F_1(s)F_2(s)$$

$$= \left[\int_0^\infty f_1(u) \epsilon^{-su} \, du\right]\left[\int_0^\infty f_2(y) \epsilon^{-sy} \, dy\right] \qquad (4)$$

$$= \int_0^\infty \int_0^\infty f_1(u)f_2(y) \epsilon^{-s(u+y)} \, dy \, du$$

(The last step is clearly justifiable since each integral in the second line is a constant with respect to the other variable of integration.) The product of integrals in the second line can be interpreted as a double integral over an area whose coordinate axes are u and y. The integration is to be performed over the entire first quadrant, as indicated in Fig. 1a.

Let us now make a transformation to a new set of variables as follows.

$$t = u + y$$

$$\qquad\qquad\qquad\qquad\qquad\qquad (5)$$

$$x = u$$

Actually, the second one of these is an identity transformation and is included only for clarity. We now need to express the double integral in terms of the new variables. The element of area $du \, dy$ in the old

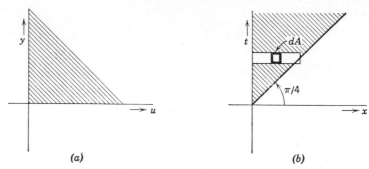

Fig. 1.   Region of integration.

variables is related to the element of area $dx\,dt$ in the new variables through the Jacobian, as follows. *

$$du\,dy = \left[\frac{\partial u}{\partial t}\frac{\partial y}{\partial x} - \frac{\partial u}{\partial x}\frac{\partial y}{\partial t}\right]dx\,dt \qquad (6)$$

Computing the partial derivatives from Eqs. (5) and substituting here leads to the result that $dx\,dt = du\,dy$.

To complete the change of variables, we must determine the new limits of integration.   Note that, since $t = u + y = x + y$, and since y takes on only positive values, then t can be no less than x.   The line $t = x$ in the x-t plane bisects the first quadrant, so the desired area of integration is the area lying between this line and the t-axis, as shown in Fig. 1b.   In order to cover this area we first integrate with respect to x from $x = 0$ to $x = t$; then we integrate with respect to t from zero to infinity.

With the change of variables given in Eqs. (5) and with the limits changed as discussed, Eq. (4) now becomes

$$F(s) = \int_0^\infty \left[\int_0^t f_1(x)f_2(t - x)\,dx\right]\epsilon^{-st}\,dt \qquad (7)$$

This is exactly in the form of Eq. (2), so that we can identify the quantity in brackets as $f(t) = \mathcal{L}^{-1}[F(s)]$.   It should be clear that, if in Eqs. (3) we write $F_1(s)$ in terms of the dummy variable y and $F_2(s)$ in terms of u, then in the result given in Eq. (7) the arguments of f_1 and f_2 will be interchanged.   The final result can therefore be written in the following two alternative forms.

$$f(t) = \int_0^t f_1(x)f_2(t - x)\,dx \qquad (8)$$

* See, A. E. Taylor, *Advanced Calculus*, Ginn and Co., New York, 1955, p. 429.

$$f(t) = \int_0^t f_1(t - x)f_2(x)\, dx \tag{9}$$

The operation performed on two functions $f_1(t)$ and $f_2(t)$ represented by these expressions is called *convolution* or *Faltung*. The two functions are said to be *convolved*. The convolution of two functions is often denoted by the short-hand notation $f_1 * f_2$. We can state the above result in the form of a theorem, as follows.

Convolution Theorem. Let the two functions $f_1(t)$ and $f_2(t)$ be Laplace transformable and have the transforms $F_1(s)$ and $F_2(s)$, respectively. The product of $F_1(s)$ and $F_2(s)$ is the Laplace transform of the convolution of $f_1(t)$ and $f_2(t)$. That is

$$\mathcal{L}[f(t)] = F(s) = F_1(s)F_2(s) \tag{10}$$

where

$$f(t) = f_1 * f_2 = \int_0^t f_1(x)f_2(t - x)\, dx = \int_0^t f_1(t - x)f_2(x)\, dx \tag{11}$$

While we are still in this general notation let us state another useful theorem concerning the derivative of the convolution of two functions. If the functions $f_1(t)$ and $f_2(t)$, in addition to being Laplace transformable, are also differentiable for $t > 0$ (they need only be continuous for $t = 0$), then their convolution will also be differentiable for $t > 0$. The derivative will be

$$\frac{df(t)}{dt} = \int_0^t f_1(x)f_2'(t - x)\, dx + f_2(0)f_1(t) \tag{12}$$

or

$$\frac{df(t)}{dt} = \int_0^t f_1'(t - x)f_2(x)\, dx + f_1(0)f_2(t) \tag{13}$$

where the prime indicates differentiation with respect to t. These expressions can be found by applying Leibnitz's formula for differentiation under an integral.* In fact we can observe that we don't really need the hypothesis that both $f_1(t)$ and $f_2(t)$ are differentiable. *If either function is differentiable and the other continuous, then the convolution $f_1 * f_2$ is differentiable.*

6.2 The Impulse Response

Let us return to our original problem of finding the response $r(t)$ of an initially relaxed network with a transfer function $H(s)$ to an excita-

---

* For an alternative proof, see Doetch, *Handbuch der Laplace-Transformation I*, Verlag Birkhauser, Basel, 1950, p. 116.

tion $e(t)$. We now have the desired result in terms of the convolution theorem, expressed by Eq. (11). Remembering the condition under which the theorem is valid, we must require that $H(s)$ have a zero at infinity, otherwise it will not be the transform of an ordinary point function. Let us denote the inverse transform of $H(s)$ by $r_\delta(t)$, for reasons which will be clear in a few paragraphs. That is,

$$\mathcal{L}^{-1}[H(s)] = r_\delta(t) \tag{14}$$

Then, with Eq. (1) used in place of Eq. (10), we will get

$$r(t) = \int_0^t r_\delta(x)e(t - x)\, dx = \int_0^t r_\delta(t - x)e(x)\, dx \tag{15}$$

This is a very valuable result. By this expression we are able to express the time response of a network to an arbitrary driving function $e(t)$, in terms of the inverse transform of the transfer function of the network.

A further interpretation is possible, if we are willing to admit the impulse function in our discussions. Such an interpretation is not really needed since Eq. (15) can stand on its own feet, so to speak. However, the interpretation may prove useful in some instances.*

Let us conceive of the situation in which the driving function is a unit impulse $\delta_1(t)$. Let us label the response of the network to this excitation $r_\delta(t)$, with transform $R_\delta(s)$ and call it the *impulse response*. Since $\mathcal{L}[\delta_1(t)] = 1$, Eq. (1) becomes

$$R_\delta(s) = H(s)$$

$$\mathcal{L}^{-1}[R_\delta(s)] = r_\delta(t) = \mathcal{L}^{-1}[H(s)] \tag{16}$$

In words, the last equation states that the inverse transform of the network transfer function is equal to the impulse response of the network. We anticipated this result by using the notation of Eq. (14).

Return now to Eq. (15). We see that this equation expresses the fact that once the impulse response of an initially relaxed network is known, the response to any other function $e(t)$ is determined. What we must do is form the product of the excitation at each point x and the impulse response, not at the same point, but at a point $(t - x)$, and then integrate. Another viewpoint is to say that the input function is "weighted" by the impulse response. This leads to the name of "weighting function" used by some authors for the impulse response.

Let us elaborate on the concept of weighting a little. Perhaps an example would be more satisfying as a means of communicating this

---

* For instance, one can find a close approximation to $r_\delta(t)$ experimentally, by using this interpretation.

point.   Therefore let us consider a system with the transfer function

$$H(s) = \frac{1}{(s+1)^2}$$

which is the transfer function $V_2(s)/V_1(s)$ of the network of Fig. 2.
Then the impulse response is given by

$$r_\delta(t) = t\epsilon^{-t}$$

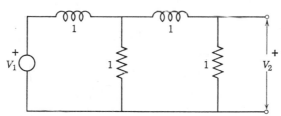

Fig. 2.   Example for the concept of weighting function.

A plot of this function is given in Fig. 3.

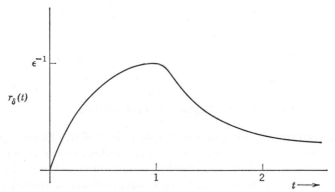

Fig. 3.   Impulse response of the network of Fig. 2.

Suppose we wish to compute the response of this network to some
driving function $e(t)$.   For convenience of interpretation, let us take the
convolution of $r_\delta(t)$ and $e(t)$ in the second form given in Eq. (15).   We
will use x as the running variable.   To get the value of the response at
any given time t, we take the input up to this point and the impulse
response up to this point.   Then we "flip over" the impulse response,
so that its value at $x = 0$ multiplies the excitation at t, and its value at
t multiplies the excitation at $x = 0$.   This is illustrated in Fig. 4, where
the functions $r_\delta(t - x)$ and $e(x)$ are shown.   Let us see what happens

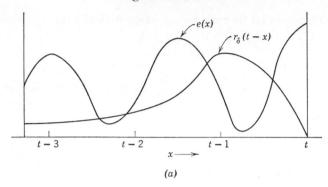

(a)

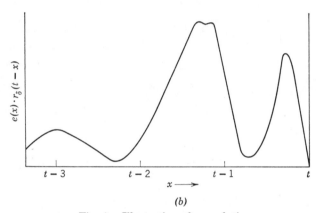

(b)

Fig. 4.   Illustration of convolution.

when we multiply these two curves point by point. Since $r_\delta(0) = 0$, the value of $e(x)$ at the point t contributes *nothing* to the response at t. This, in spite of the fact that $e(x)$ has a maximum value at this point. On the other hand the *most important* neighborhood is around $(t - 1)$, for the values of $e(x)$ in this vicinity are multiplied by the largest values that r_δ assumes. Similarly the values of $e(x)$ for x less than $(t - 2)$ do virtually nothing to the response at t. Thus r_δ decides how much *weight* to attach to the values of e at various times. In this case, the response is decided virtually by the values of $e(t)$ for the previous 2 seconds; the most significant contribution coming from the values of $e(t)$ about the point 1 second prior to the time under consideration.

   The question now arises, what should we do if the network transfer function does not have a zero at infinity? In such a case $r_\delta(t)$ will contain impulses. Since we are permitting impulses in the excitation, we might just as well relax the original condition on $H(s)$ and permit it to be nonzero at infinity. Let us see what effect this will have. If we designate the limit of $H(s)$ as s approaches infinity by $H(\infty)$, then we can write

$$H(s) = H(\infty) + H_1(s) \tag{17}$$

where $H_1(s)$ has a zero at infinity. The impulse response will then be

$$r_\delta(t) = H(\infty)\delta_1(t) + h_1(t) \tag{18}$$

where $h_1(t)$ is a well-behaved function not containing impulses. Let us use this expression in the first form of Eq. (15) to find the response of the network to an excitation $e(t)$. The result will be

$$r(t) = \int_0^t H(\infty)\delta_1(x)e(t-x)\,dx + \int_0^t h_1(x)e(t-x)\,dx$$

$$= H(\infty)e(t) + \int_0^t h_1(x)e(t-x)\,dx \tag{19}$$

The last step follows from the sampling property of impulse functions as given in Eq. (114) of Chapter 4. We see that if the transfer function of the network has a nonzero value at infinity, there is a resistance path through the network (at least conceptually) over which the input is transmitted to the output with a change in scale only.

6.3   The Step Response and the DuHamel Integral

In the last section we established that the response of an initially relaxed network to any arbitrary excitation can be found simply from a knowledge of the response of the same network to a unit impulse. In this section we shall show that the same conclusion applies as well to a knowledge of the response of the network to a unit step function $u(t)$.

Let us initially assume that a unit step excitation function is applied to a network and denote the response of the network to this excitation by $r_u(t)$, with transform $R_u(s)$. We will call $r_u(t)$ the *step response* or the *indicial response*. Carson originally referred to this as the "indicial admittance" when the response was the current and the excitation was a voltage at the same terminals. Since $\mathcal{L}[u(t)] = 1/s$, we write

$$R_u(s) = \frac{1}{s}H(s) \tag{20}$$

This expression immediately tells us something about the relationship between the step response and the impulse response, since $H(s) = R_\delta(s)$. To get the relationship between the time responses, we take the inverse transform of Eq. (20), either as it stands or after multiplying through by s. The results will be

$$r_u(t) = \int_0^t r_\delta(x)\, dx \tag{21}$$

$$r_\delta(t) = \frac{d}{dt} r_u(t) + r_u(0)\delta_1(t) \tag{22}$$

The initial value of the step response is readily found from Eq. (20) using the initial value theorem. It will be

$$r_u(0) = \lim_{s\to\infty} [sR_u(s)] = \lim_{s\to\infty} H(s) = H(\infty) \tag{23}$$

provided $H(\infty)$ exists and is finite. We conclude that the initial value of the step function response of a network will be zero if the transfer function has a zero at infinity. If $H(\infty)$ is nonzero, the initial value of the step response will be nonzero, and the impulse response will itself contain an impulse. Note that Eqs. (21) and (22) together do violence to our ordinary concepts of calculus. If $r_\delta(t)$ is an integrable function, then Eq. (21) tells us that $r_u(0)$ should be zero (simply by putting 0 as the upper limit). However, if we admit impulses, then our constitution must be strong to withstand the violence that will be done to our mathematics. Note also that even if $r_\delta(t)$ contains a first order impulse, $r_u(t)$ will not be impulsive. Hence, $r_u(t)$ is always better behaved than $r_\delta(t)$.

Let us now return to our original task and assume that an arbitrary $\mathcal{L}$-transformable excitation $e(t)$ is applied to the network. Equation (1) relates the transforms. This equation can be rewritten in one of several ways if we multiply numerator and denominator by s. Thus

$$R(s) = s\left[\frac{H(s)}{s} E(s)\right] = s[R_u(s)E(s)] \tag{24}$$

$$R(s) = \left[s\frac{H(s)}{s}\right] E(s) = [sR_u(s)]E(s) \tag{25}$$

$$R(s) = [sE(s)]\left[\frac{H(s)}{s}\right] = [sE(s)]R_u(s) \tag{26}$$

In each case we have used Eq. (20) to obtain the far right side. To find $r(t)$ we will now use the convolution theorem. Focus attention on Eq. (24). This can be written

$$R(s) = sF(s) \tag{27}$$

where

$$F(s) = R_u(s)E(s) \tag{28}$$

With the use of the convolution theorem we can write

$$f(t) = \int_0^t r_u(x)e(t - x)\,dx = \int_0^t r_u(t - x)e(x)\,dx \tag{29}$$

If we evaluate $f(0)$ we will find it to be zero, unless $r_u(t)$ contains an impulse. But we saw that this is not possible even if $H(s)$ has a finite, nonzero value at infinity. The step response will have an impulse only if $H(s)$ has a pole at infinity. Hence, if we admit only those $H(s)$ functions which are regular at infinity, then $r(t)$ will be the derivative of $f(t)$, based on Eq. (27). Thus,

$$r(t) = \frac{d}{dt}\int_0^t r_u(x)e(t - x)\,dx$$
$$= \frac{d}{dt}\int_0^t r_u(t - x)e(x)\,dx \tag{30}$$

We now have an expression for the response of an initially relaxed network to an excitation $e(t)$ in terms of the step response. This result ranks in importance with Eq. (15). Using the theorem we stated in Eqs. (12) and (13), we can put the last equation in the following form

$$r(t) = \int_0^t r_u(x)e'(t - x)\,dx + e(0)r_u(t) \tag{31}$$

$$r(t) = \int_0^t r_u'(t - x)e(x)\,dx + r_u(0)e(t) \tag{32}$$

This will require that $r_u(t)$ or $e(t)$, as the case may be, be differentiable. These same expressions can be obtained in an alternative manner starting from Eqs. (25) and (26). To use Eq. (25) let us first write

$$\mathcal{L}^{-1}[sR_u(s)] = \mathcal{L}^{-1}\left\{[sR_u(s) - r_u(0)] + r_u(0)\right\}$$
$$= \frac{dr_u}{dt} + r_u(0)\delta_1(t) \tag{33}$$

We can now use the convolution theorem on Eq. (25). The result will be

$$r(t) = \int_0^t \left[\frac{dr_u(x)}{dx} + r_u(0)\delta_1(x)\right]e(t - x)\,dx$$

$$r(t) = r_u(0)e(t) + \int_0^t r_u'(x)e(t-x)\,dx$$

$$= r_u(0)e(t) + \int_0^t r_u'(t-x)e(x)\,dx \tag{34}$$

which is the same as Eq. (32). In a similar manner Eq. (31) can be obtained starting from Eq. (26). The details are left to you.

For future reference we will collect all of the forms of these expressions which we have derived. They are

$$r(t) = e(0)r_u(t) + \int_0^t r_u(t-x)e'(x)\,dx$$

$$= e(0)r_u(t) + \int_0^t r_u(x)e'(t-x)\,dx \tag{35}$$

$$r(t) = r_u(0)e(t) + \int_0^t r_u'(x)e(t-x)\,dx$$

$$= r_u(0)e(t) + \int_0^t r_u'(t-x)e(x)\,dx \tag{36}$$

$$r(t) = \frac{d}{dt}\int_0^t r_u(x)e(t-x)\,dx$$

$$= \frac{d}{dt}\int_0^t r_u(t-x)e(x)\,dx \tag{37}$$

These expressions were originally used by DuHamel in 1833 in dynamics. They are variously known as the DuHamel Integrals, Carson Integrals, and Superposition Integrals. Carson himself called (37) the fundamental formula of circuit theory.

6.4   The Principle of Superposition

In the preceding sections of this chapter we obtained, in a formal way, expressions that relate the response of an initially relaxed network to an excitation $e(t)$ with the impulse response or step function response, through a convolution integral. It is possible to interpret these integrals as statements of the superposition principle. This will be the subject of the present section.

Consider the excitation function sketched in Fig. 5. We are interested in the time interval from 0 to t. Let x represent any value of time in this interval and suppose t is temporarily fixed. Let the interval be

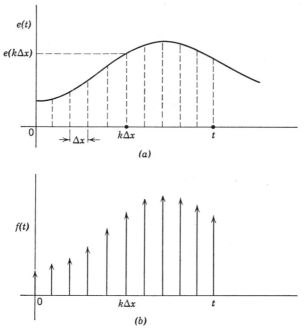

Fig. 5.   Decomposition of function into impulse train.

divided into n equal subintervals Δx (it is not necessary that they be equal but the problem is easier to formulate if they are).

Now consider the sequence of impulses labelled $f(t)$ shown in Fig. 5b. The impulse at the point $k\Delta x$ has a strength $\Delta x e(k\Delta x)$, which is the area of a rectangle formed by the base Δx and the height of the curve of Fig. 5a at the point $k\Delta x$. The heights of the arrows in the figure have been drawn proportional to this strength. However, remember that the impulses are all of infinite height. Hence, for any finite Δx, no matter how small, the string of impulses is *not* a good representation of the excitation function which is everywhere finite. Nevertheless, let us compute the response of the network to this sequence of impulses. For $f(t)$ we can write

$$f(t) = \sum_{k=1}^{n} [e(k\Delta x)\Delta x]\delta_1(t - k\Delta x) \tag{38}$$

Let us denote the response to one of these impulses by Δr_k. Then Δr_k will be equal to the strength of the impulse times the impulse response, suitably displaced. Thus,

$$\Delta r_k = [e(k\Delta x)\Delta x]r_\delta(t - k\Delta x) \tag{39}$$

Let us now concentrate on a particular point on the axis which we can call x. For a given value of Δx this point will be $k\Delta x$. If we let Δx get smaller, we will have to increase k proportionately so that the value $x = k\Delta x$ will stay the same, since it refers to a fixed point on the axis. Hence, Eqs. (38) and (39) can be rewritten

$$f(t) = \sum_{k=1}^{n} e(x)\delta_1(t - x)\Delta x \tag{40}$$

$$\Delta r_k = e(x)r_\delta(t - x)\Delta x \tag{41}$$

The response at any time t is obtained by adding the responses to each of the impulses up to time t. Let us denote by $r(t)$ the response to the sequence of impulses as we let Δx approach zero.

$$r(t) = \lim_{\Delta x \to 0} \sum_{x=0}^{t} \Delta r_k = \lim_{\Delta x \to 0} \sum_{x=0}^{t} e(x)r_\delta(t - x)\Delta x$$

$$= \int_0^t e(x)r_\delta(t - x)\,dx \tag{42}$$

(The summation has been indicated as extending from $x = 0$ to $x = t$. Actually, it should be $k = 0$ to n with the limit taken as n goes to infinity. Since $x = k\Delta x$, the notation we used is equivalent to this.) The indicated limit is by definition the integral written in the last line.

The question that remains to be answered is whether the sum of impulse functions $f(t)$ given in Eq. (40) can represent the original excitation $e(t)$ in the limit as Δx approaches zero. In the limit the strength of each impulse, being proportional to Δx, will also approach zero. In a formal way, the summation in Eq. (40) will become an integral which, by the sampling property of impulse functions, becomes $e(t)$. Thus, in the limit, the series of impulses represents the excitation.

In view of the preceding discussion, we can interpret the convolution integrals in Eq. (15) as expressing the response to an excitation $e(t)$ as the superposition of responses to a sequence of impulses which make up the function $e(t)$.

A similar development can be carried out by representing the excitation as a sum of step functions as illustrated in Fig. 6. The interval from 0 to t is divided into n equal subintervals Δx. The resulting "staircase" function is not a very good approximation to $e(t)$ but it gets better as n is increased and Δx is made smaller. When Δx is very small, the value of each step in the staircase can be approximated by the product of Δx and the slope of the curve at the jump, since each of the little figures between the curve and the staircase function approaches a triangle.

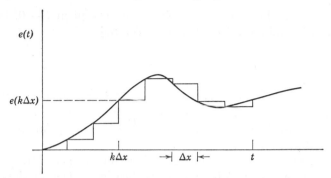

Fig. 6.   Decomposition of a function into step functions.

The response of the network to the excitation $e(t)$ can be approximated by the response to the staircase function. But this is nothing but a sum of step function responses, suitably displaced and multiplied by the value of the discontinuity. Let Δr_k be the response to the step occurring at $k\Delta x$. It will be given by

$$\Delta r_k = [e'(k\Delta x)\Delta x]r_u(t - k\Delta x) \tag{43}$$

where the prime indicates differentiation. The factor in brackets is the value of the step, while $r_u(t - k\Delta x)$ is the response to a displaced step function.

The total response will be the sum of the contributions from each step. Again if we focus attention on the point $x = k\Delta x$ and take the limit as Δx approaches zero, we will get

$$r(t) = \lim_{\Delta x \to 0} \Sigma \Delta r_k = \lim_{\Delta x \to 0} \sum_{x=0}^{t} e'(x)r_u(t - x)\Delta x$$

$$= \int_0^t e'(x)r_u(t - x)\,dx \tag{44}$$

In this development we have assumed that the excitation is a continuous function and that the initial value is zero. Now suppose it has discontinuities of value K_i occurring at times t_i, respectively. We shall consider a nonzero initial value to be a discontinuity at $t = 0$. The total excitation will then be $e(t) + \Sigma K_i u(t - t_i)$, where $e(t)$ is the continuous part of the excitation. We have already found the response to this part; to this we must now add the response due to the dicontinuities. The complete response will be

$$r(t) = \sum_i K_i r_u(t - t_i) + \int_0^t e'(x)r_u(t - x)\,dx \tag{45}$$

In particular, if there are no discontinuities except at $t = 0$, then the total response will be [with $e(0)$ written for K_0]

$$r(t) = e(0)r_u(t) + \int_0^t e'(x)r_u(t - x)\,dx \qquad (46)$$

This expression is identical with the first one in Eq. (35). We have now demonstrated that the response to an excitation $e(t)$ can be regarded as the superposition of the responses to a series of step functions which represent the excitation.

These interpretations that we have given for the convolution integral representations have two important applications. One of these is the numerical computation of network response (using a computing machine, for example), and the other is in time domain synthesis. Let us make a few remarks on the first application and briefly mention the latter. It makes little difference to the final results whether we take the impulse or the step representation. Therefore let us take the former, for the present discussion.

Suppose we wish to find the response of a network to a time function that is not easily represented as a sum of elementary functions. For instance the time function may be given simply as a curve. Or its analytical formula may be very complicated. In such cases the Laplace transform $E(s)$ may be either difficult to find, or be so involved as to be useless. If we approximate $E(s)$ by a rational function, we will not know how good an approximation of the response function we will get in the time domain. In such cases, it is more meaningful to approximate $e(t)$ in the time domain by an impulse sequence as in Fig. 5 or by a staircase function as in Fig. 6.

Let us once again resort to an example. Suppose we have a network which has the impulse response shown in Fig. 7a. This impulse response may have been found experimentally by using a short pulse as an "approximation" to the impulse. Suppose we wish to find the response of the network to the excitation in Fig. 7b, which again may be an experimental curve or the result of some other graphical computation.

We now select a suitable interval T such that the variation of $r_\delta(t)$ and $e(t)$ over an interval T are small enough to be negligible. Then we use the approximate representation.

$$e^*(t) = \sum_k e(kT)\delta_1(t - kT) \qquad (47)$$

for the excitation, and tabulate the values of $r_\delta(kT)$ and $e(kT)$. This expression is usually interpreted as the result of *multiplying* $e(t)$ by the *impulse train* $\sum_k \delta_1(t - kT)$. The function $e^*(t)$ is referred to as a *time*

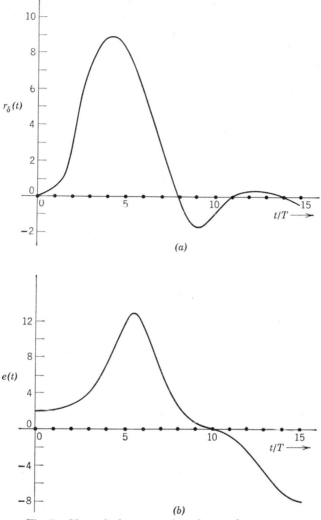

Fig. 7. Numerical computation of network response.

series. It can be shown that the same final results as we shall obtain here using these concepts can also be obtained by approximating

$$f(t) = \int_0^t e(x)\, dx \tag{48}$$

by a staircase function and using Laplace-Stieltjes transforms, without using the impulse function. Thus, our final results can be justified in the realm of rigorous mathematics.

Now, using the convolution theorem, the response of the network to the time series (47) can be written,

$$r_1(t) = \sum_{k=1}^{n} e(kT)r_\delta(t - kT) \tag{49}$$

where

$$nT \leq t < (n + 1)T$$

In particular, the value of the response at our chosen points nT will be given by *

$$r_1(nT) = \sum_{k=1}^{n} e(kT)r_\delta[(n - k)T] \tag{50}$$

Let us see the implication of this equation. We notice that the sum on the right is simply a sum of *real numbers, not functions.* Thus we can get an approximate idea of the response simply by adding these numbers, without integrating functions.

To illustrate this point a little clearer, let us find the approximate response at $t = 10$ for the example of Fig. 7. (The intervals chosen are too large for any accuracy, but the example suffices as an illustration.) Reading the values of $e(kT)$ and $r_\delta(kT)$ from the graphs, we have

						k					
	0	1	2	3	4	5	6	7	8	9	10
$r_\delta(kT)$	0	0.5	3	7	9	8.5	6	2.5	−0.3	−1.7	−1
$e(kT)$	2	2	2.7	4	8	12	11	6	2.5	0.5	0
$e[(10 − k)T]$	0	0.5	2.5	6	11	12	8	4	2.7	2	2
$e[(10 − k)T]r_\delta(kT)$	0	0.25	7.5	42	99	102	48	10	−0.81	−3.4	−2

Lines 1 and 2 of this table are found from the graphs. Line 3 is obtained by copying line 2 backwards. Line 4 is the product of the corresponding entries in lines 1 and 3. Now the approximate response at $t = 10T$ is simply the sum of the entries in the last row, or

$$r_1(10T) = 302.54$$

Quite often this method of representing the approximate response is called the time series representation of the response and is written

* Since n is the only variable in this equation, we can write this in more conventional form as

$$r_n^{(1)} = \sum_{1}^{n} e_k r_{n-k}^{(\delta)}$$

and observe that it is the Cauchy product of two time series, for e and r_δ.

$$r^*(t) = \sum_n \left\{ \sum_{k=1}^{n} e(kT)r_\delta[(n-k)T] \right\} \delta(t - nT) \qquad (51)$$

This method of representing everything by time series leads to the so called *z-transform* method of analysis used in sampled data systems.

The same concept of time series is also used in time domain synthesis. Quite often the synthesis problem is specified by means of a curve for the excitation $e(t)$ and a curve for the response $r(t)$ that is desired. Then, one of the procedures in use is to represent $e(t)$ and $r(t)$ as time series and use simultaneous equations derived from Eq. (51) to find the time series for $r_\delta(t)$. The synthesis then proceeds by finding $H(s)$. The mathematical problems that arise are too numerous for us to consider this question any further. Therefore we leave this application to advanced courses on synthesis.

6.5 Representations of Network Response

At this point we need to step back from all the algebraic (sometimes tedious) manipulations of the previous sections in order to obtain a broad view of what we have been doing.

In mathematics and in mathematical physics, of which electric network theory forms a part, we are often interested in explicit formulas for various functions of interest. For example in the theory of functions of a complex variable we write a formula for an analytic function in terms of its values on a closed contour—the Cauchy integral formula. We write another formula in terms of its derivatives at a point—the Taylor series expansion. We write a formula for a rational function in terms of its behavior at singular points—the partial fraction expansion and its generalization (the Mittag–Leffler formula) to meromorphic functions. Similarly, in potential theory we write formulas for the potential function in terms of the boundary values (the Poisson integral formula for a circle) involving the Green's function of the domain. We write another formula in terms of general harmonic functions, etc. All of these formulas give us various ways of *representing* the solution of a given problem, and we refer to this process as *representation theory*. Each new representation tells us something about the behavior of the solution. Each new representation also tells us how we can completely describe the solution for any given arbitrary conditions. Since all these representations refer to the solution of the same problem, they must all be equivalent.

We are also interested in establishing the conditions that completely specify a solution. In other words we look for minimal criteria that fix the solution completely. Then we write uniqueness theorems—the identity theorem for analytic functions, uniqueness theorems for boundary value problems and differential equations in general, etc.

In the case of the response of electric networks to arbitrary excitations and initially relaxed conditions, we found several representations. We saw that knowledge of either the impulse response or the step function response tells us the response to any excitation, through the agency of convolution integrals. We also know that the network is specified in terms of the pertinent transfer function. Of course, these representations must all be related, and we already saw some of the relationships in Eqs. (16), (21), and (22). We will now pursue this topic somewhat further.

Let us first look at the impulse response representation of the solution, as given in Eq. (15). When the network is initially relaxed this expression gives the *complete* solution for $t > 0$, steady state, transient and all. Thus the impulse response is a *representation of the network* and Eq. (15) is a *representation of the solution* in terms of the impulse response.

Let us now see what this expression will tell us about the nature of the response function $r(t)$. If the function $r_\delta(t)$ is an ordinary point function (i.e., if the transfer function $H(s)$ has a zero at ∞, meaning the denominator is of higher degree than the numerator) then the response, being an integral, will always be continuous. In fact it will satisfy a very strong continuity condition known as "absolute continuity." The response $r(t)$ will start from 0 at $t = 0$. Again if the impulse response $r_\delta(t)$ is an ordinary point function, we know it will be a sum of exponential functions and so will have derivatives of all orders. It is an entire function of the variable t. Hence, whenever the driving function $e(t)$ is continuous, the response function $r(t)$ will be differentiable and the derivative will be given by Leibnitz's formula for differentiation under the integral sign.

$$r'(t) = \int_0^t e(x) r_\delta'(t - x) \, dx + r_\delta(0)e(t) \qquad (52)$$

This statement can be generalized. If $r_\delta(t)$ and $e(t)$ are ordinary point functions, then $r(t)$ has at least one more derivative than $e(t)$. If $e(t)$ has n derivatives, then at each point where $e^{(n)}(t)$ is continuous, we will have

$$\frac{d^{(n+1)}r(t)}{dt^{(n+1)}} = \int_0^t e(x) r_\delta^{(n+1)}(t - x) \, dx$$

$$+ r_\delta(0)e^{(n)}(t) + r_\delta'(0)e^{(n-1)}(t) + \cdots + r_\delta^{(n)}(0)e(t) \qquad (53)$$

Thus, if the impulse response is an ordinary point function, the system response is always "better behaved" then the driving function.

Another piece of information we can squeeze out of the impulse response representation is the behavior of the solution near $t = 0$. The behavior near $t = 0$ is of considerable interest in systems which are constantly in a transient state, such as a servo system for example. This initial transient response is easily computed from the last equation if the impulse response is an ordinary point function. We have, quite obviously,

$$r(0) = 0 \qquad\qquad (a)$$

$$r'(0) = r_\delta(0)e(0) \qquad\qquad (b) \qquad (54)$$

$$r''(0) = r_\delta{}'(0)e(0) + r_\delta(0)e'(0) \qquad\qquad (c)$$

etc. The discussion gets slightly more complicated if the impulse response is not an ordinary point function. If the impulse response contains a first-order impulse then the response function will have as many derivatives as the driving function. Higher order impulses in the impulse response will cause the response to the excitation $e(t)$ to have fewer derivatives than does $e(t)$ itself. Note that what we have done in terms of the impulse response in the time domain can be done just as well in terms of the transfer function $H(s)$ in the complex domain.

Let us next take a brief look at the formula for the response function in terms of the step response given in Eq. (36). This is once again a representation of the complete solution, including steady state and transient, when the initial conditions are zero. If the step response starts from zero at $t = 0$, then the behavior of $r(t)$ is "one step better" than the behavior of $e(t)$, as far as differentiability is concerned. If $e(t)$ has n derivatives, then $r(t)$ has $(n + 1)$ derivatives. Conclusions similar to those arrived at from our discussion of the impulse response representation can be obtained in the present case as well. These will be left for you to carry out.

Let us now turn our attention to the "specification" problem and see if we can get any uniqueness theorems. As a first step in this direction let us see what we can learn about the response of a network to our old familiar sine function. Let us drive the network with $e(t) = \sin \omega t$ and assume that all the initial conditions are zero. Let $r_s(t)$ denote the solution. We should emphasize here that $r_s(t)$ is the *complete solution* for $t > 0$, not just the steady state. Let us see what $r_s(t)$ will tell us about the system. By our earlier discussion we know that $r_s(t)$ is related to the impulse response by the convolution integral

$$r_s(t) = \int_0^t \sin \omega x \, r_\delta(t - x) \, dx \qquad (55)$$

Formerly we knew $r_\delta(t)$ and we wrote this equation as a solution for $r_s(t)$. Now, however, we are assuming that $r_s(t)$ is known, so that Eq. (55) becomes an integral equation for $r_\delta(t)$. It is an integral equation of the convolution type. Under suitable conditions on $r_s(t)$, this equation has a unique solution. In fact the best way to solve this integral equation is through Laplace transforms. $\mathcal{L}$-transforming Eq. (55) yields

$$R_s(s) = \frac{\omega}{s^2 + \omega^2} R_\delta(s) \tag{56}$$

Solving for $R_\delta(s)$ we get

$$R_\delta(s) = \frac{s^2 + \omega^2}{\omega} R_s(s) \tag{57}$$

and so

$$r_\delta(t) = \mathcal{L}^{-1} \left\{ \frac{s^2 + \omega^2}{\omega} R_s(s) \right\} \tag{58}$$

Thus, as soon as we know the response of the network to a sine function we know its response to a unit impulse. By our earlier discussion we know the response to any arbitrary ($\mathcal{L}$-transformable) function $e(t)$ as soon as we know $r_\delta(t)$. Thus the response to any excitation can be computed from a knowledge of the complete response to a sinusoid.

Going one step further, we see that the restriction to sine functions was really unnecessary. We could have computed the transfer function $R_\delta(s)$ from the response to any arbitrary driver. Hence, the following uniqueness theorem can now be stated.

If two initially relaxed lumped linear systems N_1 and N_2 have the same response $r_f(t)$ to a $\mathcal{L}$-transformable function $f(t)$, then their responses (when initially relaxed) to any arbitrary $\mathcal{L}$-transformable input function will be the same.

Let us collect our conclusions here, as a set of uniqueness theorems. Suppose N_1 and N_2 are two networks that satisfy any one of the conditions below. Then their responses, when initially relaxed, to any arbitrary excitation will be identical.

s-domain:

    (a) $H_1(s) = H_2(s)$, all s;

    (b) $H_1(s) = H_2(s)$ on a line segment of positive length in the s-plane;

---

* This statement should be qualified, as should any statement involving inverse $\mathcal{L}$-transforms, by adding the phrase "except at a set of measure zero," or "except for a null-function." A finite or infinite sequence of isolated points is an example of a set of measure zero, and a null-function is a function which has non-zero values only at such a set of measure zero. The function $f(t)$ in the uniqueness theorem is assumed to be a non-null function.

t-domain:

(c) $r_{\delta1}(t) = r_{\delta2}(t)$;

(d) $r_{u1}(t) = r_{u2}(t)$;

(e) $r_{f1}(t) = r_{f2}(t)$

where $f(t)$ is any function such that $\displaystyle\int_0^t f(x)\,dx \not\equiv 0$

and r_f is the complete response to $f(t)$ under initially relaxed conditions.

Steady state:

(f)   Steady-state response of N_1 and N_2 to sin ωt excitation agree over a positive range of frequencies $\omega_1 \leq \omega \leq \omega_2$ ($\omega_2 - \omega_1 > 0$);

(g)   If N_1 and N_2 have a steady-state response to any periodic function and their steady-state responses agree for some periodic function $f(t)$ which has an infinite number of nonzero Fourier coefficients.

Of these, we see that (a) is obvious, and (b) follows from the identity theorem for analytic functions and the fact that $H(s)$ is rational and therefore single-valued in the complex plane. We have just observed the validity of (c), (d), and (e). Condition (f) follows from (b) and the proof is left as a problem.

Condition (g) is a consequence of the most general form of the identity theorem for analytic functions, which can be stated as follows.

If $F_1(s)$ and $F_2(s)$ are two analytic functions which agree on an infinite set of points having a limit point inside the region of regularity of both functions, then $F_1(s)$ and $F_2(s)$ agree everywhere within their common region of regularity.*

The assumption in condition (g) implies that $H(s)$ is regular at $s = \infty$. The transformation $z = 1/s$ now converts $s = \infty$ into $z = 0$, and the identity theorem can be applied with $z = 0$ as the limit point.

The last condition (g) is the basis for the "square wave testing" of audio amplifiers, where we describe the frequency response characteristics by the steady-state response to a square wave.

6.6   Relationships Between Frequency and Time Responses

We will now consider some detailed relationships between the transfer function and the step and impulse responses. Let us initially restrict ourselves to transfer functions with no poles on the $j\omega$ axis. For networks with such transfer functions, the forced response is also the steady-

---

* For a proof of this theorem see K. Knopp, *Theory of Functions*, vol. I, p. 87, Dover Publications, New York, 1945.

state for periodic excitations. That is, as $t \to \infty$ the total response is asymptotic to the steady-state. On the $j\omega$-axis the transfer function can be written

$$H(j\omega) = U(\omega) + jX(\omega) = |H(j\omega)| e^{j\theta(\omega)} \tag{59}$$

where U and X are the real and imaginary parts, respectively, and θ is the angle. It is easy to show that the real part is an even function of ω and the imaginary part is an odd function (do this). That is,

$$U(-\omega) = U(\omega) \qquad (a)$$
$$X(-\omega) = -X(\omega) \qquad (b) \tag{60}$$

Suppose the excitation is sinusoidal, given by

$$e(t) = \sin \omega t \tag{61}$$

The usual method of steady-state analysis tells us that the steady-state response will be

$$r_{ss}(t) = |H(j\omega)| \sin (\omega t + \theta)$$
$$= U(\omega) \sin \omega t + X(\omega) \cos \omega t \tag{62}$$

Let us now write the complete response to the sinusoidal excitation in terms of the superposition integral given in Eq. (35). The result will be

$$r_s(t) = \int_0^t \omega r_u(x) \cos \omega(t - x) \, dx$$
$$= \int_0^\infty \omega r_u(x) \cos \omega(t - x) \, dx - \int_t^\infty \omega r_u(x) \cos \omega(t - x) \, dx \tag{63}$$

(The notation $r_s(t)$ refers to the complete response to a sine function, while $r_{ss}(t)$ means steady-state response.) Note that the integral from zero to t has been written as the sum of two integrals. This is possible only if the improper integrals converge. It is clear that the integrals will converge if the absolute value of $r_u(t)$ is integrable over the infinite range. This will require that $r_u(t) \to 0$ as $t \to \infty$. Using the final-value theorem, which is valid because $H(s)$ is assumed regular on the $j\omega$-axis, we will get

$$\lim_{t \to \infty} r_u(t) = \lim_{s \to 0} sR_u(s) = \lim_{s \to 0} s \frac{H(s)}{s} = H(0) \tag{64}$$

If we require the limit on the left to be zero, this means the transfer function must have a zero at the origin. Let us assume that this condition is met by the transfer function. Then the last integral in Eq. (63) will approach zero at $t \to \infty$. Hence, we can interpret the first integral in that equation as the steady-state response. Thus,

$$r_{ss}(t) = \int_0^\infty \omega r_u(x) \cos \omega(t - x) \, dx$$

$$= \sin \omega t \int_0^\infty \omega r_u(x) \sin \omega x \, dx + \cos \omega t \int_0^\infty \omega r_u(x) \cos \omega x \, dx \quad (65)$$

The last step is obtained by expanding $\cos \omega(t - x)$.

This equation gives a representation of the steady-state response of a network to a sine wave when the transfer function of the network has no poles on the $j\omega$-axis and has a zero at $s = 0$. Another representation of the steady-state response was given in Eq. (62). On comparing the two equations, we can make the following identifications.

$$U(\omega) = \int_0^\infty \omega r_u(x) \sin \omega x \, dx \quad (66)$$

$$X(\omega) = \int_0^\infty \omega r_u(x) \cos \omega x \, dx \quad (67)$$

These same expressions could have been obtained, perhaps more easily, from the definition of the Laplace integral. Thus

$$R_u(s) = \int_0^\infty r_u(x) \epsilon^{-sx} \, dx = \frac{H(s)}{s} \quad (68)$$

We have already assumed that $H(s)$, and hence also $R_u(s)$, has no poles on the $j\omega$-axis. Hence, the integral will converge if we set $s = j\omega$, provided $r_u(x) \to 0$ as $x \to \infty$, which is the same condition we found before. We can now write

$$H(j\omega) = j\omega \int_0^\infty r_u(x)[\cos \omega x - j \sin \omega x] \, dx$$

$$= \int_0^\infty \omega r_u(x) \sin \omega x \, dx + j \int_0^\infty \omega r_u(x) \cos \omega x \, dx \quad (69)$$

This, of course, agrees with Eqs. (66) and (67).

Additional useful relations can also be obtained by starting from the inversion integral for the step response. In view of Eq. (20), we can write

$$r_u(t) = \frac{1}{2\pi j} \int_{Br} \frac{H(s)}{s} \epsilon^{st} \, ds \quad (70)$$

We are still assuming that $H(s)$ has no poles on the $j\omega$ axis, but let us not restrict $H(s)$ to have a zero at the origin for this development. Then the integrand in the last expression might have a pole at the origin. If it weren't for this pole the Bromwich path could be taken as the $j\omega$-axis. Instead, let us take the path shown in Fig. 8 which consists of the $j\omega$-axis

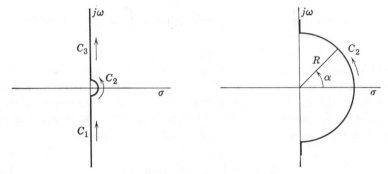

Fig. 8.   Contours of integration.

except for a semicircular arc which by-passes the origin. As the radius of the semicircle approaches zero, the path approaches the entire $j\omega$-axis. The three parts of the path have been labelled C_1, C_2, and C_3. Equation (70) can now be written.

$$r_u(t) = \frac{1}{2\pi j} \int_{C_1} \frac{H(s)}{s} \epsilon^{st} \, ds + \frac{1}{2\pi j} \int_{C_2} \frac{H(s)}{s} \epsilon^{st} \, ds + \frac{1}{2\pi j} \int_{C_3} \frac{H(s)}{s} \epsilon^{st} \, ds$$

(71)

On the parts C_1 and C_3, $s = j\omega$ and $ds = jd\omega$. On the part C_2, which is shown expanded in part (b) of the figure, we can write

$$s = R\epsilon^{j\alpha} = R \cos \alpha + jR \sin \alpha$$
$$ds = jR\epsilon^{j\alpha} \, d\alpha$$

(72)

Hence, Eq. (71) becomes

$$r_u(t) = \frac{1}{2\pi j} \left[\int_{-\infty}^{-R} \frac{H(j\omega)}{j\omega} \epsilon^{j\omega t} j \, d\omega + \int_{R}^{\infty} \frac{H(j\omega)}{j\omega} \epsilon^{j\omega t} j \, d\omega \right]$$
$$+ \frac{1}{2\pi j} \int_{-\pi/2}^{\pi/2} H(s) \epsilon^{t(R \cos \alpha + jR \sin \alpha)} j \, d\alpha \quad (73)$$

The last integral on the right involves the radius R in a complicated way. However, we intend to let R approach zero, in which case the integral reduces to $H(0)/2$ (justify this).   Note that if we place the additional restriction that $H(s)$ has a zero at $s = 0$, then this term will disappear. When we let $R \to 0$, the remaining two integrals in Eq. (73) combine to give the principal value of the integral running from $-\infty$ to $+\infty$. Hence, finally

$$r_u(t) = \frac{H(0)}{2} + \frac{1}{2\pi j} \int_{-\infty}^{\infty} \frac{H(j\omega)}{\omega} e^{j\omega t} \, d\omega \qquad (74)$$

(Note that, although it is not explicitly shown, we are to understand the last integral as representing the principal value.)   This expression can be further simplified by writing $H(j\omega)$ in terms of its real and imaginary parts, expanding the exponential and using the odd and even properties of the resulting functions to change the range of integration to the positive ω axis.   The details will be left to you.   The result is

$$r_u(t) = \frac{U(0)}{2} + \frac{1}{\pi} \int_0^{\infty} \frac{U(\omega)}{\omega} \sin \omega t \, d\omega + \frac{1}{\pi} \int_0^{\infty} \frac{X(\omega)}{\omega} \cos \omega t \, d\omega \quad (75)$$

We have replaced $H(0)$ by $U(0)$, since $X(0) = 0$.

Let us pause now and consolidate our results.   In Eq. (69) we obtained an expression for the network transfer function along the $j\omega$-axis in terms of the step function response.   The inverse relationship, giving the step response in terms of the real and imaginary parts of $H(j\omega)$, was obtained in Eq. (75).   Note that this expression is valid for negative as well as positive values of t.   However, $r_u(t) = 0$ for negative values of t.   Hence,

$$0 = \frac{U(0)}{2} - \frac{1}{\pi} \int_0^{\infty} \frac{U(\omega)}{\omega} \sin \omega t \, d\omega + \frac{1}{\pi} \int_0^{\infty} \frac{X(\omega)}{\omega} \cos \omega t \, d\omega \qquad (76)$$

or

$$\frac{U(0)}{2} + \frac{1}{\pi} \int_0^{\infty} \frac{X(\omega)}{\omega} \cos \omega t \, d\omega = \frac{1}{\pi} \int_0^{\infty} \frac{U(\omega)}{\omega} \sin \omega t \, d\omega \qquad (77)$$

When we substitute the last equation into Eq. (75) we obtain the final result

$$r_u(t) = U(0) + \frac{2}{\pi} \int_0^{\infty} \frac{X(\omega)}{\omega} \cos \omega t \, d\omega \qquad (78)$$

$$r_u(t) = \frac{2}{\pi} \int_0^{\infty} \frac{U(\omega)}{\omega} \sin \omega t \, d\omega \qquad (79)$$

Up till now we have performed various mathematical manipulations to put the relationships between $H(j\omega)$ and $r_u(t)$ in various equivalent forms.   But now we have something new.   The last equation shows that

the step response of the network can be computed knowing only the real part
of the transfer function along the jω-axis. Note that this relationship
does not require that $U(0) = H(0)$ be zero. With the step response
determined, Eq. (67) can be used to compute the imaginary part of
$H(j\omega)$. However, the asymptotic value of the step response which is to
be used in Eq. (67) must be zero. Hence, before using $r_u(t)$ as computed
from Eq. (79), we first subtract the asymptotic value in case $U(0)$ is
not originally equal to zero. In this way $H(j\omega)$ *is completely determined*
from a knowledge of its real part alone.

Similarly, starting with the imaginary part $X(\omega)$, we can compute the
step response from the integral in Eq. (78). The step response computed
from this integral will approach zero as t approaches infinity. This fact
is evident from the Riemann-Lebesgue theorem given by Eq. (83) in
Chapter 5. (Note the interchange of the roles of ω and t.) To the value
of $r_u(t)$ thus computed we can add any constant, which will become the
zero-frequency value of $H(j\omega)$, denoted by $U(0)$ in Eq. (78). However,
omitting this step, we can now compute the real part $U(\omega)$ from Eq. (66).
Thus, $H(j\omega)$ *will be completely determined, except for an additive constant,*
from a knowledge of the imaginary part alone.

Let us now turn to the impulse response. Everything we did starting
from Eq. (68) can be duplicated (with appropriate changes) in terms of
the impulse response. We will list the results and leave the details of
the development to you. It will still be required that $H(s)$ be regular
on the $j\omega$-axis, but now it need not have a zero at $s = 0$. Instead, application of the inversion integral to $H(s)$ will require that $H(s)$ have a
zero at infinity. If we retrace the steps starting at Eq. (68), we will get
the following equations.

$$U(\omega) = \int_0^\infty r_\delta(x) \cos \omega x \, dx \qquad (80)$$

$$X(\omega) = -\int_0^\infty r_\delta(x) \sin \omega x \, dx \qquad (81)$$

$$r_\delta(t) = \frac{2}{\pi} \int_0^\infty U(\omega) \cos \omega t \, d\omega \qquad (82)$$

$$r_\delta(t) = -\frac{2}{\pi} \int_0^\infty X(\omega) \sin \omega t \, d\omega \qquad (83)$$

The first two of these are the counterparts of Eqs. (66) and (67), whereas
the last two are to be compared with Eqs. (78) and (79). As a matter

of fact, the last two equations can be obtained from Eqs. (78) and (79) in view of the fact that the impulse response is the derivative of the step response. (No impulses will be involved since we assumed $H(\infty) = 0$.)

Equation (83) shows that the impulse response of the network can be computed knowing only the imaginary part $X(\omega)$. Note that $X(\omega)$ will approach zero as $\omega \to \infty$ even though $H(\infty)$ may not be zero. With the impulse response computed, the real part $U(\omega)$ can now be found from Eq. (80). Similarly, starting from a knowledge of just the real part $U(\omega)$, the impulse response can be computed from Eq. (82). However, this will be valid only if $U(\omega)$, and so also $H(j\omega)$, goes to zero as $\omega \to \infty$. Having found the impulse response, the imaginary part $X(\omega)$ is now calculated from Eq. (81). Thus again we find that a transfer function is completely determined from a knowledge of either its real part or its imaginary part along the $j\omega$-axis. Again note that the transfer function calculated from a given $X(\omega)$ will have a zero at infinity; to this we can add any positive constant without affecting the imaginary part.

In each of the above cases, once the step response or impulse response is calculated from a given $U(\omega)$ or $X(\omega)$, it is then only necessary to find the Laplace transform, since $\mathcal{L}[r_u(t)] = H(s)/s$ and $\mathcal{L}[r_\delta(t)] = H(s)$. In this way one of the integrations can be avoided.

The relationships which we have derived between the step response, or the impulse response, and the transfer function, and between the real and imaginary parts of the transfer function, are important mostly for their theoretical implications. As far as actual computations are concerned, they are not renowned for their simplicity. In the next chapter we shall discuss other relationships between the real and imaginary parts of network functions which are much more useful for computation.

Let us terminate this section with an example illustrating the application of the results we have derived. Suppose the following is specified to be the real part of a network function on the $j\omega$-axis.

$$U(\omega) = \frac{\omega^4 + 2\omega^2 + 4}{(1 + \omega^2)(4 + \omega^2)} \tag{84}$$

We see that this has a nonzero value at infinity and so Eq. (82) cannot be used directly. If we subtract its infinite frequency value, we will get

$$U_1(\omega) = U(\omega) - 1 = \frac{-3\omega^2}{(1 + \omega^2)(4 + \omega^2)} \tag{85}$$

We can now apply Eq. (82), which leads to

$$r_{\delta 1}(t) = -\frac{6}{\pi}\int_0^\infty \frac{\omega^2 \cos \omega t}{(1+\omega^2)(4+\omega^2)}\,d\omega$$

$$= -\frac{3}{\pi}\left[\int_0^\infty \frac{\omega^2 \epsilon^{j\omega t}\,d\omega}{(1+\omega^2)(4+\omega^2)} + \int_0^\infty \frac{\omega^2 \epsilon^{-j\omega t}\,d\omega}{(1+\omega^2)(4+\omega^2)}\right]$$

$$= -\frac{3}{\pi}\int_{-\infty}^\infty \frac{\omega^2 \epsilon^{j\omega t}\,d\omega}{(1+\omega^2)(4+\omega^2)} \tag{86}$$

The second line follows from the use of the exponential form of $\cos \omega t$. If in the second integral in this line we replace ω by $-\omega$ and appropriately change the limits, the last line will follow.

Now consider the following contour integral in the complex s-plane.

$$I = \int_C \frac{s^2 \epsilon^{st}\,ds}{(s^2-1)(s^2-4)} \tag{87}$$

The contour consists of the entire $j\omega$-axis and an "infinite" semi-circle to the left. The integrand satisfies the conditions of Jordan's lemma, since the rational function in the integrand vanishes at infinity as $1/s^2$. Hence, the contribution of the infinite arc will be zero, and the complete integral reduces to its value along the $j\omega$-axis. By the residue theorem, the value of the integral is equal to $2\pi j$ times the sum of the residues at the left half plane poles. In the present case there are only two simple poles, at $s = -1$ and $s = -2$, and their residues are easily computed. Hence, we get

$$I = -j\int_{-\infty}^\infty \frac{\omega^2 \epsilon^{j\omega t}\,d\omega}{(1+\omega^2)(4+\omega^2)} = 2\pi j\left(\frac{1}{6}\epsilon^{-t} - \frac{1}{3}\epsilon^{-2t}\right) \tag{88}$$

When this expression is substituted into Eq. (86), we get

$$r_{\delta 1}(t) = \epsilon^{-t} - 2\epsilon^{-2t} \tag{89}$$

The transfer function can now be found by taking the Laplace transform. The result will be

$$H_1(s) = \frac{1}{s+1} - \frac{2}{s+2} = \frac{-s}{(s+1)(s+2)} \tag{90}$$

This function has a zero at infinity. To this we should add the infinite-frequency value of $U(\omega)$, which is $H(\infty)$ and which we subtracted from the original function at the start. Thus

$$H(s) = H_1(s) + H(\infty) = \frac{-s}{(s+1)(s+2)} + 1$$

$$= \frac{s^2 + 2s + 2}{(s+1)(s+2)} \tag{91}$$

(Refer to the discussion following Eq. (17) for further clarification.)

This is the desired transfer function. We can easily verify that it has the function in Eq. (84) as its j-axis real part. The imaginary part can now be simply calculated if desired. Note that for this purpose we may use either $H_1(s)$ in Eq. (90) or $H(s)$ in Eq. (91) since they have the same imaginary part.

Note that the impulse response corresponding to the original $U(\omega)$ differs from Eq. (89) by having an impulse at $t = 0$. This statement is verified by reference to Eq. (18).

PROBLEMS

6.1 In the text the concept of the convolution of two functions is introduced; extend the concept to more than two functions.

6.2 Prove that the convolution shares the following algebraic properties with ordinary multiplication.

If f_1, f_2, and f_3 are integrable functions (so that $f_1 * f_2 = \displaystyle\int_0^t f_1(x)f_2(t - x)\, dx$ is defined and so is $f_1 * f_3$)

$(a)\quad f_1 * f_2 = f_2 * f_1$ (commutative law)
$(b)\quad f_1 * (f_2 * f_3) = (f_1 * f_2) * f_3$ (associative law)
$(c)\quad u * f = f * u = f$, where u is the unit step function   (identity)
$(d)\quad f_1 * (f_2 + f_3) = f_1 * f_2 + f_1 * f_3$ (distributive law)

6.3 Find the impulse response and the step response of the networks given in Fig. P5.7(1) in the previous chapter assuming initially relaxed conditions. The desired responses are indicated in the figures. Demonstrate that Eq. (22) is satisfied.

6.4 Use Eqs. (66) and (67) or (80) and (81) to compute the real part and imaginary part of $H(j\omega)$ for the same networks. Check your answers by computing $H(s)$, then $U(\omega)$ and $X(\omega)$ directly.

6.5 Find the indicated response of the same networks to the following excitation functions, using the impulse response or the step response and a superposition integral.

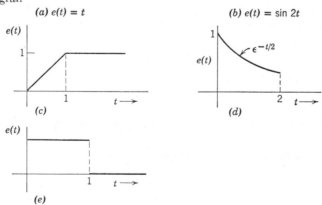

Fig. P6.5.

6.6 The response (complete response) of an initially relaxed network is given by

$$r(t) = -\tfrac{1}{2}\epsilon^{-2t} + \tfrac{1}{8}\cos 2t + \tfrac{1}{8}\sin 2t$$

when the excitation is $e(t) = \sin 2t$. Find the response of the system when $e(t)$ is the triangular wave shown in Fig. P6.6.

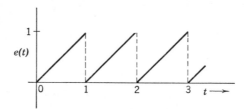

Fig. P6.6.

6.7 The equivalent circuit of a two stage RC coupled amplifier is shown in Fig. P6.7. Find the response of the amplifier to the excitations given in Problem 6.5 using a superposition integral and the impulse response or step response.

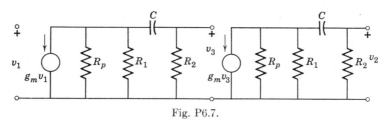

Fig. P6.7.

6.8 Solve the following integral equation of the convolution type.

$$f(t) + \int_0^t f(x)g_1(t - x)\, dx = g_2(t)$$

The unknown function is $f(t)$, and $g_1(t)$ and $g_2(t)$ are known (integrable) functions.

6.9 Obtain a solution of the following integral equations.

(a) $f(t) + \int_0^t f(x)\epsilon^{-2(t-x)}\, dx = 2t$

(b) $f(t) + \int_0^t f(x)\epsilon^{-(t-x)}\sin(t - x)\, dx = 5$

(c) $\dfrac{df}{dt} + 2f(t) + 9\int_0^t f(x)(t - x)\, dx = 1 - \epsilon^{-2t}, \quad f(0) = 0$

6.10 Given the differential equations

$$\frac{d^2y}{dt^2} + 2\frac{dy}{dt} + y = f(t)$$

$$y(0+) = y'(0+) = 0$$

get an explicit formula for $y(t)$—the solution—by first finding

$$\mathcal{L}^{-1}\left\{\frac{1}{s^2 + 2s + 1}\right\}$$

Use this formula to find the solution when $f(t)$ is a pulse of unit height and width; that is

$$f(t) = \begin{cases} 1, & 0 \le t < 1 \\ 0, & 1 \le t \end{cases}$$

6.11 Find the impulse response for $i_2(t)$ in Fig. P.6.11a and use it to find the complete solution for the first period, when $v_g(t)$ is the periodic function given in Fig. P6.11b. Compare the answer with that obtained in Problem 17 of Chapter 5.

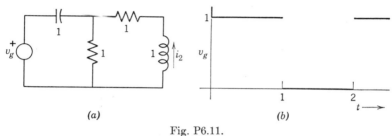

(a) $\qquad\qquad\qquad\qquad\qquad$ (b)

Fig. P6.11.

6.12 In a certain network problem the response transform is found to be

$$R(s) = \frac{(s^2 + 2s + 5)}{(s^2 + 2s + 4)(s^2 + 4)}$$

when the excitation is $e(t) = \cos 2t$, and the network is initially relaxed. Find (a) the steady-state solution, (b) the transient solution, and (c) the step response.

6.13 The triangular pulse of voltage shown in Fig. P6.13a is applied to the network of Fig. P6.13b. Find the output voltage response for all time, using the convolution theorem.

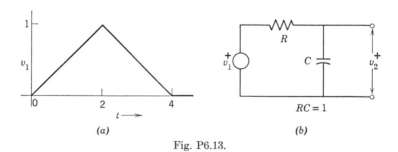

(a) $\qquad\qquad\qquad\qquad\qquad$ (b)

Fig. P6.13.

6.14 Use the convolution integral theorem to prove the translation (shifting) theorem of Laplace transform theory.

6.15 The network of Fig. P6.13b is excited by the function

$$v_1(t) = \begin{cases} \tan t, & 0 \le t \le \pi/4 \\ \tan(\pi/2 - t), & \pi/4 \le t < \pi/2 \\ 0, & \pi/2 \le t \end{cases}$$

Find the approximate response of the network for $0 \le t \le 2$, using time series representations. Estimate the maximum error in the solution for the chosen interval.

6.16 Repeat Problem 6.15, but using the excitation

$$v_1(t) = \begin{cases} \arc \sin t, & 0 \le t < 1 \quad (0 \le v_1 \le \pi/2) \\ 0, & 1 \le t \end{cases}$$

Use the staircase approximation and the step response. Estimate the error.

6.17 The network of Fig. P6.17a is excited by the function of Fig. P6.17b. Find the approximate response $v_2(t)$ for $0 \le t \le 5$.

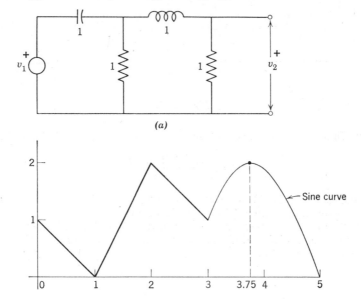

(a)

(b)

Fig. P6.17.

6.18 A voltage $v(t) = K\epsilon^{-st}$ is applied to an initially relaxed network and an oscillographic trace of the response voltage $v_2(t)$ is obtained. Discuss the procedure for finding the impulse response of the network.

6.19 Prove the following theorem. Any two initially relaxed networks which have the same steady-state response over a positive range of frequencies will have the same total response to any excitation function.

6.20 Using the inversion integral prove that

$$u(t) = \frac{1}{2} + \frac{1}{\pi} \int_0^\infty \frac{\sin \omega t}{\omega} \, d\omega$$

7 · REPRESENTATIONS OF NETWORK FUNCTIONS

In the previous chapter we saw how the response of a network may be represented in a number of different ways. Toward the end of the chapter we also saw how the value of the network function itself can be calculated from a knowledge of the network response. We shall now subject the network functions to a similar treatment. It is our purpose in the present chapter, to study the different methods of representing network functions and to see what we can learn from the different representations. We shall also study the relationships that exist between parts of a network function—real and imaginary parts, magnitude and angle—and represent the function in terms of any one of its component parts.

It is here that we begin to make real use of the Laplace transform. As a matter of fact, the mere computation of the solution of a set of ordinary linear differential equations with constant coefficients is a very trivial, and mundane, application for this elegant tool of analysis. Our real purpose in starting with a knowledge of Laplace transforms as a prerequisite, was to associate *analytic functions* with a network and hence make use of the extensive theory of analytic functions that has been developed by mathematicians over the last century. In this chapter we shall see the beginnings of the elegant science of *Network Function Theory* that owes its existence to W. Cauer, O. Brune, and H. W. Bode. Much of the present chapter is based on the work of Bode.

Network functions naturally fall into two classes depending on whether the terminals to which the output (response) relates are the same, or different from, the input (excitation) terminals. The two classes are called (1) *driving point* (or *input*) *functions*, and (2) *transfer functions*. The analytic behavior of driving point functions is significantly different from that of transfer functions. In addition to characterizing network functions this way (as driving point and transfer) we also characterize networks themselves depending on which functions are of interest. If we are only interested in the behavior of a network as viewed from one pair of external terminals (hence only in the driving point functions) we say that this network is a *one terminal-pair*, or a *one-port*. If, on the other hand, we are interested in the currents and voltages at two pairs of external terminals (hence in driving point and transfer functions) the network is a *two terminal-pair* or a *two-port*. A two-port is to be distinguished from a four terminal network. (This distinction will be discussed in more detail in Chapter 8.) Some *n*-ports are illustrated in Fig. 1.

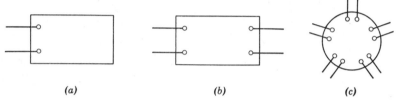

(a)   *(b)*   *(c)*

Fig. 1.   Some *n*-ports.   (*a*) One-port; (*b*) Two-port; (*c*) Five-port.

7.1   Representation by Poles and Zeros

Let us begin our discussion of network functions by observing a few elementary properties that should have become obvious to you by now, even though we have not stated them explicitly.

First of all we observe that in lumped, linear, time-invariant networks, the network functions we have seen are all *rational functions*. For, we saw in Chapter 4 that the network functions can be computed from loop or node systems of equations. They appear as ratios of determinants and cofactors, or linear combinations of such ratios (even when dependent generators are present). The elements of the loop impedance matrix and the node admittance matrix are themselves rational functions. For instance, if we choose each R, L, and C to be a network element, we have for the loop impedance matrix

$$Z_m = [c_{kj}] \qquad (a)$$

with

$$c_{kj} = \frac{1}{s}(L_{kj}s^2 + R_{kj}s + D_{kj}) \qquad (b)$$

(1)

Since sums, products, differences and quotients of rational functions are also rational functions, and these are the only operations involved, we see that all network functions are rational. This is indeed a fortunate circumstance, since rational functions are the simplest analytic functions. (We shall soon see the difficulties that arise when we take the logarithm of one of these.)

Network functions have another very simple, but very useful, property. The coefficients in the numerator and denominator of the rational function that is a network function, are all real numbers.* Thus if $F(s)$, given by

$$F(s) = \frac{a_m s^m + a_{m-1} s^{m-1} + \cdots + a_1 s + a_0}{b_n s^n + b_{n-1} s^{n-1} + \cdots + b_1 s + b_0} \tag{2}$$

is a network function, then $a_m, a_{m-1}, \cdots, a_o, b_n, \cdots, b_o$ are all real numbers.† We observe this fact through the same line of reasoning as above. Namely, the elements of the loop impedance matrix and the node admittance matrix are rational functions with real coefficients; and this characteristic is invariant under the arithmetic operations (addition, subtraction, multiplication and division).

From this simple observation follows the important property that all network functions are real on the real axis in the s-plane. If a function of a complex variable is real on the real axis, it is called a *real function*. Thus all network functions that we have so far seen are *real rational functions*. This result immediately leads to the *reflection property*

$$F(s^*) = F^*(s) \tag{3}$$

That is, network functions assume conjugate values at conjugate points in the complex plane.

A rational function is a quotient of polynomials, and a polynomial can be expressed as a product of linear factors. Thus we can write a network function as

$$F(s) = K \frac{(s - s_{01})(s - s_{02}) \cdots (s - s_{0m})}{(s - s_{p1})(s - s_{p2}) \cdots (s - s_{pn})} \tag{4}$$

The complex numbers s_{0k} are the *zeros* of the function $F(s)$ and the complex numbers s_{pk} are the *poles* of the function $F(s)$. We refer to each factor $(s - s_{0k})$ in the numerator as a *zero factor* and each factor $(s - s_{pk})$ in the denominator as a *pole factor*.

We immediately have a *representation* of the function $F(s)$, and a way to specify a network function completely. A rational function $F(s)$ can be specified completely by giving its poles and zeros and the number K, which is merely a scale factor, and is known as soon as the value of the function at any point (other than a pole or zero) is known. The scale

---

* This statement should be qualified in a trivial way, since it is possible to multiply every coefficient in the numerator and denominator by an arbitrary complex number without changing the function. This difficulty is overcome by fixing, say, the coefficient of the highest power in the denominator to be 1.

† In the last two chapters we used H as a generic symbol for a network function. We are now using F. This should cause no confusion.

factor, however, is not too significant. The analytic properties of $F(s)$ are determined by its poles and zeros. Therefore, we generally disregard K and *represent* $F(s)$ (or $F(s)/K$, to be precise) in the complex plane as in Fig. 2. The small circles refer to the zeros of F and the small crosses to the poles of F. We refer to such diagrams as *pole-zero patterns* or *pole-zero constellations*. Due to the reflection property of Eq. (3), the poles and zeros of a network function are either real or occur in complex conjugate pairs.

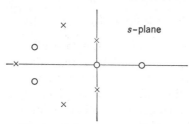

Fig. 2. Pole-zero constellation.

Another simple property possessed by network functions follows from a consideration of stability. We know that the transient response is governed by the poles of the network function. Since

$$\mathcal{L}^{-1}\left\{\frac{a_{-k}}{(s-s_p)^k}\right\} = a_{-k}t^{k-1}\epsilon^{s_p t} \qquad (5)$$

we immediately conclude that the network function of a stable network cannot have any poles in the right half plane, and any poles on the $j\omega$-axis must be simple. For otherwise, the transient response will be unbounded and the network will be unstable.

This conclusion can be strengthened in the case of the driving point functions. For, both the driving point impedance and the admittance are ratios of response to excitation transforms. Hence the driving point functions can have neither poles *nor zeros* in the right half plane; poles *and zeros* on the $j\omega$-axis must be simple.

In the case of the transfer functions, the reciprocals are not ratios of response to excitation transforms (in general). Hence we can say nothing about their zeros. They may lie anywhere in the complex plane, subject only to the symmetry requirement.

We will leave a further study of realizability of network functions to Chapter 9 and presently see what we can learn from the pole-zero representation of a network function.

7.2 Frequency Response Functions

For general complex values of s the network functions will take on complex values. These values can be represented either in terms of the real and imaginary parts, or in terms of the magnitude and angle. However, we are not usually interested in network functions for all complex values of s; of particular significance is the $j\omega$-axis. We are often interested in the behavior of one or more of the quantities: real part, imaginary part, magnitude, or its logarithm, and angle for purely imaginary values of s. We can refer to any one of these as a *frequency response function*. As we know, these values determine the steady-state response of the network to sinusoidal functions.

Let us formalize this discussion by writing

$$F(j\omega) = U(\omega) + jX(\omega) = |F(j\omega)| e^{j\phi(\omega)} \qquad (6)$$

The real and imaginary parts can be expressed in terms of $F(j\omega)$ as follows.

$$U(\omega) = \tfrac{1}{2}[F(j\omega) + F(-j\omega)] \qquad (7)$$

$$X(\omega) = \frac{1}{2j}[F(j\omega) - F(-j\omega)] \qquad (8)$$

Here we have used the information that $F(-j\omega) = F^*(j\omega)$, since $F(s)$ is a real function of s. To express the magnitude and angle in terms of $F(j\omega)$, let us write the square of $F(j\omega)$ as

$$F^2(j\omega) = F(j\omega)F(-j\omega)\frac{F(j\omega)}{F(-j\omega)} = |F(j\omega)|^2 e^{j2\phi(\omega)} \qquad (9)$$

Hence

$$|F(j\omega)|^2 = F(j\omega)F(-j\omega) \qquad (10)$$

$$j\phi(\omega) = \frac{1}{2}\ln\frac{F(j\omega)}{F(-j\omega)} \qquad (11)$$

The first of these two expressions is trivial; it is included for emphasis. (The second one has to be interpreted properly since the logarithm is multiple-valued.)

Once we know $F(s)$ these equations permit us to compute $U(\omega)$, $X(\omega)$, $|F(j\omega)|$, and $\phi(\omega)$. We can, of course, then plot these expressions in order to get a graphical picture. However, if a graphical representation is desired, there is another alternative to first computing the desired magnitude, real part, etc. This alternative procedure will give us much intuition into the relation between steady state and transient response of networks. For values of s restricted to the $j\omega$-axis, the function shown in Eq. (5) can be written as

$$\frac{F(j\omega)}{K} = \frac{(j\omega - s_{01})(j\omega - s_{02})\cdots(j\omega - s_{0m})}{(j\omega - s_{p1})(j\omega - s_{p2})\cdots(j\omega - s_{pn})} \qquad (12)$$

In the following discussion let us take the value of K to be unity since it affects the frequency response functions only as a scale change.

To find the magnitude of $F(j\omega)$ at any value of ω, we find the magnitudes of each of the zero and pole factors, then divide the product of the zero factor magnitudes by the product of the pole factor magnitudes. Similarly, the angle of $F(j\omega)$ at any frequency is found by adding the angles of all the zero factors and subtracting from this the sum of the angles of all the pole factors.

This procedure is easily performed graphically. By way of illustration consider the diagram in Fig. 3 where a pair of conjugate zeros is

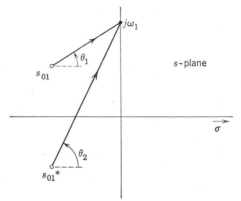

Fig. 3.   Graphical calculation of frequency response.

shown. The complex number represented by the factor $(j\omega_1 - s_{01})$ can be represented by a directed line from s_{01} to $j\omega_1$. The magnitude of the factor is simply the length of the directed line, and its angle is the one labelled θ_1 in the diagram. A similar discussion applies to the factor $(j\omega_1 - s_{01}{}^*)$, and to all other zero and pole factors in a given rational function.

To find the magnitude of a rational function for any point on the $j\omega$-axis when the poles and zeros are known, we simply measure the distances from the given point on the axis to each of the zeros and poles. The desired magnitude will be the product of the line lengths to the zeros divided by the product of the line lengths to the poles. If we do this for a number of points on the $j\omega$-axis, we will be able to make a plot of the magnitude as a function of frequency. In a similar way, a plot of the angle of $F(j\omega)$ can be drawn as a function of frequency.

As an illustration consider the impedance of the tuned circuit shown in Fig. 4. This can be written

$$Z(s) = \frac{1}{sC + 1/(sL + R)} = \frac{1}{C}\frac{s + 2a}{s^2 + 2as + \omega_0{}^2} = \frac{1}{C}\frac{s + 2a}{(s - s_1)(s - s_1{}^*)}$$

$$(13)$$

where

$$a = R/2L \qquad s_1 = -a + j\sqrt{\omega_0{}^2 - a^2}$$

$$\omega_0{}^2 = 1/LC \qquad s_1{}^* = -a - j\sqrt{\omega_0{}^2 - a^2}$$

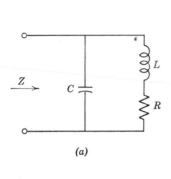

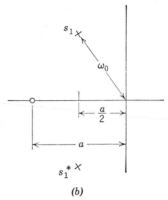

(a)

(b)

Fig. 4. Tuned circuit and its pole-zero configuration.

The pole-zero pattern is also shown in the figure. The geometrical construction for the magnitude and angle leads to the sketches shown in Fig. 5. From these curves it is possible to sketch the real part and the imaginary part as well, since

$$U(\omega) = |Z(j\omega)|\cos\phi(\omega) \qquad (a)$$

$$X(\omega) = |Z(j\omega)|\sin\phi(\omega) \qquad (b)$$

$$(14)$$

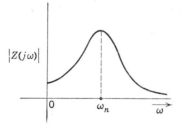

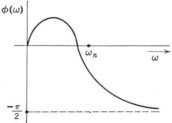

Fig. 5. Magnitude and angle functions.

These sketches are shown in Fig. 6. Note that the sketches are drawn for positive values of ω only. We have already noted that U and X are even and odd functions of ω, respectively. The same is true of $|Z(j\omega)|$ and $\phi(\omega)$.* Hence, it is only necessary to show the behavior for positive ω.

---

* We will discuss the oddness of $\phi(\omega)$ a little later. In some cases it may require some jugglery to make it an odd function of ω.

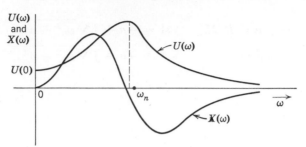

Fig. 6.   Real and imaginary parts.

We can relate these curves to familiar discussions of the tuned circuit and observe all the familiar properties, such as Q, bandwidth, the three resonant frequencies, etc.   However our purpose at this point is not a discussion of the tuned circuit, and so we leave this digression as an exercise for you.

In this graphical sketching of the magnitude and angle of the function, or the real part and the imaginary part, we have another way of representing a network function.   It is a complete representation, as we know from Problem 6.19.

7.3   Bode Diagrams

Let us now consider the magnitude function in somewhat greater detail.   Many formulas and statements become simpler if we consider the logarithm of $|F(j\omega)|$ rather than $|F(j\omega)|$ itself as the function of interest, and if we consider the logarithm of ω to be the variable.   Let us begin by writing

$$F(j\omega) = \epsilon^{\alpha(\omega)+j\phi(\omega)} \qquad\qquad (a)$$

$$\ln F(j\omega) = \alpha(\omega) + j\phi(\omega) \qquad\qquad (b) \qquad (15)$$

$$\alpha(\omega) = \ln|F(j\omega)|$$

$$= \tfrac{1}{2}\ln[F(j\omega)F(-j\omega)] \qquad\qquad (c)$$

We refer to $\alpha(\omega)$ as the *logarithmic gain* or simply the *gain*.   Its unit is the *neper*.   Alternatively we can define a quantity $\alpha'(\omega)$ as

$$|F(j\omega)| = 10^{\alpha'/20} \qquad\qquad (a)$$
$$\alpha'(\omega) = 20\log_{10}|F(j\omega)| \qquad\qquad (b) \qquad (16)$$

The two α's are related by

$$\alpha = \frac{\alpha'}{20} \ln 10 \doteq 0.1151\alpha' \qquad (a)$$

$$\alpha' = \frac{20}{\ln 10} \doteq 8.686\alpha \qquad (b)$$

$$(17)$$

The same name is commonly given to α' as to α. The unit of α' is the *decibel* (contracted to db) and the last equation relates the neper and the decibel. Since the two differ by simply a constant factor, it is common practice to use the definition of α in Eq. (15) for α' also and to say this is the logarithmic gain "measured in db." Although it sometimes may lead to confusion, we will continue this practice.

Turning next to the frequency variable let us write

$$\omega = 10^{u} \qquad (a)$$

$$u = \log_{10}\omega \qquad (b)$$

$$(18)$$

The new variable u is the logarithmic frequency. Let u_2 and u_1 correspond to two frequencies ω_2 and ω_1, respectively. The interval $u_2 - u_1$ on the u-axis will be

$$u_2 - u_1 = \log_{10}\omega_2 - \log_{10}\omega_1 = \log_{10}(\omega_2/\omega_1) \qquad (19)$$

Hence, a unit interval on the u-axis corresponds to a frequency interval $\omega_2 = 10\omega_1$, which is one *decade*. Thus, the unit of u is the decade.

Another way of transforming the frequency is also in common use. We write

$$\omega = 2^{u'} \qquad (a)$$

$$u' = \log_2 \omega = \frac{\log_{10}\omega}{\log_{10}2} \doteq \frac{u}{0.3} \qquad (b)$$

$$(20)$$

A unit of u' corresponds to a change in ω of two to one, which is an *octave*. The last expression shows that the number of decades corresponding to a given frequency range is approximately three tenths the number of octaves.

Let us now turn back to the network function in Eq. (12) and find its logarithm. We get

$$\ln F(j\omega) = \sum_{i=1}^{m} \ln (j\omega - s_{0i}) - \sum_{i=1}^{n} \ln (j\omega - s_{pi}) \qquad (a)$$

$$\alpha(\omega) = \ln |F(j\omega)| = \sum_{i=1}^{m} \ln |j\omega - s_{0i}| - \sum_{i=1}^{n} \ln |j\omega - s_{pi}| \quad (b) \qquad (21)$$

$$\phi(\omega) = \sum_{i=1}^{m} \arg (j\omega - s_{0i}) - \sum_{i=1}^{n} \arg (j\omega - s_{pi}) \qquad (c)$$

We immediately see the advantage of the change to the logarithm. Multiplication has been replaced by addition; and each zero factor and each pole factor appears separately. What we shall do next is to study the contribution to the frequency response of the various types of pole and zero factors that can occur in a network function. Then, to find the behavior of a network function as a whole, we merely have to add the curves. If we had taken the constant multiplier K into consideration, the term $\ln|K|$ would have been added to the right side of Eqs. (21a) and (21b); in case K is a negative number, $j\pi$ and π have to be added to Eqs. (21a) and (21c), respectively. The effect, in so far as the frequency response curves are concerned, is merely a translation of the axes (0 db level and 0° phase).

Let us begin our study with the factor corresponding to a real pole or zero, using the more familiar db notation. The function under consideration is therefore

$$\alpha_i = 20 \log|(a - j\omega)| \tag{22}$$

where a is a real number. It may be one of the zeros or one of the poles. At $\omega = 0$ this function is simply $\alpha_i = 20 \log a$. For small values of ω such that $\omega \ll a$, this function is still approximately $20 \log a$. For large values of ω, such that $\omega \gg a$, the function reduces to $20 \log \omega = 20\, u$. That is for large ω, α_i becomes a linear function of u with a slope of 20. The gain rises (or falls, if it is a pole factor) at the rate of 20 db per decade, or 6 db per octave. Figure 7 shows the asymptotic behavior for large and small ω. (Plot this on a linear scale, $|F(j\omega)|$ vs. ω, to see the simplicity introduced by the change to logarithmic scales.) We can use this asymptotic plot to obtain an approximate idea of the variation of gain with frequency. Suppose we assume that the asymptotic values of α_i apply for all values of u. The point of intersection of the asymptotic values, labelled u_1 in Fig. 7, is called the *break frequency* or *corner fre-*

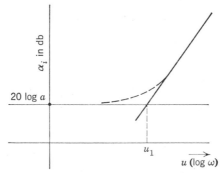

Fig. 7.   Asymptotic behavior of α_i.

quency. It occurs when $\omega = a$ or $u = \log a$ (why?). The greatest error in using the asymptotic values instead of actual values occurs at the break frequency. Since $\omega = a$ at this point, Eq. (22) shows that the actual value of α_i is

$$\alpha_i(a) = 20 \log \sqrt{a^2 + \omega^2}\big|_{\omega=a} = 20 \log a + 20 \log \sqrt{2} \doteq 20 \log a + 3 \tag{23}$$

This differs from the approximate value by 3 db, so that a 3 db error will be made at the break frequency if the asymptotic values are used. (Actually 3.010 db to four significant figures.)

Each of the terms in Eq. (21) which is due to a real pole or zero will make a contribution similar to Fig. 7 to the over-all gain. The contributions of the poles will have a negative slope beyond the break frequency. A good idea of the behavior of the gain can be obtained from the asymptotic curves, only if the break frequencies are separated widely enough so that at each break frequency the contributions from the other terms can be accurately represented by their asymptotic values. This approximate representation of gain (by straight line segments) is referred to as a *Bode diagram*, after the inventor.

In the case of complex poles or zeros, the above discussion requires some modification. Let us consider a quadratic factor $s^2 + as + b$ in the rational function due to a pair of complex zeros or poles. Its contribution to the gain will be

$$\alpha_i = \pm 20 \log |(b - \omega^2) + ja\omega| \tag{24}$$

the $+$ sign applying for a zero and the $-$ sign for a pole. The low frequency asymptote is again a constant, $\pm 20 \log b$, but the high frequency asymptote now becomes

$$\alpha_i \xrightarrow[\omega \to \infty]{} \pm 20 \log \omega^2 = \pm 40u \tag{25}$$

This is again a straight line but this time with a slope of 40 db per decade instead of 20. The break frequency can be found by equating the two asymptotic values. We see that the break frequency is $\omega = \sqrt{b}$, which is the distance of the pole or zero from the origin. In the present case, the actual value of α_i is not necessarily closely approximated by the asymptotic values except near very small and very large frequencies. This fact is easy to appreciate from a consideration of Eq. (24). The coefficient a is here twice the real part of the pole or zero. If the pole or zero is very close to the $j\omega$-axis, then a will be small. The actual value of α_i at the break frequency $\omega = \sqrt{b}$ is

$$\alpha_i(\sqrt{b}) = \pm 20 \log a \sqrt{b} \tag{26}$$

If $a \sqrt{b}$ is very small, then its logarithm will be a large negative number. In the limit, if the complex pair falls on the $j\omega$-axis, $a = 0$ and $\alpha_i(\sqrt{b}) = \pm \infty$. Figure 8 shows the possible behavior of the contribution of a pair of complex poles to the gain. It is clear that when the complex poles or zeros are not very close to the $j\omega$-axis, the asymptotic values form a fairly good approximation to the actual value of the gain contributed by the complex pair.

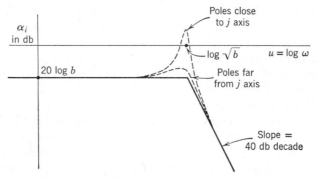

Fig. 8.   Contribution of complex poles to gain.

The behavior of a complex pair of poles or zeros is thus somewhat more complicated. In the case of the real poles, one plot of $-20 \log |F(j\omega)|$ vs. $\log \omega$ suffices to describe all poles, and if tipped over, to describe all zeros. With complex poles and zeros, we need a number of curves depending on the "damping." These curves are available however, and can be found in any text book on servomechanisms. The plots of quadratic factors, such as shown in Fig. 8, are known as *second order corner plots* as contrasted with plots of simple factors, which are referred to as *first-order corner plots*.

One other point should be mentioned before this subject is terminated. It is an easy matter to determine the asymptotic value of the over-all gain in Eq. (21) for large values of ω. Since each term contributes $\pm 20 \log \omega$, the overall gain becomes

$$\alpha \xrightarrow[\omega \to \infty]{} 20(m - n) \log \omega = -20(n - m)u \qquad (27)$$

That is, the gain will fall linearly with u, with a slope which is 20 times the difference between the number of finite poles and the number of finite zeros (which is the number of zeros at ∞).

The gain plots can be simplified if all the zeros s_{0i} and the poles s_{pi} are factored in the rational function in Eq. (12), leaving each zero factor as $(j\omega/s_{0i} - 1)$ and each pole factor as $(j\omega/s_{pi} - 1)$. The constants that are factored can then be lumped with the multiplier K. This constant has the effect of moving the entire gain curve in the vertical direction an amount $20 \log K$ db. The low frequency asymptotic value of the gain will then simply be zero (except for the value $20 \log K$).

As an example, consider the function

$$F(s) = \frac{20(s + 5)}{(s^2 + s + 1)(s + 10)} = \frac{10(1 + s/5)}{(s^2 + s + 1)(1 + s/10)} \qquad (28)$$

On the $j\omega$-axis, we can write the gain as

$$\alpha = 20 \log 10 + 20[\log|1 + j\omega/5| - \log|1 + j\omega/10| - \log|1 - \omega^2 + j\omega|] \qquad (29)$$

The zero frequency gain is 20 db and the first break frequency occurs at $\omega = 1$ ($u = 0$). The break is downward with a slope of 40 db per decade. At $\omega = 5$ ($u = 0.7$) there is a break upward with a slope of 20 db per decade. Finally, at $\omega = 10$ ($u = 1$) there is another break downward at a slope of 20 db per decade. For larger frequencies, the gain falls at a rate of 40 db per decade. The asymptotic plot is shown in Fig. 9.

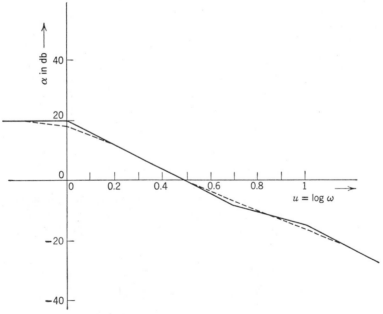

Fig. 9.   Gain plot of numerical example.

The actual plot is also shown, by the dotted curve. It is clear that the asymptotic behavior approximates the actual behavior quite closely.

7.4 Minimum-phase and Nonminimum-phase Transfer Functions

As we observed earlier in this chapter, the zeros of transfer functions can occur in any part of the complex plane. However, those functions that have no zeros in the right half plane have certain properties which are quite important. For this reason we give these functions a distinctive name for ease of identification. We define a *minimum-phase transfer function as one that has no zeros in the right half plane.* Conversely, any transfer function that has zeros (even one zero) in the right half plane is labelled *nonminimum-phase.* The reason for these names will become apparent in the sequel.

In order to determine the effect of right half plane zeros on the magnitude and angle of a transfer function, consider the diagram of Fig. 10a.

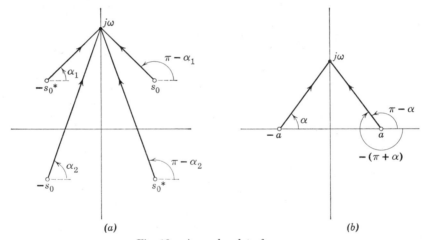

(a)   *(b)*

Fig. 10. A quadruplet of zeros.

This shows a pair of conjugate zeros in the right half plane and the left half plane image of this pair. Let $P_a(s)$ and $P_b(s)$ be quadratics which have the right half plane pair of factors and the left half plane pair of factors, respectively. That is,

$$P_a(s) = (s - s_0)(s - s_0{}^*) \qquad (a)$$

$$P_b(s) = (s + s_0)(s + s_0{}^*) \qquad (b)$$

$$(30)$$

It is clear that $P_a(s) = P_b(-s)$. The geometrical construction in the figure indicates that the magnitudes of P_a and P_b are the same when $s = j\omega$. As for the angles, we find

$$\arg P_a(j\omega) = \pi - \alpha_1 - [2\pi - (\pi - \alpha_2)] = -(\alpha_1 + \alpha_2) \quad (a)$$

$$\arg P_b(j\omega) = \alpha_1 + \alpha_2 = -\arg P_a(j\omega) \quad (b)$$

(31)

Note that, in order for the angle of P_a to be zero at $\omega = 0$ as it must be if the angle is to be an odd function, we have written the angle of $(s - s_0{}^*)$ as $-(\pi + \alpha_2)$ rather than $\pi - \alpha_2$.

This desire to have the angle function $\phi(\omega)$ an odd function of ω is quite deep seated in network theorists. The main reason for this desire is that it simplifies the statements of many theorems that we shall state later in the chapter. To achieve this aim, we do many peculiar things, such as change the sign of the function as we have done here, or introduce a discontinuity of 2π in $\phi(\omega)$ at $\omega = 0$, as we shall do in another example. The basic difficulty is the following. Although the realness of $F(s)$ on the real axis is a natural consequence of real network parameters, there is no valid reason why $F(s)$ should be a real positive number at $s = 0$, except for a driving-point function. The fact that the logarithm is a multiple-valued function adds to the fun.

Changing the sign of the function as we have done here, has the simple interpretation of changing one of the references (excitation or response) in the network. Since the procedure may be necessary only in transfer functions, the change of one reference is not serious.

Introduction of a discontinuity of 2π in $\phi(\omega)$ at $\omega = 0$ corresponds to jumping from one Riemann surface to another at $\omega = 0$ (presumably from fright at the mere thought of negative frequencies).

It is clear from the figure that $\alpha_1 + \alpha_2$, the angle contributed by the left half plane zeros, is positive for all positive ω. It runs from zero at $\omega = 0$ to π at infinity. This is illustrated in Fig. 11. It follows, then,

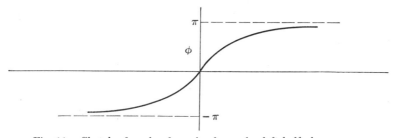

Fig. 11.   Sketch of angle of a pair of complex left half plane zeros.

that the angle of a pair of right half plane zeros is always negative for positive values of ω, running from zero at $\omega = 0$ to $-\pi$ at infinity.

Let us now consider the situation in Fig. 10b which shows a real zero on the positive real axis and its left half plane image. Again, the magnitudes of the two factors $(j\omega - a)$ and $(j\omega + a)$ are equal. The angle of the left half plane factor $(j\omega + a)$ is α for positive ω. (It will be $-\alpha$ for negative ω.) We will choose the angle of the right half plane factor $(j\omega - a)$ to be $-(\pi + \alpha)$ for positive ω and $\pi - \alpha$ for negative ω in order to make the angle an odd function. Sketches of these angles are shown in Fig. 12. Note that there is a discontinuity of 2π in the second

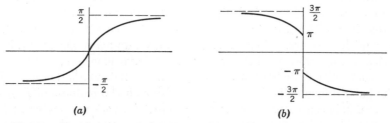

Fig. 12. Sketches of angle functions. (a) arg $(j\omega + a)$; (b) arg $(j\omega - a)$.

figure which is introduced simply by our desire to make the angle an odd function.

If we consider two real right half plane zeros, we can define the angles in such a way that this discontinuity is eliminated. The situation becomes similar to the case of a pair of complex right half plane zeros. The only difficulty occurs when there is only a single right half plane zero (or an odd number of such zeros). The alternative procedure in the case of an odd number of right half plane zeros is to reverse the reference of the output voltage or current. This will change the right half plane factor $(s - s_0)$ to $(s_0 - s)$. The angle will then be the negative of the angle of the corresponding left half plane zero, just as in the case of the complex pair of zeros.

With this discussion as a background, let us now consider the following two transfer functions.

$$F_1(s) = (s - s_0)(s - s_0{}^*)F(s) = P_b(-s)F(s) \tag{32}$$

$$F_2(s) = (s + s_0)(s + s_0{}^*)F(s) = P_b(s)F(s) \tag{33}$$

where s_0 and its conjugate lie in the right half plane. These two functions are identical except that $F_1(s)$ has a pair of right half plane zeros, whereas in $F_2(s)$ these are replaced by their left half plane images. The common function $F(s)$ may have additional right half plane factors. Suppose we multiply numerator and denominator of $F_1(s)$ by the left half plane factors $(s + s_0)(s + s_0{}^*)$. The result will be

$$F_1(s) = \frac{P_b(s)}{P_b(s)} P_b(-s)F(s) = F_2(s) \frac{P_b(-s)}{P_b(s)} = F_2(s)F_0(s) \quad (34)$$

where

$$F_0(s) = \frac{P_b(-s)}{P_b(s)} = \frac{(s - s_0)(s - s_0{}^*)}{(s + s_0)(s + s_0{}^*)} \quad (35)$$

Let us define an *all-pass function* as a transfer function all of whose zeros are in the right half plane and whose poles are the left half plane images of its zeros. A consideration of the last equation now shows that $F_0(s)$ is an all-pass function. It is a *second-order* all-pass function, the order referring to the number of poles. From the previous discussion it is clear that an all-pass function has a unit magnitude for all values of $s = j\omega$. (This is the reason for its name.) From Eqs. (31) the angle of $F_0(j\omega)$ is found to be

$$\arg F_0(j\omega) = \arg P_b(-j\omega) - \arg P_b(j\omega) = -2(\alpha_1 + \alpha_2) \quad (36)$$

For positive frequencies this is a negative angle. Thus, the angle of an all-pass function is negative for all positive frequencies.

Using this equation and Eq. (34) we can now write

$$\arg F_1(j\omega) = \arg F_2(j\omega) + \arg F_0(j\omega) < \arg F_2(j\omega), \quad \text{for } \omega > 0 \quad (37)$$

This result tells us that, at all positive frequencies the angle of a function having right half plane zeros is *less than* that of the function obtained when a pair of these zeros is replaced by its right half plane image.

This procedure of expressing a transfer function as the product of two others may now be repeated. At each step a pair of complex zeros or a real zero from the right half plane may be replaced by their left half plane images. A sequence of functions, of which F_1 and F_2 are the first two, will be obtained. Each member of the sequence will have fewer right half plane zeros than the preceding one. The last member in this sequence will have no right half plane zeros. Let us label it $F_m(s)$. By definition, $F_m(s)$ is a minimum-phase function (as the subscript is meant to imply). Using Eq. (37), and similar results for the other functions, we can write

$$\arg F_1(j\omega) < \arg F_2(j\omega) < \cdots < F_m(j\omega); \quad \omega > 0 \quad (38)$$

Each of the functions in this sequence will have the same j-axis magnitude but the angles will get progressively larger. Paradoxically, *the minimum-phase function will have the largest angle of all* (algebraically, but not necessarily in magnitude). The reason for this apparent inconsistency is the following. We have defined transfer functions as ratios of *output* transform to *input* transform. When the concept of minimum-phase was first introduced by Bode, he defined transfer functions in the opposite way. With this definition the inequalities in Eq. (38) will be reversed and the minimum-phase function will have the smallest angle.

At each step in the above procedure a second-order or first-order all-pass function is obtained. The product of any number of all-pass functions is again an all-pass function. It follows that any nonminimum-phase transfer function can be written as the product of a minimum-phase function and an all-pass function.

We can establish one other result from a consideration of the variation of the angle of an all-pass function as ω increases from zero to infinity. Equation (36), together with Fig. 10a, shows that the change in angle $\Delta\phi$, defined as the angle at infinity minus the angle at $\omega = 0$, for a second-order all-pass function is -2π. Similarly, for a first-order all-pass function, we can find from Fig. 12, that this change is $\Delta\phi = -\pi$ (not counting the discontinuity at $\omega = 0$). It is easy to appreciate that for an nth-order all-pass function the change in angle is $-n\pi$.

Consider now a nonminimum-phase function that has n zeros in the right half plane. This can be expressed as the product of a minimum-phase function and an nth-order all-pass function. The net change in angle of the nonminimum-phase function as ω varies from zero to infinity will be the net change in angle of the corresponding minimum-phase function plus the net change in angle of the all-pass function. Since this latter is a negative quantity, it follows that a nonminimum-phase function has a smaller net change in angle, again only algebraically, as ω varies from zero to infinity, than the corresponding minimum-phase function, the difference being $n\pi$, where n is the number of right half plane zeros.

It is also of interest to determine what the net change in angle of a minimum-phase function will be as ω varies from zero to infinity. The angle contributed by each zero to this net change is $\pi/2$, whereas that contributed by each pole is $-\pi/2$. Hence, the net change in angle will be $\pi/2$ times the number of finite zeros minus the number of finite poles. Thus if the transfer function is regular at $s = \infty$, the minimum phase function will have a smaller $|\Delta\phi|$ than the corresponding nonminimum phase function, since both angles are nonpositive.

7.5 Complex Loci

In the previous sections of this chapter we described two ways in which the network functions can be represented. One way involves specifying the locations of the poles and zeros in the s-plane. The second method involves an analytical or graphical presentation of the real part and imaginary part, or the magnitude and angle, as a function of frequency. Since the network functions are analytic functions of the complex variable s, we can also represent the function graphically as a mapping of the s-plane. This is best done by plotting families of curves in the F plane which are loci for constant values of σ and ω in the s plane. However, since our main interest lies in the $j\omega$ axis, we usually plot only one locus, the map of the $j\omega$ axis on the F plane. We refer to this as the *complex locus* (or complex plot) of the network function.

In simple cases the locus may have a simple geometrical shape but generally it will not. As an example let us consider the impedance function given in Eq. (13). The magnitude and angle functions are shown in Fig. 5 while the real and imaginary parts are shown in Fig. 6. From these figures it is possible to sketch the locus quite rapidly. The result is shown in Fig. 13.

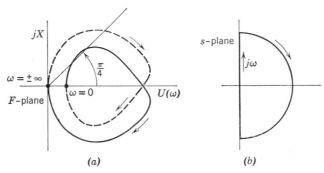

(a)   (b)

Fig. 13.   Complex locus.

The locus starts at $\omega = 0$ with a zero imaginary part and a nonzero real part. Corresponding to the points in Fig. 6 at which U and X are equal, the locus crosses the 45° line twice, the imaginary part reaching a maximum between these two frequencies. The real part reaches a maximum soon after the imaginary part becomes zero. Finally both the real part and the imaginary part become zero at infinity, so the locus approaches the origin at high frequencies. For negative frequencies the locus will be the image of that for positive frequencies due to the even and odd symmetries of the real and imaginary parts. This part of the locus is shown by the dotted curve.

According to a theorem in the theory of conformal mapping with analytic functions, if a closed path in the plane of the complex variable encircles in the clockwise direction an area throughout which the function is regular, the map of that closed path in the function plane will encircle the corresponding area also in the clockwise direction (see Problem 7.10). In the present case the area in the s-plane is the entire right half plane, the boundary being the $j\omega$-axis and an "infinite semicircle," as shown in Fig. 13b.* In accordance with the theorem, the locus does encircle an area in the clockwise direction.

As another illustration consider the complex locus of an all-pass function. Since this function has a unit magnitude for all ω, the locus is the unit circle in the F plane. As we saw in the last section, the angle of an nth order all-pass function changes by $n\pi$ as ω varies from zero to infinity, so the change will be twice this amount for the entire frequency range. This means that the locus of the nth order all-pass function will go around the unit circle n times (in the clockwise direction, as we saw). The locus is sketched in Fig. 14.

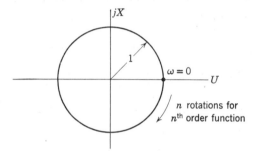

Fig. 14.   Complex locus of all-pass function.

This result is a special case of a more general result which we shall now discuss. Let $F(s)$ be a function which is regular on a closed contour C in the s plane and whose only singular points inside the contour are poles, as sketched in Fig. 15a. Suppose the map C' in the F plane of this s plane contour is the one shown in Fig. 15b. Both contours are traversed in the clockwise direction. According to a theorem in function theory, which is referred to as the Principle of Argument, *the number of times the contour C' encircles the origin in the F plane is equal to the number of zeros minus the number of poles of $F(s)$ inside the contour C in the s-plane.*

* This phrase "infinite semicircle" can be very confusing and so let us explain what we mean by it. We mean that we are going to start with a semicircle in the right half plane of finite radius R. We perform whatever operations are desired (in this case map the contour), with the finite semicircle. Then we find the *limit of the result* (of whatever operations were performed) as the radius R goes to infinity. By saying that we have the map of the infinite semicircle, we mean that only this limit is shown, not the pre-limit curve. Certainly Fig. 13b shows only a finite semicircle. An infinite semicircle can neither be drawn nor be seen. However confusing this phrase may be, it is part of the electrical engineer's jargon.

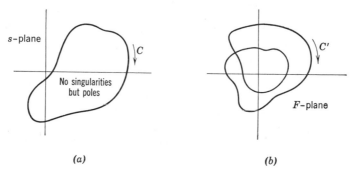

Fig. 15.   Principle of the argument.

If there are any multiple order poles or zeros, these are counted according to their multiplicity. (See Appendix.)

In applying this theorem to complex loci of network functions, note that the closed contour in the s plane consists of the entire $j\omega$ axis and the "infinite semicircle" in the right half plane, as shown in Fig. 13b. The theorem requires that the function have no poles on the $j\omega$ axis or at infinity. According to the theorem, then, the number of times the complex locus encircles the origin in a clockwise direction in the F plane is equal to the number of zeros minus the number of poles in the right half s plane.

This theorem is very useful in determining whether or not a given rational function is the transfer function of a stable network.* If the denominator is of relatively high degree, factoring it in order to determine stability may require a large amount of work. On the other hand, a sketch of the complex locus can be made relatively easily. Whether or not the locus encircles the origin will give information concerning the stability. Of course, conclusive information is not always obtained, because the number of clockwise encirclements of the origin depends on the difference between number of right half plane zeros and poles. If there are a net number of *counterclockwise* encirclements of the origin, this indicates the definite existence of right half plane poles. On the other hand, if there are no net encirclements of the origin, we can only conclude that the number of right half plane poles is equal to the number of right half plane zeros. However, if we know the function to be minimum-phase, we can then definitely say there are no right half plane poles. A similar discussion applies if there are a number of clockwise encirclements of the origin. In a passive network we can use this test to see whether the transfer function is minimum phase.

* A detailed discussion of this subject is included in Chapter 10.

7.6   Calculation of Network Function from a Given Magnitude

Up to the present time, we have concentrated on the problem of representing a given rational function in one of several ways. One method is to plot its j-axis real and imaginary parts, or magnitude and angle as a function of frequency.

We would now like to discuss the inverse operation; that of reconstructing a rational function knowing only its real part, or imaginary part, or its magnitude or angle. We have already seen in the last chapter that the real and imaginary parts of analytic functions are related through certain integral formulas. In this section we shall concentrate on the magnitude function. Since it is easier to talk about the square of the magnitude rather than the magnitude itself, we will do so from now on. Of course, if a magnitude function is given we can always square it. We assume that the magnitude squared function is given as a rational function of s and not as a curve to be approximated.

Suppose now that a rational function of ω, say $G(j\omega)$, is given and that it satisfies the necessary conditions for being the square of the magnitude of a network function. What are these conditions? Actually, they are very simple; the function should be an even function of ω, and the degree of the numerator should not exceed that of the denominator by more than two. This is because the network function cannot have more than a simple pole at infinity. In addition, if $G(j\omega)$ has any finite j-axis poles, they must be double, since poles of a network function on the $j\omega$-axis must be simple.

Glance back at Eq. (10). The given function can be written

$$G(j\omega) = |F(j\omega)|^2 = F(j\omega)F(-j\omega) \qquad (39)$$

Our task, then, is to determine the function $F(j\omega)$, knowing the function $G(j\omega)$. As a matter of fact, we can think of G as being a function of the complex variable s, $G(j\omega)$ being its value on the $j\omega$-axis. That is, we can write the relationship

$$G(s) = F(s)F(-s) \qquad (40)$$

which is valid for all values of s, not only $s = j\omega$. However $G(s)$ is *not* equal to the square of the magnitude of $F(s)$, *except for $s = j\omega$*.

Suppose we now imagine factoring the numerator and denominator of $G(s)$. We must assign some of these factors to $F(s)$ and some to $F(-s)$. Let us first determine what the pole-zero pattern of $G(s)$ will be. Remember that $G(s)$ is the ratio of two even polynomials. Now the factors of an even polynomial must take one of the following forms.

$$s^2 - a^2$$

$$s^4 + as^2 + b \qquad (41)$$

$$s^2 + a^2$$

For the function $G(s)$ the last factor can only appear as $(s^2 + a^2)^2$. The first of these will lead to a pair of real zeros, one on the positive real axis, the other its image on the negative real axis. The second factor will lead to four complex zeros symmetrically arranged around the origin. The third leads to a pair of j-axis zeros. The distribution is shown in Fig. 16. Such a symmetrical distribution of zeros (or poles)

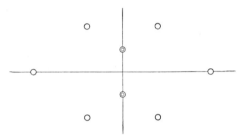

Fig. 16. Zeros arranged in quadrantal symmetry.

is referred to as *quadrantal symmetry*. We say, then, that the poles and zeros of $G(s)$, to which we can refer as the *magnitude squared* function, occur in quadrantal symmetry.

The question now is how to pick the poles and zeros of $F(s)$ from among those of $G(s)$. For the poles the answer is simple. We know that $F(s)$ must be regular in the right half plane. Since the poles of $F(-s)$ are the negatives of the poles of $F(s)$, it follows that $F(-s)$ is regular in the left half plane. Hence, the poles of $G(s)$ can be uniquely distributed; the left half plane poles of $G(s)$ belong to $F(s)$, whereas those in the right half plane belong to $F(-s)$. Poles on the $j\omega$-axis are evenly distributed. They will be double in $G(s)$ and simple in $F(s)$ and $F(-s)$.

As for the zeros, the answer is not so clear-cut. It is not essential that $F(s)$ have no zeros in the right half plane unless it is a driving point function. Hence, we need not assign all the left half plane zeros of $G(s)$ to $F(s)$. However, if it is specified that $F(s)$ is to be *minimum-phase*, then all the left half plane zeros of $G(s)$ are assigned to $F(s)$. Otherwise, it is possible to assign some right half plane zeros to $F(s)$. Remember, however, that a pair of complex zeros must be kept together since $F(s)$ must be a real function of s. Thus $F(s)$ is uniquely determined by $G(s)$ only if $F(s)$ is required to be minimum-phase.

Finally, zeros on the $j\omega$ axis must be equally divided between $F(s)$ and $F(-s)$ just as the poles were.

Let us now consider some examples which illustrate this procedure and which are of practical interest. The requirements of most common electrical filters involve transfer functions whose j-axis magnitudes are ideally constant over a given frequency interval, which is referred to as the *pass band*, and are ideally zero over the rest of the $j\omega$-axis, which is referred to as the *stop band*. It is not possible for the j-axis magnitude of a rational function to behave in this ideal manner. (Why?) However, it is possible to find transfer functions whose j-axis magnitudes approximate the desired magnitude in some fashion or other.

Consider the ideal low-pass filter function shown in Fig. 17a. Two

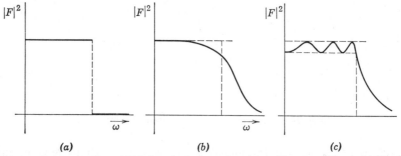

Fig. 17. Butterworth and Tchebyscheff approximations of low-pass filter. (a) Ideal; (b) Butterworth; (c) Tchebyscheff.

possible ways of approximating this ideal function are shown in parts (b) and (c) of the figure. The first of these is called a *maximally-flat* or *Butterworth* approximation, while the second one is called a *Tchebyscheff* (or equal ripple) approximation.* The maximally flat approximation is monotonic in both pass-band and stop-band, the maximum error occurring near the edge of the band. On the other hand, the Tchebyscheff approximation is oscillatory in the pass-band, the peaks of the ripples being equal. In this way, the error is distributed more uniformly over the pass-band.

The analytical forms of these functions, aside from a scale factor, are given by

$$|F(j\omega)|^2 = \frac{1}{1 + \omega^{2n}} ; \qquad \text{Butterworth} \qquad (42)$$

$$|F(j\omega)|^2 = \frac{1}{1 + \delta^2 T_n{}^2(\omega)} ; \qquad \text{Tchebyscheff} \qquad (43)$$

* We will see more of these approximations in Chapter 11.

in which δ is a small number which controls the ripple amplitude and in which $\omega = 1$ corresponds to the edge of the passband. The function $T_n(\omega)$ is a *Tchebyscheff polynomial* which is defined by

$$T_n(s/j) = \cosh(n \cosh^{-1} s/j) \tag{44}$$

which reduces on substituting $s = j\omega$ to

$$T_n(\omega) = \cos(n \cos^{-1} \omega) \qquad \text{for } |\omega| \le 1 \tag{45}$$

Our problem now is to find the transfer function $F(s)$ knowing its j-axis squared magnitude. Let us first consider the Butterworth response. According to the previous discussion, we first replace ω^2 by $-s^2$ in Eq. (42). The result is

$$G(s) = F(s)F(-s) = \frac{1}{1 + (-1)^n s^{2n}} \tag{46}$$

This function has no finite zeros, so we need only factor the denominator. In the present case, this is a relatively simple task. The zeros of the denominator are found by writing

$$s^{2n} = \epsilon^{j(2k-1+n)\pi} \tag{a}$$

which is simply $\tag{47}$

$$s^{2n} = \pm 1 \tag{b}$$

where the minus sign applies for n even. Taking the $2n$th root in Eq. (47a) we find the poles of $G(s)$ to be

$$s_k = \epsilon^{j(2k-1+n)\pi/2n}; \qquad k = 1, 2, \cdots, 2n \tag{48}$$

Thus, there are $2n$ poles each of which has unit magnitude. The poles are uniformly distributed on the unit circle as shown in Fig. 18 for the case $n = 4$.

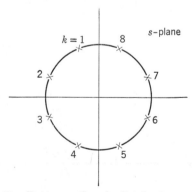

Fig. 18.   Butterworth pole distribution: $n = 4$.

To form $F(s)$ we simply take the n left half plane poles of $G(s)$. These are the ones given by values of k from 1 to n. For $n = 4$ these will be

$$s_1 = \epsilon^{j(5\pi/8)}; \qquad s_3 = \epsilon^{j(9\pi/8)}$$

$$s_2 = \epsilon^{j(7\pi/8)}; \qquad s_4 = \epsilon^{j(11\pi/8)} \tag{49}$$

Finally, for the case $n = 4$,

$$F(s) = \frac{1}{(s - s_1)(s - s_2)(s - s_3)(s - s_4)}$$

$$= \frac{1}{1 + 2.613s + 3.414s^2 + 2.613s^3 + s^4} \tag{50}$$

Next let us consider the Tchebyscheff response in Eq. (43). The first step is to replace $j\omega$ by s. We then set the denominator equal to zero in order to locate the poles. The result will be

$$T_n(s/j) = \cosh(n \cosh^{-1} s/j) = \pm j/\delta \tag{51}$$

In order to solve this equation, let us define a new variable $w = x + jy$ and write

$$s = j \cosh w = j \cosh(x + jy) \qquad (a)$$

$$T_n(s/j) = \cosh nw = \cosh n(x + jy) = \pm j/\delta \quad (b) \tag{52}$$

If we now expand $\cosh nw$ in the last equation and set reals and imaginaries equal on both sides of the equation, we will find the values of x and y which will satisfy the equation. When these values are substituted into Eq. (52a) we find the corresponding values of s. These are the pole locations. If we designate them by $s_k = \sigma_k + j\omega_k$, the result of the indicated operations will be

$$\sigma_k = \sinh\left(\frac{1}{n}\sinh^{-1}\frac{1}{\delta}\right) \sin \frac{2k - 1}{n}\frac{\pi}{2} \qquad (a)$$

$$\omega_k = \cosh\left(\frac{1}{n}\sinh^{-1}\frac{1}{\delta}\right) \cos \frac{2k - 1}{n}\frac{\pi}{2} \qquad (b) \tag{53}$$

In order to get some interpretation for these seemingly monstrous expressions, we note that if we divide each of them by the hyperbolic function, square both sides and add, we will get

$$\frac{\sigma_k{}^2}{\sinh^2\left(\dfrac{1}{n}\sinh^{-1}\dfrac{1}{\delta}\right)} + \frac{\omega_k{}^2}{\cosh^2\left(\dfrac{1}{n}\sinh^{-1}\dfrac{1}{\delta}\right)} = 1 \tag{54}$$

This is the equation of an ellipse in the s-plane. The major axis of the ellipse will lie along the $j\omega$-axis, since the hyperbolic cosine of a real variable is always greater than the hyperbolic sine. The pole locations for $n = 4$ are shown in Fig. 19.

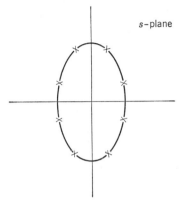

Fig. 19.   Tchebyscheff pole distribution: $n = 4$.

Finally, the left half plane poles of $G(s)$ are allotted to $F(s)$ and the task is again complete.

For a typical case, if the permissible ripple is given to be $\delta = 0.1$ and the order $n = 4$, the pole locations are found from Eq. (53) and we get the transfer function

$$F(s) = \frac{1}{(s^2 + 0.644s + 1.534)(s^2 + 1.519s + 0.823)}$$

$$= \frac{1}{s^4 + 2.16s^3 + 3.31s^2 + 2.86s + 1.26}$$

7.7   Calculation of Network Function from a Given Angle

In the last section we found that, starting with an even rational function which satisfies necessary conditions for realizability as the square of the magnitude of a network function, we can determine a rational function $F(s)$ (often more than one) such that the square of the j-axis magnitude of $F(s)$ is equal to the given function; the function becomes unique when it is required to be minimum-phase.

In the present section we will discuss the possibility of a similar procedure for determining a rational function from a given function of frequency which is claimed to be an angle function. In Eq. (11) we wrote an expression for the angle of a transfer function $F(j\omega)$. Let us repeat it here.

$$j\phi(\omega) = \frac{1}{2} \ln \frac{F(j\omega)}{F(-j\omega)} \tag{55}$$

or

$$\frac{F(j\omega)}{F(-j\omega)} = \epsilon^{j2\phi(\omega)} \tag{56}$$

In the following discussion we shall assume that the function which is given is the tangent of $\phi(\omega)$, to which we will refer as the *tangent function*.* In addition, since we shall be using the ratio on the left side of Eq. (56) quite often, let us denote it with a single symbol. As a matter of fact, we would like s to take on all values rather than simply j-axis values in this ratio. Hence, we define

$$A(s) = \frac{F(s)}{F(-s)} \tag{57}$$

We will refer to this function simply as the A function.

With these preliminaries behind us, let us now tackle our problem. In the first place, note that for $\tan \phi(\omega)$ we can write

$$j \tan \phi(\omega) = \frac{\epsilon^{j\phi} - \epsilon^{-j\phi}}{\epsilon^{j\phi} + \epsilon^{-j\phi}} = \frac{\epsilon^{j2\phi} - 1}{\epsilon^{j2\phi} + 1} = \frac{A(j\omega) - 1}{A(j\omega) + 1} \tag{58}$$

The last step follows from Eqs. (56) and (57). If we now invert this last equation and solve for $A(j\omega)$, we get

$$A(j\omega) = \frac{1 + j \tan \phi(\omega)}{1 - j \tan \phi(\omega)} \tag{59}$$

Let us now inquire into the conditions that the tangent function must satisfy if it is to be a realizable function. Note that,

$$\tan \phi(\omega) = \frac{X(\omega)}{U(\omega)} \tag{60}$$

where U and X are the real and imaginary parts of the network function. We know that these are respectively even and odd functions of ω. Hence, $\tan \phi(\omega)$ must necessarily be an odd rational function. There are no other requirements that we can place on this function unless we specify whether the desired $F(s)$ is to be a driving point function or a transfer function.

If an odd rational function is prescribed, the first step will be to form $A(j\omega)$ according to Eq. (59). If we now replace $j\omega$ by s, this will im-

---

* Once again we assume that $\tan \phi(\omega)$ is given as a rational function of ω, and not as a curve to be approximated.

mediately give us the ratio of $F(s)$ to $F(-s)$ according to Eq. (57). The question now is, how do we extract $F(s)$ from this ratio? The situation here is not as simple as it was in the case of the magnitude function.

In order to carry on, let us write $F(s)$ as the ratio of two polynomials.

$$F(s) = \frac{P_1(s)}{P_2(s)} \tag{61}$$

Then $A(s)$ can be written

$$A(s) = \frac{F(s)}{F(-s)} = \frac{P_1(s)}{P_1(-s)} \frac{P_2(-s)}{P_2(s)} \tag{62}$$

Our problem can now be restated as the problem of finding $P_1(s)$ and $P_2(s)$ when the function on the right side of the last equation is known. Note that $A(s)$ will always have zeros in the right half plane and it will usually have poles in the right half plane also. It differs from an all-pass function in that it may have poles in the right half plane as well as zeros. On the other hand, it is similar to an all pass function in that each zero is the negative of a pole. As a matter of fact, it can be expressed as the ratio of two all-pass functions, but this has no utility for our present purpose. It can have neither zeros nor poles on the $j\omega$-axis, since, if $P_1(s)$ has a pair of such zeros, so also will $P_1(-s)$ so that they will cancel in the ratio; similarly if $P_2(s)$ has j-axis zeros.

Let us now consider assigning the poles of $A(s)$ to $P_1(-s)$ or $P_2(s)$. If $A(s)$ has any right half plane poles these must belong to $P_1(-s)$, since $P_2(s)$ cannot have right half plane zeros. On the other hand, the left half plane poles cannot uniquely be assigned to either $P_2(s)$ or $P_1(-s)$. If we assign one of the left half plane poles of $A(s)$ to $P_1(-s)$, then $P_1(s)$ will have the corresponding right half plane factor, indicating that the transfer function is nonminimum-phase. Of course, the distribution of poles and zeros will be dictated by the permissible degrees of numerator and denominator of $F(s)$.

Once $P_2(s)$ and $P_1(-s)$ have been established from the denominator of $A(s)$ it is not necessary to examine the numerator since the transfer function will now be known; it is only necessary to replace $-s$ by s in $P_1(-s)$ to get $P_1(s)$.

Let us now illustrate this procedure with an example. Suppose we are given

$$\tan \phi(\omega) = \frac{\omega^3 - 4\omega}{2 - 3\omega^2} \tag{63}$$

The first step is to substitute this into Eq. (59) to obtain $A(j\omega)$. The result is

$$A(j\omega) = \frac{2 - 3\omega^2 + j\omega^3 - j4\omega}{2 - 3\omega^2 - j\omega^3 + j4\omega} \tag{64}$$

If we now replace $j\omega$ by s, we get

$$A(s) = \frac{-s^3 + 3s^2 - 4s + 2}{s^3 + 3s^2 + 4s + 2} = \frac{(1 - s)(s^2 - 2s + 2)}{(s + 1)(s^2 + 2s + 2)} \tag{65}$$

We find that all the poles of $A(s)$ are in the left half plane, whereas all the zeros are in the right. Hence, there is no unique way to assign the zeros and poles of $F(s)$. Any one of the following functions will be suitable.

$$F_1(s) = \frac{1}{(s + 1)(s^2 + s + 2)} \tag{a}$$

$$F_2(s) = \frac{1 - s}{s^2 + s + 2} \tag{b} \tag{66}$$

$$F_3(s) = \frac{(s^2 - 2s + 1)}{s + 1} \tag{c}$$

Notice that the last two have right half plane zeros. Each of these functions will have the same angle for all values of ω, but their magnitudes will be quite different. If $F(s)$ is required to be minimum-phase, the answer is once again unique—in this case the first function of Eq. (66a).*

In our computations so far, we have assumed that $\phi(\omega)$ is specified to be a continuous function of ω. If however, the function $F(s)$ has either poles or zeros on the $j\omega$-axis the corresponding phase function $\phi(\omega)$ will have discontinuities of $\pm\pi$ at each pole and zero. In such cases we consider the discontinuities separately, applying the procedure above to the "continuous part" of the function. That is, we write

$$\phi(\omega) = \phi_c(\omega) + \sum_j \pm \pi u(\omega - \omega_j) \tag{67}$$

where $\phi_c(\omega)$ is a continuous function. The index j runs over all zeros and poles on the $j\omega$-axis; the minus sign applying to the poles.

We now have to identify the step discontinuities. For this, we remember our earlier discussion about the $F(j\omega)$ locus. $F(s)$ is regular in the right half plane. Therefore the locus of $F(j\omega)$ as ω varies from $-\infty$ *to* $+\infty$ must have the right half plane to its right as it goes through the origin or the point ∞ (think of the Riemann sphere for the latter). Therefore as we go through a zero on the $j\omega$-axis, in the direction of

---

* Even this uniqueness is only to within a constant multiplier. The angle is obviously independent of a real positive *gain constant*.

increasing ω, the angle of $F(s)$ *increases* abruptly by π; and as we go through a pole, $\phi(\omega)$ *decreases* by π. We can draw the same conclusions by examining a typical factor in $F(s)$ (pole or zero factor)

$$(s - j\omega_0)|_{s=j\omega} = j(\omega - \omega_0) \tag{68}$$

Obviously this factor changes from $-j$ to $+j$ as ω increases through ω_0. Thus we can restore all the poles and zeros of $F(s)$ on the $j\omega$-axis.

7.8 Calculation of Network Function from a Given Real Part

In the last two sections we discussed the possibility of determining a network function from a specified rational function of ω which is to be the j-axis magnitude of the function or the tangent of its angle on the $j\omega$-axis. We found that in most cases it is not possible to obtain a unique answer unless the function is minimum phase. Nevertheless, it is possible to calculate a number of functions that will satisfy the requirements. In the case of a specified magnitude, we are able to find a number of transfer functions which have the given j-axis magnitude but which differ from each other in their angles. Similarly, from a given tangent function, we are able to find a number of transfer functions which have the same angle on the $j\omega$ axis but which differ in magnitude.

In Chapter 6 we derived some relationships between the j-axis real and imaginary parts of a network function. These are in the form of integral formulas. Although they are quite useful for theoretical considerations, they are extremely unsatisfactory for computational purposes. In the present section we will discuss some computational procedures which will permit us to calculate a network function from its j-axis real part.

Again the question of uniqueness must be answered. Is a network function uniquely determined if its j-axis real part is known? We can very quickly think of several different networks whose network functions have the same real part, so that the question must be answered in the negative. As an example, suppose the desired function is a driving point admittance function. Consider the network shown in Fig. 20a. In part

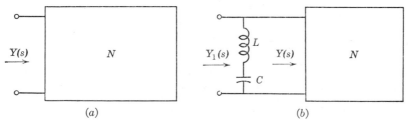

(a)   (b)

Fig. 20.   Two networks whose admittances have the same real part.

(b) of the figure an additional branch is connected at the input terminals. The admittance of the second network is

$$Y_1(s) = Y(s) + \frac{sC}{s^2 LC + 1} \tag{69}$$

Its j-axis real part is

$$Re[Y_1(j\omega)] = Re[Y(j\omega)] + Re\left[\frac{j\omega C}{1 - \omega^2 LC}\right] = Re[Y(j\omega)] \tag{70}$$

That is, the real parts of both admittances are the same, yet the admittances themselves are different. $Y_1(s)$ differs from $Y(s)$ by having a pair of poles on the $j\omega$-axis. If the real part is given, we can't tell whether to choose $Y(s)$ or $Y_1(s)$ corresponding to this real part. As a matter of fact, an infinite number of functions which differ from $Y(s)$ by having additional poles on the $j\omega$-axis will have the same real part on the $j\omega$-axis. What we can hope to do from a given real part, then is to find that function which has no poles on the $j\omega$ axis.* This is in agreement with the results of Chapter 6, where we required the network function to have no poles on the $j\omega$-axis in deriving those results.

Turn back to Eq. (7). The j-axis real part of a function is expressed as

$$U(\omega) = \tfrac{1}{2}[F(j\omega) + F(-j\omega)] \tag{71}$$

Suppose we now replace $j\omega$ by s on the right-hand side. This will no longer be the real part of $F(s)$. However, it *will* be the *even part* of $F(s)$. That is, if we express $F(s)$ as

$$F(s) = \text{``Ev''}\, F(s) + \text{``Odd''}\, F(s) \tag{72}$$

where the notation "Ev" means "even part of $F(s)$" and "Odd" means "odd part of $F(s)$," then it will follow that

$$\tfrac{1}{2}[F(s) + F(-s)] = \text{``Ev''}\, F(s) \tag{73}$$

The even part of $F(s)$ is *not* related to the real part of $F(s)$, *except when* $s = j\omega$; then they are the same.

When the j-axis real part, which is $U(\omega)$, is specified, we replace $j\omega$ by s (or ω^2 by $-s^2$). The result is the even part of $F(s)$. The question now is how to find $F(s)$ from its even part. Note from Eq. (73) that "Ev" $F(s)$ has the poles of both $F(s)$ and $F(-s)$; those of $F(s)$ are in the left half plane, whereas those of $F(-s)$ are in the right. Note also that if $F(s)$ has a nonzero value at infinity, $F(-s)$ will have this same value. Now it becomes clear how we can find $F(s)$; we expand "Ev" $F(s)$

---

* Such a function is a *minimum susceptance* function if it is an admittance, and a *minimum reactance* function if it is an impedance. This condition on driving point functions is the analog of the minimum-phase condition on the transfer function.

in partial fractions and group all the terms contributed by poles in the left half plane. If there is a constant term in the expansion, we add half of this to the group. Finally, we multiply by 2 and this is $F(s)$. This procedure was first described by Bode, and we shall refer to it as the Bode procedure. We don't really need to find the entire partial fraction expansion of "Ev" $F(s)$. All we need do is to find the principal parts at the left half plane poles.

The same result can be obtained in an alternative manner by a procedure which was first developed by Gewertz. To outline this procedure, let us write $F(s)$ as the ratio of two polynomials

$$F(s) = \frac{a_0 + a_1 s + \cdots + a_m s^m}{b_0 + b_1 s + \cdots + b_n s^n} = \frac{m_1 + n_1}{m_2 + n_2} \qquad (74)$$

where the m's refer to the even parts of the numerator and denominator and the n's refer to the odd parts. We would like to be able to express the even part of $F(s)$ in terms of the even and odd parts of the numerator and denominator. Suppose we multiply numerator and denominator by $m_2 - n_2$ (this is equivalent to rationalizing when $s = j\omega$). The result will be

$$F(s) = \frac{m_1 m_2 - n_1 n_2}{m_2{}^2 - n_2{}^2} + \frac{m_2 n_1 - m_1 n_2}{m_2{}^2 - n_2{}^2} \qquad (75)$$

The first term on the right is obviously even, whereas the second term is odd. Hence, we can write

$$\text{"Ev"} \, F(s) = \frac{m_1 m_2 - n_1 n_2}{m_2{}^2 - n_2{}^2} \qquad (76)$$

This is the function which is given (it is obtained by setting $\omega^2 = -s^2$ in the given j-axis real part). It will be given in the form

$$\text{"Ev"} F(s) = \frac{A_0 + A_1 s^2 + \cdots + A_m s^{2m}}{B_0 + B_1 s^2 + \cdots + B_n s^{2n}} \qquad (77)$$

Let us first go to work on the denominator. We have already seen that the poles of "Ev" $F(s)$ are those of both $F(s)$ and $F(-s)$. The ones belonging to $F(s)$ are those that lie in the left half plane. The procedure here is the same as the one we discussed in connection with finding a network function from its magnitude. We factor the denominator of "Ev" $F(s)$ and assign all the left half plane factors to $F(s)$.

Turn now to the numerator on the right side of Eq. (76). In the previous step we determined m_2 and n_2 so that only m_1 and n_1 are unknown. Suppose we now write $F(s)$ as a ratio of polynomials as in Eq. (74) with unknown coefficients in the numerator but with known denominator coefficients. We then form the expression $m_1 m_2 - n_1 n_2$ and set it equal to the numerator of the given function in Eq. (77). Equating coefficients of like powers of s on the two sides of this equation will permit us to solve for the unknowns. Note that three sets of coefficients are involved: the small a's, the capital A's and the small b's. Of these the last two sets are known at this point; only the small a's are unknown.

Let us carry out the process just indicated. Identifying m_1, m_2, n_1 and n_2 from Eq. (74), we can write

$$m_1 m_2 - n_1 n_2 = (a_0 + a_2 s^2 + \cdots)(b_0 + b_2 s^2 + \cdots)$$
$$- (a_1 s + a_3 s^3 + \cdots)(b_1 s + b_3 s^3 + \cdots)$$
$$= A_0 + A_1 s^2 + \cdots A_m s^{2m} \tag{78}$$

Equating the coefficients yields

$$A_0 = a_0 b_0$$
$$A_1 = a_0 b_2 + b_0 a_2 - a_1 b_1$$
$$A_2 = a_0 b_4 + a_2 b_2 + a_4 b_0 - a_1 b_3 - a_3 b_1$$

. . . .

$$A_k = \sum_{j=-k}^{k} (-1)^{k+j} a_{k+j} b_{k-j} \tag{79}$$

To find the unknown a's, we must solve this set of linear equations simultaneously.

Let us now illustrate these procedures. Suppose the following function is given as the real part of a network function.

$$U(\omega) = \frac{1}{1 + \omega^6} \tag{80}$$

The first step is to replace ω^2 by $-s^2$. The resulting function will be "Ev" $F(s)$.

$$\text{"Ev"} \ F(s) = \frac{1}{1 - s^6} = \frac{1}{(s + 1)(s^2 + s + 1)(1 - s)(s^2 - s + 1)} \tag{81}$$

We have already discussed the pole locations of this particular function; it is a third-order Butterworth response function, and the denominator is easily factored. From the left half plane poles, we can immediately write the denominator of the desired $F(s)$ as

$$m_2 + n_2 = (s + 1)(s^2 + s + 1) = s^3 + 2s^2 + 2s + 1 \tag{82}$$

Since the given real part function is zero at infinity, this must also be true of the desired network function (why?). Hence, the numerator of $F(s)$ must be of the form

$$m_1 + n_1 = a_2 s^2 + a_1 s + a_0 \qquad (83)$$

Using the last two equations in Eq. (78) and the fact that all the capital A coefficients are zero except A_0 which is unity, we get

$$1 = a_0$$
$$0 = 2a_0 + a_2 - 2a_1 \qquad (84)$$
$$0 = 2a_2 - a_1$$

Finally, solving these equations, we get $a_0 = 1$, $a_1 = \frac{4}{3}$ and $a_2 = \frac{2}{3}$. The desired function is, therefore,

$$F(s) = \frac{1}{3} \frac{2s^2 + 4s + 3}{s^3 + 2s^2 + 2s + 1} \qquad (85)$$

As for the Bode procedure, note that the given function will have no constant term in its partial fraction expansion. So it is only required to calculate the residues of "Ev" $F(s)$ in Eq. (80) at the left half plane poles. Of course, the final result will be the same. The details are left to you.

7.9 Integral Relationships Between Real and Imaginary Parts

Let us now contemplate our achievements in relating the components of a network function (by components of a function we will mean one of the quantities: real part, imaginary part, magnitude, gain, or angle). In the first place, the driving point and transfer functions of the networks under consideration are analytic functions of a complex variable. Hence, their real and imaginary parts are related through the Cauchy–Riemann equations. However, these are implicit relationships, and one component is not expressed directly in terms of the other.

In the preceding chapter explicit relationships were found relating the real and imaginary parts of a function satisfying certain additional conditions. This was done by first relating the frequency response and the time response. Finally, in the last three sections of this chapter, we were able to determine a network function as a rational function of s by algebraic methods, given one of the components of the function as a rational function. The drawback here is that the given component of the desired function must already be in a realizable rational form. If, say, the real part is given graphically, or even analytically in some other form, we must first find a realizable rational approximation before we can proceed. In this section we shall discuss a number of relationships first used in network theory by Bode, which are generally referred to as "Bode formulas," that enable us to get some information about one component when the other component is given merely as a graph. In addition to this advantage, these formulas have many useful implications, as we shall see.

Since we are dealing with analytic functions of a complex variable, we should be able to use our knowledge of such functions to establish additional relationships among the components. One point of departure might be Cauchy's integral formula (see appendix) which states

$$F(s) = \frac{1}{2\pi j} \int_C \frac{F(z)}{z - s} \, dz \qquad (86)$$

In this expression C is a closed contour within and on which $F(s)$ is regular, and z represents points on the contour, whereas s is any point inside. If we let the contour be a circle and express both z and s in polar coordinates, we shall be able to express the real and imaginary parts of $F(s)$ in terms of either its real part or its imaginary part on the circle. Finally, by means of a transformation the circle is mapped into the imaginary axis. The resulting expressions relating the real and imaginary parts are referred to as Hilbert transforms.*

An alternative approach is to start with Cauchy's integral theorem (see appendix). This theorem states that the contour integral of a function around a path within and on which the function is regular will vanish. In order to apply this theorem, two things must be known: the integration contour and the function to be integrated. In the present problem, the contour of integration should include the $j\omega$-axis, since we want the final result to involve the j-axis real and imaginary parts of a network function. Since the functions we are dealing with are regular in the entire right half plane, then the contour of integration we will choose will consist of the $j\omega$-axis and an infinite semicircular arc in the right half plane. By Cauchy's theorem the complete contour integral will be zero. Hence, it remains to calculate the contributions of each part of the contour.

Let $F(s)$ be a network function, either driving point or transfer, and in the usual way write

$$F(j\omega) = U(\omega) + jX(\omega) \qquad (87)$$

$$\ln F(j\omega) = \alpha(\omega) + j\phi(\omega) \qquad (88)$$

where $\alpha(\omega) = \ln|F(j\omega)|$ is the gain function, and $\phi(\omega)$ is the angle

---

* See E. A. Guillemin, *Mathematics of Circuit Analysis*, Wiley, 1949, New York, for a detailed discussion of these.

function. If $F(s)$ is a driving-point function it will have neither zeros nor poles in the right half plane. Hence, ln $F(s)$ will be regular there. If $F(s)$ is a transfer function, then ln $F(s)$ will be regular in the right half plane *only if $F(s)$ is minimum-phase.* Hence, the results we develop will apply both to $F(s)$ and to ln $F(s)$ so long as $F(s)$ is minimum-phase.

Let us now consider possible poles of $F(s)$ on the $j\omega$-axis. We know that any such poles must be simple. In carrying out the contour integration such poles must be by-passed by a small indentation. The contribution of this indentation to the total integral is $2\pi j$ times half the residue of the integrand at the pole (see Appendix). Our objective is to be able to obtain expressions relating the real part of a network function to the imaginary part, so that when one of these is given, the other can be calculated. Thus, we are not likely to know the residues at j-axis poles. Hence, we will assume that $F(s)$ has no poles on the $j\omega$-axis; this includes the points zero and infinity as well, so that $F(s)$ is assumed regular at zero and infinity.

If $F(s)$ has a pole on the $j\omega$-axis, then ln $F(s)$ will have a logarithmic singularity there. If the integrand in question involves ln $F(s)$, we shall again indent the contour about this singularity. But because the singularity is logarithmic, this indentation will contribute nothing to the contour integral (see Appendix). Hence, in case the integrand we choose involves ln $F(s)$, we can permit $F(s)$ to have simple poles on the $j\omega$-axis. In the following discussion we will always take the function in the integrand to be $F(s)$. However, identical results apply if we replace $F(s)$ by ln $F(s)$.

Let us now consider integrating a network function $F(s)$, which is regular on the $j\omega$-axis including zero and infinity, around the contour shown in Fig. 21a, which consists of the entire $j\omega$ axis and an infinite

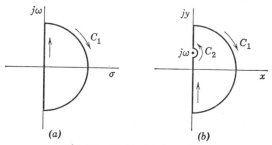

Fig. 21.   Path of integration.

semicircular arc to the right. By Cauchy's theorem the integral will be zero. Our procedure will be to evaluate the contributions of those parts of the contour which we can evaluate, and then express the remaining parts in terms of these. With these ideas, we can readily appreciate that we will not be able to obtain the type of relationship we are looking for with $F(s)$ alone as the integrand. No particular point on the $j\omega$-axis is singled out and attention directed thereto.

Suppose we divide $F(s)$ by $s - j\omega_0$ before integrating, where ω_0 is any value of ω. This will put a pole of the integrand on the $j\omega$-axis. In order to apply Cauchy's theorem, we shall have to by-pass this pole with a small semicircular arc C_2, as shown in Fig. 21b. The complete contour now consists of three parts, and the contribution of arc C_2 will have to be evaluated. This will focus attention on the value of $F(s)$ at $s = j\omega_0$. Note that the result of the integration will not be a function of s, which is only a dummy variable of integration, but of ω_0, which is an arbitrary point on the $j\omega$-axis. It will be convenient to use a different symbol for the dummy variable; let us use $z = x + jy$. Then the point $j\omega_0$ can be relabelled $j\omega$.

If $F(s)$ is a network function which is regular on the entire $j\omega$ axis as well as the right half plane, application of Cauchy's theorem leads to the result

$$\oint \frac{F(z)}{z - j\omega}\, dz = 0 \tag{89}$$

where the closed contour is the one shown in Fig. 21b.

The complete contour consists of three parts: the large semicircle C_1, the small semicircular indentation C_2 about the point $z = j\omega$, and the imaginary axis. The contribution of the small indentation to the overall integral is $2\pi j$ times half the residue of the integrand at $z = j\omega$, which is simply $F(j\omega)$. (See Appendix.) To compute the contribution of the "infinite" semicircle, let us initially assume it to be of finite radius, with $z = R_0 \epsilon^{j\theta}$. Then

$$\int_{C_1} \frac{F(z)}{z - j\omega}\, dz = \int_{C_1} \frac{F(R_0\epsilon^{j\theta})}{R_0\epsilon^{j\theta} - j\omega}\, jR_0\epsilon^{j\theta}d\theta \xrightarrow[R_0 \to \infty]{} jF(\infty)\int_{\pi/2}^{-\pi/2} d\theta$$

$$= -j\pi F(\infty) \tag{90}$$

where $F(\infty)$ is the value of $F(s)$ at $s = \infty$. Thus as R approaches ∞, the integral on C_1 approaches $-j\pi F(\infty)$. Since the imaginary part must be zero at infinity, $F(\infty)$ is also equal to $U(\infty)$.

Now it remains to consider the remainder of the contour. This can be written

$$\lim_{\substack{R_0 \to \infty \\ r \to 0}} \left[\int_{-R_0}^{\omega - r} \frac{F(jy)}{y - \omega}\, dy + \int_{\omega + r}^{R_0} \frac{F(jy)}{y - \omega}\, dy \right] = \int_{-\infty}^{\infty} \frac{F(jy)}{y - \omega}\, dy \tag{91}$$

Note that the integration along the imaginary axis must avoid the pole at $z = j\omega$ in a symmetrical manner. This will yield the *principal value* of the integral on the right. In all the subsequent integrals we must keep this point in mind. Now collecting all these results and substituting into Eq. (89) we can write

$$\int_{-\infty}^{\infty} \frac{F(jy)}{y - \omega} \, dy = j\pi[F(\infty) - F(j\omega)] \tag{92}$$

If we now write $F(j\omega)$ and $F(jy)$ in terms of real and imaginary parts, then equate reals and imaginaries, we get finally

$$U(\omega) = U(\infty) - \frac{1}{\pi} \int_{-\infty}^{\infty} \frac{X(y)}{y - \omega} \, dy \tag{93}$$

$$X(\omega) = \frac{1}{\pi} \int_{-\infty}^{\infty} \frac{U(y)}{y - \omega} \, dy \tag{94}$$

We are leaving the algebraic details of these steps for you to work out.

The message carried by these two expressions is very important. The second one states that when a function is specified to be the real part of a network function over all frequencies, the imaginary part of the function is completely determined, assuming the network function has no poles on the $j\omega$-axis. Similarly, if the imaginary part is specified over all frequencies, the real part is completely determined to within an additive constant.

Remember that the same results apply if $F(s)$ is replaced by its logarithm. However, now we must require that $F(s)$ be minimum-phase (if it represents a transfer function). On the other hand we can relax the requirement of regularity of $F(s)$ on the $j\omega$-axis. A simple pole of $F(s)$ on the $j\omega$-axis becomes a logarithmic singularity of $\ln F(s)$, and such a singularity will contribute nothing to the integral (see Appendix). Thus, for minimum-phase transfer functions Eqs. (93) and (94) relate the gain and phase functions over all frequencies.

Let us now obtain alternative forms for the two basic expressions in Eqs. (93) and (94) which will throw additional light on the relationships and will bring out points which are not at once apparent from these expressions.

Remember that the real and imaginary parts are even and odd functions of frequency, respectively. Let us use this fact. Equation (94) can be written

$$X(\omega) = \frac{1}{\pi} \int_{-\infty}^{0} \frac{U(y)}{y - \omega} \, dy + \frac{1}{\pi} \int_{0}^{\infty} \frac{U(y)}{y - \omega} \, dy \tag{95}$$

In the first of these integrals, replace y by $-y$ and change the limits accordingly. The result is

$$\int_{-\infty}^{0} \frac{U(y)}{y - \omega}\, dy = \int_{\infty}^{0} \frac{U(-y)}{-(y + \omega)}\, (-dy) = -\int_{0}^{\infty} \frac{U(y)}{y + \omega}\, dy \qquad (96)$$

The last step follows from the fact that $U(y) = U(-y)$. Substituting this into Eq. (95) we get

$$X(\omega) = \frac{1}{\pi} \int_{0}^{\infty} U(y) \left[\frac{1}{y - \omega} - \frac{1}{y + \omega} \right] dy = \frac{2\omega}{\pi} \int_{0}^{\infty} \frac{U(y)}{y^2 - \omega^2}\, dy \qquad (97)$$

In a completely similar way, starting with Eq. (93) we will get

$$U(\omega) = U(\infty) - \frac{2}{\pi} \int_{0}^{\infty} \frac{y X(y)}{y^2 - \omega^2}\, dy \qquad (98)$$

In the last two expressions it still appears that the integrand goes to infinity on the path of integration at the point $y = \omega$. This is really illusory, since we must understand the integral as the principal value. Even this illusory difficulty can be removed if we note by direct integration that

$$\int_{0}^{\infty} \frac{dy}{y^2 - \omega^2}\, dy = 0 \qquad (99)$$

again using the principal value of the integral. Hence, we can subtract $U(\omega)/(y^2 - \omega^2)$ from the integrand in Eq. (97) and $\omega X(\omega)/(y^2 - \omega^2)$ from the integrand in Eq. (98) without changing the values of these integrals. The results of these steps will be

$$U(\omega) = U(\infty) - \frac{2}{\pi} \int_{0}^{\infty} \frac{y X(y) - \omega X(\omega)}{y^2 - \omega^2}\, dy \qquad (100)$$

$$X(\omega) = \frac{2\omega}{\pi} \int_{0}^{\infty} \frac{U(y) - U(\omega)}{y^2 - \omega^2}\, dy \qquad (101)$$

A very important feature of the results which we have established is the fact that it is unimportant to have the real part (or the imaginary part) as a realizable rational function. Corresponding to any given real part, whether in analytical or in graphical form, an imaginary part can be computed from the integral. As a matter of fact, the expressions are quite useful when a desired real part is specified in a vague sort of way and it is desired to obtain an approximate behavior of the imaginary part.

For example, suppose it is desired to know the approximate behavior of the angle function in the pass band of a low-pass filter. In this discussion we will interpret U and X to represent the gain α and the angle ϕ, respectively.   In the pass band the gain is approximately zero up to some frequency ω_0.   Hence, in Eq. (101) the lower limit becomes ω_0. Furthermore, the point ω, which lies in the pass band, is less than ω_0, so that in the integrand we can neglect ω compared with y, since y varies from ω_0 to infinity.   Furthermore, the pass band gain $U(\omega)$ is zero.   Thus, an approximate value is given by

$$X(\omega) \doteq \frac{2\omega}{\pi} \int_{\omega_0}^{\infty} \frac{U(y)}{y^2}\, dy \qquad (102)$$

Now make the change of variable $y = 1/p$; then $dy/y^2 = -dp$.   After appropriately modifying the limits of integration as well, this equation becomes

$$X(\omega) \doteq \frac{2\omega}{\pi} \int_{0}^{1/\omega_0} U(1/p)\, dp \qquad (103)$$

Note that the integral is no longer a function of ω, and, for a given value of the band edge ω_0, it will be simply a constant.   Thus, the angle will be approximately a linear function of ω within the pass band.*   Of course, the approximation will get progressively worse as we approach the band edge, since then ω can no longer be neglected in comparison to y in the integrand.

The relationships between the real and imaginary parts can be placed in a still different form which is more convenient for computation.   This form is most relevant when $\ln F(s)$ (the gain and angle) is involved, rather then a network function itself.   The first step is to change to a logarithmic frequency variable according to Eq. (18).   However, it is more useful to use the natural logarithmic base rather than base 10. Accordingly, let us define

$$y/\omega = \epsilon^u; \qquad u = \ln(y/\omega) \qquad (104)$$

To be completely consistent, we should use a symbol other than u for the logarithmic variable defined here, since it is different from the one defined in Eq. (18).   One difference is that here we have "normalized" the frequency variable by setting y/ω, instead of y, equal to ϵ^u.   The second difference is in the base of the logarithm, which simply introduces a constant factor, $\ln 10 = 2.3$, in the variable here defined, when compared with the u in Eq. (18).   In order to avoid introducing new notation

---

* Such a linear phase characteristic corresponds to a constant time delay in the transmission of sinusoidal functions over this range of frequencies.   Therefore for signals that have essentially only this frequency range, we get a distortionless transmission.   For this reason, a linear phase characteristic is desirable.

we will use the same symbol for the logarithmic frequency variable, always remembering the slight differences involved.

Let us now start with Eq. (101) and perform some preliminary manipulations utilizing the change of frequency variable.

$$X(\omega) = \frac{2}{\pi} \int_0^\infty \frac{U(y) - U(\omega)}{(y/\omega) - (\omega/y)} \frac{dy}{y}$$

$$= \frac{2}{\pi} \int_{-\infty}^\infty \frac{U(y) - U(\omega)}{\epsilon^u - \epsilon^{-u}} du$$

$$= \frac{1}{\pi} \int_{-\infty}^\infty \frac{U(y) - U(\omega)}{\sinh u} du \tag{105}$$

Note the change in the lower limit, since $u = -\infty$ when $y = 0$. The argument of $U(y)$ has been retained as y, although in reality we should write it as $U(\omega\epsilon^u)$. Alternatively, we can define a new function $U_1(u)$ which is equal to $U(\omega\epsilon^u)$, and use this in the integrand. However, this introduces additional new notation, which is a disadvantage. One thing we should *not* do is simply to write $U(u)$ instead of $U(y)$. In all the subsequent equations, we shall retain $U(y)$ in the integrand with the understanding that we mean to convert to a function of u by the substitution $y = \omega\epsilon^u$ before performing any operations.

As the next step, we integrate the last form by parts. Using the general formula

$$\int a\,db = ab - \int b\,da \tag{106}$$

we set

$$a = U(y) - U(\omega); \qquad db = \frac{du}{\sinh u}$$

$$da = \frac{dU(y)}{du} du; \qquad b = -\ln \coth \frac{u}{2} \tag{107}$$

Hence, Eq. (105) becomes

$$X(\omega) = -\frac{1}{\pi} \left\{ [U(y) - U(\omega)] \ln \coth \frac{u}{2} \right\} \Big|_{-\infty}^{\infty} + \frac{1}{\pi} \int_{-\infty}^\infty \frac{dU(y)}{du} \ln \coth \frac{u}{2} du$$

$$\tag{108}$$

Note that $\coth u/2$ is an odd function of u, being strictly positive when u is positive and strictly negative when u is negative. Hence, its logarithm for negative u will be complex, the imaginary part being simply π. For negative u it can be written

$$\ln \coth u/2 = \ln \coth |u|/2 + j\pi, \quad u < 0 \tag{109}$$

When $u = +\infty$, $\ln \coth u/2 = 0$, and when $u = -\infty$, $\ln \coth u = j\pi$. Hence, the integrated part of the last equation becomes simply $j[U(0) - U(\omega)]$. Now consider the remaining integral. If we use Eq. (109) for negative values of u, the result will be

$$\int_{-\infty}^{\infty} \frac{dU(y)}{du} \ln \coth \frac{u}{2} \, du = \int_{-\infty}^{\infty} \frac{dU(y)}{du} \ln \coth \frac{|u|}{2} \, du$$

$$+ j\pi \int_{-\infty}^{0} \frac{dU(y)}{du} \, du$$

$$= \int_{-\infty}^{\infty} \frac{dU(y)}{du} \ln \coth \frac{|u|}{2} \, du$$

$$+ j\pi U(y) \Big|_{u=-\infty}^{u=0} \tag{110}$$

Finally, using all of these results in Eq. (108), we will get

$$X(\omega) = \frac{1}{\pi} \int_{-\infty}^{\infty} \frac{dU(y)}{du} \ln \coth \frac{|u|}{2} \, du \tag{111}$$

This equation is quite easy to interpret even though it looks somewhat complicated. Note that the real part U is not an even function of the logarithmic frequency u and so, it is not possible to integrate over only half the range. The equation states that the imaginary part at any frequency depends on the slope of the real part at all frequencies (when plotted against logarithmic frequency), the relative importance of different frequencies being determined by the weighting factor

$$\ln \coth \frac{|u|}{2} = \ln \left| \frac{y + \omega}{y - \omega} \right| \tag{112}$$

This function is shown plotted in Fig. 22. It rises sharply in the vicinity of $u = 0$ ($y = \omega$), falling off to very small values on both sides of this point. This means that most of the contribution to the imaginary part at a frequency ω comes from the slope of the real part in the immediate vicinity of ω.

Another useful form can be obtained by simply adding and subtracting the slope evaluated at $u = 0$ ($y = \omega$) under the integral in Eq. (111). We will leave the details of this operation to you. The result will be

$$X(\omega) = \frac{\pi}{2} \frac{dU(\omega)}{du} + \frac{1}{\pi} \int_{-\infty}^{\infty} \left[\frac{dU(y)}{du} - \frac{dU(\omega)}{du} \right] \ln \coth \frac{|u|}{2} \, du \tag{113}$$

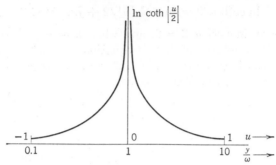

Fig. 22.   Plot of weighting factor $\ln \coth \dfrac{|u|}{2} = \ln \left| \dfrac{y + \omega}{y - \omega} \right|$.

Note that by $dU(\omega)/du$ we mean the slope of the real part as a function of u, evaluated when $u = 0$ $(y = \omega)$.

Suppose X refers to the angle and U to the gain function. The slope $dU(\omega)/du$ is measured in nepers per unit change of u. A unit change of u means a change in frequency by a factor ϵ, which is $1/\ln 10$ decade. Thus, a gain slope of 20 db per decade is the same as a neper per unit change in u. This means that if the gain slope is expressed in db per decade we should first divide by 20 before using it in this equation.

Let us continue interpreting U and X as gain and phase. We see that the angle at any frequency is $\pi/2$ times the gain slope at the same frequency plus another term given by the integral. If the gain is a continuous function, then the difference which appears in the integrand will be small in the vicinity of $y = \omega$, just where the weighting factor has large values. Hence, in this case the contribution of the integral to the angle will always be small. As a first approximation, then, we can say that the angle will have a value of $\pi/2$ radians whenever the gain slope is 20 db per decade, a value of π radians when the gain slope is 40 db per decade, etc.

Now suppose a gain function is given in graphical form. We can first approximate the curve by a series of straight line segments. An approximation to the (minimum-phase) angle function corresponding to the given gain function can now be quickly sketched according to the discussion of the last paragraph.

As an example of this procedure, suppose the Bode plot shown in Fig. 23 is given. An approximate sketch of the angle is the discontinous function shown by the solid lines in the figure. The actual angle function might have the form shown by the dotted curve.

The expressions which we have obtained so far have related the imaginary part at any frequency to the real part at all frequencies;

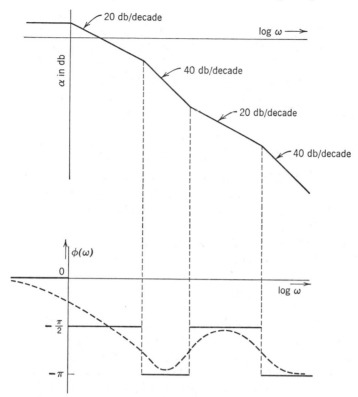

Fig. 23.   Approximate angle corresponding to a given gain function.

or the real part at any frequency to the imaginary part at all frequencies. We should be able to find limiting forms for these expressions when frequency approaches zero or infinity.

Consider, first of all, Eq. (100) when ω approaches zero. This immediately leads to the result

$$\int_0^\infty \frac{X(y)}{y}\, dy = \frac{\pi}{2}[U(\infty) - U(0)] \tag{114}$$

This expression is referred to as the *reactance integral theorem* (it is also called the *phase area theorem* since the result remains valid when $F(s)$ is replaced by its logarithm). In fact, if we make the change to logarithmic frequency as in Eq. (18), then dy/y becomes du and the last equation can be written

$$\int_0^\infty X(y)\, du = \frac{\pi}{2}[U(\infty) - U(0)] \tag{115}$$

Thus, we see that the area under the curve of the imaginary part, when plotted against logarithmic frequency, is proportional to the net change in the real part between zero and infinite frequency.

Next let us multiply both sides of Eq. (101) by ω and then take the limit as ω approaches infinity. Remember that the upper limit on the integral means that we integrate up to R_0 and then let R_0 approach infinity. Thus, Eq. (101) becomes

$$\lim_{\omega \to \infty} \omega X(\omega) = \frac{2}{\pi} \lim_{\omega \to \infty} \left[\lim_{R_0 \to \infty} \int_0^{R_0} \frac{U(y) - U(\omega)}{y^2/\omega^2 - 1} \, dy \right] \qquad (116)$$

There are two limiting operations involved on the right-hand side. If we interchange these two operations, the expression can be evaluated readily. But we must inquire whether this interchange is permissible. The answer is affirmative if the integral is uniformly convergent for all values of ω, which it is. Hence interchanging the two operations and taking the limits leads to

$$\int_0^\infty [U(y) - U(\infty)] \, dy = -\frac{\pi}{2} \lim_{\omega \to \infty} \omega X(\omega) \qquad (117)$$

The result expressed by this equation is referred to as the *resistance-integral theorem*. (It is also called the *attenuation integral theorem*, since the result remains valid if $F(s)$ is replaced by its logarithm.) If the asymptotic behavior of the imaginary part of a network function is specified, then no matter how the j-axis real part behaves with frequency, the area under the curve of the real part, with the horizontal axis shifted upward by an amount $U(\infty)$, must remain constant. Looking at it from the opposite viewpoint, when the integral of the real part of a function over all frequencies is specified, then the infinite frequency behavior of the imaginary part is fixed.

Consider the special case in which $F(s)$ has a simple zero at infinity; then $F(\infty) = U(\infty) = 0$. Observe that in this case

$$-\lim_{\omega \to \infty} \omega X(\omega) = \lim_{s \to \infty} sF(s) \qquad (118)$$

But, according to the initial value theorem, the limit on the right hand side is simply the initial value of the impulse response of the network represented by $F(s)$. In this case, then, Eq. (117) becomes

$$\int_0^\infty U(\omega) \, d\omega = \frac{\pi}{2} \lim_{s \to \infty} sF(s) = \frac{\pi}{2} r_\delta(0) \qquad (119)$$

where $r_\delta(t) = \mathcal{L}^{-1} F(s)$ is the impulse response. Note that the dummy variable has been changed to ω to suggest the physical meaning.

The resistance integral theorem can be used to develop an important result about a particular class of networks. Consider the impedance of the network shown in Fig. 24a. The feature of this network is that its terminals are shunted by a capacitance. This impedance is

$$Z(s) = \frac{Z_1(s)}{CsZ_1(s) + 1}$$

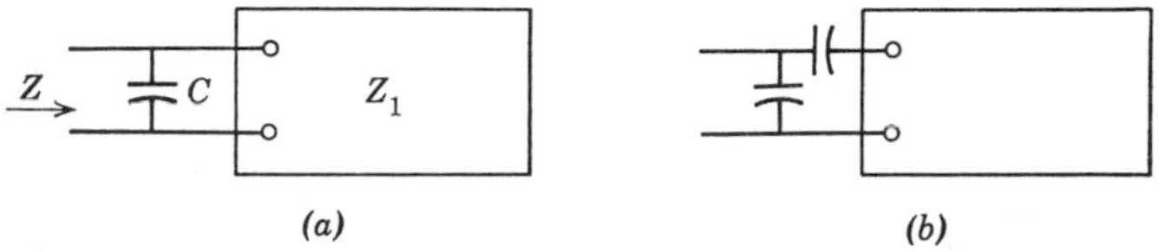

(a)   (b)

Fig. 24.   Illustration of resistance integral theorem.

We see that $Z(s)$ will have a simple zero at infinity no matter what the impedance $Z_1(s)$ may be. We will still require that $Z(s)$ be regular on the $j\omega$-axis, including the origin. Note that, even if $Z_1(s)$ has poles on the $j\omega$-axis, $Z(s)$ will not, except if $Z_1(s)$ has a pole at $s = 0$. Hence, we will not permit $Z_1(s)$ to have a pole at $s = 0$. This means that a network such as the one shown in Fig. 24b will be excluded. Similarly $Z_1(s)$ should not have a zero at infinity. If it does, then the network can be represented by one shunted by a capacitance. This capacitance can then be lumped with C.

In the present case Eq. (118) is valid with $F(s) = Z(s)$. When, we evaluate the limit, we get

$$\lim_{s \to \infty} sZ(s) = \lim_{s \to \infty} \frac{sZ_1(s)}{CsZ_1(s) + 1} = \frac{1}{C} \tag{120}$$

Hence, for this case Eq. (119) becomes

$$\int_0^\infty U(\omega)\, d\omega = \pi/2C \tag{121}$$

Thus, the capacitance across the input terminals limits the area under the curve of the real part.

Remember that this result applies only to impedance functions which have no poles on the $j\omega$-axis. If a function does have poles on the $j\omega$-axis, the contour of integration must be indented around these poles and the contribution of these poles must be taken into account. If you go through the preceding development carefully, you will find that additional terms will be subtracted from the right side of Eq. (121), these terms being proportional to the residues of $F(s)$ at the poles on the $j\omega$-axis. In Chapter 9 we will show that all such residues of driving point functions are real and positive. Hence, when $Z(s)$ has poles on the $j\omega$-axis, the right side of Eq. (121) is reduced. This means that we can write

$$\int_0^\infty U(\omega)\, d\omega \leq \pi/2C \qquad (122)$$

which will apply for any driving-point impedance function whether or not it has poles on the $j\omega$-axis, so long as the corresponding network has a shunt capacitance C across the input terminals.

In deriving the integral relationships of this section we started with the integrand in Eq. (89) and the contour shown in Fig. 21. The same expressions can be derived in alternate ways using different integrands but the same basic contour of integration. Of course, if the integrands introduce additional poles in the $j\omega$-axis, we must avoid these poles by small indentations. For example, the resistance integral theorem can be derived in short order by integrating the function $[F(s) - U(\infty)]$ around the basic contour. Similarly, the reactance integral theorem follows readily when we integrate the function $F(s)/s$ around the basic contour with an indentation around the origin.

From this discussion it seems likely that additional relationships between the real and imaginary parts can be established by choosing different integrands. In fact a great variety of relationships can be derived, but we have already presented the most important and useful ones. If we consider the two cases mentioned in the preceding paragraph, the criterion for choosing an integrand appears to be to choose it in such a way that the term in which the known component of the network function appears is an even function of frequency, whereas the term in which the unknown component appears is an odd function. In this way the unknown component will disappear from the integration along the $j\omega$-axis and will appear only in the contributions from the indentations and from the infinite arc. It seems that this consideration in choosing an integrand will apply quite generally.

So far in this section we have found that, for a suitably restricted network function, when the real part is specified over all frequencies, the imaginary part is completely determined. Similarly, when the imaginary part is specified over all frequencies, the real part is completely determined (to within a constant). The question now may be asked: suppose the real part is specified over some frequency intervals and the imaginary part over the remainder of the entire frequency spectrum; what then?

Instead of considering this problem in a completely general form, let us suppose that the real part is known for all frequencies less than ω_0

and the imaginary part for all frequencies greater than ω_0. We wish to find an expression which will give the unknown parts of the two components. The discussion concerning the choice of integrand suggests that if we can choose an integrand which changes character at ω_0 so that below ω_0 the term involving the real part is even while above ω_0 the term involving the imaginary part is even, our problem will be solved. What we need is a multi-valued function in the integrand.

Suppose we choose the following function as integrand

$$\frac{F(z)}{(z^2 + \omega^2)\sqrt{1 + z^2/\omega_0^2}}$$

Again $z = x + jy$ is taken as a dummy variable. The irrational factor in the denominator is multivalued, with branch points at $z = \pm j\omega_0$. We must choose the branch cut in such a way that the integration along the j-axis will stay on a single sheet of the Riemann surface. This will be the case if, when $z = jy$, we take

$\sqrt{1 - y^2/\omega_0^2}$ real and positive for $-\omega_0 < y < \omega_0$

$\sqrt{1 - y^2/\omega_0^2}$ imaginary and positive for $y > \omega_0$

$\sqrt{1 - y^2/\omega_0^2}$ imaginary and negative for $y < -\omega_0$

With this choice, $\sqrt{1 - y^2/\omega_0^2}$ is an even function in the interval $-\omega_0 < y < \omega_0$, whereas over the remainder of the axis it is odd.

The contour of integration consists of the basic contour shown in Fig. 21 with indentations at $z = \pm j\omega$. In the present case the infinite arc contributes nothing since the integrand goes down at least as fast as $1/z^3$ at infinity. The contributions of the indentations are $j\pi$ times the residue of the integrand at the corresponding pole, which is easily evaluated. There remains the integration along the $j\omega$-axis. This is broken up into two parts, one between 0 and ω_0, the other between ω_0 and ∞. The details will be left to you to work out. The result will be

$$\frac{2\omega}{\pi}\int_0^{\omega_0} \frac{U(y)}{\sqrt{1 - y^2/\omega_0^2}} \frac{dy}{(y^2 - \omega^2)} + \frac{2\omega}{\pi}\int_{\omega_0}^{\infty} \frac{X(y)}{\sqrt{y^2/\omega_0^2 - 1}} \frac{dy}{(y^2 - \omega^2)}$$

$$= \frac{X(\omega)}{\sqrt{1 - \omega^2/\omega_0^2}} \; ; \quad \omega < \omega_0$$

$$= \frac{-U(\omega)}{\sqrt{\omega^2/\omega_0^2 - 1}} \; ; \quad \omega > \omega_0 \quad (123)$$

We have now answered the question posed at the start of this discussion, insofar as the present problem is concerned. If we are given the real part of a function over part of the imaginary axis and the imaginary part over the rest of the axis, then the function is completely defined. Our method of obtaining the result in the last equation can be extended if there are more than two intervals over which one or the other of the two components are known. Additional irrational factors are introduced giving additional branch points at appropriate points on the axis. The resulting expressions, however, become rather complicated and hence, limited in usefulness.

Let us now summarize the results of this section. Our objective is to obtain relationships between the real and imaginary parts of a network function $F(s)$ (or between the gain and the phase), so that when one of these is prescribed the other can be calculated. The point of departure is Cauchy's integral theorem, the contour of integration consisting of the imaginary axis with an infinite semicircular arc joining the ends. An integrand is chosen which involves $F(s)$ or $\ln F(s)$, multiplied or divided by additional factors. The contour is indented to by-pass poles of the integrand introduced by these factors.

If the integrand involves a network function $F(s)$, then the only restriction is that $F(s)$ be regular on the $j\omega$-axis, including the points zero and infinity. If the integrand involves $\ln F(s)$, then $F(s)$ need not be regular on the $j\omega$-axis, but now it must have no zeros in the right half plane.

The over-all contour is divided into the straight segment consisting of the imaginary axis, and the semicircular contours which by-pass j-axis poles deliberately introduced into the integrand, plus the one at infinity. The contributions of the semicircular contours can be computed, leaving only the integral along the imaginary axis.

A very useful feature of these expressions is the fact that the prescribed function need not be given in a realizable analytical form. An approximate graphical form is sufficient. Furthermore, the integrations themselves can be performed graphically.

7.10   The Potential Analog

The driving-point and transfer functions of electric networks are analytic functions of a complex variable. We know that the real and imaginary parts of such a function satisfy Laplace's equation; they are called *harmonic functions*. Thus, the real and imaginary parts of network functions can be interpreted as *potentials* arising from some electric charge or current distributions. It remains to determine the types of such charge and current distributions whose potentials represent the real and imaginary parts of network functions of lumped networks.

Consider an infinitely long static line charge distribution, the charge per unit length being q. The potential of such a charge distribution in a plane perpendicular to the line charge can be found as a two-dimensional problem. Let this be the s-plane and let the line charge pierce the plane at a point $s = s_i$. At a point s located a distance r from the line charge, the potential is given by

$$V = \frac{-q}{2\pi\epsilon} \ln r = \frac{-q}{2\pi\epsilon} \ln |s - s_i| \tag{124}$$

with a suitable reference for potential, where ϵ is the dielectric permittivity.

Now turn back to the logarithm of a network function given in Eq. (21). Consider particularly the expression for the gain. Each term in that expression has the form just given for the potential of a line charge. Suppose we were to place a set of parallel line charges which pierce the s-plane at the points determined by the poles and zeros of a network function $F(s)$. The lines which go through the zeros of the function are to have negative charges while those that go through the poles are to have positive charges. Furthermore, the magnitudes of these charges are all to be the same and equal to $2\pi\epsilon$. For simple reference purposes, we will refer to these charges as *unit charges*. The potential at any point $s = j\omega$ due to all of these line charges, will be given precisely by Eq. (21). Thus, the variation of potential along the $j\omega$-axis due to a set of parallel lines carrying unit positive or negative charges is exactly the same as the variation of the gain function with zeros located at the positions of the negative charges and poles at the positions of the positive charges. As a matter of fact, this equality of potential and gain will hold at any point in the plane, but our main interest lies on the $j\omega$-axis.

Consider the situation in which, instead of having discrete line charges perpendicular to the s-plane, we have continuously distributed charge on a cylindrical surface which is perpendicular to the s-plane, and cuts the plane in one or more contours. Instead of being a sum of discrete terms such as given in Eq. (21), the potential will now be an integral. If we let z represent points on the contour along which the cylindrical surface cuts the s-plane, and $q(z)$ represent the charge distribution, the potential along the $j\omega$-axis will be

$$V = -\frac{1}{2\pi\epsilon} \int_C q(z) \ln |j\omega - z| \, |dz| \tag{125}$$

The contours along which the charge is distributed correspond to poles and zeros of a network function. In the present case this would mean a continuous distribution of poles and zeros, which is certainly not possible for lumped networks.

Let us pursue this topic somewhat further. Due to the presence of the line charges, there will be an electric field parallel to the s-plane. Let us consider the component of this field located at the $j\omega$-axis, perpendicular to the $j\omega$-axis and in the direction of the negative σ axis. This is illustrated in Fig. 25. Since the electric field is the negative gradient of the potential, the normal component ($E_{-\sigma}$) we are interested in is simply $\partial V/\partial\sigma$ evaluated at $\sigma = 0$.

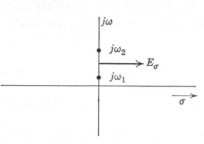

Fig. 25. Component of electric field normal to $j\omega$-axis.

Now consider the flux of the electric field across the $j\omega$-axis in the direction of the negative σ-axis between two points ω_1 and ω_2. This is given by

$$\text{Flux} = \int_{\omega_1}^{\omega_2} \frac{\partial V}{\partial\sigma}\, d\omega = \int_{\omega_1}^{\omega_2} E_{-\sigma}\, d\omega \tag{126}$$

(Note that the flux is given by a surface integral but we are taking a unit width perpendicular to the s-plane.)

Let us turn back temporarily to the gain and angle functions. These are the real and imaginary parts of an analytic function and hence satisfy the Cauchy-Riemann equations. The total differential in the angle anywhere in the complex plane if both σ and ω vary is given by

$$d\phi = \frac{\partial\phi}{\partial\sigma}\, d\sigma + \frac{\partial\phi}{\partial\omega}\, d\omega \tag{127}$$

If we restrict ourselves to the $j\omega$-axis, $d\sigma$ will be zero. The change in angle as ω goes from ω_1 to ω_2 will be

$$\Delta\phi = \int_{\omega_1}^{\omega_2} \frac{\partial\phi}{\partial\omega}\, d\omega = \int_{\omega_1}^{\omega_2} \frac{\partial\alpha}{\partial\sigma}\, d\omega \tag{128}$$

The right-hand side follows from the use of the Cauchy-Riemann equation $\partial\alpha/\partial\sigma = \partial\phi/\partial\omega$. If we compare this expression with Eq. (126) and we note that the potential and the gain are analogous quantities, we see that the flux of the electric field across a portion of the $j\omega$-axis is analogous to the change in phase over the same interval.

As a matter of fact, comparing Eq. (126) and Eq. (128) we see that the normal component of the electric field across the $j\omega$-axis (in the direction of negative σ) is analogous to the slope of the phase along the $j\omega$-axis. The *delay function* is defined as the negative derivative of the phase on the $j\omega$-axis. Hence, the delay is analogous to the normal component of the electric field in the direction of the positive σ-axis.

In arriving at the analogy between the gain and phase on the one hand and the electrostatic potential and E-field flux on the other, we used the fact that the functional form of the potential of a set of line charges is the same as that of the gain function of a lumped network. Other analogies may be possible if we can find other quantities whose functional form is also the same as that of the gain.

Suppose the s-plane is covered with a conducting sheet having a finite conductivity ρ. Current having a surface density $\mathbf{i}_s$ is assumed to flow on the surface. ($\mathbf{i}_s$ is a vector quantity.) Assume that there are regions having zero dimensions at which current can be generated; we will call these "current sources." Consider an arbitrary closed contour C encircling a region R, as shown in Fig. 26.

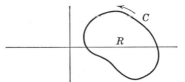

Fig. 26.   Region in s-plane.

If there are no sources within the contour C, no net current can flow out of the contour. If there are sources within the contour, the net outward current flow must be equal to the total current generated. This can be expressed as

$$\int_C \mathbf{i}_s \cdot d\mathbf{l} = \text{all current originating in } R \tag{129}$$

where $d\mathbf{l}$ is an element of arc along C. This line integral can be replaced by a surface integral according to the divergence theorem (applied to two dimensions). Suppose the current sources are distributed over the region R with a density I_s. (This is a scalar quantity.) Then, applying the divergence theorem, Eq. (129) becomes

$$\int_R \text{div } \mathbf{i}_s \, dA = \int_R I_s \, dA \tag{130}$$

where dA is an element of area in R and the symbol "div" stands for divergence. Since R is an arbitrary region, it follows that

$$\text{div } \mathbf{i}_s = I_s \tag{131}$$

Since the conducting sheet has a finite conductivity ρ, the current density can be expressed in terms of the electric field $\mathbf{E}$. The field itself can then be written as the negative gradient of the potential. These results can finally be substituted into the last equation. The steps are as follows.

$$\mathbf{i}_s = \rho\mathbf{E} = -\rho \ \mathrm{grad} \ V$$

$$\mathrm{div} \ \mathbf{i}_s = -\rho \ \mathrm{div} \ \mathrm{grad} \ V = I_s$$

$$\nabla^2 V = -\frac{I_s}{\rho} \tag{132}$$

where $\nabla^2 V$ stands for "divergence of the gradient of V." The last expression is Poisson's equation, whose solution under the present conditions is

$$V = \frac{1}{2\pi\rho} \int_R I_s \ln r \, dA \tag{133}$$

where r is the distance from the sources to the point at which the potential is computed, and a suitable level of potential has been chosen.

In the preceding discussion it is assumed that the current sources are distributed throughout region R. Let us now consider the case of a single discrete source located at the point s_i and let the current generated by this source be $2\pi\rho$. We will refer to this as a *unit current*. The source density function I_s then becomes an impulse of strength $2\pi\rho$ situated at s_i. Equation (133) becomes

$$V = \int_R \delta(s - s_i) \ln|s - s_i| \, dA = \ln|s - s_i| \tag{134}$$

The right-hand side follows from the sampling property of an impulse, which is as valid in the case of a surface integral as it is for a simple integral.

If instead of a single discrete source there are a number of such sources, some positive some negative but all having unit value, then the expression for the potential will have the exact form of the gain function given in Eq. (21) for $s = j\omega$. (A negative source current means that current is removed from the conducting sheet at a point instead of being generated there.)

We have now established a second analog for the gain. If equal steady electric currents are injected on and removed from discrete points of a conducting (but not perfectly conducting) sheet, the potential at any point in the plane (and in particular, on the $j\omega$-axis) will be the same as the gain function of a network, if the corresponding network function has simple zeros at the points of current injection and simple poles at the points of current removal. The flux of the E-field across an interval of the $j\omega$-axis and the change in phase over this same interval will still be analogous, since the preceding discussion on this point remains unmodified.

The analogy which we have just discussed provides a basis for the construction of an experimental device which can be used for both analysis and synthesis. The current injection or removal is achieved by feeding current to the conducting plane through very thin conductors, needle points. In a very simple form of such a device, called Teledeltos Paper,* a conducting material is coated on paper. In more elaborate devices, which are called *electrolytic tanks*, the conductor is a layer of electrolyte, the needle points being immersed into the electrolyte.

Consider what can be accomplished with the use of such an analog device. If a network function is given, the poles and zeros are set up by introducing current probes at the appropriate points, currents entering at the zeros and leaving at the poles. A sampling of the potential at various points on the $j\omega$-axis is quickly obtained by means of another probe. This permits a plot of the gain function along the $j\omega$-axis in rapid fashion. What is perhaps more interesting, a determination of the effect on the gain due to the perturbation or motion of one or more poles or zeros is rapidly obtained simply by moving the current probes a given amount and again sampling the potential. As a matter of fact, this measuring of the j-axis potential can be performed automatically and a plot of the gain obtained on recording paper.

The phase can also be measured, although not quite as satisfactorily, by utilizing the analogy to the flux. The recording probe is moved perpendicularly off the $j\omega$-axis small equal distances to the right and left. The difference in the readings is divided by the total excursion off the $j\omega$-axis to yield an approximate value for $\partial V/\partial \sigma$. If this is done at several points along the axis, the integral in Eq. (126) can be approximated.

In a synthesis problem in which, say, the gain is specified along a portion of the $j\omega$-axis, a first guess as to the locations of suitable poles and zeros can be set up in the electrolytic tank. A scan of the $j\omega$-axis with the probe quickly shows the error between the desired gain and the one given by the chosen poles and zeros. The poles and zeros can now be moved around and an optimum pole-zero configuration can be obtained experimentally which will give the "best" (according to some criterion) approximation to the desired gain.

At this point a few very disconcerting questions may arise. In the first place the s-plane extends to infinity whereas any physical analog device must of necessity have finite dimensions. How can this difficulty be overcome? Secondly, if there are more finite poles than there are

* This is a copyrighted name.

finite zeros, it appears that more current must be removed from the conducting plane than is being supplied to it. Such a condition obviously cannot be maintained. This second difficulty is easily remedied. If we count zeros at infinity as well, a rational function will always have the same number of zeros as poles. Hence, the total current supplied will be equal to the current removed if we supply as many units of current through a probe located at infinity as the order of the zero at infinity demands. But, where in the analog is the point at infinity? This brings us back to the first question.

One solution of this problem is as follows. Let us choose the scale in the electrolytic tank in such a way that the edges of the tank are far from the locations of pole-zero constellations, at least as compared with the points at which the gain is to be computed. Then, the fact that the plane is not infinite will have little effect. The edge of the tank can be made conducting and the required amount of current introduced there.

An alternative solution of the problem can be obtained if we apply a conformal transformation which maps the s-plane into another plane in which infinity in the s-plane becomes a finite point in the new plane. The $j\omega$-axis will be transformed to some other curve, as well, so that now we will be interested in the potential along this new curve. Many such transformations are possible. Here we will simply be content to point out this possibility and will not explore the details any further.

We have seen that the potential analog provides an experimental aid for both network analysis and network synthesis. This would be reason enough for us to discuss the topic here. However, the analogy between the gain and phase of a lumped network and the two-dimensional potential and flux field of discrete line charges is a very useful conceptual tool. It allows us to formulate network problems in analog terms, the solutions of which may be facilitated in the domain of the analog. If nothing else, it gives a new vantage point from which to survey network problems. The insight thus obtained serves to sharpen our perceptions regarding these problems.

In network analysis, the problem is to find the response of a given network when a given excitation is applied. We have been examining this problem in great detail in all of its facets. In potential analog terms, we might say this problem is equivalent to finding the potential and flux of a given set of charges. But if the charge locations are known, this corresponds to knowing the pole and zero locations in the network analog. In such a case it is not necessary to resort to the potential analog to solve the network analysis problem.

Now consider the inverse of this problem. Suppose a gain or phase function is prescribed over an interval of the $j\omega$-axis, and it is desired to find a network having the given function as its gain or phase. The given function is likely to be an ideal one, such as, say, the low-pass filter function shown in Fig. 17a, and so, not exactly realizable. The first problem is to determine a realizable network function such that the given gain or phase is approximated (in some manner). This is referred to as the *approximation problem* in network synthesis. In terms of the potential analog, the problem is to find a charge distribution which will produce a prescribed potential along a given curve (a portion of the $j\omega$-axis) or a prescribed normal derivative of potential across a given curve. Such problems have been studied in potential theory and we may find solutions to our approximation problems if we think in terms of the potential analog.

Let us pursue this line of thought somewhat further. For concreteness, let us suppose that the gain is prescribed along a portion of the $j\omega$-axis. In analog terms, the potential is prescribed on the same part of the $j\omega$-axis. In potential theory when a potential function is given, known methods can often be employed to determine a *continuous* charge distribution over some convenient contour (or more than one) which gives rise to the prescribed potential. In order to be applicable to lumped networks, such a continuous charge must first be approximated by a set of lumped charges, all of unit value, spaced on the same contour. We refer to this process as *quantization*. The continuous charge is said to be *quantized*. In order to establish the unit of charge, we must compute the total charge on a contour and choose the unit of charge such that there are an integral number of unit charges on the whole contour. Then we must divide the contour into segments each carrying a unit charge. Finally, we must place a discrete unit charge somewhere on each segment. If the continuous charge is uniformly distributed, the lumped charges can be placed in the center of each segment. More generally, the best approximation is probably obtained if each lumped charge is placed at the center of charge of the corresponding segment.

In a given problem, more than one contour may be involved, each carrying charge of a different sign. Remember that positive charges correspond to poles and negative charges to zeros. If the charge distribution is to lead to a realizable network function, several conditions must be satisfied. In the first place, the charge distribution must be symmetrical with respect to the real axis, because complex poles and zeros must be accompanied by their conjugates. Secondly, there must be no positive charges in the right half plane. For special types of network function, other conditions must also be satisfied. For example, if the network function is to be regular at infinity, the net charge cannot be positive.

Let us now illustrate these ideas by means of some simple examples. As a first example, suppose it is desired to design a network such that the phase is a linear function of frequency along a portion of the $j\omega$-axis, say in the range $-\omega_0 < \omega < \omega_0$. This means a constant delay is required over this range. In terms of the potential analog, what is required is a constant value of electric field normal to the $j\omega$-axis in this same frequency range. From previous experience we know that if we have a pair of infinitely long oppositely charged parallel plates, the field is constant between the plates and directed from one plate to the

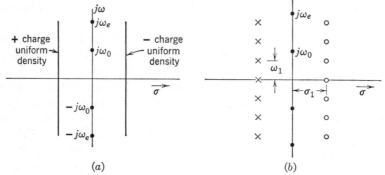

Fig. 27. Potential analog solution of the linear phase problem.

other. The potential problem is then solved by placing the $j\omega$-axis between such a pair of parallel plates. This gives a constant normal component of electric field over the whole $j\omega$-axis, which is more than we actually require. We can make the plates finite without introducing much error in the desired frequency range due to fringing effects by extending the plates somewhat beyond the desired frequency range so long as the spacing between plates is kept small relative to their length. The situation is illustrated in Fig. 27a. We must place the positively charged plate in the left half plane in order that the corresponding network function be regular in the right half plane. For convenience let us assume a uniform charge density on the plates.*

The next step is to quantize the continuous charge. Because the continuous charge density is uniform, the spacing between the lumped charges will be the same. They will be located at the points $\sigma_1 \pm jk\omega_1$, where k goes from zero to n, as shown in Fig. 27b. Here we have chosen an odd number of lumped charges so that one appears on the real axis. We can just as well choose an even number. If we let $\pm j\omega_e$ represent

* Such a uniform charge distribution over a finite conductor is impossible in a potential field; but this is only one of several approximations.

the ends of the plates and q_d the charge per unit length (remembering that a unit width perpendicular to the s-plane is always assumed), then the total charge on a plate is $2\omega_e q_d$. The unit of charge is then taken as $2\omega_e q_d/(n + 1)$, since there are $n + 1$ lumped charges; the value of ω_1 is $2\omega_e/(n + 1)$.

There are two sources of error in this procedure. One of these is due to using finite plates instead of the infinite ones. This source of error will not always be present in other problems; it will arise whenever an infinite contour is replaced by a finite one. We refer to this error as the *truncation error*. The second source of error is due to quantizing the continuous charge. It is referred to as the *quantization* or *granularity error*. This error will always be present.

Note that the network function defined by the poles and zeros shown in Fig. 27 is an all-pass function. From our knowledge of such functions the gain should be constant; its derivative with respect to ω should then be zero. Note that the analog of the gain slope is the negative of the electric field along the $j\omega$-axis. Now the field along the $j\omega$-axis produced by any one of the poles is exactly canceled by the field due to the zero which is its image. Hence, the net field along the $j\omega$-axis is zero. This means that the gain slope is zero, in agreement with our previous knowledge.

Having noted that a pole in the left half plane and a zero located at the image point in the right half plane produce exactly opposite electric fields along the $j\omega$-axis, we can also note that they produce identical fields normal to the $j\omega$-axis. If we were to remove all of the right half plane zeros, nothing serious would happen; the delay would be simply cut in half. This factor of two can be restored by placing a pole in the left half plane at the mirror image of each removed zero. Since there is one there already, this step implies doubling the order of all the poles when all the zeros are removed. As a matter of fact, it is not necessary to remove all zeros and double all poles. Any number of zeros can be removed so long as the order of the corresponding pole is doubled. In this way a large variety of network functions are obtained, for each of which the delay is exactly the same. However, the gain function will now be different for each of these.

As a second example, consider the filter problem. Here we require the gain to be high and constant over one or more frequency bands; it must be low, but not necessarily constant over the rest of the $j\omega$-axis. For concreteness, let us consider a low-pass filter. Here we require a constant high gain over the interval $-\omega_0 < \omega < \omega_0$. In terms of the potential analogy, what we want is an equipotential line along the $j\omega$-axis from $-\omega_0$ to ω_0. An equipotential suggests a conductor since the potential

on a conductor is constant. However, laying a charged conductor on
the $j\omega$-axis may solve the potential problem but it does not help the
filter problem. When we eventually quantize the charge on the conductor, we will end up with a set of poles on the $j\omega$-axis right in the region
where we want a constant gain.

The idea of using a conductor need not be lost, however. The potential is constant not only *on* a conductor, but everywhere in a region
bounded by a conductor. This suggests surrounding the desired region
of the $j\omega$-axis by a conductor as shown in Fig. 28a. We have here shown

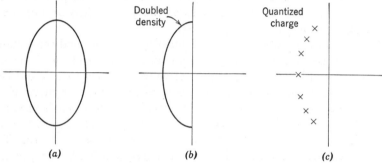

Doubled density

Quantized charge

(a)   *(b)*   *(c)*

Fig. 28.   Potential analog solution of the filter problem.

an elliptical contour but this is not necessary; any shape will do so
long as it is symmetrical with respect to the σ-axis. However, the
quantization error will be different for different shaped contours. If
there are no other charges anywhere, then the charge on this contour
should be positive. (It can't be negative because the network function
will then have a multiple pole at infinity.) But this means there will be
positive charge (which corresponds to poles) in the right half plane.
This is disconcerting, to say the least, but not devastating. Recall
that the j-axis magnitude of a pole factor such as $j\omega - s_i$, and hence the
gain, depends only on the distance from the pole to the $j\omega$-axis. This
means that the gain on the $j\omega$-axis will not change if we move all right
half plane poles to their left half plane images, since the distances from
any point on the $j\omega$-axis will remain the same. If the original contour
is symmetrical this means removing the right half and doubling the
charge density of the left half. This step, while keeping the gain invariant, does change the phase. The final step is again the quantization
of charge.

The discussion of the potential analog in this section must be considered only as an introduction to the subject. Much in the way of
details has been omitted. However, the basic principles have been

outlined. Actual solution of any but the simplest problems would of necessity take us far afield into potential theory and conformal mapping. We will leave the further development of the subject to books on network synthesis.*

PROBLEMS

7.1 Figure P7.1 shows a double-tuned transformer. The coupling coefficient $k = M/L$, and Q are variable. For the network in (a) $Q = (1/R)\sqrt{L/C}$ while for the network in (b) $Q = R\sqrt{C/L}$. Also let $\omega_0^2 = 1/LC$. Determine the poles and zeros of the transfer impedance function, V_2/I_1, in terms of k, Q, and ω_0. Sketch the variations in the locations of these points as k and Q vary. Sketch $|Z_{21}(j\omega)|$ as a function of ω for different values of k and Q.

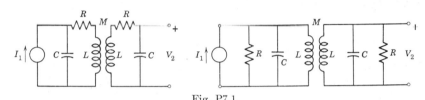

Fig. P7.1.

7.2 The network in Fig. P7.2 is called a capacitance-coupled double-tuned circuit. Again let $Q = R\sqrt{C/L}$ and $\omega_0^2 = 1/LC$. Determine the locations of the poles and zeros of the transfer impedance function $Z_{21}(s) = V_2/I_1$ in terms of ω_0, Q and the coupling capacitance C_c. Sketch the variations in these locations as Q and C_c vary. Compare the rate at which the logarithmic gain decreases in this and in the previous problem as $s = j\omega$ approaches infinity.

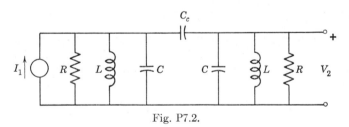

Fig. P7.2.

7.3 The following functions are given as the tangent functions of a transfer function. Find the corresponding transfer function. In case the answer is not unique, give all possibilities.

(a) $\dfrac{\omega^3 + 2\omega}{\omega^4 - 3\omega^2 - 6}$;   (b) $\dfrac{2\omega}{1 - 6\omega^2}$;   (c) $-\omega^3$;   (d) $\dfrac{-\omega^3}{\omega^4 - 4\omega^2 + 24}$

* For further reading see S. Darlington, The Potential Analogue Method of Network Synthesis, *BSTJ*, 30, pp. 315–365, April, 1951; and D. F. Tuttle, Jr., *Network Synthesis*, Vol. I, John Wiley and Sons, New York, 1958.

7.4 Suppose an odd rational function of ω is prescribed as a tangent function, the odd power of ω appearing in the denominator instead of the numerator. What does this imply about the transfer function? How should the procedure for finding $F(s)$ given in section 7.7 be modified? Illustrate on the following functions.

(a) $\dfrac{1}{\omega}$;   (b) $\dfrac{2 - 3\omega^2}{\omega(4 - \omega^2)}$

7.5 For each of the following functions sketch the complex locus and the gain and phase plots. Also find the value of ω at which $F(j\omega) = 1 + j0$.

(a) $F(s) = \dfrac{1}{s}$

(b) $F(s) = \dfrac{1}{s + 2}$

(c) $F(s) = \dfrac{1}{s(s + 2)}$

(d) $F(s) = \dfrac{1}{s^2(s + 1)}$

(e) $F(s) = \dfrac{(s + 1)(s + 3)}{(s + 2)(s + 4)}$

(f) $F(s) = \dfrac{s + 1}{s^2 + 3s + 3}$

7.6 The following even rational functions of ω are given. Assume that each one is the real part of a network function $F(s)$. Find this function using both the Bode and the Gewertz procedures. Now assume that each given function is the j-axis magnitude squared of a network function. Find the corresponding function. If there is more than one possibility, find them all.

(a) $\dfrac{1}{1 + \omega^8}$

(b) $\dfrac{-\omega^2 + 2\omega^4 - \omega^8}{1 + \omega^8}$

(c) $\dfrac{(1 - \omega^2)^2}{1 + \omega^6}$

(d) $\dfrac{1 - 2\omega^2 + \omega^4}{1 - 2\omega^2 + \omega^4 + 4\omega^6}$

(e) $\dfrac{(1 - \omega^2 + \omega^4)^2}{(\omega^4 - 4\omega^2 + 3)^2 + \omega^2(\omega^4 - 6\omega^2 + 8)^2}$

7.7 The twin Tee R-C network shown in Fig. P7.7 can be used in a feedback network to produce a selective amplifier at very low frequencies. The function of interest in this application is $z_{21}(s) = V_2(s)/I_1(s)$. Find the locus of $z_{21}(j\omega)$. Find the condition that the locus should pass through the origin at a given frequency $\omega_0(\neq 0, \infty)$.

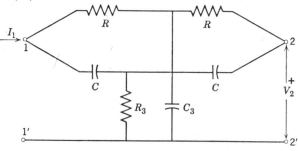

Fig. P7.7.

7.8 With reference to the tuned circuit of Fig. 4, compute the frequencies at which

(a) $|Z(j\omega)|$

(b) $Re|Z(j\omega)|$

are maximum and the frequency at which $\text{Im}|Z(j\omega)| = 0$. The first of these is the frequency of *amplitude resonance* and the last is the frequency of *phase resonance* or *unity power factor*. Relate these concepts as well as the familiar concepts of $Q_0 (= \omega_0 L/R)$ and *half power bandwidth* $\Delta\omega/\omega_0$ to the magnitude and angle of the pole. ($\Delta\omega$ is the difference between the two frequencies at which $|Z(j\omega)|$ is equal to $1/\sqrt{2}$ times the maximum value of $|Z(j\omega)|$.)

7.9 Design two networks such that the voltage ratio transfer function $G_{21}(s)$ of each network is a minimum-phase function but the *sum* of the two functions is nonminimum-phase. Show how we can get the sum as a voltage ratio transfer function. (Isolating amplifiers may be used.)

7.10 By applying the argument principle to the function $F(s) - F(s_0)$ where s_0 is any point in the right half plane, show that the image of the contour of Fig. 13*b* must enclose the area in the F-plane in the clockwise direction, assuming that $F(s)$ is a network function.

7.11 Let $Z(s)$ be the driving-point impedance function of a passive network; further let $Z(s)$ be regular on the $j\omega$-axis inclusive of $s = \infty$. From the fact that a passive network cannot generate energy, we have the familiar conclusion $Re[Z(j\omega)] \geq 0$, for all ω. By using the results of Problem 7.10 and this fact prove that $Re[Z(s)] \geq 0$ for *all s in the right half plane*. (We will prove this result in Chapter 9 without the additional hypothesis of regularity on the $j\omega$-axis using a different argument.)

7.12 Extend Problem 7.11 to stable active networks as follows. Continue the assumption of regularity on the $j\omega$-axis and $s = \infty$, so that $Re[Z(j\omega)]$ has a finite minimum value on the $j\omega$-axis. Now show that the real part of $Z(s)$ in the right half plane is never less than this minimum. Thus an active driving point function can differ from a passive one only by an additive constant.

7.13 Use the corner plot technique to obtain a rapid sketch of the locus of $G_{21}(j\omega)$ for the RC coupled amplifier of Fig. P7.13. Remark on any significant points, such as phase shift near 0 and infinite frequencies, other critical points that are easily computed etc.

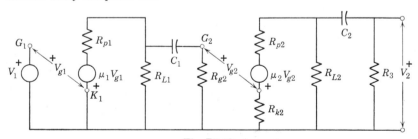

Fig. P7.13.

7.14 Using what you know about corner plots, find a function $F(s)$ that has approximately the frequency response characteristic $20 \log |F(j\omega)|$ shown in Fig. P7.14.

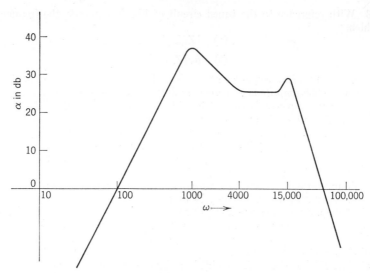

Fig. P7.14.

7.15   Derive Eq. (113) in the text starting from Eq. (111).

7.16   Derive Eq. (123) in the text.

7.17   Derive the resistance integral theorem by integrating the function $F(s) - U(\infty)$ around the basic contour consisting of the $j\omega$-axis and an infinite semicircle to the right.

7.18   Derive the reactance integral theorem by integrating the function $F(s)/s$ around the basic contour with a small indentation around the origin.

7.19   Derive Eq. (97) by integrating the function $F(z)/(z^2 + \omega^2)$ around the basic contour with indentations at $z = \pm j\omega$.

7.20   Derive Eq. (98) by integrating the function $z[F(z) - U(\infty)]/(z^2 + \omega^2)$ around the basic contour with indentations at $z = \pm j\omega$.

7.21   By integrating the function $[F(z) - U(0)]/z(z^2 + \omega^2)$ around the basic contour with indentations at $z = \pm j\omega$, derive the following relationship.

$$U(\omega) = U(0) - \frac{2\omega^2}{\pi} \int_0^\infty \frac{X(y)/y - X(\omega)/\omega}{y^2 - \omega^2} \, dy$$

Compare this with Eq. (100).

8 · TWO-PORT NETWORKS

As mentioned in the last chapter, networks can be classified according to the number of terminals that are available for external connection. When we are interested in the transmission of energy or information from one point to another, the number of *pairs* of terminals becomes important. If there are *n* pairs of terminals, we refer to the network as an *n-terminal-pair* or *n-port*. The two-port network is the most common and the most important of this class of networks.

A two-port is defined as a network with two accessible pairs of terminals, the network being electrically and magnetically isolated except for these two pairs of terminals. By calling these "terminal-pairs," or "ports," we imply that external connections are not to be made between one terminal of a terminal-pair and another terminal of a different terminal-pair. For example, if the black box of Fig. 1 denotes a two terminal-pair network where (1,1') is one terminal-pair and (2,2') is another terminal-pair, no connection is to be made, externally, between

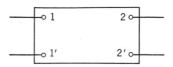

Fig. 1. Two port.

terminals 1 and 2 or 1' and 2' (or 1 and 2' or 1' and 2). Thus the external network is considered to be in two different pieces which are interconnected by the two port as shown in Fig. 2, where *N* denotes the

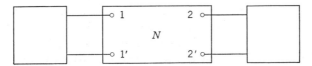

Fig. 2. External connection to a two-port.

two-port network. The name "port" arises from microwave network theory where the "terminal-pair" becomes the cross section of a waveguide. In network theory "port" and "terminal-pair" are used interchangeably. Because of the applications of two-ports as transmission networks, one of the terminal-pairs is called the "input" and the other terminal-pair, the "output." Normally the terminals (1,1') are known as the input terminals and (2,2') as the output terminals.

By focussing attention on the terminal-pairs (1,1'), (2,2'), we are implying that we are interested in the behavior of the network only in so far as it modifies the signals transmitted from one side to the other and are not too interested in its internal structure. Thus the variables of interest to us, in the study of two-ports, are the voltages and currents at the terminal-pairs only and not the voltages and currents of the branches inside the network N. We therefore establish a convention for the references of these voltages and currents as in Fig. 3.

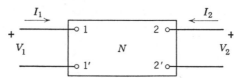

Fig. 3.   Reference convention.

Our discussion in this chapter will be entirely in terms of transformed functions under the assumption of zero initial values and so capital V's and I's are used in Fig. 3. Some authors choose a reference for I_2 opposite to the one shown in Fig. 3. In comparing formulas among textbooks it is necessary to find out the reference convention adopted by each.

We look upon the network as something interrelating the quantities V_1, V_2, I_1, and I_2. Since we are dealing with linear networks, we can expect this interrelationship also to be linear. In this chapter we are going to study the different ways of interrelating these quantities as different descriptions of the two-port.

The discussion of this chapter may appear somewhat unmotivated to you. When we are immersed in some of the details which will follow, you may question the need for all this. In restricting ourselves to analysis, we have lost much of the motivation for finding various ways of describing the behavior of two-port networks. The need for these various schemes arises from the demands made by the many applications of two-ports. The usefulness of the different methods of description comes clearly into evidence when the problem is one of synthesizing or designing networks—filters, matching networks, wave-shaping networks, and a host of others. A method of description which is convenient for a power system may be less so for a filter network, and may be completely unsuited for a transistor amplifier. For this reason we will describe many alternate, but equivalent, ways of describing two-port behavior.

Often, in the problem of synthesizing a network for a specific application, it is very convenient to break down a complicated problem into several parts. The pieces of the over-all network are designed separately and then put together in a manner consistent with the original decomposition. In order to carry out this procedure, it is necessary to know how the description of the behavior of the over-all network is related to the behavior of the components whose interconnection makes up the over-all network. For this reason we will spend some time on the problem of interconnecting two-port networks.

Many of the results obtained in this chapter require a considerable amount of algebraic manipulation which is quite straightforward. We will not attempt to carry through all the steps, but will merely outline the desired procedure leaving for you the task of filling in the omitted steps.

8.1   Two-Port Parameters and Their Interrelations

It is conventional practice to begin the discussion of two-port parameters by defining them as coefficients in certain equations relating the

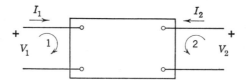

Fig. 4.   Loop analysis of two-port.

quantities V_1, V_2, I_1, and I_2. In this text we shall deviate from this convention and start at a familiar point, namely the loop or node equations for the network.

Consider the two-port network "terminated" in V_1 and V_2, shown in Fig. 4. That is, let us replace the external networks connected to terminals (1,1′) and (2,2′) by their terminal voltages so that we can deal with the two-port alone.

Let us choose our loops so that loop 1, and only loop 1, contains V_1 and similarly loop 2 alone contains V_2. Except in degenerate two-ports of the type shown in Fig. 5, it will always be possible to choose loops 1

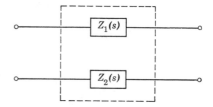

Fig. 5.   Degenerate two-port.

and 2 in this fashion. If the two-port network contains no *independent* generators, the loop equations will have the following general form.*

$$
\begin{bmatrix}
c_{11} & c_{12} & c_{13} & \cdots & c_{1\mu} \\
c_{21} & c_{22} & c_{23} & \cdots & c_{2\mu} \\
c_{31} & c_{32} & c_{33} & \cdots & c_{3\mu} \\
\cdot & \cdot & \cdot & \cdot & \cdot \\
c_{\mu 1} & c_{\mu 2} & c_{\mu 3} & \cdots & c_{\mu\mu}
\end{bmatrix}
\begin{bmatrix}
I_1(s) \\
I_2(s) \\
I_3(s) \\
\cdot \\
I_\mu(s)
\end{bmatrix}
=
\begin{bmatrix}
V_1(s) \\
V_2(s) \\
0 \\
\cdot \\
0
\end{bmatrix}
\tag{1}
$$

We note that the right side contains only two nonzero terms $V_1(s)$ and $V_2(s)$. There are no initial conditions; we assume that the network is initially relaxed. What we wish to do now is somehow to extract from Eq. (1) an equation that contains only the terminal variables V_1, V_2, I_1, and I_2. For this we make use of the fact that the right side contains only two nonzero terms. To do this, we solve Eq. (1) for the loop current transforms. The result will be

$$
\begin{bmatrix}
I_1(s) \\
I_2(s) \\
I_3(s) \\
\cdot \cdot \\
I_\mu(s)
\end{bmatrix}
= \frac{1}{\Delta}
\begin{bmatrix}
\Delta_{11} & \Delta_{21} & \Delta_{31} & \cdots & \Delta_{\mu 1} \\
\Delta_{12} & \Delta_{22} & \Delta_{32} & \cdots & \Delta_{\mu 2} \\
\Delta_{13} & \Delta_{23} & \Delta_{33} & \cdots & \Delta_{\mu 3} \\
\cdot & \cdot & \cdot & \cdot & \cdot \\
\Delta_{1\mu} & \Delta_{2\mu} & \Delta_{3\mu} & \cdots & \Delta_{\mu\mu}
\end{bmatrix}
\begin{bmatrix}
V_1(s) \\
V_2(s) \\
0 \\
\cdot \cdot \\
0
\end{bmatrix}
\tag{2}
$$

By appropriately partitioning the right-hand matrices, we get

$$
\begin{bmatrix}
I_1(s) \\
I_2(s) \\
I_3(s) \\
\cdot \cdot \\
I_\mu(s)
\end{bmatrix}
= \frac{1}{\Delta}
\begin{bmatrix}
\Delta_{11} & \Delta_{21} \\
\Delta_{12} & \Delta_{22} \\
\Delta_{13} & \Delta_{23} \\
\cdot & \cdot & \cdot \\
\Delta_{1\mu} & \Delta_{2\mu}
\end{bmatrix}
\begin{bmatrix}
V_1(s) \\
V_2(s)
\end{bmatrix}
\tag{3}
$$

Since we are interested in the terminal currents only, we solve for these only. The result will be

$$
\begin{bmatrix}
I_1(s) \\
I_2(s)
\end{bmatrix}
=
\begin{bmatrix}
\dfrac{\Delta_{11}}{\Delta} & \dfrac{\Delta_{21}}{\Delta} \\[2mm]
\dfrac{\Delta_{12}}{\Delta} & \dfrac{\Delta_{22}}{\Delta}
\end{bmatrix}
\begin{bmatrix}
V_1(s) \\
V_2(s)
\end{bmatrix}
\tag{4}
$$

* We are assuming that any dependent sources not on loops 1 or 2 do not depend explicitly on V_1 or V_2. The general results are still valid in this case also, but the specific forms in the first four equations will be different.

We have now achieved our objective—namely, to get an equation relating the terminal variables. As we anticipated, the relationship is a linear one. Since the coefficient matrix in Eq. (4) multiplies voltage transforms to give current transforms, the entries are dimensionally admittances. So we write

$$\begin{bmatrix} I_1 \\ I_2 \end{bmatrix} = \begin{bmatrix} y_{11} & y_{12} \\ y_{21} & y_{22} \end{bmatrix} \begin{bmatrix} V_1 \\ V_2 \end{bmatrix} \tag{5}$$

The coefficient matrix of this transformation is known as the "short-circuit admittance matrix" and the entries—for which the lower case y is reserved as the standard symbol—are *short-circuit admittance parameters* or the y parameters, for short. The reason for the name "short-circuit" becomes obvious on noting from Eq. (5) that

$$y_{11} = \left. \frac{I_1}{V_1} \right|_{V_2=0} \qquad\qquad y_{12} = \left. \frac{I_1}{V_2} \right|_{V_1=0}$$

$$\tag{6}$$

$$y_{21} = \left. \frac{I_2}{V_1} \right|_{V_2=0} \qquad\qquad y_{22} = \left. \frac{I_2}{V_2} \right|_{V_1=0}$$

The short-circuit admittance matrix is denoted by $\mathbf{Y}_{sc}$. A given voltage is made zero by short circuiting the proper terminals. For example, to get y_{12} we short-circuit terminals $(1,1')$ and connect a voltage generator across $(2,2')$. Then the ratio of the transform of the current at the short-circuited end to the transform of the voltage input is the short-circuit transfer admittance y_{12}. Similarly, y_{11} and y_{22} are short-circuit driving-point admittances.

Equation (5) relates the four terminal quantities, the two currents being given in terms of the two voltages. Once we have these equations, we may rearrange them in any order we choose. One possible rearrangement is to invert and solve for the V's in terms of the I's. If we do this we get

$$\begin{bmatrix} V_1(s) \\ V_2(s) \end{bmatrix} = \frac{1}{y_{11}y_{22} - y_{12}y_{21}} \begin{bmatrix} y_{22} & -y_{12} \\ -y_{21} & y_{11} \end{bmatrix} \begin{bmatrix} I_1(s) \\ I_2(s) \end{bmatrix}$$

$$= \begin{bmatrix} z_{11} & z_{12} \\ z_{21} & z_{22} \end{bmatrix} \begin{bmatrix} I_1(s) \\ I_2(s) \end{bmatrix} \tag{7}$$

In the last step we defined a new set of parameters whose relationships to the y parameters are evident by comparing the last two steps. Dimensionally they are impedances and they are called the *open-circuit impedance parameters*, or simply the z parameters. We will consistently use the lower case z for these parameters. The open-circuit impedance matrix is denoted by $\mathbf{Z}_{oc}$.

The reason for the name becomes clear by noting from Eq. (7) that

$$z_{11}(s) = \frac{V_1(s)}{I_1(s)}\bigg|_{I_2=0} \qquad\qquad z_{12}(s) = \frac{V_1(s)}{I_2(s)}\bigg|_{I_1=0}$$

$$z_{21}(s) = \frac{V_2(s)}{I_1(s)}\bigg|_{I_2=0} \qquad\qquad z_{22}(s) = \frac{V_2(s)}{I_2(s)}\bigg|_{I_1=0} \tag{8}$$

The currents are made zero by leaving the corresponding pair of terminals open. Thus, to find z_{21} we leave the $(2,2')$ terminals open and we connect a current source at the terminals $(1,1')$. Then, the ratio of the transform of the voltage at the open-circuited end to the transform of the input current is $z_{21}(s)$. Similarly, z_{11} and z_{22} are the driving-point impedances at the ports when the other port is open-circuited.

Up to this point the only restrictions on the network have been the linear, lumped and time-invariant restrictions. If we now restrict the network to be *reciprocal*, we know that the loop imedance matrix $\mathbf{Z}_m$ will be symmetric, so that

$$\Delta_{12} = \Delta_{21} \tag{9}$$

Hence for *reciprocal* networks we find that

$$y_{12} = y_{21}$$
$$z_{12} = z_{21} \tag{10}$$

This result is likewise evident from the reciprocity theorem (which also is established from the condition $\Delta_{12} = \Delta_{21}$).

Another rearrangement of Eq. (5), which was historically the first set of terminal relationships used in transmission line analysis, can be obtained by solving for the input quantities in terms of the output quantities. The result will take the form

$$\begin{bmatrix} V_1(s) \\ I_1(s) \end{bmatrix} = \begin{bmatrix} A & B \\ C & D \end{bmatrix} \begin{bmatrix} V_2(s) \\ -I_2(s) \end{bmatrix} \tag{11}$$

The relationships between this new set of parameters and the y or z parameters are obtained easily by going through the steps of actually rearranging Eq. (5) in the form of Eq. (11).

The parameters introduced in Eq. (11) are called the $ABCD$ parameters, or the *chain* parameters. The last name follows from the fact that these parameters are natural ones for describing the *tandem*, or *cascade*, or *chain* connection of two-ports, as we shall soon see. Make a note of the negative sign in $-I_2$ which is a consequence of our choice of reference for I_2.

From Eq. (11) we can interpret the $ABCD$ parameters as follows.

$$A = \frac{V_1}{V_2}\bigg|_{I_2=0} \qquad\qquad B = \frac{-V_1}{I_2}\bigg|_{V_2=0}$$

$$C = \frac{I_1}{V_2}\bigg|_{I_2=0} \qquad\qquad D = \frac{-I_1}{I_2}\bigg|_{V_2=0} \tag{12}$$

These expressions show that A is the reciprocal of the open-circuit voltage gain for transmission from terminals $(1,1')$ to $(2,2')$, whereas D is the negative reciprocal of the short-circuit current gain for the same direction of transmission. Similarly, B and C are reciprocals of short-circuit transfer admittance and open-circuit transfer impedance, again for the same direction of transmission.

By direct computation, it is possible to find an expression for the determinant of the $ABCD$ matrix. If we denote this determinant by the symbol $|ABCD|$, then we will find that

$$|ABCD| = \det\begin{bmatrix} A & B \\ C & D \end{bmatrix} = AD - BC = \frac{z_{12}}{z_{21}} = \frac{y_{12}}{y_{21}} \tag{13}$$

For the important case of *reciprocal* networks, this simplifies to

$$|ABCD| = AD - BC = 1 \tag{14}$$

For the case of reciprocal networks, then, we can invert Eq. (11), using the last expression, to get

$$\begin{bmatrix} V_2 \\ I_2 \end{bmatrix} = \begin{bmatrix} D & B \\ C & A \end{bmatrix} \begin{bmatrix} V_1 \\ -I_1 \end{bmatrix} \tag{15}$$

This expression relates the output quantities to the input quantities. We see that, in addition to the interpretations in Eq. (12), the $ABCD$ parameters have alternate interpretations from this inverse expression in the case of reciprocal networks.

$$A = -\frac{I_2}{I_1}\bigg|_{V_1=0} \qquad\qquad B = -\frac{V_2}{I_1}\bigg|_{V_1=0}$$

$$C = \frac{I_2}{V_1}\bigg|_{I_1=0} \qquad\qquad D = \frac{V_2}{V_1}\bigg|_{I_1=0} \tag{16}$$

In this case the $ABCD$ parameters refer to transmission from terminals $(2,2')$ to $(1,1')$.

We have now obtained four sets of equations relating the terminal voltages and currents. Two of these sets express the two voltages in terms of the two currents, and vice-versa. The other two sets express voltage and current at one pair of terminals in terms of voltage and current at the other. Two other sets of equations can be obtained by expressing I_1 and V_2 in terms of I_2 and V_1, and vice-versa. These are obtained by rearranging Eq. (11). Again we will leave the details for you to work out. The results will take the following forms.

and

$$\begin{bmatrix} V_1 \\ I_2 \end{bmatrix} = \begin{bmatrix} h_{11} & h_{12} \\ h_{21} & h_{22} \end{bmatrix} \begin{bmatrix} I_1 \\ V_2 \end{bmatrix} \tag{17}$$

$$\begin{bmatrix} I_1 \\ V_2 \end{bmatrix} = \begin{bmatrix} g_{11} & g_{12} \\ g_{21} & g_{22} \end{bmatrix} \begin{bmatrix} V_1 \\ I_2 \end{bmatrix} \tag{18}$$

The interpretations of these parameters can be easily determined from the preceding equations to be the following.

$$h_{11} = \frac{V_1(s)}{I_1(s)} \bigg|_{V_2=0} \qquad h_{12} = \frac{V_1(s)}{V_2(s)} \bigg|_{I_1=0}$$

$$h_{21} = \frac{I_2(s)}{I_1(s)} \bigg|_{V_2=0} \qquad h_{22} = \frac{I_2(s)}{V_2(s)} \bigg|_{I_1=0} \tag{19}$$

$$g_{11} = \frac{I_1}{V_1} \bigg|_{I_2=0} \qquad g_{12} = \frac{I_1}{I_2} \bigg|_{V_1=0}$$

$$g_{21} = \frac{V_2}{V_1} \bigg|_{I_2=0} \qquad g_{22} = \frac{V_2}{I_2} \bigg|_{V_1=0} \tag{20}$$

Thus, we see that the h and g parameters are interpreted under a mixed set of terminal conditions, some of them under open-circuit and some under short-circuit conditions. The h parameters are referred to as the *hybrid* parameters, although both the h and g parameters deserve this name.

From Eq. (19) we see that h_{11} is the reciprocal of y_{11}, and h_{22} is the reciprocal of z_{22}. However, h_{12} is the open-circuit voltage transfer function for transmission from right to left. Similarly, h_{21} is the short-circuit current transfer ratio for transmission from left to right.

From Eq. (20) we see that g_{11} is the reciprocal of z_{11}, and g_{22} is the reciprocal of y_{22}. But g_{12} and g_{21} are dimensionless; g_{12} is the short-circuit current transfer ratio for transmission from right to left, whereas g_{21} is the open-circuit voltage transfer ratio for transmission from left to right.

By direct computation we can find the following relationships

$$h_{12} = -\frac{z_{12}}{z_{21}} h_{21} \qquad (a)$$

$$(21)$$

$$g_{12} = -\frac{y_{12}}{y_{21}} g_{21} \qquad (b)$$

In the special case of reciprocal networks these expressions simplify even further. We can see that in this case $h_{12} = -h_{21}$ and $g_{12} = -g_{21}$. In words, this means that the open-circuit voltage gain for transmission in one direction through the network is equal to the negative of the short-circuit current gain for transmission in the other direction. (The negative sign appears only because of the chosen reference direction of I_2.)

We need to make one remark here about the various equations that we have written relating V_1, V_2, I_1, and I_2. Although the various parameters have interpretations only under suitable open- or short-circuit conditions, the basic equations defining these parameters—Eqs. (5), (7), (11), (17), and (18)—are valid for all two-ports, for all types of external connections, not just for open- or short-circuit conditions. The restrictions are needed only for the purposes of interpreting individual parameters. (Incidentally, these interpretations lead to methods of experimental determination of the parameters.)

A special kind of reciprocal two-port, but one that is very important, is a *symmetrical* two-port. We say that a two-port is symmetrical when there is no effect on the external behavior when the terminal-pairs, or ports, are interchanged. We can easily find the effect of two-port symmetry on the various parameters by interchanging V_1 and I_1 with V_2 and I_2. We find that

$$z_{11} = z_{22} \qquad (a)$$

$$y_{11} = y_{22} \qquad (b)$$

$$A = D \qquad (c) \qquad (22)$$

$$h_{11} = g_{22} \qquad (d)$$

$$g_{11} = h_{22} \qquad (e)$$

One other point should be mentioned. The starting point of the discussion in this chapter was the loop equations. We can just as easily start with the node equations and solve for the terminal voltages initially, rather than the loop currents. The z and y parameters, and, through them, all the others, will then be expressed in terms of the node admittance determinant and its cofactors.

The preceding discussion is in rather great detail and can become tedious if you lose sight of our objective of developing methods of representing the external behavior of two-ports by giving various relationships among the terminal voltages and currents. Each of these sets of relationships finds useful applications. For future reference we will tabulate the interrelationships among the various parameters. The result is given in Table 1. Note that these relationships are valid for a general nonreciprocal two-port.

Let us now give some illustrative examples of the computation of two-port parameters. As the first example consider the network shown

TABLE 1

	z		y		$ABCD$		h		g	
z	z_{11}	z_{12}	$\dfrac{y_{22}}{\lvert y\rvert}$	$\dfrac{-y_{12}}{\lvert y\rvert}$	$\dfrac{A}{C}$	$\dfrac{AD-BC}{C}$	$\dfrac{\lvert h\rvert}{h_{22}}$	$\dfrac{h_{12}}{h_{22}}$	$\dfrac{1}{g_{11}}$	$\dfrac{g_{12}}{g_{11}}$
	z_{21}	z_{22}	$\dfrac{-y_{21}}{\lvert y\rvert}$	$\dfrac{y_{11}}{\lvert y\rvert}$	$\dfrac{1}{C}$	$\dfrac{D}{C}$	$\dfrac{-h_{21}}{h_{22}}$	$\dfrac{1}{h_{22}}$	$\dfrac{g_{21}}{g_{11}}$	$\dfrac{\lvert g\rvert}{g_{11}}$
y	$\dfrac{z_{22}}{\lvert z\rvert}$	$\dfrac{-z_{12}}{\lvert z\rvert}$	y_{11}	y_{12}	$\dfrac{D}{B}$	$\dfrac{-(AD-BC)}{B}$	$\dfrac{1}{h_{11}}$	$\dfrac{-h_{12}}{h_{11}}$	$\dfrac{\lvert g\rvert}{g_{22}}$	$\dfrac{g_{12}}{g_{22}}$
	$\dfrac{-z_{21}}{\lvert z\rvert}$	$\dfrac{z_{11}}{\lvert z\rvert}$	y_{21}	y_{22}	$\dfrac{-1}{B}$	$\dfrac{A}{B}$	$\dfrac{h_{21}}{h_{11}}$	$\dfrac{\lvert h\rvert}{h_{11}}$	$\dfrac{-g_{21}}{g_{22}}$	$\dfrac{1}{g_{22}}$
AB CD	$\dfrac{z_{11}}{z_{21}}$	$\dfrac{\lvert z\rvert}{z_{21}}$	$\dfrac{-y_{22}}{y_{21}}$	$\dfrac{-1}{y_{21}}$	A	B	$\dfrac{-\lvert h\rvert}{h_{21}}$	$\dfrac{-h_{11}}{h_{21}}$	$\dfrac{1}{g_{21}}$	$\dfrac{g_{22}}{g_{21}}$
	$\dfrac{1}{z_{21}}$	$\dfrac{z_{22}}{z_{21}}$	$\dfrac{-\lvert y\rvert}{y_{21}}$	$\dfrac{-y_{11}}{y_{21}}$	C	D	$\dfrac{-h_{22}}{h_{21}}$	$\dfrac{-1}{h_{21}}$	$\dfrac{g_{11}}{g_{21}}$	$\dfrac{\lvert g\rvert}{g_{21}}$
h	$\dfrac{\lvert z\rvert}{z_{22}}$	$\dfrac{z_{12}}{z_{22}}$	$\dfrac{1}{y_{11}}$	$\dfrac{-y_{12}}{y_{11}}$	$\dfrac{B}{D}$	$\dfrac{AD-BC}{D}$	h_{11}	h_{12}	$\dfrac{g_{22}}{\lvert g\rvert}$	$\dfrac{-g_{12}}{\lvert g\rvert}$
	$\dfrac{-z_{21}}{z_{22}}$	$\dfrac{1}{z_{22}}$	$\dfrac{y_{21}}{y_{11}}$	$\dfrac{\lvert y\rvert}{y_{11}}$	$\dfrac{-1}{D}$	$\dfrac{C}{D}$	h_{21}	h_{22}	$\dfrac{-g_{21}}{\lvert g\rvert}$	$\dfrac{g_{11}}{\lvert g\rvert}$
g	$\dfrac{1}{z_{11}}$	$\dfrac{-z_{12}}{z_{11}}$	$\dfrac{\lvert y\rvert}{y_{22}}$	$\dfrac{y_{12}}{y_{22}}$	$\dfrac{C}{A}$	$\dfrac{-(AD-BC)}{A}$	$\dfrac{h_{22}}{\lvert h\rvert}$	$\dfrac{-h_{12}}{\lvert h\rvert}$	g_{11}	g_{12}
	$\dfrac{z_{21}}{z_{11}}$	$\dfrac{\lvert z\rvert}{z_{11}}$	$\dfrac{-y_{21}}{y_{22}}$	$\dfrac{1}{y_{22}}$	$\dfrac{1}{A}$	$\dfrac{B}{A}$	$\dfrac{-h_{21}}{\lvert h\rvert}$	$\dfrac{h_{11}}{\lvert h\rvert}$	g_{21}	g_{22}

in Fig. 6, which can be considered as a model for a vacuum triode under certain conditions. (The capacitances are the grid-plate and plate-

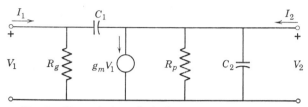

Fig. 6.   Example for calculating two-port parameters.

cathode capacitances.) Let us compute the y parameters for this network. The simplest procedure is to use the interpretations in Eqs. (6). If we short-circuit the output terminals, the resulting network will take the form shown in Fig. 7. As far as the input terminals are concerned,

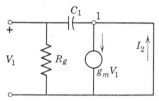

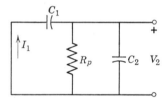

Fig. 7.   Example with output   Fig. 8.   Example with input
terminals shorted.   terminals shorted.

the dependent source has no effect. Hence, y_{11} is the admittance of the parallel combination of R_g and C_1.

$$y_{11}(s) = \frac{1}{R_g} + sC_1 \tag{23}$$

To find y_{21}, let us assume that a voltage source with transform $V_1(s)$ is applied at the input terminals. By applying Kirchhoff's current law at the node labeled 1 in Fig. 7, we find that $I_2 = g_m V_1 - sC_1 V_1$. Hence, y_{21} becomes

$$y_{21} = \frac{I_2(s)}{V_1(s)}\bigg|_{V_2=0} = g_m - sC_1 \tag{24}$$

Now let us short-circuit the input terminals of the original network. The result will take the form of Fig. 8. Since V_1 is zero, the dependent source current is also zero. It is now a simple matter to compute y_{22} and y_{12}. They are

$$y_{22} = \frac{I_2}{V_2}\bigg|_{V_1=0} = s(C_1 + C_2) + \frac{1}{R_p} \qquad (a)$$

$$(25)$$

$$y_{12} = \frac{I_1}{V_2}\bigg|_{V_1=0} = -sC_1 \qquad (b)$$

We see that y_{12} is different from y_{21}, as it should be, because of the presence of the dependent source.

Knowing the y parameters we can now compute any of the other sets of parameters using Table 1. Note that even under the conditions that C_1 and C_2 are zero and R_g infinite, the y parameters exist, but the z parameters do not (both z_{22} and z_{12} will become infinite).

As a second example, consider the model of a transistor (in the common base connection) shown in Fig. 9. Let us compute the open-circuit

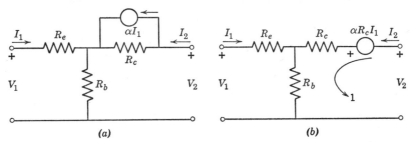

(a)   (b)

Fig. 9.   Transistor model.

parameters for this model. With the output end left open, it is clear that the dependent source will have no effect on the input voltage-current relationship. Hence, z_{11} is the impedance of R_e and R_b in series. On the other hand, the output voltage transform will be affected by the dependent source. In Fig. 9b from Kirchhoff's voltage law around the loop labeled 1, we find that V_2 is $-\alpha R_c I_1 + R_b I_1$. Thus, we have

$$z_{11} = R_e + R_b \qquad (a)$$

$$(26)$$

$$z_{21} = R_b - \alpha R_c \qquad (b)$$

With the input terminals left open ($I_1 = 0$) the dependent source will vanish. Hence, z_{22} and z_{12} are immediately found to be

$$z_{22} = R_b + R_c \qquad (a)$$

$$(27)$$

$$z_{12} = R_b \qquad (b)$$

Again we find that the 12 parameter is not the same as the 21 parameter.

8.2   The Scattering Parameters

Two other methods of expressing the external behavior of two-ports are in common use. Unlike the parameters discussed so far, these parameters are not obtained by a simple rearrangement of Eq. (5). Nevertheless, the description of the terminal behavior afforded by these parameters is just as good as that of the other sets of parameters.

The classical theory of filters is based on the *image parameters*. Consequently, these parameters have been extensively studied and a great deal is known about them. We will defer discussion of these parameters to Chapter 11, which will be devoted exclusively to image parameters and classical filter theory.

The set of parameters that we shall discuss in this section are known as the *scattering parameters*. They are sufficiently different from the other sets to warrant a section all to themselves. Like the image parameters, scattering parameters originated in the theory of transmission lines. They are particularly useful in microwave network theory. In microwave networks the concept of power is much more important than the concepts of voltage and current. In fact the latter become artificial. The scattering parameters are defined in such a fashion that the various quantities of interest in power transmission have very simple expressions in terms of scattering parameters. This fact also makes scattering parameters useful in the design of lumped power transmission networks —filters designed for specified insertion loss, for example. It is possible for us to define scattering parameters starting with the two-port equations; but such a definition would perforce be artificial. Therefore, we shall start from a different point and freely use concepts from transmission line theory, in order to motivate the discussion.

It will perhaps be instructive to begin by considering a one-port. Figure 10 shows a one-port whose driving-point impedance is Z'. It can

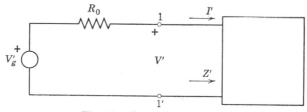

Fig. 10.   Scattering one-port.

be considered as a load on another network whose Thévenin equivalent is shown to the left of terminals $(1,1')$. Using the picture and terminology of wave propagation, we say that if the load is matched to the "source," there will be no reflection at the terminals; otherwise, there will be.

The voltage transform V' at the terminals is pictured as having contributions from the "incident wave" arriving from the left and the "reflected wave" coming back from the load. Similarly for the current transform I'. (We are using primed quantities here because we wish to reserve the unprimed symbols for normalized quantities later.) Thus, we can write

$$V' = V_i' + V_r' \qquad (a)$$
$$I' = I_i' + I_r' \qquad (b)$$

(28)

where the subscripts i and r refer to incident and reflected, respectively. Suppose we think of R_0 as the "characteristic impedance" of the transmission system to the left of terminals $(1,1')$. Then, the incident and reflected quantities are related by

$$\frac{V_i'}{I_i'} = -\frac{V_r'}{I_r'} = R_0 \qquad (29)$$

Using this result, Eqs. (28) will become

$$V' = V_i' + V_r' \qquad (a)$$
$$I' = \frac{V_i'}{R_0} - \frac{V_r'}{R_0} \qquad (b)$$

(30)

When we solve these equations for V_i' and V_r', we get

$$V_i' = \tfrac{1}{2}(V' + R_0 I') \qquad (a)$$
$$V_r' = \tfrac{1}{2}(V' - R_0 I') \qquad (b)$$

(31)

It is now possible to define a *reflection coefficient* or *scattering coefficient* S_{11} as the ratio between the reflected and incident voltage transforms. (The usual symbol for reflection coefficient is ρ but we shall use S_{11} in order to conveniently generalize to a two-port or n-port later.) Thus,

$$S_{11} = \frac{V_r'}{V_i'} = \frac{V' - R_0 I'}{V' + R_0 I'} = \frac{Z' - R_0}{Z' + R_0} = \frac{Z'/R_0 - 1}{Z'/R_0 + 1} \qquad (32)$$

The wave propagation concepts which we used in the preceding discussion are artificial in the case of lumped networks. Nevertheless, it is possible to look upon Eqs. (31) as formal definitions of V_i' and V_r', without attaching any interpretive significance to these quantities which reflect their intuitive origin. In the development, we used R_0 as the Thévenin source resistance or as the characteristic impedance. However, neither of these ideas is necessary in the definitions expressed by Eqs. (31) or (32); R_0 is simply an arbitrary real positive number which has the dimensions of impedance.

Although it is not obvious from the preceding discussion, it is quite convenient to normalize all current and voltage transforms, and therefore also impedances. We define the normalized quantities as follows.

$$V = \frac{V'}{\sqrt{R_0}} \qquad (a)$$

$$\qquad (33)$$

$$I = \sqrt{R_0}\, I' \qquad (b)$$

In terms of these, the incident and reflected voltage transforms in Eq. (31) become

$$V_i = \frac{V_i'}{\sqrt{R_0}} = \frac{1}{2}(V + I) \qquad (a)$$

$$\qquad (34)$$

$$V_r = \frac{V_r'}{\sqrt{R_0}} = \frac{1}{2}(V - I) \qquad (b)$$

Eq. (29) now becomes

$$\frac{V_i}{I_i} = -\frac{V_r}{I_r} = 1 \qquad (35)$$

The scattering coefficient in Eq. (32) becomes

$$S_{11} = \frac{V_r}{I_i} = \frac{V - I}{V + I} = \frac{Z - 1}{Z + 1} \qquad (36)$$

where $Z = Z'/R_0$ is the normalized impedance. When using the preceding expressions, always keep in mind that all voltages and currents are normalized. The normalization can be interpreted in terms of the network shown in Fig. 11. From the diagram it is clear that

$$V_g = V + I \qquad (37)$$

On comparing this with Eq. (34a), we find that

$$V_i = \tfrac{1}{2}V_g \qquad (38)$$

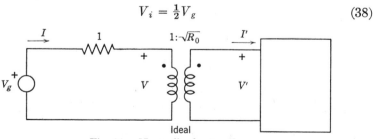

Fig. 11. Normalized network.

That is, the normalized incident voltage is equal to half the normalized source voltage.

Now let us return to the case of a two-port as shown in Fig. 12. The voltage source in series with a resistance at each end of the two-port

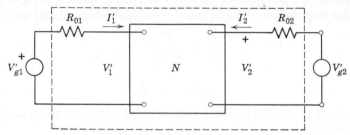

Fig. 12.   Terminated two-port.

can be looked upon as a model for a physical generator. In the most usual case $V_{g2} = 0$ and R_{02} represents the load resistance. The terminal voltage and current transforms have again been primed because we intend to use unprimed symbols for the corresponding normalized quantities, which we define as follows.

$$V_1 = \frac{V_1'}{\sqrt{R_{01}}} \; ; \qquad V_2 = \frac{V_2'}{\sqrt{R_{02}}} \tag{39}$$

$$I_1 = \sqrt{R_{01}} \, I_1'; \qquad I_2 = \sqrt{R_{02}} \, I_2' \tag{40}$$

The network inside the dashed lines in Fig. 12 is known as the *augmented network*. We can interpret the normalization in terms of the network in Fig. 13. An ideal transformer with the turns ratio shown is connected

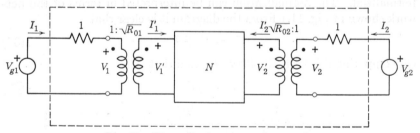

Fig. 13.   Normalized augmented network.

at each pair of terminals. The normalized voltage and current transforms are those at the far sides (looking out from the network) of the ideal transformers.

We now define incident and reflected voltages at each of the ports in a manner quite similar to the corresponding quantities for a one-port as given in Eq. (34). Thus,

$$V_{i1} = \tfrac{1}{2}(V_1 + I_1); \qquad V_{r1} = \tfrac{1}{2}(V_1 - I_1) \tag{41}$$

$$V_{i2} = \tfrac{1}{2}(V_2 + I_2); \qquad V_{r2} = \tfrac{1}{2}(V_2 - I_2) \tag{42}$$

What we wish to do now is to express the relationship between the incident voltages and the reflected voltages, which will serve the same function for the two-port that the scattering coefficient in Eq. (36) serves for the one-port. We write this relationship as

$$\begin{bmatrix} V_{r1} \\ V_{r2} \end{bmatrix} = \begin{bmatrix} S_{11} & S_{12} \\ S_{21} & S_{22} \end{bmatrix} \begin{bmatrix} V_{i1} \\ V_{i2} \end{bmatrix} \tag{43}$$

The coefficient matrix of this transformation is called the *scattering matrix* and is designated **S**; the entries are the *scattering parameters*. These parameters can be interpreted as follows.

$$S_{11} = \left. \frac{V_{r1}}{V_{i1}} \right|_{V_{i2}=0} \qquad\qquad S_{12} = \left. \frac{V_{r1}}{V_{i2}} \right|_{V_{i1}=0}$$

$$S_{21} = \left. \frac{V_{r2}}{V_{i1}} \right|_{V_{i2}=0} \qquad\qquad S_{22} = \left. \frac{V_{r2}}{V_{i2}} \right|_{V_{i1}=0} \tag{44}$$

(Lower case letters, s_{11}, s_{12}, etc., are usually used for the scattering parameters in the literature. We will use capitals to avoid possible confusion with the complex variable $s = \sigma + j\omega$.)

Let us now relate the scattering matrix with the short-circuit admittance or open-circuit impedance matrix of the two-port N. We should point out that N may not have a y matrix or a z matrix (as, for example, the network in Fig. 7). Nevertheless, the augmented network will always have a y matrix because of the augmenting unit resistances. Let us designate this matrix by $\mathbf{Y}_a$. That is,

$$\mathbf{I} - \mathbf{Y}_a \mathbf{V}_g \tag{45}$$

where

$$\mathbf{I} = \begin{bmatrix} I_1 \\ I_2 \end{bmatrix}, \qquad \mathbf{V}_g = \begin{bmatrix} V_{g1} \\ V_{g2} \end{bmatrix} \tag{46}$$

It is always possible to relate the scattering matrix to $\mathbf{Y}_a$. In order to do this, let us first solve Eqs. (41) and (42) for I_1 and I_2. We will get

$$\mathbf{I} = \mathbf{V}_i - \mathbf{V}_r \tag{47}$$

where

$$\mathbf{V}_i = \begin{bmatrix} V_{i1} \\ V_{i2} \end{bmatrix}, \qquad \mathbf{V}_r = \begin{bmatrix} V_{r1} \\ V_{r2} \end{bmatrix} \tag{48}$$

Next, from a consideration of Fig. 13, we find the generalization of Eq. (34) to the two-port to be

$$\mathbf{V}_i = \tfrac{1}{2}\mathbf{V}_g \tag{49}$$

This expression throws new light on the interpretations of the scattering parameters in Eqs. (44). We now interpret the ratios expressed in those equations to apply when the *pertinent terminals of the augmented network are shorted*. Thus, the scattering parameters are short-circuit parameters (but not *admittances*) of the augmented networks.

By substituting Eqs. (45) and (49) into Eq. (47), and solving for the reflected voltage matrix, we get

$$\mathbf{V}_r = (\mathbf{U} - 2\mathbf{Y}_A)\mathbf{V}_i \tag{50}$$

where $\mathbf{U}$ is the unit matrix. Hence, the scattering matrix is

$$\mathbf{S} = \mathbf{U} - 2\mathbf{Y}_A \tag{51}$$

This is the desired relationship. It is valid whether or not the network N has an admittance or impedance matrix. However, when N does have an admittance matrix $\mathbf{Y}_{sc}$, or an impedance matrix $\mathbf{Z}_{oc}$, it is possible to express $\mathbf{Y}_A$ in terms of one of these and, thus, to express the scattering matrix in terms of $\mathbf{Y}_{sc}$ or $\mathbf{Z}_{oc}$.

First of all, we should normalize the impedance and admittance matrices. Let the normalized matrices be designated $\mathbf{Z}_n$ and $\mathbf{Y}_n$, respectively. We define $\mathbf{Z}_n$ as

$$\mathbf{Z}_n = \begin{bmatrix} \dfrac{z_{11}}{R_{01}} & \dfrac{z_{12}}{\sqrt{R_{01}R_{02}}} \\[2ex] \dfrac{z_{21}}{\sqrt{R_{01}R_{02}}} & \dfrac{z_{22}}{R_{02}} \end{bmatrix} \tag{52}$$

with a similar definition for $\mathbf{Y}_n$. These relationships can be expressed concisely as

$$\mathbf{Z}_n = (\sqrt{\mathbf{R}_0}\,)^{-1}\mathbf{Z}_{oc}(\sqrt{\mathbf{R}_0}\,)^{-1} \qquad (a)$$
$$\mathbf{Y}_n = (\sqrt{\mathbf{R}_0}\,)\mathbf{Y}_{sc}(\sqrt{\mathbf{R}_0}\,) \qquad (b)$$
$$\tag{53}$$

where

$$\sqrt{\mathbf{R}_0} = \begin{bmatrix} \sqrt{R_{01}} & 0 \\[2ex] 0 & \sqrt{R_{02}} \end{bmatrix}; \qquad (\sqrt{\mathbf{R}_0}\,)^{-1} = \begin{bmatrix} \dfrac{1}{\sqrt{R_{01}}} & 0 \\[2ex] 0 & \dfrac{1}{\sqrt{R_{02}}} \end{bmatrix} \tag{54}$$

(You can verify these by carrying out the indicated multiplications.)

The next job is to express the admittance matrix of the augmented network in terms of $\mathbf{Z}_n$ or $\mathbf{Y}_n$. This is easy, since the impedance matrix of the augmented network is $\mathbf{U} + \mathbf{Z}_n$, and $\mathbf{Y}_A$ is simply the inverse of this. Hence,

$$\mathbf{S} = \mathbf{U} - 2(\mathbf{U} + \mathbf{Z}_n)^{-1} \tag{55}$$

is one form of the desired relationship. Several alternative forms can be obtained with some algebraic manipulation. We will present them here but leave the derivations to you. They are

$$\mathbf{S} = (\mathbf{Z}_n + \mathbf{U})^{-1}(\mathbf{Z}_n - \mathbf{U}) = (\mathbf{Z}_n - \mathbf{U})(\mathbf{Z}_n + \mathbf{U})^{-1} \quad (a)$$
$$\mathbf{S} = (\mathbf{U} + \mathbf{Y}_n)^{-1}(\mathbf{U} - \mathbf{Y}_n) = (\mathbf{U} - \mathbf{Y}_n)(\mathbf{U} + \mathbf{Y}_n)^{-1} \quad (b) \tag{56}$$
$$= 2(\mathbf{U} + \mathbf{Y}_n)^{-1} - \mathbf{U}$$

Everything we have done up to this point is valid for both reciprocal and nonreciprocal networks. However, if network N is reciprocal, then the scattering matrix will be symmetric, as evidenced most clearly by Eq. (51).

Let us now consider a simple example in order to illustrate some of the concepts which have been introduced. We wish to calculate the scattering parameters of an ideal transformer, shown in Fig. 14. The

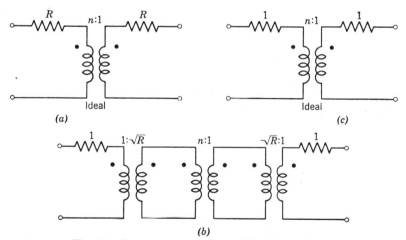

Fig. 14. Scattering parameters of ideal transformers.

series resistances are equal. (If they are unequal to start with, we can change the turns ratio). The augmented network is formed as in part (b) of the figure. But the cascade connection of the three ideal transformers reduces to the original transformer. (This is most easily seen by calculating the chain matrix according to the discussion in section 8.5.)

Note that the ideal transformer alone has neither a z matrix nor a y matrix. Hence, Eqs. (55) and (56) will be of no use; we fall back on Eq. (51) which involves calculating the y matrix of the augmented network. But this is a relatively easy task. By direct calculation we find $\mathbf{Y}_A$ to be

$$\mathbf{Y}_A = \begin{bmatrix} \dfrac{1}{n^2+1} & \dfrac{-n}{n^2+1} \\ \dfrac{-n}{n^2+1} & \dfrac{n^2}{n^2+1} \end{bmatrix} \tag{57}$$

Hence, using Eq. (51), the scattering matrix is

$$\mathbf{S} = \begin{bmatrix} \dfrac{n^2-1}{n^2+1} & \dfrac{2n}{n^2+1} \\ \dfrac{2n}{n^2+1} & \dfrac{1-n^2}{n^2+1} \end{bmatrix} \tag{58}$$

Note that S_{22} is the negative of S_{11}. Two-ports which satisfy this condition are called *antimetric* two-ports (in contrast with symmetric two-ports for which $S_{11} = S_{22}$). In order to check on the reasonableness of, at least, S_{11} and S_{22}, go back to Fig. 14a. Shorting the output terminals and calculating the reflection coefficient between the series resistance R and the input impedance at the terminals of the transformer, we get the same S_{11}. We should be able to obtain S_{22} simply by replacing n by $1/n$, which is also correct.

Let us now restrict ourselves to passive, reciprocal two-ports and interpret the scattering parameters in terms of power transfer. Up until now we have been dealing with transforms of voltage and current. Let us continue to use the same symbols but think of the variables as phasors which represent sinusoidal quantities. From the discussion in Chapter 5 we know that such a procedure is valid.

Refer to Fig. 13 and let $V_{g2} = 0$; we then have a transmission network excited on the left. The maximum power available from the source (with the unit resistance fixed) is $|V_{g1}|^2/2$, of which half is dissipated in the unit resistance. The maximum power available to the two-port is then

$$P_A = \tfrac{1}{4}|V_{g1}|^2 = |V_{i1}|^2 \tag{59}$$

The last step follows from Eq. (49). The power output at the unit resistance load is

$$P_L = |I_2|^2 = |V_2|^2 = |V_{i2} + V_{r2}|^2 = |V_{r2}|^2 \qquad (60)$$

The last step follows from the fact that $V_{i2} = \frac{1}{2}V_{g2} = 0$; the preceding step follows from Eq. (42). The ratio of the power output to the maximum power available is

$$\frac{P_L}{P_A} = \frac{|V_{r2}|^2}{|V_{i1}|^2} = |S_{21}(j\omega)|^2 \qquad (61)$$

Since V_{r2} and V_{i1} are phasors, S_{21} in the last step is to be evaluated on the $j\omega$-axis only, as indicated. Note that this power ratio is invariant under normalization, so that the same result applies to the unnormalized network. In a similar manner, we can interpret the j-axis squared magnitude of S_{12} to be equal to the ratio of power output to maximum power input when transmission is from right to left.

The preceding brief discussion of scattering parameters is by no means exhaustive. However, we shall not discuss the subject any further in this text.*

Let us here restate the reasons why we use so many different sets of parameters to describe the behavior of a two-port when they are all admittedly equivalent descriptions. The main reason is to obtain algebraically simple formulas for the various quantities of interest under many different operating conditions. In particular the way in which the network is to be operated and the methods in which two-ports are to be interconnected decide the choice of parameters to be used. For example, when a two-port network is used as an interstage coupling network between vacuum tubes, it is (approximately) operating between open circuits and so the open-circuit parameters are the most suitable set. On the other hand, in a transistor circuit one end is approximately an open circuit, whereas the other is approximately a short circuit. Then the hybrid parameters are the most natural method of description. If we are interested in combining networks in parallel it would seem reasonable to expect that the short-circuit admittance parameters will lead to the simplest formulas for the composite network parameters in terms of the individual network parameters. Similarly in cascading two terminal pairs, the $ABCD$ parameters lead to the simplest formulas. In conventional filter design image parameters are used mainly because the components of a lattice are very simply related to the image parameters, thus leading to simple computations.

* Many good papers on scattering parameters appear in *Transactions*, IRE, Vol. CT-3, June, 1956. (This is the scattering matrix issue of the Professional Group on Circuit Theory.)

8.3   Equivalence of Two-Ports

When it is desired to design a network to satisfy certain given performance criteria, it may be that the design procedure gives a network that
contains many undesirable features.   These features may be in the
structure of the network, in the number of elements in the network, or
in the type of elements.   It would be desirable to replace this network
with another which would be "equivalent" to the first in some sense.
The same is true if the objective is to analyze a given network.   If the
network can be replaced by a simpler "equivalent" of some sort, the
analysis will be simplified.   For these reasons we are quite interested
in the topic of equivalence of networks.

We already have available the Thévenin or Norton equivalent of a
network.   These are equivalent to a given network at a single pair of
terminals.   We would now like to discuss equivalence of two-ports.   We
say that *a two-port N_1 is equivalent to a second two-port N_2 at the two pairs
of terminals if replacing N_2 by N_1 leaves the terminal voltages and currents
unchanged independent of external networks connected at the terminals.*
This is illustrated in Fig. 15.

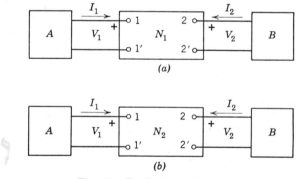

(a)

(b)

Fig. 15.   Equivalence of two-ports.

The same networks are connected to corresponding pairs of terminals
in the two parts of the figure.   The three parts A, N_1, and B are isolated
(electrically and magnetically) except for the interconnections shown.
Similarly A, N_2, and B are isolated except for the interconnections
shown.

The definition of two-port equivalence implies that the relationships
among the terminal voltages and currents remain unchanged if N_1 is
substituted for N_2.   Hence, two equivalent two-ports have the same z
or y, or $ABCD$, or any other set of parameters.   Thus, if we have a two-

port and we wish to find a second two-port, perhaps one whose structure we specify, to be equivalent to the first, we require that one of the sets of two-port parameters be equal for both networks. The simplest set to use may depend on the structure of the networks and on the ultimate application that is to be made of the equivalent two-port.

Let us now consider two simple but very general two-ports which are to be equivalent to an arbitrary two-port. The first of these is based on a consideration of the z parameters. The pertinent equations are repeated here.

$$V_1 = z_{11}I_1 + z_{12}I_2 \qquad (a)$$
$$V_2 = z_{21}I_1 + z_{22}I_2 \qquad (b)$$
$$(62)$$

These equations suggest the two-port shown in Fig. 16. By direct calculation we can verify that the voltages and currents of this two-port

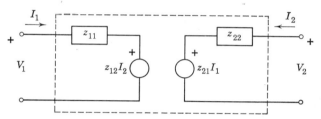

Fig. 16.   General two-port equivalent.

satisfy Eqs. (62). Note that the two-port contains two dependent voltage sources.

In a completely similar manner, the system of y parameter equations, which are

$$I_1 = y_{11}V_1 + y_{12}V_2 \qquad (a)$$
$$I_2 = y_{21}V_1 + y_{22}V_2 \qquad (b)$$
$$(63)$$

leads to the equivalent two-port shown in Fig. 17. This one contains two dependent current sources. Other such equivalent two-ports can be found, either based on the z and y parameters, or based on the other sets of two-port parameters. Some of these are suggested as problems

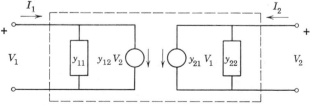

Fig. 17.   Another general two-port equivalent.

at the end of the chapter. These equivalent two-ports find their greatest use when dealing with nonreciprocal networks.

Let us now discuss some simple equivalent two-ports for the case of *reciprocal* networks. Consider the Tee network shown in Fig. 18. Since

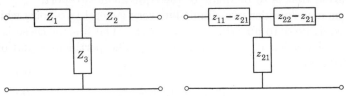

Fig. 18.   Tee equivalent.

for reciprocal two-ports $z_{12} = z_{21}$, we can immediately write the z parameters of the Tee by inspection. They are

$$z_{11} = Z_1 + Z_3 \qquad (a)$$

$$z_{22} = Z_2 + Z_3 \qquad (b) \qquad (64)$$

$$z_{12} = z_{21} = Z_3 \qquad (c)$$

If we now consider that the z parameters on the left are given, or that they are calculated from a given two-port, we must adjust the branch impedances of the Tee in order to satisfy these equations. Solving for the branch impedances, we get

$$Z_1 = z_{11} - z_{21} \qquad (a)$$

$$Z_2 = z_{22} - z_{21} \qquad (b) \qquad (65)$$

$$Z_3 = z_{21} \qquad (c)$$

Hence, if the Tee is to be equivalent to any other reciprocal two-port the branch impedances of the Tee must satisfy these equations. This is illustrated in Fig. 18b.

Note that the Tee equivalent is a mathematical equivalent. No claim is made that it can actually be constructed as a realizable network. Nevertheless, the results of any mathematical operations performed with the Tee equivalent used in place of any reciprocal two-port will be valid.

Let us now illustrate with an example the use of the Tee equivalent in deriving analytical results in the analysis of networks when a specific network is not involved, just a set of two-port parameters. It is desired to develop the formula for the driving point impedance at the terminals $(1,1')$ of a general reciprocal two-port when an impedance (Z_L) is connected at terminals $(2,2')$ as in Fig. 19a. Let the open-circuit parameters of the two-port be z_{11}, z_{12}, and z_{22}. Then, we can replace the two-port

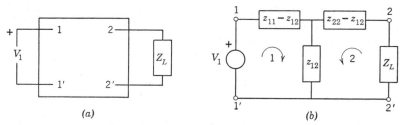

Fig. 19.   Use of Tee equivalent.

by its Tee equivalent as in Fig. 19b.   The loop equations for the two loops shown in the figure are

$$\begin{bmatrix} V_1 \\ 0 \end{bmatrix} = \begin{bmatrix} z_{11} & z_{12} \\ z_{21} & z_{22} + Z_L \end{bmatrix}\begin{bmatrix} I_1 \\ I_2 \end{bmatrix} \tag{66}$$

Immediately we get the driving-point impedance as

$$Z = \frac{V_1(s)}{I_1(s)} = \frac{z_{11}(z_{22} + Z_L) - z_{12}{}^2}{z_{22} + Z_L} = z_{11} - \frac{z_{12}{}^2}{z_{22} + Z_L} \tag{67}$$

This is the desired result.   Note that the same result can be obtained directly from the z system of equations without using the Tee equivalent by setting $V_2 = -Z_L I_2$.   Equation (66) (and its consequences) then follows immediately.   However, it may sometimes be more helpful and satisfying to have a network to analyze rather than some equations to manipulate.

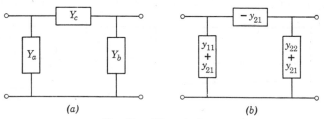

Fig. 20.   Pi equivalent.

As a second simple equivalent of reciprocal two-ports consider the Pi network shown in Fig. 20a.   We can easily compute its y parameters by inspection; they are

$$y_{11} = Y_a + Y_c \qquad\qquad (a)$$

$$y_{22} = Y_b + Y_c \qquad\qquad (b) \qquad (68)$$

$$y_{21} = y_{12} = -Y_c \qquad\qquad (c)$$

If the Pi network is to be equivalent to any arbitrary two-port, then the branch admittance must be adjusted to satisfy these equations. Solving these equations for the branch admittances, we get

$$Y_a = y_{11} + y_{21} \qquad (a)$$
$$Y_b = y_{22} + y_{21} \qquad (b) \qquad (69)$$
$$Y_c = -y_{21} \qquad (c)$$

The resulting network is shown in Fig. 20b. It is again clear that these branch admittances do not necessarily represent realizable networks. However, the mathematical equivalence is valid and useful.

Of course, since the Pi and Tee are themselves two-ports, we can find a Tee equivalent of the Pi or a Pi equivalent of the Tee. To find the relationships among the branch impedances and admittances when a Pi and a Tee are equivalent, we must set one of the sets of two-port parameters of the Tee equal to the corresponding ones of the Pi. For example, using the relationships between the y and z parameters from Table 1, we can compute the y parameters of the Tee from Eqs. (64) and then set them equal to the y parameters of the Pi given in Eqs. (68). The result will be the well-known Tee to Pi (or $Y - \Delta$) transformation. The details are simply algebra and will be left to you. Note, however, that the Tee equivalent of a Pi (or Pi equivalent of a Tee) may not be a realizable network.

Before leaving the topic of equivalent two-ports, let us emphasize that the ideas of equivalent two-ports that have been developed are valid only for *two-ports* and not for arbitrary networks with four terminals. As an example consider the network shown in Fig. 21a which

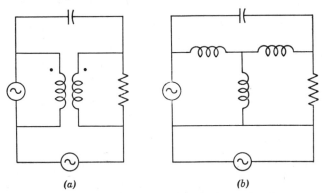

(a)   (b)

Fig. 21. Erroneous use of equivalent network.

contains a transformer. What will happen if the transformer is replaced by a Tee "equivalent"? Clearly the voltage source at the bottom of the figure will become short-circuited. The voltages and currents at the original terminals of the transformer will not be the same as they were. This should be expected, because the equivalences we have been discussing are for two-ports only, and the transformer in this figure does not constitute a two-port.

8.4 Transformer Equivalents

Very often in the analysis of networks containing transformers it is convenient to have an equivalent of the transformer. Somehow, we feel more at home with a connected network with no mutual coupling. Quite often such equivalent networks suggest other networks by which the transformer may be replaced while providing the same type of behavior that was expected of the transformer. (An example of this is the double-tuned, capacitively coupled circuit. See Problem 7.2.) The usefulness of a transformer equivalent is sometimes felt in the opposite direction as well. That is, in a synthesis situation it may be possible to arrive at a network which is not realizable as it stands, but may be replaced by an equivalent transformer. (An example of this is the famous Brune synthesis of a driving-point function.) For these reasons we will devote a separate section to a discussion of transformer equivalent two-ports.

To start with, let us look for a Tee equivalent of the transformer shown in Fig. 22. The z system of equations can be written down im-

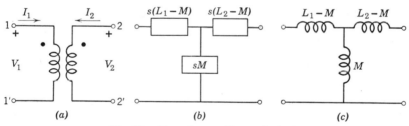

(a)   (b)   (c)

Fig. 22. Transformer Tee equivalent.

mediately from the definition of the v–i relationships of a transformer. It is

$$\begin{bmatrix} V_1 \\ V_2 \end{bmatrix} = \begin{bmatrix} sL_1 & sM \\ sM & sL_2 \end{bmatrix} \begin{bmatrix} I_1 \\ I_2 \end{bmatrix} \tag{70}$$

Hence, the Tee equivalent takes the form of Fig. 22b. Since each impedance in this Tee equivalent is s times a constant, we might be tempted to call the elements "inductances" and draw the network as in Fig. 22c. There is nothing wrong with this procedure provided we keep in mind that some of the inductances so drawn may be negative, since it is possible for M to be larger than one or the other of the self-inductances, or for M to be negative. As a matter of fact, we shall follow this practice.

Next let us consider a Pi equivalent. For this we should invert Eq. (70) and obtain the y parameters. As we saw in Chapter 2 from a different viewpoint, this can be done except in the case of a perfect transformer. For a perfect transformer the z matrix is singular. Assuming that this is not the case, the inversion of Eq. (70) gives

$$\begin{bmatrix} I_1 \\ I_2 \end{bmatrix} = \frac{1}{s(L_1 L_2 - M^2)} \begin{bmatrix} L_2 & -M \\ -M & L_1 \end{bmatrix} \begin{bmatrix} V_1 \\ V_2 \end{bmatrix} \tag{71}$$

Hence, the Pi equivalent takes the form shown in Fig. 23. Again note that some of the branch inductances may be negative, depending on the value and sign of M.

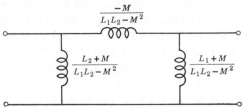

Fig. 23.   Transformer Pi equivalent.

In both of these equivalent circuits of a transformer, a connected network is obtained. One of the features of a transformer, that of isolation, is thus lost. Let us now use a slightly different approach and transform the output current and voltage. Let us write

$$V_2(s) = \frac{1}{n} V_2{}'(s) \tag{a}$$

$$I_2(s) = n I_2{}'(s) \tag{b}$$

$$\tag{72}$$

where n is a real number. We immediately recognize this transformation to represent an ideal transformer (see Chapter 1) in which n is the turns ratio. With these changes, the z system of equations given in Eq. (70) can be written

$$\begin{bmatrix} V_1 \\ V_2{}' \end{bmatrix} = \begin{bmatrix} sL_1 & snM \\ snM & sn^2 L_2 \end{bmatrix} \begin{bmatrix} I_1 \\ I_2{}' \end{bmatrix} \tag{73}$$

It is now a simple matter to find the Tee network whose z system of equations is given by this expression. The complete equivalent, including the ideal transformer, takes the form of Fig. 24.

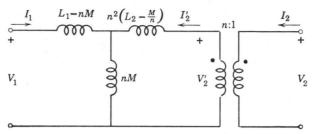

Fig. 24.   Transformer equivalent.

No restriction has been placed on the turns ratio n other than realness. For special values of n, the transformer equivalent shown in Fig. 24 will take on special forms. In particular, when $n = 1$ the ideal transformer is no longer necessary and the Tee equivalent of Fig. 22 results. For the case $n = kL_1/M = M/kL_2$, where k is the coupling coefficient, the equivalent takes the form shown in Fig. 25a.   In the still further

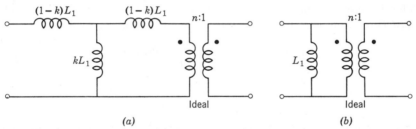

(a)   *(b)*

Fig. 25.   More transformer equivalents.   (a) $n = kL_1/M = M/kL_2$; (b) $n = L_1/M = M/L_2$.

case in which $k = 1$, corresponding to a perfect transformer, the network of Fig. 25b is obtained.   This agrees with Fig. 13 in Chapter 1, as it should.

8.5   Interconnection of Two-Port Networks

Practical two-port networks are built by combining simple two-port structures as "building blocks."   There are two simple reasons for this procedure.   From the design engineer's point of view it is much easier to design simple blocks and interconnect them, than to design a complex network in one piece.   The second reason is practical.   It is much easier to shield smaller units and to reduce the effect of parasitic capacitances to ground.

There are three basic methods in which simple two-ports can be interconnected to make up a complex two-port.   These three combinations are known as the *series*, *parallel*, and *tandem* interconnections.   The tandem connection is also called a *cascade* connection.   Of these, the cascade connection is the most common, the parallel is less common, and the series is the least popular.   We will study these interconnections in their order of importance.

Two two-ports are said to be connected in cascade, if the output terminals of one two-port are the input terminals of the second, as in Fig. 26.

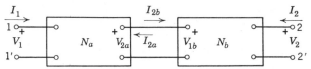

Fig. 26.   Tandem connection of two-ports.

Our main interest in the problem of "interconnection" is, from the analysis point of view, to study how the parameters of the over-all networks are related to the parameters of the individual building blocks. The tandem combination is most conveniently studied by means of the $ABCD$ parameters.   From the references in the figure, we see that

$$V_1 = V_{1a} \qquad\qquad I_1 = I_{1a}$$

$$V_2 = V_{2b} \qquad\qquad I_2 = I_{2b} \tag{74}$$

$$V_{2a} = V_{1b} \qquad\qquad I_{2a} = -I_{1b}$$

Hence, for the $ABCD$ system of equations of the N_b network we can write

$$\begin{bmatrix} V_{2a} \\ -I_{2a} \end{bmatrix} = \begin{bmatrix} V_{1b} \\ I_{1b} \end{bmatrix} = \begin{bmatrix} A_b & B_b \\ C_b & D_b \end{bmatrix} \begin{bmatrix} V_2 \\ -I_2 \end{bmatrix} \tag{75}$$

If we now write the $ABCD$ system of equations for the N_a network and substitute the last equation, we get

$$\begin{bmatrix} V_1 \\ I_1 \end{bmatrix} = \begin{bmatrix} A_a & B_a \\ C_a & D_a \end{bmatrix} \begin{bmatrix} V_{2a} \\ -I_{2a} \end{bmatrix} = \begin{bmatrix} A_a & B_a \\ C_a & D_a \end{bmatrix} \begin{bmatrix} A_b & B_b \\ C_b & D_b \end{bmatrix} \begin{bmatrix} V_2 \\ -I_2 \end{bmatrix} \tag{76}$$

Thus the $ABCD$ matrix of the over-all network is equal to the product of the $ABCD$ matrices of the individual networks; that is,

$$\begin{bmatrix} A & B \\ C & D \end{bmatrix} = \begin{bmatrix} A_a & B_a \\ C_a & D_a \end{bmatrix} \begin{bmatrix} A_b & B_b \\ C_b & D_b \end{bmatrix} \tag{77}$$

Once we know the relationship between the parameters of the over-all network and those of the components for any one set of parameters, it is merely algebraic computation to get the relationship for any other set. For example, the open-circuit parameters of the over-all network can be found in terms of those of the two cascaded ones by expressing the z parameters in terms of the $ABCD$'s, and then using Eq. (77). The result will be

$$z_{11} = \frac{z_{11a}(z_{22a} + z_{11b}) - z_{12a}z_{21a}}{z_{22a} + z_{11b}}$$

$$= z_{11a} - \frac{z_{12a}z_{21a}}{z_{22a} + z_{11b}} \qquad (a)$$

$$z_{12} = \frac{z_{12a}z_{12b}}{z_{22a} + z_{11b}} \qquad (b)$$

$$(78)$$

$$z_{21} = \frac{z_{21a}z_{21b}}{z_{22a} + z_{11b}} \qquad (c)$$

$$z_{22} = z_{22b} - \frac{z_{12b}z_{21b}}{z_{11b} + z_{22a}} \qquad (d)$$

The details of this computation and the corresponding computation of the short-circuit parameters are left as exercises.

One important feature of Eqs. (78)(*b*), (*c*) should be emphasized. The zeros of z_{12} or z_{21} of the composite network (which are known as "zeros of transmission") are the zeros of the corresponding parameters of the individual networks. This fact is the basis of some of the well-known methods of two-port synthesis.

Let us next turn our attention to the parallel combination of two-ports. Two two-ports are said to be connected in parallel if the corresponding terminals (1,1′, 2,2′) of the two are connected together as in Fig. 27. This condition forces the equality of the terminal voltages

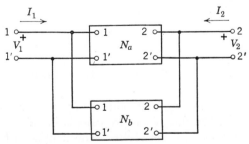

Fig. 27.   Parallel connection of two-ports.

of the two networks. If we can assume that the relationships among the voltages and currents of the individual networks N_a and N_b remain unaltered when the two are connected in parallel, then we can write

$$\begin{bmatrix} I_1 \\ I_2 \end{bmatrix} = \begin{bmatrix} I_{1a} \\ I_{2a} \end{bmatrix} + \begin{bmatrix} I_{1b} \\ I_{2b} \end{bmatrix} = \begin{bmatrix} y_{11a} & y_{12a} \\ y_{21a} & y_{22a} \end{bmatrix} \begin{bmatrix} V_1 \\ V_2 \end{bmatrix} + \begin{bmatrix} y_{11b} & y_{12b} \\ y_{21b} & y_{22b} \end{bmatrix} \begin{bmatrix} V_1 \\ V_2 \end{bmatrix}$$

$$= \begin{bmatrix} y_{11a} + y_{11b} & y_{12a} + y_{12b} \\ y_{21a} + y_{21b} & y_{22a} + y_{22b} \end{bmatrix} \begin{bmatrix} V_1 \\ V_2 \end{bmatrix} \qquad (79)$$

Thus the short-circuit admittance matrix of the composite network is the sum of the short-circuit admittance matrices of the individual networks.

We must now inquire into the conditions under which the two networks can be connected in this way without causing the voltage-current relationships at the terminals of each to be modified in any way. For example, we can see that if there is a straight-through connection between terminals 1′ and 2′ of network b but not in network a, then the branch between terminals 1′ and 2′ of network a will be shorted when the parallel connection is made. Equation (79) will not be valid in such a case.

In order for the voltage-current relationships of the individual networks to remain unaltered under interconnection, the following condition (due to O. Brune) is necessary and sufficient. When the two two-ports are interconnected at either of the two ends and the other ends are short-circuited as in Fig. 28 the voltage marked V must be zero.

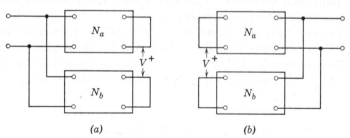

(a)   *(b)*

Fig. 28.   Brune's test for parallel-connected two-ports.

If this condition is not satisfied, the matrix addition will not give the correct answer for the parameters of the composite network, unless isolating ideal transformers are introduced at one of the two ends. It is a simple matter to prove this result by calculating the voltage between terminals 1′ and 2′ of both networks. The details will be left to you.

An important special case of the parallel combination of two-ports, which is useful in practical applications, is the parallel connection of common terminal networks, that is, networks in which the terminals 1′ and 2′ are the same. A typical example is the "parallel ladders" network of Fig. 29. You should verify (by Brune's test) that the matrix addition is valid for this structure.

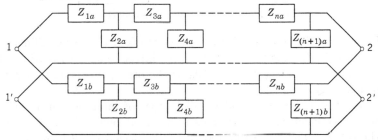

Fig. 29.   Parallel ladders network.

Finally, let us consider the series connection of two-ports. We say that two two-ports are connected in series if they are connected as shown in Fig. 30.

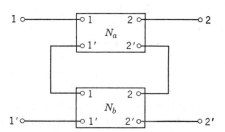

Fig. 30.   Series connection of two-ports.

If, as before, we assume that the voltage-current relationships of the individual networks are unaltered, the open-circuit impedance matrix of the composite network is the sum of the open-circuit matrices of the individual two-ports; that is,

$$\begin{bmatrix} z_{11} & z_{12} \\ z_{21} & z_{22} \end{bmatrix} = \begin{bmatrix} z_{11a} & z_{12a} \\ z_{21a} & z_{22a} \end{bmatrix} + \begin{bmatrix} z_{11b} & z_{12b} \\ z_{21b} & z_{22b} \end{bmatrix} \qquad (80)$$

The proof of this result is left as an exercise.

Brune's test to verify whether matrix addition is valid for the series combination is the following. Connect one end of the two networks in series as in Fig. 31 leaving the other terminals open. Then the matrix

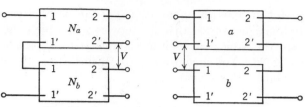

Fig. 31.   Brune's test for series connection.

addition is valid if and only if the voltage marked V is zero.   (This must be true for both ends.)   Once again, by introducing an isolating ideal transformer at one pair of terminals or the other, this condition can be dispensed with.

Variations of the series and parallel types of interconnection are obtained by connecting the terminals in series at one end and in parallel at the other.   These are referred to as the *series-parallel* and *parallel-series* connections.   As we might surmise, the h and g parameters of the individual two-ports are added to give the over-all h and g parameters, respectively.   We will not pursue this topic any further here.*

8.6   Certain Simple Reciprocal Two-Ports

In the preceding parts of this chapter we have concentrated heavily on the general description of the behavior of two-ports.   It is now time for us to take up some examples of the most common two-port networks and briefly study their transmission properties and frequency response. We shall here restrict ourselves to passive, reciprocal and time invariant networks.

Let us start by noting that two-ports can be classified broadly in two categories: (1) *common-terminal* and (2) *noncommon terminal*.   Sometimes these classes are called *unbalanced* and *balanced*, respectively.   In the common-terminal two-port, one terminal of each pair is common to both.   Such a two-port is essentially a three terminal network, one terminal belonging to the input, a second to the output, and the third is common to both.

The most common example of a common terminal two-port is a ladder network as shown in Fig. 32.   None of the branches is assumed to be coupled magnetically to any other branch.   Of course, the ladder may start or end, or both, with a shunt branch instead of a series branch.

Purely from physical intuition we can make some interesting observations about a ladder.   These observations can also be confirmed by formal analysis.   Suppose the ladder is excited from the left.   Quite

* For further details, see E. A. Guillemin, *Communication Networks*, Vol. II, John Wiley and Sons, 1935.

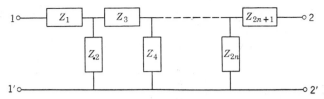

Fig. 32.   General ladder network.

evidently, the output voltage can go to zero only under one of two conditions.   Either one of the series impedances Z_1, Z_3, etc., becomes an open circuit at some value of s, or one of the shunt impedances Z_2, Z_4, etc., becomes a short circuit.   Such values of s are zeros of z_{12} and are referred to as *transmission zeros*.   However, if a series impedance Z_k has a pole at some value of s (thus effectively open-circuiting the branch), and the impedance of the rest of the network to the right of Z_k also has a pole there, this value of s will not be a transmission zero.   This fact is clarified from a consideration of Fig. 33.   If both Z_k and Z have a pole

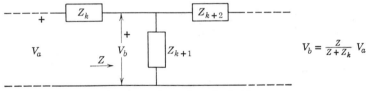

Fig. 33.   A section of a ladder.

at the same point, then the voltage V_a will divide between them according to the voltage divider law (in accordance with the values of the residues) and will cause V_b to have a nonzero value.   A similar statement applies when a shunt branch impedance becomes a short circuit and the impedance of the rest of the network to the right also becomes shorted at the same value of s.   These results can be proved more formally.   (See, for example, Problem 10.9.)   (The words "rest of the network to the right" should be changed to "rest of the network to the left" if transmission is from right to left.)

Since the branch impedances of a ladder can have zeros and poles only in the left half plane or on the imaginary axis, it follows that the transfer impedance z_{12} of a ladder cannot have any zeros inside the right half plane.   In other words, a ladder is always a minimum-phase network. This condition is no longer true if we admit mutual coupling between the branches, for then the network may become nonminimum-phase.

Let us now consider some specific examples of ladders.   A typical interstage RC coupling network for an audio amplifier is shown in Fig.

34. R_p represents the equivalent load resistance (including the plate resistance of the tube); C_c is the coupling capacitance; R_T and C_T constitute the tone control; R_1 and R_2 represent the volume control, and

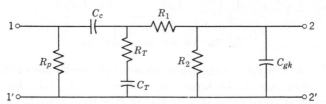

Fig. 34.   Interstage coupling network.

C_{gk} represents the grid-cathode capacitance of the following stage.   For a typical circuit we may have the following values.   Both actual and

	Actual	Normalized	
R_p	100 K	1	
C_c	0.01 μf	10	$R_n = \dfrac{R}{R_0}$
R_T	1 meg	10	
C_T	0.001 μf	1	$C_n = \omega_0 R_0 C$
R_1	500 K	5	$R_0 = 10^5$
R_2	500 K	5	$\omega_0 = 10^4$
C_{gk}	20 μμf	0.02	

normalized values are given.   The relationship between the actual and the normalized values was first given in Chapter 2 and is repeated here. The normalizing constants are chosen to be $R_0 = 10^5$ and $\omega_0 = 10^4$.

Let us calculate the open-circuit transfer impedance of this network. Perhaps the simplest method is to use the procedure outlined in section 4.7.   We assume a unit voltage output and work back through the ladder to calculate the input current.   The details will be left to you. The result is

$$z_{12} = \frac{500s}{65s^2 + 1201s + 10}$$

We find that the transmission zeros lie at zero and infinity.   This is disconcerting, because we expect a transmission zero at the zero of the R_T–C_T branch, which lies at $s = -\frac{1}{10}$.   However, if we compute the impedance of C_c in series with R_p, we find it to be $(10s + 1)/10s$.   This also has a zero at $s = -\frac{1}{10}$.   Hence, according to our earlier deductions, even though a shunt branch becomes a short circuit, the impedance of the rest of the network to the left also becomes a short circuit, and so there should be no transmission zero at the corresponding value of s.

As another example of a ladder network let us take a conventional filter for a power supply, with a 120 cycle "trap." The network is shown in Fig. 35. Let us again calculate the open-circuit transfer imped-ance by the same method we used before. Without normalizing this time, the result will be

$$z_{12} = \frac{s^2 + 5.66 \times 10^5}{9.4 \times 10^{-7} s (s^4 + 1.67 \times 10^7 s^2 + 1.08 \times 10^{12})}$$

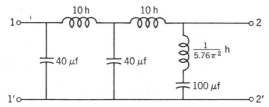

Fig. 35.   Power supply filter.

The zeros of z_{12} are at $s = \pm j240\pi$ (120 cps) and at ∞. The poles of z_{12} are at $s = 0$, $0 \pm j288$ and $0 \pm j290$ (45.8 and 46.2 cps). The fre-quency response is shown in Fig. 36.

Since ladder networks can have zeros of transmission only where the

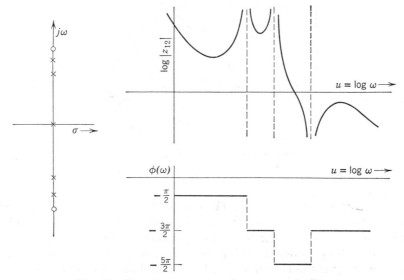

Fig. 36.   Frequency response of power supply filter.

branches of the ladder have zeros or poles, they are somewhat inflexible. In many applications it is desirable to have zeros of transmission more or less unrestricted. But it is still required that the network be common-terminal, like the ladder. Some networks that satisfy this requirement are the twin-Tee and the bridged-Tee. Let us now examine these two networks briefly.

A bridged-Tee network is the network shown in Fig. 37. It is a Tee network with a branch "bridging" the top terminals. Each of the

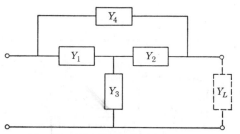

Fig. 37. The bridged-Tee structure.

branches may itself be a complex one terminal-pair network. The bridged-Tee can be redrawn as a Wheatstone bridge as shown in Fig. 38. The element Y_L is the load between terminals $(2,2')$ and G is the

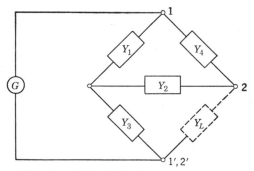

Fig. 38. Bridged-Tee drawn as a bridge.

source connected between $(1,1')$. The load now becomes one of the bridge arms. Thus, the bridged-Tee is somewhat similar to a lattice (which we will discuss shortly) and is essentially different from a ladder.

We can also consider the bridged-Tee as a parallel connection of two simpler two-ports as shown in Fig. 39. To find the short-circuit parameters of the bridged-Tee we simply add the short-circuit parameters of the two simpler two-ports. The result is

$$y_{11} = \frac{Y_1(Y_2 + Y_3)}{Y_1 + Y_2 + Y_3} + Y_4 \qquad (a)$$

$$y_{22} = \frac{Y_2(Y_1 + Y_3)}{Y_1 + Y_2 + Y_3} + Y_4 \qquad (b) \qquad (81)$$

$$y_{12} = y_{21} = -\frac{Y_1 Y_2}{Y_1 + Y_2 + Y_3} - Y_4 \qquad (c)$$

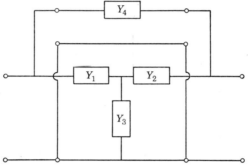

Fig. 39.   Bridged-Tee as parallel connection of components.

Alternatively, we can look upon the bridged-Tee as a series connection of two simpler two-ports as shown in Fig. 40. The open-circuit parameters of the bridged-Tee can then be computed as the sum of the

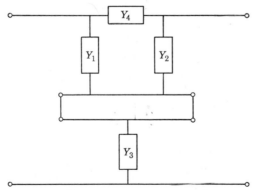

Fig. 40.   Bridged-Tee as series connection of components.

open-circuit parameters of the two simpler two-ports. If we do this, the result will be

$$z_{11} = \frac{Z_1(Z_2 + Z_4)}{Z_1 + Z_2 + Z_4} + Z_3 \qquad (a)$$

$$z_{22} = \frac{Z_2(Z_1 + Z_4)}{Z_1 + Z_2 + Z_4} + Z_3 \qquad (b) \qquad (82)$$

$$z_{21} = z_{12} = \frac{Z_1 Z_2}{Z_1 + Z_2 + Z_4} + Z_3 \qquad (c)$$

We shall now consider two specific examples of a bridged-Tee network and we shall examine the pole-zero locations and the other representations. The network of Fig. 41 is a typical RLC "equalizer" network. For this network the branch admittances are

$$Y_1 = Y_2 = 1 \qquad (a)$$

$$Y_3 = \frac{1}{1 + \dfrac{1}{s + (1/s)}} = \frac{s^2 + 1}{s^2 + s + 1} \qquad (b) \qquad (83)$$

$$Y_4 = 1 + \frac{1}{s + (1/s)} = \frac{s^2 + s + 1}{s^2 + 1} = \frac{1}{Y_3} \qquad (c)$$

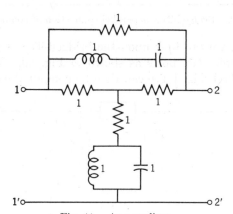

Fig. 41. An equalizer.

The z parameters are obtained by substituting these into Eqs. (82). Thus,

$$z_{22} = z_{11} = \frac{7s^4 + 9s^3 + 14s^2 + 9s + 7}{(s^2 + 1)(3s^2 + 2s + 3)} \qquad (a)$$

$$\qquad (84)$$

$$z_{21} = z_{12} = \frac{2(s^2 + s + 1)}{s^2 + 1} \qquad (b)$$

The poles and zeros z_{12}, the gain-phase plot and the z_{12} locus are shown in Fig. 42.

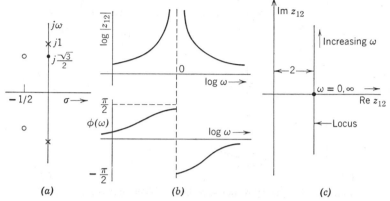

Fig. 42.   Frequency response of equalizer.

As a second example of a bridged-Tee network we will take an *RC* network of a very simple type as shown in Fig. 43. By substituting into Eqs. (82) we find the open-circuit parameters to be

$$z_{11} = z_{22} = \frac{s^2 + 6s + 4}{4s(s + 2)} \quad (a)$$

$$(85)$$

$$z_{21} = z_{12} = \frac{s^2 + 2s + 4}{4s(s + 2)} \quad (b)$$

The poles and zeros, frequency response and locus for z_{12} are shown in Fig. 44.

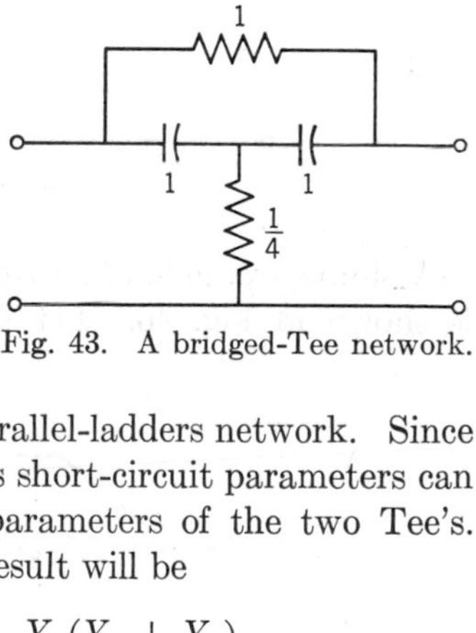

Fig. 43.   A bridged-Tee network.

Let us now turn to the twin-Tee network shown in Fig. 45. This is a simple parallel-ladders network. Since it is a parallel connection of two-ports, its short-circuit parameters can be obtained by adding the short-circuit parameters of the two Tee's. In terms of the branch admittances, the result will be

$$y_{11} = \frac{Y_1(Y_2 + Y_3)}{Y_1 + Y_2 + Y_3} + \frac{Y_4(Y_5 + Y_6)}{Y_4 + Y_5 + Y_6} \quad (a)$$

$$y_{21} = y_{12} = \frac{-Y_1Y_2}{Y_1 + Y_2 + Y_3} - \frac{Y_4Y_5}{Y_4 + Y_5 + Y_6} \quad (b) \quad (86)$$

$$y_{22} = \frac{Y_2(Y_1 + Y_3)}{Y_1 + Y_2 + Y_3} + \frac{Y_5(Y_4 + Y_6)}{Y_4 + Y_5 + Y_6} \quad (c)$$

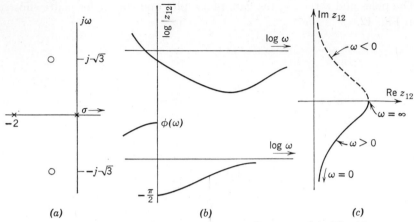

(a)   (b)   (c)

Fig. 44.   Frequency response of bridged-Tee network in Fig. 43.

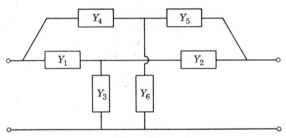

Fig. 45.   Twin-Tee structure.

A simple example of an RC twin-Tee used in the design of equalizers is shown in Fig. 46.   Let us compute only the open-circuit transfer

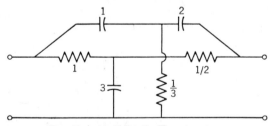

Fig. 46.   An RC twin-Tee structure.

impedance.   This can be found by first using Eqs. (86) to get the y parameters and then using the z–y relationships.   The details will be left to you.   The result is

$$z_{12}(s) = \frac{(s+1)(s^2+1)}{6s(s+1)^2} = \frac{s^2+1}{6s(s+1)} \tag{87}$$

The pole-zero configuration is shown in Fig. 47a. It is seen that the two zeros of transmission are on the $j\omega$-axis, even though this is only an

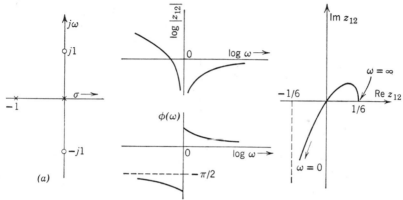

Fig. 47.   Frequency response of the twin-Tee in Fig. 46.

RC network. The gain and phase plots and the complex locus are shown in the other parts of the figure. Note that the phase plot has a positive discontinuity of π at the j-axis zero of z_{12}, in accordance with the discussion in section 7.7.

All of the two-ports we have been studying in this section have been common-terminal. Let us now turn our attention to noncommon terminal two-ports. The most important structure of this type is the symmetrical balanced lattice shown in Fig. 48. It is usually drawn with

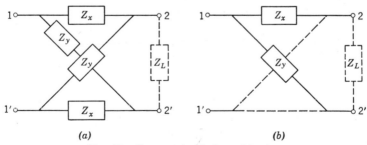

Fig. 48.   Symmetrical balanced lattice.

dotted lines replacing two of the branches, as in the second part of the figure, to avoid cluttering up the diagram. The lattice is the same network as a Wheatstone bridge. This is illustrated by redrawing the lattice as in Fig. 49. The zeros of transmission (the zeros of the transfer function) may now be interpreted as the frequencies at which the bridge is balanced.

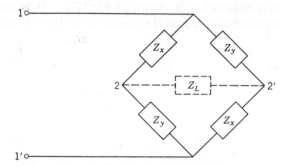

Fig. 49.   Lattic drawn as a bridge.

The lattice owes its place of prominence to two factors. First, it can be proved that every symmetric (passive, reciprocal, lumped, and time-invariant) two-port has a physically realizable lattice equivalent. Thus the lattice is the "most general" symmetric two-port. Secondly, the lattice network plays an important role in the general image parameter theory of filter design, which has occupied a large portion of the interest in networks in the past.

To start with, let us compute the open-circuit parameters of the lattice. We shall do this by using the interpretive results given in Eq. (8). From Fig. 49 we see that with terminals $(2,2')$ open, the network at terminals $(1,1')$ looks like the parallel connection of two branches each of which is the series connection of Z_x and Z_y. Hence,

$$z_{11} = \tfrac{1}{2}(Z_y + Z_x) \tag{88}$$

This is also equal to z_{22} by symmetry.

To compute $z_{12} = z_{21}$ remember that what we want is the ratio of the voltage across terminals $(2,2')$ to the current into terminal 1. It is clear from Fig. 49 that

$$V_{22'} = V_{21'} - V_{2'1'} \tag{89}$$

Each of the voltages on the right can be expressed in terms of the voltage $V_{11'}$ by means of the voltage divider law. Thus

$$V_{21'} = \frac{Z_y}{Z_y + Z_x} V_{11'} \tag{a}$$

$$(90)$$

$$V_{2'1'} = \frac{Z_x}{Z_y + Z_x} V_{11'} \tag{b}$$

If we substitute these expressions into Eq. (89) and divide both sides by I_1, the current at the input terminals, we get

$$\frac{V_{22'}}{I_1} = \frac{Z_y - Z_x}{Z_y + Z_x} \frac{V_{11'}}{I_1} \qquad (91)$$

But the left-hand side is simply z_{21}, whereas the ratio $V_{11'}/I_1$ on the right is z_{11}. Hence, using Eq. (88) we get, finally,

$$z_{21} = \tfrac{1}{2}(Z_y - Z_x) \qquad (92)$$

Having obtained the z parameters of the lattice we can now determine any of the other sets of two-port parameters using the proper relationships.

Notice that the expression for z_{21} involves a subtraction of two impedances. That is, the transmission zeros occur at those values of s for which the two branch impedances have equal values. This can happen for *any* value of s; hence, the locations of the transmission zeros of a lattice are unrestricted and may occur anywhere in the s-plane.

Let us now consider some examples of lattice networks. One very common lattice is shown in Fig. 50. This lattice is the prototype of

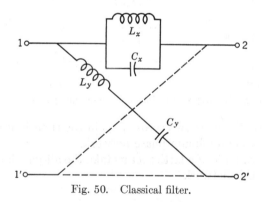

Fig. 50.   Classical filter.

image parameter filters. If $L_x = L_y = L$ and $C_x = C_y = C$ then from Eqs. (88) and (92) we get

$$z_{11} = \frac{1}{2}\left(\frac{s^4 L^2 C^2 + 3s^2 LC + 1}{sC(1 + s^2 LC)}\right) \qquad (a)$$

$$z_{12} = \frac{1}{2}\left(\frac{s^4 L^2 C^2 + s^2 LC + 1}{sC(1 + s^2 LC)}\right) \qquad (b)$$

$$(93)$$

Besides poles at zero and infinity there are a pair of poles on the $j\omega$-axis at $s = \pm j\omega_0$, where $\omega_0 = 1/\sqrt{LC}$. The zeros of z_{11} are all on the $j\omega$-axis at the points

$$s = \pm j\omega_0 \sqrt{(3 \pm \sqrt{5})/2} \qquad (94)$$

and the zeros of z_{12} are in quadrantal symmetry. They are located at the points

$$s = \frac{\omega_0}{2}(-1 \pm j\sqrt{3}) \qquad (a)$$

$$\qquad\qquad\qquad\qquad\qquad\qquad\qquad\qquad (95)$$

$$s = \frac{\omega_0}{2}(1 \pm j\sqrt{3}) \qquad (b)$$

The corresponding plots are shown in Fig. 51.

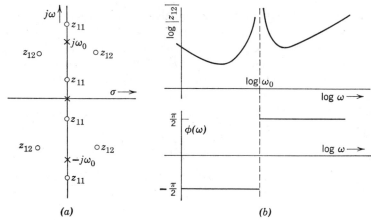

(a)   (b)

Fig. 51.   Representations of open-circuit parameters.

We note that there are two zeros of z_{12} in the right half plane. Thus, this lattice is a nonminimum-phase network.

As another example of a lattice let us take the all-pass lattice shown in Fig. 52.   For this network

$$Z_x = \frac{4s}{s^2 + 2s + 2} \qquad (a)$$

$$\qquad\qquad\qquad\qquad\qquad\qquad\qquad\qquad (96)$$

$$Z_y = 1 \qquad (b)$$

Hence, from Eqs. (88) and (92) we get

$$z_{11} = \frac{s^2 + 6s + 2}{2(s^2 + 2s + 2)} \qquad (a)$$

$$\qquad\qquad\qquad\qquad\qquad\qquad\qquad\qquad (97)$$

$$z_{12} = \frac{1}{2}\frac{s^2 - 2s + 2}{s^2 + 2s + 2} = \frac{1}{2}\frac{(s - 1 + j)(s - 1 - j)}{(s + 1 + j)(s + 1 - j)} \qquad (b)$$

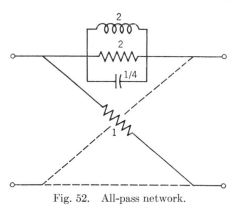

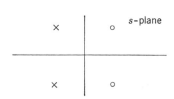

Fig. 52.   All-pass network.

Fig. 53.   Pole-zero locations of z_{12} for all-pass network.

The location of the poles and zeros of z_{12} are illustrated in Fig. 53. They exhibit a very special symmetry. The poles are the mirror images of zeros with respect to the $j\omega$-axis. When $s = j\omega$, we therefore get

$$|z_{12}(j\omega)| = \frac{1}{2}\left|\frac{-1 + j(\omega + 1)}{1 + j(\omega + 1)}\right| \cdot \left|\frac{-1 + j(\omega - 1)}{1 + j(\omega - 1)}\right| = \frac{1}{2} \quad (98)$$

This verifies our previous knowledge that the magnitude of an all-pass function is independent of ω. The gain and phase plots and the complex locus are shown in Fig. 54. As we already know, the locus is a circle which encloses the origin twice, since there are two right half plane zeros.

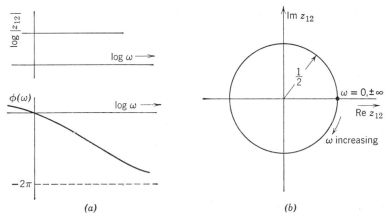

Fig. 54.   Frequency response of all-pass network.

PROBLEMS

8.1 Find the $ABCD$ parameters, and scattering parameters of the Tee and Pi networks of Fig. P8.1.

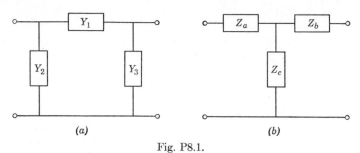

(a)   *(b)*

Fig. P8.1.

8.2 Find the Tee equivalent of Fig. P8.1a and the Pi equivalent of Fig. P8.1b, thus obtaining the $\Delta - Y$ and $Y - \Delta$ transformations.

8.3 Find the $ABCD$ parameters of each of the networks in Fig. P8.3.

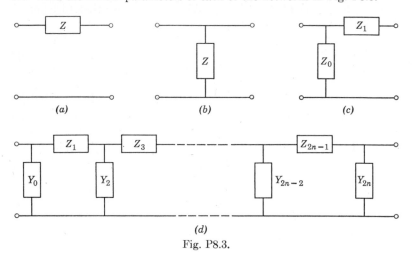

(a)   *(b)*   *(c)*

(d)

Fig. P8.3.

8.4 Fig. P8.4 shows a two-port N terminated in an impedance Z_L. Show that

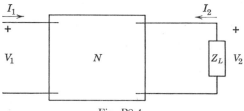

Fig. P8.4.

$$Z_{21}(s) = \frac{V_2(s)}{I_1(s)} = \frac{z_{21}Z_L}{Z_L + z_{22}}$$

$$Y_{21}(s) = \frac{I_2(s)}{V_1(s)} = \frac{y_{21}Y_L}{Y_L + y_{22}}$$

8.5 Find the zeros and poles of the transfer voltage ratio $G_{21}(s)$ of the networks of Fig. P8.5. Plot them in the complex plane. Find the scattering parameters of the same networks. Plot the zeros and poles of $S_{21}(s)$ and compare with those of $G_{21}(s)$.

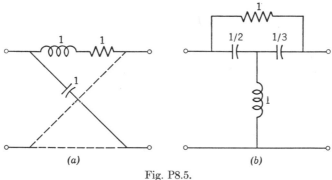

(a)   (b)

Fig. P8.5.

8.6 In the network of Fig. P8.6 the transformers are perfectly coupled. Use matrix methods to find the $ABCD$ parameters of the over-all network.

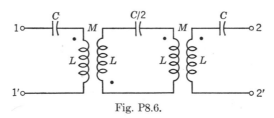

Fig. P8.6.

8.7 Find the scattering parameters of Fig. P8.6. Does this network have a $\mathbf{Z}_{oc}$ or $\mathbf{Y}_{sc}$ matrix?

8.8 Given a reciprocal two-port N_1, it is desired to find another two-port N_2 such that the open-circuit impedance matrix $\mathbf{Z}_{oc}$ of one of them is equal to the short-circuit admittance matrix $\mathbf{Y}_{sc}$ of the other. We will refer to such networks as *two-port duals*. One method of doing this is to find the dual of the given two-port by geometrical means, according to the procedure outlined in Chapter 4. However, this is not possible for all two-ports, even if the terminated network can be drawn planar (for instance Fig. 49). Find the condition which the given two-port must satisfy in order for this procedure to be possible.

8.9 Using the method of the last problem, show that the two-port dual of the bridged-Tee network shown in Fig. P8.9 is also a bridged-Tee with branches 4 and 3 interchanged and each branch replaced by its dual. Also find the two-port duals of Figs. P8.1 and P8.3.

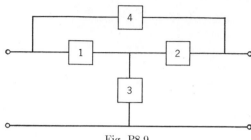

Fig. P8.9.

8.10 Consider the series-parallel and parallel-series connections of two-ports shown in Fig. P8.10. Determine the sets of two-port parameters which lead to the simplest relationship of the over-all parameters in terms of those of the components. Find expressions for these over-all parameters.

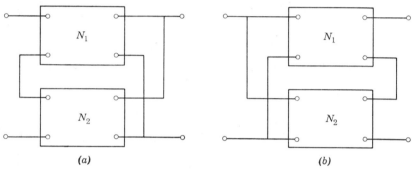

(a)   (b)

Fig. P8.10.

8.11 Prove Brune's test for the validity of the series and parallel connection of two-ports. State and prove similar tests for the series-parallel and parallel-series connections.

8.12 Derive a pair of equivalent two-port networks based on the h and g sets of parameters.

8.13 Consider the cascade connection of two two-ports shown in Fig. P8.13. Show that the short-circuit transfer admittance and the open-circuit transfer impedance of the over-all two-port are given by

$$y_{12} = \frac{-y_{12a}y_{12b}}{y_{22a} + y_{11b}} \; ; \qquad z_{12} = \frac{z_{12a}z_{12b}}{z_{22a} + z_{11b}}$$

where the subscripts a and b refer to the component two-ports. These expressions are sometimes referred to as the *partitioning theorem*. Use the definitions of z_{21} and y_{21} in arriving at the answers.

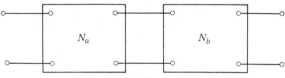

Fig. P8.13.

8.14   Consider a reciprocal two-port N which is both structurally and electrically symmetrical. Its z and y parameters are denoted by $z_{11} = z_{22}$, z_{12} and $y_{11} = y_{22}$, y_{12}, respectively. If we consider bisecting the two-port at its structural line of symmetry, a number of terminals (two or more) will be created at the junction between the two halves. Assume that none of the leads from which these terminals are formed are crossed. Now consider the two cases shown in Fig. P8.14 in which these terminals are left open and are short-circuited, respectively. The input impedance and input admittance are designated z_{11h} and y_{11h} in the two cases, respectively, where the subscript h stands for *half*. Show that

$$z_{11h} = z_{11} + z_{12} \quad \text{and} \quad \frac{1}{y_{11h}} = z_{11} - z_{12}$$

or

$$\frac{1}{z_{11h}} = y_{11} + y_{12} \quad \text{and} \quad y_{11h} = y_{11} - y_{12}$$

(*Hint:* Apply voltages $V_1 = V_2 = V$ at the terminals of the original network and show that no current will flow across the structural line of symmetry. Then apply voltages $V_1 = -V_2 = V$ and show that the voltage at each point on the structural line of symmetry will be the same.) This result is known as Bartlett's bisection theorem.

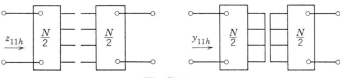

Fig. P8.14.

8.15   Find the short-circuit admittance parameters of the networks in Fig. P8.15 by decomposing the networks into suitable series or parallel connected two-ports.

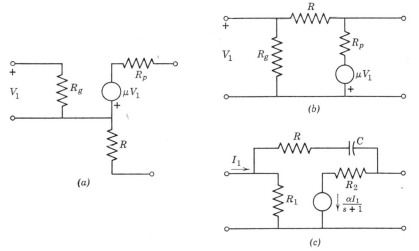

Fig. P8.15.

8.16 Find "two-generator equivalent networks" for the networks in the last problem. (See Problem 8.12 and Figs. 16 and 17 in the text.)

8.17 A three terminal network is shown in Fig. P8.17. This network is to be used as a common-terminal two-port in three ways, each time with a different terminal acting as the common terminal. When b is the common terminal, the h parameters are known. That is, the coefficients in the following equations are known.

$$V_{ab} = h_{11b}I_a + h_{12b}V_{bc}$$

$$I_b = h_{21b}I_a + h_{22b}V_{bc}$$

The subscript on the h parameters indicates the common terminal. Express the h parameters of the other two connections in terms of the known h parameters. (Can we hope to do a similar thing with a noncommon terminal two-port?) All the current references are directed into the network.

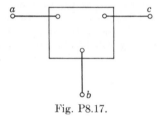

Fig. P8.17.

8.18 The driving point impedance of a reciprocal network is denoted by $Z(s)$. Figure P8.18 shows such a network with one of the resistances shown explicitly. Consider cutting the branch in which the kth resistance of the network is located; assume that the terminals so formed are the $(1,1')$ terminals of a two-port whose $(2,2')$ terminals are the external terminals of the network. Designate the g_{21} parameter of this two-port by $g_{21k}(s)$. Show that if the network contains n resistances, the real part of $Z(j\omega)$ is given by

$$Re[Z(j\omega)] = \sum_{k=1}^{n} R_k |g_{21k}(j\omega)|^2$$

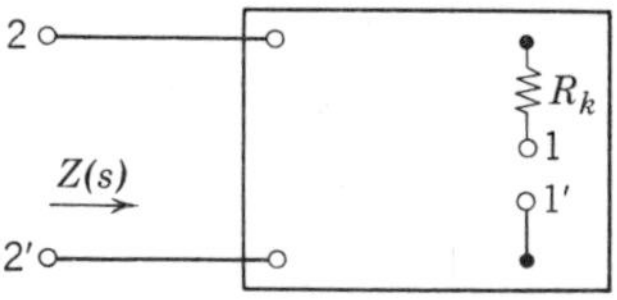

Fig. P8.18.

8.19 Complete Table 1 of section 1 by adding two columns, one giving the expressions for the parameters in terms of loop determinants and cofactors, and the other, the corresponding expressions in terms of node determinants and cofactors.

9 · ANALYTIC PROPERTIES OF NETWORK FUNCTIONS

In Chapter 4 we defined various network functions as ratios of Laplace transforms of an output (response) to an input (excitation), under initially relaxed conditions. In the later chapters, we hinted at several analytic properties that the network functions possess. It is now our purpose to provide reasonable proofs for all the properties that we have hinted at, as well as to carry the analytic discussion deeper. Such analytic properties as we shall discuss are of the greatest interest in the theory of network synthesis. On this basis, the present chapter could well be titled "Foundations of Network Synthesis."

Before we begin our formal discussion, let us collect together all the properties of network functions that we have stated so far. The only networks which we will consider in this chapter are linear, passive, reciprocal, lumped, and time-invariant networks. Let $F(s)$ denote a general network function (driving-point or transfer impedance or admittance, or voltage or current ratio) defined as the ratio of a response transform to an excitation transform with all initial conditions zero. Then $F(s)$ has the following general properties.

1. $F(s)$ is a rational function with real coefficients.
2. Poles and zeros of $F(s)$ are either real or occur in complex conjugate pairs.
3. $F(s)$ has no poles in the right half s-plane and poles on the $j\omega$-axis are simple.
4. On the $j\omega$-axis the real part of $F(j\omega)$ is an even function of ω and the imaginary part of $F(j\omega)$ is an odd function of ω.
5. On the $j\omega$-axis, $|F(j\omega)|$ is an even function of ω. If $\arg F(j\omega)$ is zero when $\omega = 0$ (corresponding to a suitable choice of references in the network), then $\arg F(j\omega)$ is an odd function of ω.

The first property expresses the fact that the network elements are real, whereas the third one is a consequence of the stability of the network.   The other three are a direct consequence of the first property.

In case $F(s)$ is a driving point (impedance or admittance) function, it has the following additional properties.

1. $F(s)$ has no zeros in the right half plane.
2. Re $F(j\omega) \geq 0$.
3. Poles *and* zeros on the $j\omega$-axis are simple, including $s = 0, \infty$.

9.1   Preliminary

In this section we are going to make strong use of the matrix formulation of loop and node equations in sections 1 and 2 of Chapter 4.   Therefore it is advisable to review these sections before proceeding.

Consider a general one terminal-pair network N (a one-port), driven by a voltage generator as shown in Fig. 1.   The network N is assumed to

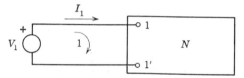

Fig. 1.   One terminal-pair network.

consist of linear, passive, lumped, reciprocal, and time-invariant elements only.   Since we wish to discuss network functions, we will assume that all initial conditions are zero.

The loop equations of the network can be written in matrix form as

$$\mathbf{Z}_m(s)\mathbf{I}_m(s) = \mathbf{V}_m(s) \tag{1}$$

or in the alternative form

$$\{\mathbf{R}_m + s\mathbf{L}_m + (\mathbf{D}_m/s)\}\mathbf{I}_m(s) = \mathbf{V}_m(s) \tag{2}$$

Remember that $\mathbf{Z}_m(s)$ is the loop impedance matrix, whereas $\mathbf{R}_m$, $\mathbf{L}_m$, and $\mathbf{D}_m$ are the loop resistance, inductance, and inverse capacitance matrices, respectively.   We saw in Chapter 4 that the loop parameter matrices can be written in terms of the branch parameter matrices as follows.

$$\mathbf{R}_m = \mathbf{B}\mathbf{R}_b\mathbf{B}' \qquad (a)$$

$$\mathbf{L}_m = \mathbf{B}\mathbf{L}_b\mathbf{B}' \qquad (b) \qquad (3)$$

$$\mathbf{D}_m = \mathbf{B}\mathbf{D}_b\mathbf{B}' \qquad (c)$$

where $\mathbf{B}$ is the coefficient matrix of Kirchhoff's voltage law equations.

Equations (1) and (2) are transform equations valid for any excitation. In Chapter 5 we saw that, when the excitation is sinusoidal, loop equations can be written in terms of voltage and current phasors. Thus, if the driving voltage in Fig. 1 is $v_1(t) = |U_1| \sin (\omega_0 t + \phi)$, we can write phasor (steady-state) loop equations as

$$\mathbf{Z}_m(j\omega_0)\mathbf{J}_m = \mathbf{U}_m \qquad (a)$$

$$\left\{ \mathbf{R}_m + j\omega_0 \mathbf{L}_m + \frac{1}{j\omega_0} \mathbf{D}_m \right\} \mathbf{J}_m = \mathbf{U}_m \qquad (b)$$

(4)

where capital J and U are used for current and voltage phasors, respectively, and the matrix $\mathbf{Z}_m(j\omega_0)$ is obtained by replacing s by $j\omega_0$ in the loop impedance matrix in Eq. (1). Thus, the parameter matrices $\mathbf{R}_m$, $\mathbf{L}_m$, and $\mathbf{D}_m$ in Eqs. (2) and (4) are the same whether we are using phasor equations or transform equations.

Let us now assume that the excitation is sinusoidal and deal with the phasor equations. We shall derive some properties of the parameter matrices $\mathbf{R}_m$, $\mathbf{L}_m$, and $\mathbf{D}_m$, and later use these properties in connection with the transform equations, Eq. (1). Note that due to the choice of loops in Fig. 1, only loop 1 has a source. Thus, the phasor source voltage and loop current matrices can be written

$$\mathbf{U}_m = \begin{bmatrix} U_1 \\ 0 \\ 0 \\ \cdot \\ \cdot \\ \cdot \\ 0 \end{bmatrix} ; \qquad \mathbf{J}_m = \begin{bmatrix} J_1 \\ J_2 \\ \cdot \\ \cdot \\ \cdot \\ J_m \end{bmatrix} \qquad (5)$$

Let us now compute the power supplied to the network, the "complex power." In terms of the phasors this is given by $J_1{}^*U_1$. To obtain this result from the matrices in Eq. (5), you can see that we should premultiply $\mathbf{U}_m$ by the conjugate transpose of $\mathbf{J}_m$, which is

$$\mathbf{J}_m{}^{*\prime} = [J_1{}^* \quad J_2{}^* \cdots J_n{}^*] \qquad (6)$$

If we now premultiply both sides of Eq. (4) by $\mathbf{J}_m{}^{*\prime}$, the right side will be the complex power supplied to the network. The result will be

$$\mathbf{J}_m{}^{*\prime}\mathbf{R}_m\mathbf{J}_m + j\omega_0\mathbf{J}_m{}^{*\prime}\mathbf{L}_m\mathbf{J}_m + \frac{1}{j\omega_0}\mathbf{J}_m{}^{*\prime}\mathbf{D}_m\mathbf{J}_m = J_1{}^*U_1 \qquad (7)$$

This is a scalar equation. On the left side there are three terms each of which contains the product of three matrices in an ordered manner. Quantities such as these appear quite often and have been extensively studied. We shall now digress slightly in order to develop some of the mathematical properties of these terms which we will need in the subsequent discussion. In order to indicate that the results are general we will use a general notation.

9.2   Quadratic Forms

Let $\mathbf{A} = [a_{ij}]$ be a real square matrix and $\mathbf{X} = [x_i]$ be a column matrix, real or complex. The expression

$$\mathbf{X'AX} = \begin{bmatrix} x_1 & x_2 & \cdots & x_n \end{bmatrix} \begin{bmatrix} a_{11} & a_{12} & \cdots & a_{1n} \\ a_{21} & a_{22} & \cdots & a_{2n} \\ \cdot & \cdot & \cdots & \cdot \\ a_{n1} & a_{n2} & & a_{nn} \end{bmatrix} \begin{bmatrix} x_1 \\ x_2 \\ \cdot \\ \cdot \\ x_n \end{bmatrix} \tag{8}$$

when $\mathbf{X}$ is a real matrix, and the expression

$$\mathbf{X^{*'}AX} = \begin{bmatrix} x_1^* & x_2^* & \cdots & x_n^* \end{bmatrix} \begin{bmatrix} a_{11} & a_{12} & \cdots & a_{1n} \\ a_{21} & a_{22} & \cdots & a_{2n} \\ \cdot & \cdot & \cdots & \cdot \\ a_{n1} & a_{n2} & \cdots & a_{nn} \end{bmatrix} \begin{bmatrix} x_1 \\ x_2 \\ \cdot \\ \cdot \\ x_n \end{bmatrix} \tag{9}$$

when $\mathbf{X}$ is a complex matrix, are called *quadratic forms*. The reason for the name becomes clear when we perform the indicated matrix multiplications and get

$$\mathbf{X'AX} = \sum_{i=1}^{n} \sum_{j=1}^{n} a_{ij} x_i x_j \tag{10}$$

when the x's are real, and

$$\mathbf{X^{*'}AX} = \sum_{i=1}^{n} \sum_{j=1}^{n} a_{ij} x_i^* x_j \tag{11}$$

when the x's are complex. We see that these are homogeneous expressions of degree 2 in the variables $x_1, x_2, \cdots, x_n$.

The matrix $\mathbf{A}$ in Eqs. (8) through (11) is called the *matrix of the quadratic form*. We consider the x's to be variables, so that the matrix essentially defines the quadratic form. We shall concern ourselves with quadratic forms in which the matrix $\mathbf{A}$ is real and *symmetric*. Actually, *any* real quadratic form with a real matrix can be converted into a quadratic form with a symmetric matrix. For, if the x's are real and the a_{ij}'s are real, we can write

$$a_{ij} x_i x_j + a_{ji} x_j x_i = 2 \left(\frac{a_{ij} + a_{ji}}{2} \right) x_i x_j \tag{12}$$

We see that the contribution to the quadratic form of the two terms on the left of this equation will remain unchanged if we replace both a_{ij} and a_{ji} in the matrix by half their sum. Thus, if $\mathbf{A}$ is not symmetric, we define the symmetric matrix $\mathbf{B}$ as

$$\mathbf{B} = \tfrac{1}{2}(\mathbf{A} + \mathbf{A}') \tag{13}$$

The matrix $\mathbf{B}$ is called the *symmetric part of* $\mathbf{A}$. This operation leaves the diagonal elements of $\mathbf{A}$ unchanged while the off-diagonal elements are modified in the manner just described. From the preceding discussion it follows that

$$\mathbf{X}'\mathbf{A}\mathbf{X} = \mathbf{X}'\mathbf{B}\mathbf{X} \tag{14}$$

Let us now turn our attention to a quadratic form in which the matrix of the variables $\mathbf{X}$ is complex. We can show that, so long as the matrix $\mathbf{A}$ of the quadratic form is real and symmetric, then the quadratic form $\mathbf{X}^{*\prime}\mathbf{A}\mathbf{X}$ is real. To prove this result, observe that

$$\sum_{i=1}^{n}\sum_{j=1}^{n} a_{ij}x_i{}^*x_j = \sum_{i=1}^{n} a_{ii}x_i{}^*x_i + \sum_{\substack{i=1 \\ }}^{n}\sum_{\substack{j=1 \\ i \neq j}}^{n} a_{ij}x_i{}^*x_j$$

$$= \sum_{i=1}^{n} a_{ii}|x_i|^2 + \sum_{\substack{i=1 \\ }}^{n}\sum_{\substack{j=1 \\ i \neq j}}^{n} a_{ij}(x_i{}^*x_j + x_j{}^*x_i)$$

$$= \sum_{i=1}^{n} a_{ii}|x_i|^2 + \sum_{i=1}^{n}\sum_{j=1}^{n} 2a_{ij}\,\mathrm{Re}\,(x_i{}^*x_j) \tag{15}$$

The second line is a consequence of $\mathbf{A}$ being symmetric, whereas the last term in the last line is a result of the fact that $x_j{}^*x_i$ is the conjugate of $x_i{}^*x_j$. Everything in the last line is now real, thus proving the result.

Although the quadratic forms we are considering are real, their sign will normally depend on the values of the variables, the x's. However, it may happen that a quadratic form remains of one sign, independent of the values of the variables. Such forms are called *definite*. In particular, a real quadratic form $\mathbf{X}^{*\prime}\mathbf{A}\mathbf{X}$ is *positive definite* if for any set of complex or real numbers $x_1, x_2, \cdots, x_n$, *not all zero*, the value of the quadratic form is strictly positive. Similarly, we say the quadratic form is *positive semidefinite* if

$$\mathbf{X}^{*\prime}\mathbf{A}\mathbf{X} \geq 0 \tag{16}$$

for all $\mathbf{X} \neq \mathbf{0}$, provided there is at least one set of values of the variables for which the equality holds. Since the positive property of such a quadratic form is not dependent on the values of the variables, it must be associated with the matrix **A** of the quadratic form. It appears natural, then, to refer to the matrix **A** as positive definite or semi-definite according as the quadratic form itself is positive definite or semi-definite.

Quadratic forms having these particular qualifications are very important in network theory. It is important for us to know some of the properties of definite quadratic forms. However, a thorough discussion will take us far afield in the theory of linear transformations. Hence, in establishing the results that are important for us, we will prove only some of them and attempt to show the reasonableness of the others.

To start with, let us look at a few examples of positive definite quadratic forms. As the first example consider the following quadratic form

$$[x_1{}^* \quad x_2{}^* \quad x_3{}^*]\begin{bmatrix} 1 & 0 & 0 \\ 0 & 2 & 0 \\ 0 & 0 & 2 \end{bmatrix}\begin{bmatrix} x_1 \\ x_2 \\ x_3 \end{bmatrix} = |x_1|^2 + 2|x_2|^2 + 2|x_3|^2 \quad (17)$$

This is obviously positive definite, since it is the sum of magnitudes squared of the variables. We can easily extend this result to see that any diagonal matrix of positive elements defines a positive definite quadratic form.

As a more complicated example, consider the following.

$$\mathbf{X^{*\prime}AX} = [x_1{}^* \quad x_2{}^* \quad x_3{}^*]\begin{bmatrix} 3 & -1 & -1 \\ -1 & 2 & 1 \\ -1 & 1 & 2 \end{bmatrix}\begin{bmatrix} x_1 \\ x_2 \\ x_3 \end{bmatrix} \quad (18)$$

If we expand this quadratic form, we get

$$\mathbf{X^{*\prime}AX} = 3|x_1|^2 - x_1{}^*x_2 - x_2{}^*x_1 - x_1{}^*x_3 - x_3{}^*x_1$$
$$+ 2|x_2|^2 + x_2{}^*x_3 + x_3{}^*x_2 + 2|x_3|^2 \quad (19)$$

It is not easy to see whether or not this expression is positive definite, since the result is not in the form of a sum of magnitudes squared. However, after some manipulation, Eq. (19) can be put in the form

$$\mathbf{X^{*\prime}AX} = \tfrac{1}{3}(3x_1 - x_2 - x_3)(3x_1{}^* - x_2{}^* - x_3{}^*)$$
$$+ \tfrac{1}{15}(5x_2 + 2x_3)(5x_2{}^* + 2x_3{}^*) + \tfrac{7}{5}x_3x_3{}^* \quad (20)$$

If we now make the substitutions

$$y_1 = 3x_1 - x_2 - x_3 \qquad (a)$$
$$y_2 = 5x_2 + 2x_3 \qquad (b) \qquad (21)$$
$$y_3 = x_3 \qquad (c)$$

the quadratic form finally becomes

$$\mathbf{X}^{*\prime}\mathbf{A}\mathbf{X} = \tfrac{1}{3}|y_1|^2 + \tfrac{1}{15}|y_2|^2 + \tfrac{7}{5}|y_3|^2 \qquad (22)$$

We have succeeded in writing the quadratic form as a sum of magnitudes squared. It is clear from Eqs. (21) that if the x's are not all zero, then the y's also will not all be zero. Hence, the quadratic form is positive definite.

As the last example take

$$\mathbf{X}^{*\prime}\mathbf{A}\mathbf{X} = [x_1^* \quad x_2^*] \begin{bmatrix} 1 & 2 \\ 2 & 2 \end{bmatrix} \begin{bmatrix} x_1 \\ x_2 \end{bmatrix}$$

$$= x_1 x_1^* + 2x_1 x_2^* + 2x_1^* x_2 + 2x_2 x_2^*$$

$$= (x_1 + 2x_2)(x_1^* + 2x_2^*) - 2x_2 x_2^*$$

$$= |y_1|^2 - 2|y_2|^2 \qquad (23)$$

The last line is obtained with the substitution

$$y_1 = x_1 + 2x_2 \qquad (a)$$
$$y_2 = x_2 \qquad (b)$$
$$(24)$$

It is clear that the quadratic form can become positive, negative, or zero depending on the values of y_1 and y_2, and, through Eqs. (24), on the values of x_1 and x_2. Hence, it is neither positive definite nor semidefinite.

These examples have illustrated a procedure for determining whether or not a given quadratic form is positive definite or semidefinite. In the examples we "reduced" the quadratic form to an expression such as Eq. (22) or the last line of Eq. (23), involving squares of magnitudes. We did this by means of linear transformations as in Eqs. (21) and (24). On examination we see that these transformations are nonsingular.* The question arises whether it is always possible to do this for any given quadratic form. The answer can be given in the following theorem.

Theorem 1. *Every quadratic form* $\mathbf{X}^{*\prime}\mathbf{A}\mathbf{X}$ *in which* $\mathbf{A}$ *is a real, symmetric matrix can be reduced by means of a real nonsingular transformation* $\mathbf{X} = \mathbf{BY}$ *to the canonical form*

$$\mathbf{X}^{*\prime}\mathbf{A}\mathbf{X} = |y_1|^2 + |y_2|^2 + \cdots + |y_p|^2 - |y_{p+1}|^2 - \cdots - |y_r|^2 \quad (25)$$

where r *is the rank of the matrix* $\mathbf{A}$.

The number p is called the *index* of the quadratic form. Suppose now that the index p is equal to the rank r so that all the signs in Eq. (25) are positive. There are two cases to consider: (1) the rank r equal to

---

* By this we mean that for any set of y_k's there is a unique solution for the x_j's.

the order n of matrix $\mathbf{A}$, and (2) $r < n$. In the second case we can choose $y_1 = y_2 = \cdots = y_r = 0$ and the rest of the y's nonzero. Hence, with $\mathbf{X} = \mathbf{BY}$, not all the x's will be zero, but according to Eq. (25) the quadratic form will be zero. For any other choice of the variables the quadratic form will be positive. Hence, the quadratic form will be positive semidefinite.

If the rank of $\mathbf{A}$ is equal to its order (in addition to the index being equal to its rank) then every nonzero choice of the y's (and hence of the x's) will lead to a positive value of the quadratic form, indicating that it will be positive definite. This shows that a positive definite matrix is always nonsingular and a positive semidefinite matrix is always singular.

This theorem is a standard one in the theory of quadratic forms. We will forego the proof here, since it will require a lengthy discussion of linear transformations.* We have seen the validity of the theorem in the case of two of our examples.

Actually the theorem constitutes an existence proof and does not help very much in testing a given quadratic form for positive definiteness. However, we can develop such a test by using the theorem. Suppose a quadratic form $\mathbf{X'AX}$ is positive definite. We are using a real matrix $\mathbf{X}$ but the same conclusion will apply for a complex $\mathbf{X}$. According to the theorem we can find a transformation $\mathbf{X} = \mathbf{BY}$ in which $\mathbf{B}$ is real and nonsingular such that

$$\mathbf{X'AX} = \mathbf{Y'UY} \tag{26}$$

the right-hand side being simply a sum of squares of the y variables. If we substitute the transformation $\mathbf{X} = \mathbf{BY}$ into the quadratic form, we will get

$$\mathbf{X'AX} = (\mathbf{BY})'\mathbf{A}(\mathbf{BY}) = \mathbf{Y'B'ABY} \tag{27}$$

Here we have used the result that the transpose of a product of two matrices is equal to the product of the individual transposed matrices, but in the opposite order. On comparing the last two equations, we see that

$$\mathbf{B'AB} = \mathbf{U} \tag{28}$$

Thus, the theorem is equivalent to the statement that a real, symmetric positive definite matrix $\mathbf{A}$ can be reduced to a unit matrix by a nonsingular transformation $\mathbf{B}$ applied symmetrically.

Let us now find the determinant of both sides of Eq. (28). The determinant of a unit matrix is unity, while the determinant of a product of matrices of the same order is equal to the product of the determinants.

---

* For a more complete discussion of quadratic forms see Birkhoff and MacLane, *A Survey of Modern Algebra*, Macmillan, New York, 1955; or Bôcher, *Introduction to Higher Algebra*, Macmillan, New York, 1927.

Hence,

$$(\det \mathbf{B}')(\det \mathbf{A})(\det \mathbf{B}) = 1 \qquad (29)$$

Since matrix $\mathbf{B}$ and its transpose have the same (nonzero) determinant, we get

$$\det \mathbf{A} = \frac{1}{(\det \mathbf{B})^2} \qquad (30)$$

This result expresses the fact that *the determinant of a positive definite matrix is positive*. Furthermore, suppose we set the last variable x_n in the quadratic form equal to zero. Then none of the coefficients a_{ni} or a_{in} of the matrix $\mathbf{A}$ will appear in the quadratic form. This is most easily seen from the expression in Eq. (10) with $x_n = 0$. Hence, we might as well remove the last row and column of $\mathbf{A}$ and consider it to be of the $(n-1)$th order. For this new matrix Eq. (30) still applies. But the determinant of the new matrix is the principal cofactor * of the old matrix, with the last row and column removed. Since permuting the variables has no effect on the quadratic form, which one of the variables we call x_n is immaterial. It follows that all the first principal cofactors of a positive definite matrix will be positive.

This argument can now be repeated by setting two of the variables equal to zero, then three, and so on, up to all but one. We shall find that all the principal cofactors of $\mathbf{A}$ will be positive. In the last case, with all but one of the variables equal to zero, we find that all the elements of $\mathbf{A}$ on the principal diagonal must be positive (these elements are the $(n-1)$th principal cofactors of $\mathbf{A}$).

What we have succeeded in proving is that, if a matrix is known to be positive definite, then its determinant and all its principal cofactors will be positive. Actually, what we need for testing a given matrix is the converse of this result, which is also true. The proof, however, is quite lengthy and will not be given. For future reference we will list this result as Theorem 2.

Theorem 2. *A real symmetric matrix* $\mathbf{A}$ *is positive definite if and only if its determinant and principal cofactors are all positive. It is positive semidefinite if and only if its determinant and principal cofactors are all nonnegative and at least one is zero.* (In fact the determinant of a positive semidefinite matrix is necessarily zero.)

---

* By *principal minor* of a determinant we shall mean the determinant formed by removing one or more rows and their corresponding columns from the original determinant. *First, second*, etc. principal minors refer to those with one, two, etc. rows and columns removed. Since in all these cases the cofactor has the same sign as the minor, we shall refer to these quantities as the *first, second*, etc. principal cofactors. Examples are Δ_{2255}, Δ_{33}, where Δ is the determinant.

9.3   Energy Functions

After this digression into a discussion of quadratic forms, let us return to Eq. (7) which we will repeat here.

$$J_1^*U_1 = \mathbf{J}_m^{*\prime}\mathbf{R}_m\mathbf{J}_m + j\omega_0\mathbf{J}_m^{*\prime}\mathbf{L}_m\mathbf{J}_m + \frac{1}{j\omega_0}\mathbf{J}_m^{*\prime}\mathbf{D}_m\mathbf{J}_m \qquad (31)$$

With our recently acquired knowledge, we recognize the terms on the right as quadratic forms. Let us now attempt to interpret these quadratic forms taking first the one involving the loop resistance parameters. If we substitute for $\mathbf{R}_m$ from Eq. (3), the result will be

$$\mathbf{J}_m^{*\prime}\mathbf{R}_m\mathbf{J}_m = \mathbf{J}_m^{*\prime}\mathbf{B}\mathbf{R}_b\mathbf{B}'\mathbf{J}_m = (\mathbf{B}'\mathbf{J}_m)^{*\prime}\mathbf{R}_b(\mathbf{B}'\mathbf{J}_m) \qquad (32)$$

To obtain the last step we have used the fact that the transpose of a product of matrices is equal to the product of the transposes in the reverse order, in addition to the fact that $\mathbf{B}$ is real and hence $\mathbf{B} = \mathbf{B}^*$. That is,

$$\mathbf{J}_m^{*\prime}\mathbf{B} = \mathbf{J}_m^{*\prime}(\mathbf{B}^*)' = \{\mathbf{J}_m'(\mathbf{B}')'\}^* = (\mathbf{B}'\mathbf{J}_m)^{*\prime} \qquad (33)$$

Remember that $\mathbf{B}$ is the coefficient matrix of Kirchhoff's voltage law equations, and according to the mesh transformation expressed by Eq. (19) in Chapter 4, we have

$$\mathbf{B}'\mathbf{J}_m = \mathbf{J}_b \qquad (34)$$

where $\mathbf{J}_b$ is the (column) matrix of phasor *branch* currents. Hence, Eq. (32) can now be written

$$\mathbf{J}_m^{*\prime}\mathbf{R}_m\mathbf{J}_m = \mathbf{J}_b^{*\prime}\mathbf{R}_b\mathbf{J}_b \qquad (35)$$

We have now brought the quadratic form to a point where we can interpret it. Since the branch resistance matrix $\mathbf{R}_b$ is diagonal, the quadratic form in the last equation is simply

$$\mathbf{J}_m^{*\prime}\mathbf{R}_m\mathbf{J}_m = \mathbf{J}_b^{*\prime}\mathbf{R}_b\mathbf{J}_b = \sum_{k=1}^{N_b} R_k|J_k|^2 \qquad (36)$$

where J_k is the phasor branch current in branch k. Thus the quadratic form is simply twice the average power dissipated in the resistances of the network.

Tracing through identical arguments for the other two quadratic forms involving the loop inductance and capacitance parameters, we find

$$\mathbf{J}_m^{*\prime}\mathbf{L}_m\mathbf{J}_m = \mathbf{J}_b^{*\prime}\mathbf{L}_b\mathbf{J}_b = \sum_{k=1}^{N_b} L_k|J_k|^2 \qquad (37)$$

$$\mathbf{J}_m^{*\prime}\mathbf{D}_m\mathbf{J}_m = \mathbf{J}_b^{*\prime}\mathbf{D}_b\mathbf{J}_b = \sum_{k=1}^{N_b} D_k |J_k|^2 \qquad (38)$$

The extreme right side of Eq. (37) is valid only if the loop inductance matrix is diagonal. This will be the case if there is no mutual inductance. In this case, then, Eq. (37) represents four times the average energy stored in the inductances. If mutual inductance is present, the $\mathbf{L}_b$ matrix will not be diagonal and the right side of Eq. (37) will not be valid. The quadratic form still represents four times the average stored magnetic energy, but to prove this we must appeal to field theory. Similarly, the right side of Eq. (38) represents $4\omega_0^2$ times the average energy stored in the capacitances.

We have now obtained physical interpretations for the three quadratic forms appearing in Eq. (31). Let us define some notation in order to refer to these quadratic forms conveniently.

$$F(j\omega_0) = \tfrac{1}{2}\mathbf{J}_m^{*\prime}\mathbf{R}_m\mathbf{J}_m \qquad\qquad (a)$$

$$T(j\omega_0) = \tfrac{1}{4}\mathbf{J}_m^{*\prime}\mathbf{L}_m\mathbf{J}_m \qquad\qquad (b) \qquad (39)$$

$$V(j\omega_0) = \frac{1}{4\omega_0^2}\,\mathbf{J}_m^{*\prime}\mathbf{D}_m\mathbf{J}_m \qquad\qquad (c)$$

Because of the physical interpretations, we call these quantities *energy functions*. Again from the physical viewpoint, we know that the energy functions can never be negative but may be zero; hence, *they are positive semidefinite quadratic forms*.

From a mathematical point of view, $\mathbf{R}_b$ and $\mathbf{D}_b$ are diagonal matrices of nonnegative real numbers, and so they are positive semidefinite. Hence, the quadratic forms in Eqs. (36) and (38), which we have named $F(j\omega_0)$ and $V(j\omega_0)$, are positive semidefinite. The same argument applies to $T(j\omega_0)$ also when there is no mutual inductance. In the presence of mutual inductance, the positive semidefiniteness of $\mathbf{L}_b$ (and hence of $\mathbf{L}_m$) is essentially a postulate based on empirical observations. If every transformer has only two coupled coils, this postulate is equivalent to the usual constraint that the coefficient of coupling cannot exceed 1. If more than two coils are magnetically coupled, the restriction of the coupling coefficient to values less than unity is not sufficiently strong to insure positive semidefiniteness. That is, in the case of more than two magnetically coupled coils, physical realizability imposes the condition of positive semidefiniteness on the inductance matrix, which is a stronger requirement than unity coupling. At the end of the chapter a problem is suggested to illustrate this point.

Let us consider an example to clarify these concepts. A network supplied with a sinusoidal voltage source of frequency ω_0 is shown in Fig. 2. For this network the parameter matrices are

$$\mathbf{R}_m = \begin{bmatrix} R_1 & 0 \\ 0 & R_2 \end{bmatrix}; \quad \mathbf{L}_m = \begin{bmatrix} L_1 & 0 \\ 0 & L_2 \end{bmatrix}; \quad \mathbf{D}_m = \begin{bmatrix} D & -D \\ -D & D \end{bmatrix} \quad (40)$$

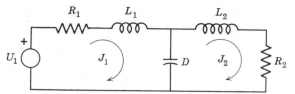

Fig. 2.   Network to illustrate energy functions.

Let us now form the energy functions

$$F = \tfrac{1}{2}[J_1{}^* \quad J_2{}^*] \begin{bmatrix} R_1 & 0 \\ 0 & R_2 \end{bmatrix} \begin{bmatrix} J_1 \\ J_2 \end{bmatrix} = \tfrac{1}{2}(R_1|J_1|^2 + R_2|J_2|^2) \quad (a)$$

$$T = \tfrac{1}{4}[J_1{}^* \quad J_2{}^*] \begin{bmatrix} L_1 & 0 \\ 0 & L_2 \end{bmatrix} \begin{bmatrix} J_1 \\ J_2 \end{bmatrix} = \tfrac{1}{4}(L_1|J_1|^2 + L_2|J_2|^2) \quad (b) \qquad (41)$$

$$V = \frac{1}{4\omega_0{}^2}[J_1{}^* \quad J_2{}^*] \begin{bmatrix} D & -D \\ -D & D \end{bmatrix} \begin{bmatrix} J_1 \\ J_2 \end{bmatrix} = \frac{D}{4\omega_0{}^2}|J_1 - J_2|^2 \quad (c)$$

The energy interpretations are immediately seen since J_1 and J_2 are the phasor branch currents of branches 1 and 2 and $J_1 - J_2$ is the branch current in the capacitance.

To summarize the results we have obtained so far, we can state that, *for a linear, passive, lumped, reciprocal, and time-invariant network, the loop resistance, inductance, and reciprocal capacitance matrices $\mathbf{R}_m$, $\mathbf{L}_m$, and $\mathbf{D}_m$ are positive semidefinite.* We established this result with the help of sinusoidal steady-state analysis. Now, however, we can return to the more general formulation in terms of Laplace transforms.

The starting point is the loop equations given in Eq. (2). Let us repeat it here for convenience.

$$(\mathbf{R}_m + s\mathbf{L}_m + \mathbf{D}_m/s)\mathbf{I}_m(s) = \mathbf{V}_m(s) \qquad (42)$$

where

$$\mathbf{V}_m(s) = \begin{bmatrix} V_1(s) \\ 0 \\ \cdot \\ \cdot \\ 0 \end{bmatrix} \qquad (43)$$

Let us now parallel the steps we took in the case of the phasor equations. Premultiply both sides of Eq. (42) by $\mathbf{I}_m^{*\prime}(s)$; the result will be

$$\mathbf{I}_m^{*\prime}(s)\mathbf{R}_m\mathbf{I}_m(s) + s\mathbf{I}_m^{*\prime}(s)\mathbf{L}_m\mathbf{I}_m(s) + \frac{1}{s}\mathbf{I}_m^{*\prime}(s)\mathbf{D}_m\mathbf{I}_m(s) = V_1(s)I_1^*(s)$$

$$(44)$$

We again get quadratic forms which are the same as we had before; only now the variables are loop current transforms rather than phasors. The quadratic forms in this equation do not have an energy interpretation like those of Eq. (31). However, the matrices of these quadratic forms are identical with the former ones. Hence, these quadratic forms are positive semidefinite. We therefore give these quadratic forms symbols similar to those of Eq. (39) and continue to call them energy functions although even dimensionally they do not represent energy.

$$F_0(s) = \mathbf{I}_m^{*\prime}(s)\mathbf{R}_m\mathbf{I}_m(s) \qquad (a)$$

$$T_0(s) = \mathbf{I}_m^{*\prime}(s)\mathbf{L}_m\mathbf{I}_m(s) \qquad (b) \qquad (45)$$

$$V_0(s) = \mathbf{I}_m^{*\prime}(s)\mathbf{D}_m\mathbf{I}_m(s) \qquad (c)$$

Using this notation, Eq. (44) becomes

$$F_0(s) + sT_0(s) + V_0(s)/s = V_1(s)I_1^*(s) \qquad (46)$$

The choice of symbols for the energy functions is an unfortunate one as we mentioned in Chapter 1. However, these symbols have become standard notation and we will continue to use them.

Let us digress here for a moment. This entire development started from the loop equations. Alternatively, a completely dual development can proceed on the basis of the node equations. Instead of the loop parameter matrices $\mathbf{R}_m$, $\mathbf{L}_m$, and $\mathbf{D}_m$, the node parameter matrices $\mathbf{G}_n$, $\mathbf{\Gamma}_n$, and $\mathbf{C}_n$ will appear, where G, Γ, and C refer to conductance, inverse inductance, and capacitance, respectively. Energy functions can now be defined in terms of these parameter matrices and the node voltage matrix $\mathbf{V}_n$. These will have the same form as Eqs. (45) with $\mathbf{V}_n$ in place of $\mathbf{I}_m$ and the node parameter matrices in place of the loop parameter matrices. An equation similar to Eq. (46) can now be written with these new energy functions, but with V_1 and I_1 interchanged. This alternative development is not needed to carry on the subsequent discussion, just as the node system of equations itself is really superfluous. However, just as node equations provide helpful viewpoints and often simplify computation, so also this alternative approach may sometimes be useful.   If you are interested, you can supply the details in the procedure which was outlined.

Up to this point everything we have done may be considered as preliminary to our major effort, which is to establish analytic properties of network functions.   We are now ready to embark on this task.   As a first step we can compute the driving-point impedance of the network of Fig. 1 from Eq. (46).   (Remember that there are zero initial conditions.) To do this divide both sides by the real positive quantity $I_1(s)I_1^*(s)$ and get

$$Z(s) = \frac{V_1(s)}{I_1(s)} = \frac{1}{|I_1(s)|^2} \{F_0(s) + sT_0(s) + V_0(s)/s\} \qquad (47)$$

This is an important equation; the properties of driving-point impedance functions follow directly from it.   Suppose we now separate the right side into real and imaginary parts.   The result will be

$$\operatorname{Re}[Z(s)] = \frac{1}{|I_1(s)|^2}\left(F_0(s) + \sigma T_0(s) + \frac{\sigma}{\sigma^2 + \omega^2}V_0(s)\right) \qquad (48)$$

$$\operatorname{Im}[Z(s)] = \frac{\omega}{|I_1(s)|^2}\left(T_0(s) - \frac{V_0(s)}{\sigma^2 + \omega^2}\right) \qquad (49)$$

Notice that these equations apply no matter what the value of s may be, except at zeros of $I_1(s)$.   These two are extremely important equations from which we can draw some interesting conclusions.   For later reference let us state these results as a theorem.

Theorem 3.   Let $Z(s)$ be the driving-point impedance of a linear, passive, lumped, reciprocal, and time-invariant network N.   Then the following statements are true.

(a)   Whenever $\sigma \geq 0$, $\operatorname{Re}[Z(s)] \geq 0$.

(b)   If N contains no resistances ($F_0(s) = 0$), then

$$\sigma > 0 \quad \text{implies} \quad \operatorname{Re}[Z(s)] > 0$$

$$\sigma = 0 \quad \text{implies} \quad \operatorname{Re}[Z(s)] = 0$$

$$\sigma < 0 \quad \text{implies} \quad \operatorname{Re}[Z(s)] < 0$$

(c)   If N contains no capacitances ($V_0(s) = 0$), then

$$\omega > 0 \quad \text{implies} \quad \operatorname{Im}[Z(s)] > 0$$

$$\omega = 0 \quad \text{implies} \quad \operatorname{Im}[Z(s)] = 0$$

$$\omega < 0 \quad \text{implies} \quad \operatorname{Im}[Z(s)] < 0$$

(d)   If N contains no inductances ($T_0(s) = 0$), then

$$\omega > 0 \quad \text{implies} \quad \text{Im}\,[Z(s)] < 0$$

$$\omega = 0 \quad \text{implies} \quad \text{Im}\,[Z(s)] = 0$$

$$\omega < 0 \quad \text{implies} \quad \text{Im}\,[Z(s)] > 0$$

These results follow immediately from Eqs. (48) and (49). Part (a) leads to the discussion of positive real functions which we shall take up next. Part (b) leads to the historically important Reactance Theorem of Foster. Parts (c) and (d) lead to Cauer's results on RL and RC networks.

9.4   Positive Real Functions

A *positive real function* $F(s)$ is an analytic function of the complex variable $s = \sigma + j\omega$ which has the following properties.

(a) $F(s)$ is regular in $\sigma > 0$,
(b) $F(\sigma)$ is real,
(c) $\sigma \geq 0$ implies $\text{Re}\,[F(s)] \geq 0$.

This is a mathematical definition and defines a class of mathematical functions. Our motivation in making this definition is the fact that a network function of interest, namely the driving-point impedance, possesses these properties. By making a mathematical study of positive real functions we can perhaps determine things about impedances which we could not establish from physical reasoning alone. The concept of a positive real function, as well as many of the properties of positive real functions which we will consider, are due to Otto Brune.

We will now show that if a function is rational and satisfies the last two of these conditions, it will automatically satisfy condition (a). We will do this by showing that a pole of order n of a real rational function is surrounded by $2n$ sectors in which the real part of the function is alternately positive and negative. Let s_0 be a pole of order n of the rational function $F(s)$. The case $n = 3$ is illustrated in Fig. 3. In the neighborhood of the pole of order n, the function has a Laurent expansion of the form

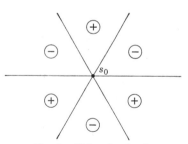

Fig. 3.   Pole of order 3.

$$F(s) = \frac{a_{-n}}{(s - s_0)^n} + \frac{a_{-n+1}}{(s - s_0)^{n-1}} + \cdots + \frac{a_{-1}}{s - s_0} + \sum_{k=0}^{\infty} a_k (s - s_0)^k \quad (50)$$

If a sufficiently small neighborhood of s_0 is chosen, the first term of the Laurent expansion can be made much larger in magnitude than the rest; so that the real part of $F(s)$ in this neighborhood will be positive or negative according as the real part of the first term is positive or negative. If we write

$$a_{-n} = k\epsilon^{j\theta} \qquad\qquad (a)$$

$$(s - s_0) = \rho\epsilon^{j\phi} \qquad\qquad (b)$$

(51)

then

$$\mathrm{Re}\left[\frac{a_{-n}}{(s - s_0)^n}\right] = \frac{k}{\rho^n}\cos(\theta - n\phi) \qquad\qquad (52)$$

Since θ is a fixed angle and ϕ can vary from 0 to 2π in this neighborhood, we see that the real part of the dominant term changes sign $2n$ times as ϕ varies from 0 to 2π. Therefore the real part of $F(s)$ also changes sign $2n$ times (although not necessarily at the same values of ϕ, due to the other terms in the Laurent expansion).

Now suppose that the function $F(s)$ satisfies the last two conditions in the definition of a positive real function but it has a pole in the interior of the right half plane. According to what we have just proved, the real part of $F(s)$ will then take on both negative and positive values in the right half plane, which contradicts condition (c).

We conclude that in the case of rational functions, whose only singular points are poles, condition (a) of the definition of a positive real function is a consequence of the other two conditions and hence, is unnecessary.

Let us now interpret the definition of a positive real function as a mapping property of the function so that we can use our knowledge of conformal mapping to advantage. A positive real function $W = F(s)$ maps the real s-axis into the real W-axis, and maps the right half s-plane into the right half W-plane. This is illustrated in Fig. 4.

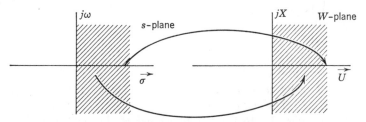

Fig. 4.   Mapping by positive real functions.

An immediate consequence of this interpretation is the fact that a positive real function of a positive real function is itself positive real.

That is, if $F_1(s)$ and $F_2(s)$ are pr (this is used as an abbreviation for positive real), then

$$F_3(s) = F_1[F_2(s)] \tag{53}$$

For, the right half s-plane goes into the right half F_2-plane since $F_2(s)$ is pr. Also, the right half F_2-plane goes into the right half F_1-plane since F_1 is pr. The composite mapping therefore maps the right half s-plane into the right half F_3-plane. The real axis is preserved throughout.

This is a useful result. We can use it to show immediately that if $F(s)$ is pr so are $1/F(s)$ and $F(1/s)$. To prove this result we merely observe that

$$\frac{1}{s} = \frac{\sigma}{\sigma^2 + \omega^2} - j\frac{\omega}{\sigma^2 + \omega^2} \tag{54}$$

is a pr function. Now we use $1/s$ and $F(s)$ as $F_1(s)$ and $F_2(s)$ in Eq. (53) both ways, and the result follows immediately.

From the fact that the reciprocal of a pr function is itself pr, it follows that a pr function can have no zeros in the right half plane. For if it did, then its reciprocal would have poles in the right half plane, which is impossible.

From a conformal mapping point of view, the points $F(s) = 0$ and ∞ (these are the zeros and poles of the function), which are on the *boundary* of the right half F-plane, cannot be images of any *interior points* of the right half s-plane. Let us now inquire into the possibility of boundary points of the right half F-plane being images of boundary points of the right half s-plane. That is, let a point on the $j\omega$-axis be mapped by a pr function F into a point on the imaginary axis of the F-plane. If $j\omega_0$ is the point in question, then

$$F(j\omega_0) = jX_0 \tag{55}$$

where X_0 is real (positive, negative, or zero).

Consider a neighborhood of $j\omega_0$ in the s-plane and the corresponding neighborhood of jX_0 in the F-plane as shown in Fig. 5. Let s_1 denote a

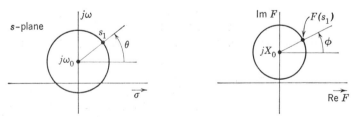

Fig. 5. Conformal mapping by pr functions.

point in the right half plane, in this neighborhood of $j\omega_0$. Let us now expand $F(s)$ in a Taylor series about $j\omega_0$ and evaluate it at $s = s_1$. The result is

$$F(s_1) - jX_0 = F^{(n)}(j\omega_0)(s_1 - j\omega_0)^n + F^{(n+1)}(j\omega_0)(s_1 - j\omega_0)^{n+1} + \cdots$$

$$(56)$$

where $F^{(n)}(j\omega_0)$ is the first nonvanishing derivative of $F(s)$ at $j\omega_0$.

As s_1 approaches $j\omega_0$ the dominant term on the right will be the first term. Let us define

$$\phi = \arg [F(s_1) - jX_0] \qquad (a)$$

$$\theta = \arg (s_1 - j\omega_0) \qquad (b) \qquad (57)$$

$$\beta = \arg [F^{(n)}(j\omega_0)] \qquad (c)$$

Then, in the limit, we will find from Eq. (56) that

$$\lim_{s_1 \to j\omega_0} \phi = \beta + n \lim_{s_1 \to j\omega_0} \theta \qquad (58)$$

But the pr condition requires that $|\phi| \leq \pi/2$ as long as $|\theta| \leq \pi/2$. Therefore we conclude from Eq. (58) that

$$n = 1 \qquad (a)$$

$$\beta = 0 \qquad (b) \qquad (59)$$

Thus the first nonvanishing derivative is the first one and its angle is zero at $s = j\omega_0$. This is a very important result. For future reference we will state it as a theorem.

Theorem 4. *If any point on the $j\omega$-axis is mapped by a pr function F into a point on the imaginary axis in the F-plane, then at this point the derivative dF/ds is real and positive.*

A number of other results follow from this important theorem. Note that if $F(s)$ has a zero or a pole on the $j\omega$-axis, the conditions of the theorem are satisfied. In the case of a zero ($X_0 = 0$), a point on the $j\omega$-axis is mapped into the origin of the F-plane, which is on the imaginary axis. Hence, the derivative dF/ds is real and positive. This also implies that the zero is a simple one, since at a higher order zero the first derivative will be zero. If $F(s)$ has a pole on the $j\omega$-axis, its reciprocal will have a zero there and the theorem will apply to the reciprocal. However, $d(1/F)/ds$ evaluated at a pole of $F(s)$ is the reciprocal of the residue of $F(s)$ at the pole (see appendix). These considerations can now be stated as the following theorem.

Theorem 5. *If a pr function has any poles or zeros on the $j\omega$-axis (including $s = 0, \infty$) such poles or zeros must be simple. At a simple zero on* *the jω-axis the derivative is real and positive. At a simple pole on the jω-axis, the residue is real and positive.*

We have up to this point collected quite a number of necessary conditions that a positive real function satisfies. What we should like to do is to find a set from among these necessary conditions which proves to be sufficient as well. The result is contained in the following theorem.

Theorem 6. *A rational function $F(s)$ with real coefficients is positive real if and only if*

(a) $F(s)$ *is regular in $\sigma > 0$;*
(b)   *Poles on the jω-axis (including $s = 0, \infty$) are simple and with real positive residues;*
(c) $Re\,[F(j\omega)] \geq 0$ *for all ω, except at poles.*

That these conditions are necessary is obvious from the definition of a pr function and from the immediately preceding theorem. Therefore, only the sufficiency needs to be proved. That is, let us assume that a function $F(s)$ satisfies these conditions and show that the function must be pr. Let $\omega_1, \omega_2, \cdots, \omega_k$ be the poles on the jω-axis and let us examine the principal parts at these poles. If there is a pole at the origin, the principal part is

$$F_0(s) = k_0/s \qquad (60)$$

where k_0 is real and positive. It is evident that $F_0(s)$ is itself pr and that

$$Re\,[F_0(j\omega)] = 0 \qquad (61)$$

Similarly, the principal part at a possible simple pole of $F(s)$ at infinity is

$$F_\infty(s) = k_\infty s \qquad (62)$$

where k_∞ is real and positive. $F_\infty(s)$ is also pr and its real part on the jω-axis is zero. That is,

$$Re\,[F_\infty(j\omega)] = 0 \qquad (63)$$

Any other poles on the jω-axis must occur in conjugate pairs and with conjugate residues, since $F(s)$ is a real function. Since the residues are real by hypothesis, the two residues are equal. Taking the principal parts at the conjugate poles $j\omega_j$ and $-j\omega_j$ together, we get

$$F_j(s) = \frac{k_j}{s - j\omega_j} + \frac{k_j}{s + j\omega_j} = \frac{2k_j s}{s^2 + \omega_j^2} \qquad (64)$$

where k_j is real and positive. This function is also positive real and has the property

$$Re\,[F_j(j\omega)] = 0 \qquad (65)$$

(We may note parenthetically that $F_0(s)$ is the impedance of a capacitance, $F_\infty(s)$ that of an inductance, and $F_j(s)$ that of a parallel tuned circuit.)

Thus we can subtract from the given function $F(s)$, the principal parts at all of its poles on the $j\omega$-axis, including $s = \infty$. Since each principal part has a zero real part on the $j\omega$-axis, the remainder function $F_r(s)$ still has property (c) of the theorem. That is,

$$\text{Re}\,[F_r(j\omega)] = \text{Re}\,[F(j\omega)] \geq 0 \tag{66}$$

The remainder function $F_r(s)$ is a function which is regular in the right half plane and its entire boundary, the $j\omega$-axis, including the point infinity. For such a function, the minimum value of the real part throughout its region of regularity lies on the boundary. This can be proved using the maximum modulus theorem (see appendix) in the following way. Let $G(s) = \epsilon^{-F_r(s)}$. This function will have the same region of regularity as $F_r(s)$. Hence, according to the maximum modulus theorem, the maximum magnitude of $G(s)$ for all $\sigma \geq 0$ lies on the $j\omega$-axis. But

$$|G(s)| = \epsilon^{-\text{Re}\,[F_r(s)]} \tag{67}$$

The maximum magnitude of $G(s)$ will correspond to the smallest value of $\text{Re}\,[F_r(s)]$. This proves the desired result that the minimum value of $\text{Re}\,[F_r(s)]$ for all $\sigma \geq 0$ occurs on the $j\omega$-axis. But according to Eq. (66) this value is nonnegative. Hence, the real part of $F_r(s)$ must be nonnegative everywhere in the right half plane. That is,

$$\text{Re}\,[F_r(s)] \geq 0 \qquad \text{in } \sigma \geq 0 \tag{68}$$

Since in addition $F_r(\sigma)$ is real, $F_r(s)$ is a positive real function. Now we can write

$$F(s) = F_r(s) + k_\infty s + \frac{k_0}{s} + \sum_j \frac{2k_j s}{s^2 + \omega_j^2} \tag{69}$$

We have shown that each term on the right is pr. You can easily show that the sum of two (or more) pr functions is itself pr. Hence, $F(s)$ is pr. This completes the proof of the sufficiency of the stated conditions.

Since the reciprocal of a pr function is also pr, we can restate these necessary and sufficient conditions in terms of the zeros of $F(s)$.

Theorem 7. *A real rational function $F(s)$ is positive real if and only if*

(a) $F(s)$ *has no zeros in $\sigma > 0$.*

(b)   *Zeros on the $j\omega$-axis (including $s = \infty$) are simple and with real positive derivatives.*

(c) $\text{Re}\,[F(j\omega)] \geq 0$ *for all ω, except at poles.*

This theorem follows directly from the previous one if we remember that the residue of a function at a simple pole is the reciprocal of the derivative of the reciprocal of the function.

In testing a given function to determine positive realness, it may not always be necessary to use the necessary and sufficient conditions listed in the preceding two theorems. It may be possible to eliminate some functions from consideration by inspection because they violate certain simple necessary conditions. Let us now discuss some of these conditions.

We have seen that a rational positive real function has neither zeros nor poles in the right half s-plane. We define a *Hurwitz polynomial* as one that has no zeros in the right half s-plane. This definition permits zeros on the $j\omega$-axis. To describe a polynomial which has zeros neither inside the right half plane nor on the $j\omega$-axis, we say the polynomial is *strictly Hurwitz*. With this terminology, we see that a pr function is the ratio of two Hurwitz polynomials.

The factors which constitute a strictly Hurwitz polynomial must have one of the following two forms: $(s + a)$ for real zeros or $(s^2 + as + b)$ for a pair of complex zeros, both a and b being positive. If any number of such factors are multiplied, the result must be a polynomial all of whose coefficients are strictly positive, that is, no powers of s can be missing. Note, however, that even though this is a necessary condition for a Hurwitz polynomial, it is not sufficient, as the following counter-example readily demonstrates.

$$(s^2 - s + 4)(s + 2) = s^3 + s^2 + 2s + 8 \tag{70}$$

This polynomial has no missing powers of s and all coefficients are positive, yet it has a pair of zeros in the right half plane.

Hence, if a rational function is presented as a candidate for positive realness, this criterion can serve as a negative type of test. If the numerator or denominator polynomials have any negative coefficients, or missing coefficients, the function can be discarded.* On the other hand, if this test is passed, nothing definite can be said about the function.

Another simple test follows from the fact that a pr function can have no more than a simple pole or a simple zero at zero or infinity (which are on the $j\omega$-axis). This requires that the highest powers of s in numerator and denominator not differ by more than unity; and similarly for the lowest powers.

---

* Of course, if every other coefficient in both numerator and denominator is missing, the candidate function might be a reactance function, which is a positive real function. We will discuss reactance functions and their properties in the next section.

Before leaving the general theory of positive real functions, let us briefly examine the behavior of the real part of such a function $F(s)$ on the $j\omega$-axis. Remember that the j-axis real part of F is equal to the even part evaluated at $s = j\omega$. That is,

$$U(\omega) = \text{Re}\,[F(j\omega)] = \text{``Ev''}F(s)\,|_{s=j\omega} = \tfrac{1}{2}[F(j\omega) + F(-j\omega)] \quad (71)$$

so that statements made about the even part can easily be interpreted in terms of the real part on the $j\omega$-axis.

We already know that $U(\omega)$ is necessarily an even function of ω and nonnegative for all ω. It is also easy to establish that the even part of $F(s)$ can have no poles on the $j\omega$-axis. Any poles of the even part would also have to be poles of $F(s)$. But on the $j\omega$-axis, these are simple. If we consider $F(s)$ expanded in partial fractions as in Eq. (69), the function $F(-s)$ will contain the same terms but all those involving the poles on the $j\omega$-axis will have a negative sign. Hence, in forming the even part, $F(s) + F(-s)$, these will all cancel, leaving a function with no poles on the $j\omega$-axis. Interpreted in terms of the real part, this means that $U(\omega)$ must be bounded for all ω.

Now let us consider a possible zero of $U(\omega)$. Figure 6 shows a sketch of $U(\omega)$ versus ω in the vicinity of a zero. Because of the pr requirement,

Fig. 6.   Sketch of real part of a pr function.

$U(\omega)$ must remain positive on both sides of the zero. It follows that a zero of $U(\omega)$ on the ω-axis cannot be of odd multiplicity; it must be of even multiplicity.

We have here determined certain necessary conditions for the j-axis real part of a positive real function. Let us now list a set of necessary and sufficient conditions as a theorem.

Theorem 8.   *A real function $U(\omega)$ of a real variable ω is the j-axis real part of a rational pr function $F(s)$ if and only if:*

(a)   *$U(\omega)$ is an even rational function with real coefficients.*
(b)   *$U(\omega)$ is bounded for all ω.*
(c)   *$U(\omega) \geq 0$ for all ω.*

We have already seen that these conditions are necessary. As a matter of fact we have already demonstrated in Chapter 7, by actual construction, that conditions (a) and (b) are sufficient to find a real rational function. If condition (c) is included as well, this is sufficient to make the rational function in question, a positive real function.

The discussion of this section is by no means an exhaustive treatment of the general properties of positive real functions. However, we will not go any further, since elaboration on this subject will take us into topics which are primarily of interest in network synthesis.*

Let us now summarize the broad results we have obtained so far in this chapter. We started with a class of networks (linear, passive, lumped, reciprocal, and time-invariant). For such networks we found an expression for the driving-point impedance in terms of the energy functions. Because of the known physical properties of the energy functions, we were able to establish that the driving-point impedance of the class of networks under consideration is necessarily a member of the class of functions called positive real. We then studied many properties of positive real functions, one of which states that the reciprocal of a positive real function is also positive real. This means that the admittance function, as well as the impedance, is necessarily positive real.

The converse of these results, namely, that any given positive real rational function can be realized as the driving-point impedance or admittance of a network in the class of networks under consideration, is also true and was first established by Brune in 1931. We will not discuss this aspect of the subject any further since discussion of this theorem and elucidation of its consequences would take us far afield into network synthesis.

9.5 Reactance Functions

Let us now turn our attention to some special types of positive real functions. We shall find that these arise from a consideration of networks containing only two types of elements (LC, RC, RL). Historically such networks were studied before the more general ones, starting with the work done by Foster in 1924.

We shall initially consider networks that have no resistance. Such networks are referred to as *lossless* or *reactance* networks. In section 9.3 (Theorem 3) we noted that the driving-point impedance of a lossless network is purely imaginary on the $j\omega$-axis; that is, Re $[Z(j\omega)] = 0$. Stated in terms of a transformation, the impedance of a lossless net-

* The interested readers are referred to:
1. O. Brune, *J. Math. Phys.*, vol. 10, 1931, pp. 195–236.
2. P. I. Richards, *Duke Math. J.*, vol. 14, 1947, pp. 777–786.
3. E. A. Guillemin, *Mathematics of Circuit Analysis*, Wiley, 1949, pp. 395–422.
4. N. Balabanian, *Network Synthesis*, Prentice-Hall, Inc., 1958.

work maps the imaginary axis of the s-plane into the imaginary axis of the Z-plane. We shall make this property the basis of a definition. We shall define a *reactance function* as a *positive real function which maps the imaginary axis into the imaginary axis*. These functions are also called *pri functions* (i standing for imaginary). In this terminology *the driving point impedance of a lossless network is a reactance function*.

Let us now establish some properties of reactance functions. In the first place we will show that *the poles and zeros of a reactance function all lie on the $j\omega$-axis*.

To prove this theorem, note that, just as a function that maps the real axis into the real axis has symmetry about the real axis [that is, $F(s^*) = F^*(s)$], so a function that maps the imaginary axis into the imaginary axis has symmetry about the imaginary axis. To see this clearly let us rotate the two planes (the s-plane and the F-plane) clockwise by $\pi/2$ radians. We do this by defining

$$z = s/j \qquad\qquad (a)$$

$$\phi(s) = \frac{1}{j} F(jz) = \psi(z) \qquad\qquad (b)$$

(72)

The function $\phi(s)$ has been renamed $\psi(z)$ on the extreme right. These transformations are illustrated in Fig. 7. Note that the real s-axis

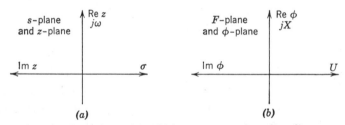

Fig. 7.   Transformation which rotates axes by $\pi/2$ radians.

becomes the imaginary z-axis and vice versa. Similarly for the other transformation. When z is real, the argument of $F(jz)$ is imaginary, so by hypothesis $F(jz)$ will also be imaginary. Hence $\psi(z)$ will be real when z is real. It follows that

$$\psi(z^*) = \psi^*(z) \qquad\qquad (73)$$

If we now translate back through the transformations in Eqs. (72) this relation becomes

$$F(-s^*) = -F^*(s) \qquad\qquad (74)$$

Note that the point $-s^*$ is the image of the point s with respect to the imaginary axis. Likewise for the points $-F^*$ and F. Hence, the result in Eq. (74) states that image points with respect to the imaginary axis in the s-plane go into image points with respect to the imaginary axis in the F-plane.

It follows that, if $F(s)$ has a pole or a zero in the left half plane, then the image point in the right half plane is also a pole or a zero which is not possible for a pr function. Hence, the poles and zeros of a reactance function must all lie on the $j\omega$-axis.

Let us turn back to Theorem 4 for a moment. There we saw that if a pr function maps a point on the $j\omega$-axis into a point on the imaginary axis, then the derivative of the function at that point is real and positive. But according to Theorem 3 a reactance function maps the entire $j\omega$-axis into the imaginary axis in the F-plane. Hence for such a function, the derivative property will hold at all points on the $j\omega$-axis (except at poles). This is the basis of another very important property, namely, that *the poles and zeros of a reactance function alternate on the $j\omega$-axis. That is, between any two poles is a zero and between any two zeros is a pole.*

As we just mentioned, theorem 4 applies at all points on the $j\omega$-axis except at poles. Hence, the derivative dF/ds evaluated at $s = j\omega$ is real and positive. Let us compute the derivative along the $j\omega$-axis, which we are permitted to do since the derivative exists. The result will be

$$\frac{dF}{ds}\bigg|_{s=j\omega} = \frac{dF(j\omega)}{d(j\omega)} = \frac{d[jX(\omega)]}{d(j\omega)} = \frac{j\,dX(\omega)}{j\,d\omega} = \frac{dX(\omega)}{d\omega} > 0 \qquad (75)$$

We have used the usual notation $F(j\omega) = U(\omega) + jX(\omega)$, and, since F is here a reactance function, $U(\omega)$ is zero. Notice that $X(\omega)$ is a real function of a real variable. Therefore, if there is no pole between two zeros of $X(\omega)$, the derivative will become negative somewhere in between, which, as we have just shown, is impossible. A similar conclusion applies to successive poles. Figure 8 illustrates the form of $X(\omega)$ required for successive zeros or poles without intervening poles or zeros, respectively.

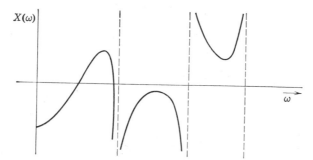

Fig. 8.   Impossible behavior of a reactance function.

The property which we have just proved is referred to as the *alternation* property of the poles and zeros. From this property it is clear that the plot of $X(\omega)$ vs ω must have the general shape shown in Fig. 9.

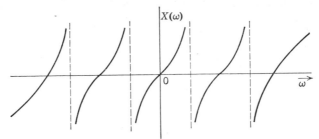

Fig. 9.   Behavior of a reactance function.

Since $X(\omega)$ is an odd function of ω and the alternation of poles and zeros must hold on the entire imaginary axis (positive and negative values of ω), we conclude that *the point $s = 0$ is either a zero or a pole of a reactance function.*

Note that, if $F(s)$ is a pr function mapping the imaginary axis into the imaginary axis, so is the function $F(1/s)$. With the transformation $s \rightarrow 1/s$, the point ∞ in the s-plane goes into the origin in the $1/s$-plane. Hence, using the immediately preceding result we find that *the point $s = \infty$ is either a zero or a pole of a reactance function.*

We have now discussed several properties of reactance functions. We should also note that certain properties of general pr functions apply in particular to reactance functions. Thus, since we have shown that poles and zeros of a pr function which lie on the $j\omega$-axis are simple and that residues at such poles are real and positive, we conclude that *all poles and zeros of reactance functions are simple and that residues at all poles are real and positive.*

We are now in a position to consolidate our results about reactance functions and to state necessary and sufficient conditions for a rational function of s to be a reactance function.

Theorem 9. *A real rational function $\psi(s)$ is a reactance function if and only if (a) all of its poles are simple and lie on the $j\omega$-axis; (b) the residues are all real and positive; (c) the function has either a pole or a zero at $s = 0$ and at $s = \infty$; and (d) Re $\psi(j\omega) = 0$ for some ω.*

Notice that this statement involves only the poles and the residues, not the zeros. We have already shown these conditions to be necessary; it remains to prove that they are sufficient. That is, assuming a rational function to satisfy the stated conditions, we must show that the function is a reactance function. This is most easily done by considering the partial fraction expansion of such a function. If we combine the two terms due to conjugate poles, the most general form of the partial fraction expansion will be

$$\psi(s) = \frac{k_0}{s} + k_\infty s + \sum_{i=1} \frac{2k_i s}{s^2 + \omega_i^2} \qquad (76)$$

where the summation runs over all the poles, and all the k's are positive. Of course, the pole at the origin or at infinity, or both, may be absent. This expression is consistent with Eq. (69) with $F_r(s) = 0$, since in the present case there are no other poles except those on the $j\omega$-axis. The desired result follows immediately. Each term in this expansion is imaginary for imaginary values of s, so that $\psi(s)$ maps the imaginary axis into the imaginary axis, which makes $\psi(s)$ a reactance function by definition.

The alternation property of the poles and zeros forms the basis of an alternate set of necessary and sufficient conditions as follows.

Theorem 10. *A real rational function of s is a reactance function if and only if all of its poles and zeros are simple and lie on the $j\omega$-axis, and alternate with each other.*

Again, we have already proved that a reactance function necessarily satisfies these conditions. It remains to show that the conditions are sufficient. A rational function which satisfies the given conditions must have the following form.

$$\psi(s) = K \frac{s(s^2 + \omega_1^2)(s^2 + \omega_3^2) \cdots (s^2 + \omega_{2n-1}^2)}{(s^2 + \omega_0^2)(s^2 + \omega_2^2) \cdots (s^2 + \omega_k^2)} \qquad (77)$$

where

$$0 \leq \omega_0 < \omega_1 < \omega_2 < \omega_3 < \cdots < \omega_{2n-2} < \omega_{2n-1} < \omega_{2n} < \infty \qquad (78)$$

and K is a positive constant, with $k = 2n - 2$ or $2n$ accordingly as $\psi(s)$ has a zero or a pole at infinity. Similarly, if $\psi(s)$ has a pole at $s = 0$, we take ω_0 to be zero.

The desired result now follows immediately. Each of the quadratic pole and zero factors in Eq. (77) is real when s is imaginary. This means that $\psi(s)$ is imaginary when s is imaginary due to the factor s. Hence, $\psi(s)$ is a reactance function, by definition.

At the start of this discussion of reactance functions we showed that the driving-point impedance of a lossless network is necessarily a reactance function. Note that the driving-point admittance of a lossless network is also a reactance function. That is,

$$Y(s) = 1/Z(s) \qquad (79)$$

is also imaginary for imaginary values of s.

The question now arises whether the converse of this condition is also true. That is, given a reactance function, is this the driving-point impedance or admittance of some lossless network? In order to answer this question in the affirmative, we shall have to construct a lossless network which has the given reactance function as its impedance or admittance. The question was answered by Foster in his famous Reactance Theorem in 1924 (although not in the form given here).

Theorem 11. *A rational function of s is a reactance function if and only if it is the driving-point impedance or admittance of a lossless network.*

We have already established the sufficiency. It remains to show that, given a reactance function, it is necessarily the impedance or admittance of a lossless network. To show this, turn back to the partial fraction expansion of a reactance function given in Eq. (76). We can recognize each of the summands of the partial fraction expansion to be the impedance or admittance of a very simple reactance structure. The structures are shown in Fig. 10. Thus if $\psi(s)$ is to be an impedance, we can represent it as a series combination of the elementary one-port networks in column 2 of Fig. 10. Or if $\psi(s)$ is to be an admittance we can represent it as a

Function	Network representation	
	Impedance	Admittance
$\dfrac{k_0}{s}$	$C = 1/k_0$	$L = 1/k_0$
$k_\infty s$	$L = k_\infty$	$C = k_\infty$
$\dfrac{2k_i s}{s^2 + \omega_i^2}$	$L = 2k_i/\omega_i^2$ $C = 1/2k_i$	$C = 2k_i/\omega_i^2$ $L = 1/2k_i$

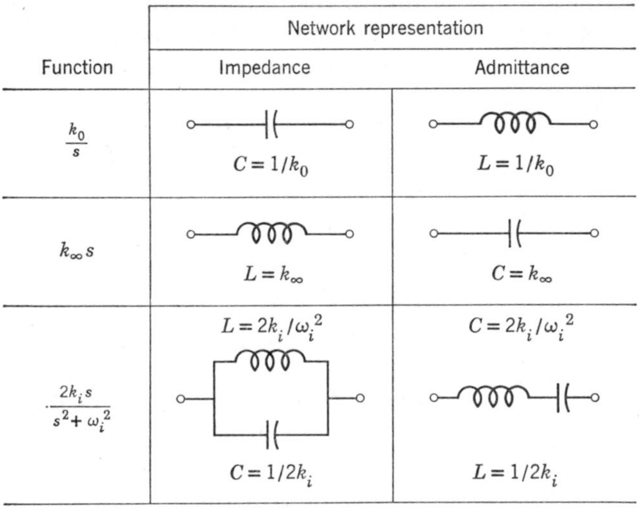

Fig. 10. Representation of partial fraction summands.

parallel combination of the elementary one-ports in column 3. The forms of the resulting networks are shown in Fig. 11. They are referred to as *Foster's first and second form*.

We have now proved the theorem with a vengeance. We found that a given reactance function can be *both* impedance *and* admittance of

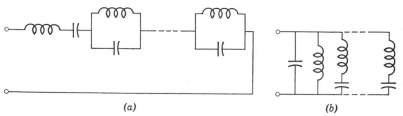

Fig. 11. Foster's forms of lossless one-ports.

some lossless network (not the same network, of course). In fact, an infinite number of lossless networks can be found which are equivalent to the ones shown in Fig. 11. However, we will stop the discussion here since we wish to present only the fundamentals in this book. We shall leave the further exploration of this subject to the books on network synthesis.

9.6   *RC* and *RL* Impedances

Let us now turn to the other two types of two-element networks, *RL* and *RC*. We can, if we like, carry out a complete discussion of these two cases, without referring to the discussion of *LC* networks. However, this would be a waste of time, since we can interrelate the driving-point functions by means of suitable transformations. The procedure we will follow was first used by W. Cauer in extending Foster's work to *RC* and *RL* networks. Cauer also gave a realization procedure in the form of ladder representations of driving-point functions of *RL*, *RC*, and *LC* networks but we will leave this subject also to the synthesis books.*

Let $Z(s)$ be the driving-point impedance of an *RC* network N. With the usual choice of loops, let the loop impedance matrix of N be

$$\mathbf{Z}_m(s) = [c_{ij}(s)] \tag{80}$$

where the elements of the matrix are

$$c_{ij}(s) = R_{ij} + \frac{1}{sC_{ij}} \tag{81}$$

Let us replace each resistance in N by an inductance of equal value (R ohms becomes R henries). Then the loop impedance matrix of the new network N' becomes

$$\boldsymbol{\mathfrak{z}}_m(s) = \left[\left(sR_{ij} + \frac{1}{sC_{ij}} \right) \right] = \left[s \left(R_{ij} + \frac{1}{s^2 C_{ij}} \right) \right] = s\mathbf{Z}_m(s^2) \tag{82}$$

* For example, N. Balabanian, *Network Synthesis*, Prentice-Hall, 1958, and E. A. Guillemin, *Synthesis of Passive Networks*, Wiley, 1957.

Remembering the effect on the determinant of multiplication of a matrix by a scalar s, we shall find the driving-point impedance of the network N' to be

$$\psi(s) = sZ(s^2) \tag{83}$$

The network N' contains only capacitance and inductance, so that $\psi(s)$ in the last equation is a reactance function. Thus, we have found that the impedance of an RC network can be transformed to a reactance function by replacing s by s^2 and then multiplying by s.

It would be of interest to see if the converse is also true; that is, given a reactance function $\psi(s)$, can we convert to the impedance of an RC network with the opposite transformation? To do this, consider the reactance function to be expanded in partial fractions as shown in Eq. (76). Now replace s by $\sqrt{s}$ (or s^2 by s) and divide the entire result by $\sqrt{s}$. (This is the opposite of the transformation just used.) The result will be

$$\frac{1}{\sqrt{s}}\psi(\sqrt{s}) = \frac{1}{\sqrt{s}}\left(\frac{k_0}{\sqrt{s}} + k_\infty\sqrt{s} + \sum_i \frac{2k_i\sqrt{s}}{s + \omega_i^2}\right)$$

$$= \frac{k_0}{s} + k_\infty + \sum_i \frac{2k_i}{s + \omega_i^2} \tag{84}$$

Each term on the right can be recognized as the impedance of a simple RC structure. As a matter of fact, the representations of column 2 in Fig. 10 will apply but with inductances replaced by resistances. For convenient reference let us state this result as follows.

Theorem 12. *If $Z_{RC}(s)$ is the driving-point impedance of an RC network, then*

$$\psi(s) = sZ_{RC}(s^2) \tag{85}$$

is a reactance function. Conversely, if $\psi(s)$ is a reactance function, then

$$Z_{RC}(s) = \frac{1}{\sqrt{s}}\psi(\sqrt{s}) \tag{86}$$

is the driving-point impedance of an RC network.

A similar theorem can be established for RL impedances using a similar method. We shall state the result and leave the details of the proof as an exercise.

Theorem 13. *If $Z_{RL}(s)$ is the driving-point impedance of an RL network, then*

$$\psi(s) = \frac{1}{s}Z_{RL}(s^2) \tag{87}$$

is a reactance function. Conversely, if $\psi(s)$ is a reactance function, then

$$Z_{RL}(s) = \sqrt{s}\,\psi(\sqrt{s}) \tag{88}$$

is the driving-point impedance of an RL network.

The last two theorems have involved impedances. Let us now consider the admittance of an *RC* network. Using Eq. (86) the admittance of an *RC* network can be expressed as

$$Y_{RC}(s) = \sqrt{s}\,\frac{1}{\psi(\sqrt{s})} \tag{89}$$

But the reciprocal of a reactance function is itself a reactance function. Hence, the right side of this equation is the same kind of function as the right side of Eq. (88), which is the impedance of an *RL* network.

In a similar manner, starting from Eq. (88) we can show that the driving-point admittance of an *RL* network is the same, functionally, as the driving-point impedance of an *RC* network.

We see here a basic distinction between reactance functions and *RC* or *RL* functions. Whereas the reciprocal of a reactance function is again a member of the same class of functions, the reciprocal of an *RC* impedance is a member of the class of *RL* impedances, and vice versa.

With the preceding transformations we are in a position to translate all the properties of reactance functions into properties of *RC* and *RL* driving-point functions. The procedure for establishing these results is quite straightforward. To start with, let us apply Eqs. (86) and (88) to the partial fraction expansion of a reactance function given in Eq. (76). The results will be

$$Z_{RC}(s) = k_\infty + \frac{k_0}{s} + \sum_i \frac{k_i}{s + \sigma_i} = Y_{RL}(s) \tag{90}$$

$$Z_{RL}(s) = k_\infty s + k_0 + \sum_i \frac{k_i s}{s + \sigma_i} = Y_{RC}(s) \tag{91}$$

where the k's and σ's are all real and positive. Note that we have used the same symbols for the residues and poles in both cases, but these are general expressions and the two are not supposed to be related.

Equation (91) is not a partial fraction expansion of $Z_{RL}(s)$. Rather it is an expansion of $Z_{RL}(s)/s$, after which the result is multiplied through by s. If we divide Eq. (91) by s, we find that the form is identical with Eq. (90). This shows that *an RL impedance function (or RC admittance) divided by s is an RC impedance function.* We see that the poles of both these functions are all negative real and the residues of Z_{RC} and Z_{RL}/s are all positive.

By differentiating the last two equations along the real axis ($s = \sigma$), we obtain a result which is the counterpart of the positive slope property of a reactance function. That is,

$$\frac{dZ_{RC}(\sigma)}{d\sigma} = \frac{dY_{RL}(\sigma)}{d\sigma} < 0 \qquad (a)$$

$$\frac{dZ_{RL}(\sigma)}{d\sigma} = \frac{dY_{RC}(\sigma)}{d\sigma} > 0 \qquad (b)$$

(92)

Thus, the curves of RC and RL driving-point functions plotted for real values of s are monotonic; $Z_{RC}(\sigma)$ and $Y_{RL}(\sigma)$ are strictly decreasing, whereas $Z_{RL}(\sigma)$ and $Y_{RC}(\sigma)$ are strictly increasing. Just as in the case of reactance functions, this implies that the zeros and poles of both must alternate.

Sketches of typical RC and RL driving-point functions for real values of s are shown in Figs. 12 and 13. In Fig. 12 note that the first pole near the origin may in fact move into the origin making $F(0)$ infinite.

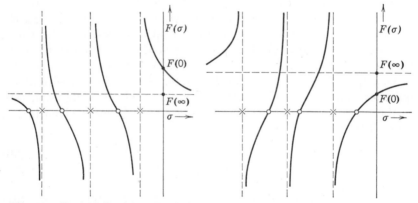

Fig. 12.   Typical $Z_{RC}(\sigma)$ or $Y_{RL}(\sigma)$.   Fig. 13.   Typical $Z_{RL}(\sigma)$ or $Y_{RC}(\sigma)$.

Also, the last zero on the negative real axis may move out to infinity causing $F(\infty)$ to become zero. Similarly, in Fig. 13 the first zero may be at the origin causing $F(0)$ to be zero. Also, the final pole may move out to infinity causing $F(\infty)$ to become infinite.

Let us now collect all of these results and state them in the form of theorems.

Theorem 14. (First characterization of RC impedances and RL admittances.) *A rational function $F(s)$ is the driving-point impedance of an RC network or the admittance of an RL network if and only if all of its poles are simple and are restricted to the finite negative real axis (including*

$s = 0$ but excluding $s = \infty$) with real positive residues at all poles and with $F(\infty)$ real and nonnegative. (This is the counterpart of theorem 9 for reactance functions.)

Theorem 15. (Second characterization of RC impedances and RL admittances.) A rational function $F(s)$ is the driving-point impedance of an RC network or the admittance of an RL network if and only if all the poles and zeros are simple, lie on the negative real axis and alternate with each other, the first critical point (pole or zero), starting at the origin and moving down the negative real axis, being a pole. (This is the counterpart of theorem 10 for reactance functions.)

Theorem 16. (First characterization of RL impedances and RC admittances.) A rational function $F(s)$ is the driving-point impedance of an RL network or the admittance of an RC network if and only if all of its poles are simple and are restricted to the negative real axis, excluding the point $s = 0$ (but including infinity), with $F(0)$ real and nonnegative, and with all the residues of $F(s)/s$ real and positive.

Theorem 17. (Second characterization of RL impedances and RC admittances.) A rational function $F(s)$ is the driving-point impedance of an RL network or the admittance of an RC network if and only if all the poles and zeros are simple, lie on the negative real axis and alternate with each other, the first critical point (pole or zero), starting at the origin and moving down the negative real axis, being a zero. (The only difference between this theorem and theorem 15 is the last word.)

We have already sketched the proofs of all these theorems in the preceding discussion. You can organize the proofs as an exercise.

We have now stated several sets of necessary and sufficient conditions for a rational function to be the driving-point impedance or admittance of RC or RL one-ports. Generally, when it is desired to prove the sufficiency of a set of conditions that a given function be the driving-point (or transfer) function of a class of network, it is done by showing that a network (at least one) of the given class can be realized from the given function. In the present case, we tied up the proof with reactance functions by showing that the given function can always be transformed to a reactance function. This function can then be realized as an LC network. The desired RC or RL network is then obtained by performing the inverse transformation. (This step amounts to replacing, in the LC network, each L with an R of equal value for RC networks or each C with an R of value $1/C$ for RL networks.)

Alternatively, we can work on the given RC or RL driving-point function itself, expanding it in partial fractions just as we did for reactance functions. We have already obtained the desired forms in Eqs. (90) and (91). Each term in these expressions can be recognized as the impedance or admittance of a simple RC or RL structure. The series or parallel connection of these structures (depending on whether the function is to be impedance or admittance) gives the desired result. The networks have the same form as the Foster forms of lossless networks shown in Fig. 11. Hence, they are referred to as Foster realizations of RC and RL networks, although it was Cauer who first gave these results. Figure 14 shows the realizations of the terms in Eqs. (90) and (91).

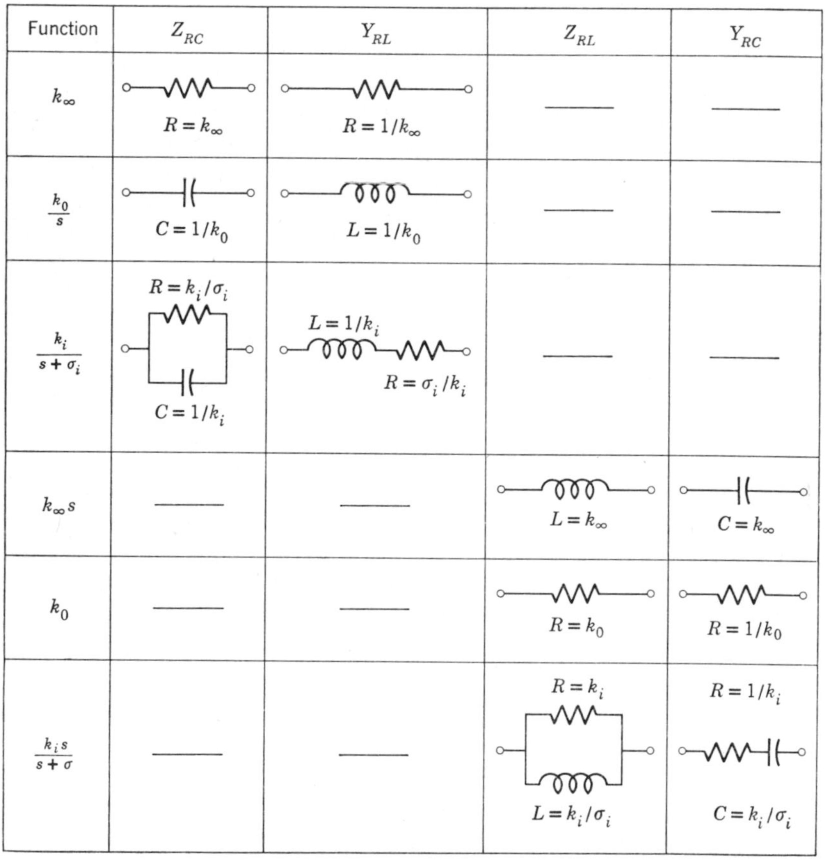

Function	Z_{RC}	Y_{RL}	Z_{RL}	Y_{RC}
k_∞	$R = k_\infty$	$R = 1/k_\infty$	———	———
$\dfrac{k_0}{s}$	$C = 1/k_0$	$L = 1/k_0$	———	———
$\dfrac{k_i}{s + \sigma_i}$	$R = k_i/\sigma_i$ $C = 1/k_i$	$L = 1/k_i$ $R = \sigma_i/k_i$	———	———
$k_\infty s$	———	———	$L = k_\infty$	$C = k_\infty$
k_0	———	———	$R = k_0$	$R = 1/k_0$
$\dfrac{k_i s}{s + \sigma}$	———	———	$R = k_i$ $L = k_i/\sigma_i$	$R = 1/k_i$ $C = k_i/\sigma_i$

Fig. 14. RL and RC Foster components.

This will terminate our discussion of RC and RL one-ports. However, this does not exhaust the subject by any means. The discussion can be extended in two directions: (1) additional analytic properties of the driving-point functions can be derived, and (2) alternative realizations of a given RC or RL driving-point function can be investigated. Some of these extensions will be suggested as problems at the end of the chapter.

9.7 Open- and Short-Circuit Functions

In the last three sections we studied some of the most important properties of driving-point immittance functions of linear, passive, lumped, reciprocal, and time-invariant networks. Let us now extend our scope and take up the functions which describe the behavior of two-ports. We shall consider only the open-circuit and short-circuit matrices.

The open-circuit and short-circuit parameter matrices are defined as the coefficient matrices in the following systems of equations

$$\begin{bmatrix} V_1 \\ V_2 \end{bmatrix} = \begin{bmatrix} z_{11} & z_{12} \\ z_{21} & z_{22} \end{bmatrix} \begin{bmatrix} I_1 \\ I_2 \end{bmatrix} \tag{93}$$

$$\begin{bmatrix} I_1 \\ I_2 \end{bmatrix} = \begin{bmatrix} y_{11} & y_{12} \\ y_{21} & y_{22} \end{bmatrix} \begin{bmatrix} V_1 \\ V_2 \end{bmatrix} \tag{94}$$

with the reference conventions shown in Fig. 15. As we observed earlier, for reciprocal networks these two matrices are *symmetric;* that is,

$$z_{12} = z_{21} \qquad (a)$$
$$\tag{95}$$
$$y_{12} = y_{21} \qquad (b)$$

Fig. 15. Two-port and its references.

To derive the more important analytic properties of these two matrices, we follow a procedure analogous to the one adopted in section 9.3, when only one pair of terminals was involved. The starting point is again the set of loop equations for the network of Fig. 15. These are

$$\{\mathbf{R}_m + s\mathbf{L}_m + \mathbf{D}_m/s\}\mathbf{I}_m(s) = \mathbf{V}_m(s) \tag{96}$$

where, in the present case,

$$\mathbf{V}_m(s) = \begin{bmatrix} V_1(s) \\ V_2(s) \\ 0 \\ \cdot \\ \cdot \\ \cdot \\ 0 \end{bmatrix} \tag{97}$$

Again, we premultiply Eq. (96) by $\mathbf{I}_m{}^{*\prime}(s)$ obtaining

$$\mathbf{I}_m{}^{*\prime}\mathbf{R}_m\mathbf{I}_m + s\mathbf{I}_m{}^{*\prime}\mathbf{L}_m\mathbf{I}_m + \frac{1}{s}\mathbf{I}_m{}^{*\prime}\mathbf{D}_m\mathbf{I}_m = V_1 I_1{}^* + V_2 I_2{}^* \qquad (98)$$

The three quadratic forms on the left side of this equation are precisely the energy functions defined in Eqs. (45). Hence, we may rewrite this equation as

$$F_0(s) + sT_0(s) + \frac{1}{s}V_0(s) = V_1 I_1{}^* + V_2 I_2{}^* \qquad (99)$$

But as we saw in section 9.3, the left side of this equation is a positive real function. Hence, the right side is also. That is,

$$\text{Re } (V_1 I_1{}^* + V_2 I_2{}^*) \geq 0 \qquad \text{in Re } (s) \geq 0 \qquad (100)$$

Note that the right side of Eq. (99) can be modified by substituting Eq. (93) for V_1 and V_2, or substituting Eq. (94) for I_1 and I_2 after first taking the conjugate. The result of these steps will be

$$V_1 I_1{}^* + V_2 I_2{}^* = [I_1{}^* \quad I_2{}^*] \begin{bmatrix} z_{11} & z_{12} \\ z_{21} & z_{22} \end{bmatrix} \begin{bmatrix} I_1 \\ I_2 \end{bmatrix} \qquad (101)$$

and

$$(V_1 I_1{}^* + V_2 I_2{}^*)^* = [V_1{}^* \quad V_2{}^*] \begin{bmatrix} y_{11} & y_{12} \\ y_{21} & y_{22} \end{bmatrix} \begin{bmatrix} V_1 \\ V_2 \end{bmatrix} \qquad (102)$$

Since the left sides of these two equations are conjugates, their real parts will be equal. But we have already shown the left side of Eq. (101) to have a positive real part when s lies in the right half plane. Hence, we conclude that the quadratic forms on the right sides of Eq. (101) and Eq. (102) are both positive real.

This conclusion remains valid if I_1 and I_2 in Eq. (101) or V_1 and V_2 in Eq. (102) are complex (or real) constants instead of being Laplace transforms. To see this fact, note that the positive realness of the left side of Eq. (99) is a result of the positive definiteness of the energy functions, which, in turn, is a function of the loop parameter matrices and not the variables. Just as we say that the matrix of a positive definite quadratic form is positive definite, so we say that a matrix $\mathbf{W}(s)$ which satisfies the condition that $\mathbf{X}^{*\prime}\mathbf{W}\mathbf{X}$ is positive real for all nonzero complex (or real) values of $\mathbf{X}$ is itself a *positive real matrix*.

We have now established the fact that *the open-circuit impedance and short-circuit admittance matrices of a linear, passive, lumped, reciprocal, and time-invariant network are positive real matrices.* This result was initially stated by Gewertz.

The same result was demonstrated by Brune in a different way. Consider the network shown in Fig. 16. The two pairs of terminals of the two-port are connected in series through ideal transformers whose turns ratios are $x_1:1$ and $x_2:1$, respectively. The voltage and current at the input terminals will be given by

$$V = x_1 V_1 + x_2 V_2 \qquad (a)$$

$$I = \frac{I_1}{x_1} = \frac{I_2}{x_2} \qquad (b)$$

(103)

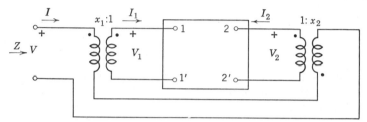

Fig. 16.   Brune's demonstration that the z and y matrices are pr.

If we now compute the driving-point impedance $Z(s) = V/I$ at the input terminals, we will get

$$Z(s) = x_1^2 z_{11} + 2x_1 x_2 z_{21} + x_2^2 z_{22}$$

$$= [x_1 \quad x_2] \begin{bmatrix} z_{11} & z_{12} \\ z_{21} & z_{22} \end{bmatrix} \begin{bmatrix} x_1 \\ x_2 \end{bmatrix} \qquad (104)$$

Since the impedance is positive real, this proves that the quadratic form on the right is also positive real. To prove the condition for the y matrix, the two pairs of terminals can be connected in parallel through ideal transformers and the over-all input admittance calculated. This is left for you as an exercise.

Gewertz's Theorem has a very important consequence known as the *residue condition*. Let x_1 and x_2 be two arbitrary real numbers. Since the quadratic forms

$$Q_1 = [x_1 \quad x_2] \begin{bmatrix} z_{11} & z_{12} \\ z_{21} & z_{22} \end{bmatrix} \begin{bmatrix} x_1 \\ x_2 \end{bmatrix} \qquad (a)$$

$$Q_2 = [x_1 \quad x_2] \begin{bmatrix} y_{11} & y_{12} \\ y_{21} & y_{22} \end{bmatrix} \begin{bmatrix} x_1 \\ x_2 \end{bmatrix} \qquad (b)$$

(105)

are positive real functions, it follows that any pole of these functions on the $j\omega$-axis must be simple and the residue at such a pole must be real and positive. Suppose, for instance, that the z parameters have a pole at $s = j\omega_i$. Since this pole is a simple pole of the quadratic form, the residue of Q_1 is

$$\text{Residue of } Q_1 = \lim_{s \to j\omega_i} (s - j\omega_i)[x_1 \quad x_2] \begin{bmatrix} z_{11} & z_{12} \\ z_{21} & z_{22} \end{bmatrix} \begin{bmatrix} x_1 \\ x_2 \end{bmatrix}$$

$$= \lim_{s \to j\omega_i} [x_1 \quad x_2] \begin{bmatrix} (s - j\omega_i)z_{11} & (s - j\omega_i)z_{12} \\ (s - j\omega_i)z_{21} & (s - j\omega_i)z_{22} \end{bmatrix} \begin{bmatrix} x_1 \\ x_2 \end{bmatrix} \quad (106)$$

If we give the residues of z_{11}, $z_{21}(=z_{12})$, and z_{22} at the pole $s = j\omega_i$ the labels $k_{11}{}^{(i)}$, $k_{21}{}^{(i)}$ and $k_{22}{}^{(i)}$, respectively, then the residue of the quadratic form will become

$$\text{Residue of } Q_1 = [x_1 \quad x_2] \begin{bmatrix} k_{11}{}^{(i)} & k_{21}{}^{(i)} \\ k_{21}{}^{(i)} & k_{22}{}^{(i)} \end{bmatrix} \begin{bmatrix} x_1 \\ x_2 \end{bmatrix} \quad (107)$$

Thus, the residue itself is a quadratic form whose matrix is the matrix of residues of the z parameters. However this residue must be real and nonnegative for all values of x_1 and x_2. Hence, the matrix of residues of the z parameters at any poles on the $j\omega$-axis must be *positive definite* or *semidefinite*. As discussed in section 9.2, this requires that the determinant of the matrix and all of its principal cofactors be nonnegative. That is,

$$k_{11}{}^{(i)} \geq 0, \qquad k_{22}{}^{(i)} \geq 0 \quad (108)$$

$$k_{11}{}^{(i)}k_{22}{}^{(i)} - (k_{21}{}^{(i)})^2 \geq 0 \quad (109)$$

The first of these equations we already know, since z_{11} and z_{22} are driving-point functions and therefore positive real. But Eq. (109) is a new and important result. It is known as the *residue condition*.

We have shown that the z matrix of a two-port, in the class of networks under consideration, is positive real and, by definition, positive realness is linked with the real part of a function. Hence, we should expect to obtain some relationship among the real parts of the z parameters. Let us denote these real parts r_{11}, $r_{21}(=r_{12})$, and r_{22}. The real part of the quadratic form Q_1 in Eq. (105) can then be written

$$\text{Re}(Q_1) = [x_1 \quad x_2] \begin{bmatrix} r_{11} & r_{12} \\ r_{21} & r_{22} \end{bmatrix} \begin{bmatrix} x_1 \\ x_2 \end{bmatrix} \quad (110)$$

Whenever s lies in the right half plane or on the $j\omega$-axis, this quadratic form must be positive semidefinite or definite, since Q_1 is a positive real function. As in the case of the matrix of residues, it follows that

$$r_{11} \geq 0; \qquad r_{22} \geq 0$$

$$r_{11}r_{22} - r_{21}{}^2 \geq 0; \qquad \text{Re } s \geq 0 \quad (111)$$

This important result is known as the *real part condition*. In fact, it alone is a sufficient condition that the open-circuit impedance matrix be positive real. (Demonstrate this fact.)

Although we derived these two results, the residue condition and the real part condition, for the z matrix, they are equally valid for the y matrix, as you can show by repeating the same steps on the quadratic form Q_2 that we performed on Q_1.

Let us now briefly consider the special case of two-ports with two kinds of elements only. In the case of a lossless network the z or y parameters must have all their poles on the $j\omega$-axis. Hence, the residue condition must apply at all the poles. One of the implications of this fact is that it is impossible for z_{21} to have a pole which is not also a pole of both z_{11} and z_{22}. (Likewise for the y parameters.) For, if either k_{11} or k_{22} is zero when k_{21} is not, the residue condition will be violated. On the other hand, it is possible for either z_{11} or z_{22} (or both) to have a pole not shared by the remaining parameters. We refer to such poles as private poles of z_{11} or z_{22}.

What we have just said about lossless two-ports applies equally well to RC and RL two-ports through the Cauer transformations, with appropriate and obvious modifications. For these networks the z and y parameters have all their poles on the negative real axis and the residue condition will apply at all these poles; z_{21} cannot have poles not possessed by z_{11} and z_{22}, and so on.

We will terminate this discussion rather abruptly at this point. The subject is by no means exhausted; however, further pursuit of the subject will be left to more advanced treatises.

9.8 Topological Formulas for Network Functions

In the preceding part of this chapter we have been concerned with establishing the analytic properties of the functions pertinent to linear, lumped, passive, time-invariant, and reciprocal networks. We have been careful to prove each of the results that were established.

In the present section we will change our objective somewhat. Whereas previously we developed general properties of the functions of certain classes of networks, we shall now be concerned with the calculation of the network functions when a specific network is given. We shall discuss some old methods due to Kirchhoff and Maxwell which permit the evaluation of network functions simply by inspection. The techniques which we will discuss are based on topological considerations. Hence, a review of section 3.3 will be advisable at this point. However, to prove many of the results we will discuss, would require careful development of the concepts of topology and matrix algebra. In this section we will often be content to give "reasonableness" arguments in the interest of maintaining a manageable size.*

To start the discussion, let us recall the loop and node equations of a network under zero initial conditions from Chapter 4. These are

$$\mathbf{B}\mathbf{Z}_b\mathbf{B}'\mathbf{I}_m(s) = \mathbf{V}_m(s) \tag{112}$$

$$\mathbf{A}\mathbf{Y}_b\mathbf{A}'\mathbf{V}_n(s) = \mathbf{I}_n(s) \tag{113}$$

where $\mathbf{A}$ and $\mathbf{B}$ are the incidence and circuit matrices; $\mathbf{Z}_b$ and $\mathbf{Y}_b$ are branch impedance and admittance matrices; and $\mathbf{I}_m$ and $\mathbf{V}_n$ are loop current and node voltage matrices, all respectively. In addition to the already listed restrictions on the type of network under consideration, we will assume that there are *no mutual inductances*. Under this condition the matrices $\mathbf{Z}_b$ and $\mathbf{Y}_b$ are diagonal.

Let us also recall some of the properties of the incidence and circuit matrices from section 3.3 and from Problems 3.21 and 3.22.

The Incidence Matrix.

1. The *incidence matrix* $\mathbf{A}_a$ is of order (N_v, N_b) and rank $N_v - 1$. If any row of $\mathbf{A}_a$ is deleted the resulting matrix $\mathbf{A}$ is also of rank $N_v - 1$.

2. A square submatrix of $\mathbf{A}$ of order $N_v - 1$ is nonsingular if and only if the columns of this submatrix correspond to the branches of a tree.

The Circuit Matrix.

1. The *circuit matrix* $\mathbf{B}_a$ is of order (N_m, N_b) and rank $N_b - N_v + 1$.

2. Let $\mathbf{B}$ be a circuit matrix of order $(N_b - N_v + 1, N_b)$ and rank $N_b - N_v + 1$. (That is, we delete from $\mathbf{B}_a$ a number of rows equal to the difference between the total number of loops and the number of independent loop equations.) Then a square submatrix of $\mathbf{B}$ of order $N_b - N_v + 1$ is nonsingular if and only if the columns of this submatrix correspond to a set of links for some tree of the network.

Let us now interpret these statements in terms of Kirchhoff's laws before proceeding. Kirchhoff's current law states

$$\mathbf{A}_a\mathbf{i}_b(t) = \mathbf{0} \tag{114}$$

Property 1 of the incidence matrix states the fact that exactly $N_v - 1$ of these equations are linearly independent. (The network is assumed to be connected.) Suppose we order the columns of the matrix $\mathbf{A}$ according to the tree branches and the links for some tree, and then

---

* Proofs of all the topological formulas in this section may be found in Mayeda, W., and Seshu, S., "Topological Formulas for Network Functions," Bulletin No. 446, Engineering Experiment Station, University of Illinois, 1956.

partition it.   Then, partitioning $i_b(t)$ correspondingly, we can write Eq. (114) as

$$[\mathbf{A}_T \quad \mathbf{A}_C]\begin{bmatrix} \mathbf{i}_T \\ \mathbf{i}_C \end{bmatrix} = \mathbf{A}_T\mathbf{i}_T + \mathbf{A}_C\mathbf{i}_C = 0 \qquad (115)$$

(The subscripts T and C stand for tree and chord.)

Now property 2 of the incidence matrix can be interpreted as saying: the tree branch currents can be expressed as linear combinations of the chord currents.   For, since $\mathbf{A}_T$ is nonsingular by property 2, we can solve Eq. (115) for $\mathbf{i}_T$ and get

$$\mathbf{i}_T = -\mathbf{A}_T^{-1}\mathbf{A}_C\mathbf{i}_C \qquad (116)$$

We know this interpretation to be true from the following argument. Suppose we form the fundamental loops for this tree.   Then the link currents are the same as the loop currents.   We know that all the tree branch currents can be expressed as linear combinations of loop currents, which in this case are the link currents.   This is all that Eq. (116) says.   Property 2 of the incidence matrix makes a stronger statement, namely, the converse is also included.

Similarly, property 1 of the circuit matrix $\mathbf{B}_a$ states that exactly $N_b - N_v + 1$ of the KVL equations, which can be written

$$\mathbf{B}_a\mathbf{v}_b(t) = 0 \qquad (117)$$

are linearly independent, which we know.   To interpret property 2, let us order the columns of $\mathbf{B}$ as tree branches and chords for a tree, and then partition, getting

$$[\mathbf{B}_T \quad \mathbf{B}_C]\begin{bmatrix} \mathbf{v}_T \\ \mathbf{v}_C \end{bmatrix} = \mathbf{B}_T\mathbf{v}_T + \mathbf{B}_C\mathbf{v}_C = 0 \qquad (118)$$

We see from property 2 that this equation can be solved for $\mathbf{v}_C$ yielding

$$\mathbf{v}_C = -\mathbf{B}_C^{-1}\mathbf{B}_T\mathbf{v}_b \qquad (119)$$

This last statement can be interpreted to state that link voltages are linear combinations of branch voltages.   This statement is again seen to be valid by considering fundamental loops.   Property 2 includes the converse as well.

In order to carry on with our development, we will need one more property of the incidence matrix, which states that *the determinant of a nonsingular submatrix of A is equal to + 1 or − 1*.   We shall refer to this as *property 3 of the incidence matrix*.

To prove this result let us recall the structure of $\mathbf{A}$, namely that each column contains at most a single 1 and a single −1, all others being zero. In a nonsingular submatrix there can be no column in which all entries are zeros. Also every column cannot contain both a $+1$ and a -1, for then the rows would be linearly dependent. Therefore, there is at least one column in which there is only one nonzero element, ± 1. We expand the determinant by this column, which yields

$$\Delta = \pm 1 \Delta_{ij} \tag{120}$$

where Δ_{ij} is the cofactor of this nonzero element. Δ_{ij} has the same structure as the original determinant, namely, it has at most a single $+1$ and -1 per column. Therefore, it also must have a column with a single nonzero entry, ± 1. Hence we may expand Δ_{ij} by this column. Continuing this way, we find that

$$\Delta = (\pm 1)(\pm 1) \cdots (\pm 1) = \pm 1 \tag{121}$$

thus establishing the result.

A similar statement is not true in general of the circuit matrix.[*] However, in two special cases we can assert that a nonsingular submatrix of **B** has a ± 1 determinant. One of these is the case where we choose the regions (meshes) of a planar graph as loops. (In this case the above proof holds.) Another special case is the matrix $\mathbf{B}_f$ of fundamental loops. We will assume in this section that fundamental loops have been chosen, so that the analog of property 3 holds for the circuit matrix as well.

Recall that, for the type of network under consideration here, the network functions, be they driving-point or transfer, are expressed as the ratio of a loop or node determinant and a cofactor, or as the ratio of two cofactors. In order to express the network functions as rational functions, the determinants must be expanded. But in the usual method of expanding determinants, much effort is wasted due to the fact that a large number of terms cancel in the final result. Considerable effort will be saved, if these terms that cancel are not brought into the picture at all. The formulas which we shall now discuss accomplish precisely this objective.

All of these results are based on a theorem from matrix algebra called the *Binet-Cauchy Theorem*. This theorem goes as follows.

Let **P** of order (m,n) and **Q** of order (n,m) be matrices of elements from a field (real or complex numbers or functions, for our purposes). Let $m < n$. Then the determinant of the product **PQ** is given by

$$\det \mathbf{PQ} = \Sigma \text{ Products of corresponding majors of } \mathbf{P} \text{ and } \mathbf{Q} \tag{122}$$

the summation being over all such majors.

---

[*] In the general case the determinant of a nonsingular submatrix of **B** is $\pm 2^i$ where i is a nonnegative integer, fixed for a given matrix **B**. See Okada, *Proc. I.R.E.*, vol. 43, 1955, p. 1527.

By a *major* or a *major determinant* is meant the determinant of a largest square submatrix (in this case of order m). The phrase "corresponding major" implies that if we choose *columns* $i_1, i_2, \cdots, i_m$ of $\mathbf{P}$ for a major, we should choose *rows* $i_1, i_2, \cdots, i_m$ of $\mathbf{Q}$ to form the corresponding major.

The proof of this result is too long to be given here, but it is readily available in the literature.* We shall be content to illustrate it with an example. Let

$$\mathbf{P} = \begin{bmatrix} 1 & -1 & 3 \\ 2 & 1 & 0 \end{bmatrix} \qquad (a)$$

$$\qquad\qquad\qquad\qquad\qquad\qquad (123)$$

$$\mathbf{Q} = \begin{bmatrix} 2 & 1 \\ -1 & 1 \\ 1 & 0 \end{bmatrix} \qquad (b)$$

In this case $m = 2$ and $n = 3$. By direct multiplication we find that

$$\mathbf{PQ} = \begin{bmatrix} 6 & 0 \\ 3 & 3 \end{bmatrix} \qquad (124)$$

The determinant of this matrix is easily seen to be 18. Now let us apply the Binet-Cauchy theorem. We see that there are 3 determinants of order 2 to be considered. Applying Eq. (122), we get

$$\det \mathbf{PQ} = \begin{vmatrix} 1 & -1 \\ 2 & 1 \end{vmatrix} \begin{vmatrix} 2 & 1 \\ -1 & 1 \end{vmatrix} + \begin{vmatrix} 1 & 3 \\ 2 & 0 \end{vmatrix} \begin{vmatrix} 2 & 1 \\ 1 & 0 \end{vmatrix} + \begin{vmatrix} -1 & 3 \\ 1 & 0 \end{vmatrix} \begin{vmatrix} -1 & 1 \\ 1 & 0 \end{vmatrix}$$

$$= 3 \cdot 3 + (-6)(-1) + (-3)(-1) = 18 \qquad (125)$$

This agrees with the value calculated by direct evaluation of the determinant.

Let us now proceed to use this result in calculating the node admittance determinant Δ_n. From Eq. (113) this is the determinant of the matrix $\mathbf{AY}_b\mathbf{A}'$. Let us identify $\mathbf{AY}_b$ with the matrix $\mathbf{P}$ in the Binet-Cauchy theorem and $\mathbf{A}'$ with the matrix $\mathbf{Q}$. Remember that $\mathbf{Y}_b$ is a diagonal matrix; let us designate the diagonal elements y_j, $j = 1, 2, \cdots$, N_b. Therefore, the product $\mathbf{AY}_b$ has the same structure as the matrix $\mathbf{A}$ except that column j is multiplied by y_j, $j = 1, 2, \cdots, N_b$. Therefore the nonsingular submatrices of $(\mathbf{AY}_b)$ still correspond to the trees of the network, but the value of the determinant of each nonsingular submatrix instead of being ± 1 is now

$$(\pm 1)y_{i_1}y_{i_2}\cdots y_{i_k}, \qquad \text{where } k = N_v - 1$$

* See, for instance, F. E. Hohn, *Elementary Matrix Algebra*, Macmillan Co., New York, 1958, or M. Bocher, *Higher Algebra*, Macmillan Co., New York, 1938.

and i_1, i_2, $\cdots$, i_k are the branches of a tree. The corresponding sub-matrix of $\mathbf{A}'$ is merely the transpose of the submatrix of $\mathbf{A}$, and so it is also nonsingular, and has the same determinant (± 1) as the submatrix of $\mathbf{A}$. The product of the two is simply $y_{i_1}y_{i_2}\cdots y_{i_k}$, which we will call the *tree admittance product*. All the other majors, which do not correspond to trees, are zero and hence do not contribute anything to the sum on the right side of Eq. (122). Hence, using the Binet-Cauchy theorem, we get

$$\Delta_n = \det \mathbf{A}\mathbf{Y}_b\mathbf{A}' = \sum_{\substack{\text{All} \\ \text{trees}}} \text{tree admittance products of the network} \quad (126)$$

This result is referred to as *Maxwell's rule or formula*. In order to calculate the node admittance determinant, this expression says we must locate all the trees of the network, multiply together the branch admittances of each tree, then add the resulting products for all the trees.

Before Maxwell developed the formula we have just discussed, Kirchhoff gave the corresponding one for the loop impedance determinant. This is simply the dual of Maxwell's formula and is proved by the same argument. We will merely state it and leave the details of the proof to you. From Eq. (113), the loop impedance determinant Δ_m is the determinant of the matrix $\mathbf{B}\mathbf{Z}_b\mathbf{B}'$. Let us define a *chord set impedance product* as the product of the branch impedances of all the chords, or links, corresponding to a given tree. Then *Kirchhoff's rule or formula* for the loop impedance determinant states

$$\Delta_m = \sum_{\substack{\text{All} \\ \text{trees}}} \text{chord set impedance products of the network} \quad (127)$$

Thus, to find the loop impedance determinant, we must locate all the trees, multiply together the chord impedances for each tree, then add the resulting products for all the trees.

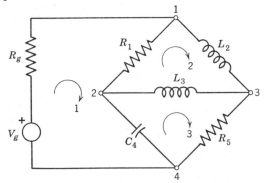

Fig. 17.   Example for Maxwell's and Kirchhoff's rules.

Let us now illustrate these rules by means of an example. Consider the network shown in Fig. 17. For this example, there are four nodes, so the trees will have three branches. All the trees are easily found to be: $g12$, 134, 235, $g45$, $g13$, $g23$, $g43$, $g53$, 125, 145, 124, 245, 135, 234, $g15$, $g24$; where R_g in series with the source is counted as a single branch, labeled g.

Inserting the values of the admittances and collecting coefficients, Maxwell's formula gives

$$\Delta_n = sC_4(G_gG_5 + G_1G_5)$$

$$+ (G_gG_1G_5 + G_1\Gamma_3C_4 + G_g\Gamma_3C_4 + G_1\Gamma_2C_4 + \Gamma_2C_4G_5 + G_g\Gamma_2C_4)$$

$$+ \frac{1}{s}(G_gG_1\Gamma_2 + G_gG_1\Gamma_3 + G_g\Gamma_3G_5 + G_1\Gamma_2G_5 + G_1\Gamma_3G_5 + \Gamma_2\Gamma_3C_4)$$

$$+ \frac{1}{s^2}\Gamma_2\Gamma_3(G_5 + G_g) \quad (128)$$

The chord sets will also contain three branches. They are easily found, by taking the complements of the tree branches, to be: 345, $g25$, $g14$, 123, 245, 145, 125, 124, $g34$, $g23$, $g35$, $g13$, $g24$, $g15$, 234, 135.

Inserting the values of the impedances and collecting coefficients, Kirchhoff's formula gives

$$\Delta_m = s^2L_2L_3(R_1 + R_g)$$

$$+ s(L_2L_3D_4 + R_gL_2R_5 + L_2R_1R_5 + L_3R_gR_5 + L_3R_gR_1 + L_3R_1R_5)$$

$$+ (R_gR_1R_5 + L_3D_4R_5 + L_2D_4R_5 + R_1L_2D_4 + R_gL_3D_4 + R_gL_2D_4)$$

$$+ \frac{1}{s}D_4(R_gR_1 + R_1R_5) \quad (129)$$

It is left for you to verify that the same answers are obtained by evaluating the determinants directly, but that considerably more effort is required in evaluating a number of terms that eventually cancel. Notice that it is not necessary to write the loop or the node equations to find these determinants.

But let us observe a more important fact implied in these two formulas.* Suppose we multiply a tree admittance product by the product of all the branch impedances of the network. Then the tree branch impedances cancel with the tree branch admittances, leaving a chord set

---

* This was first pointed out by N. F. Tsang, *J. Math. Phys.*, vol. 33, 1954, pp. 185–193. Since then it has been extended in the form given in Eq. (131) to networks with mutual inductances by I. Cederbaum, *J. Math. Phys.*, vol. 34, 1956, pp. 236–244.

impedance product. Hence, since the node admittance determinant is simply a sum of tree admittance products, and the loop impedance determinant is a sum of chord impedance products, it follows that

$$\Delta_m = (Z_1 Z_2 \cdots Z_b)\Delta_n \tag{130}$$

Since the branch impedance matrix $\mathbf{Z}_b$ is diagonal, the product of impedances on the right is simply the determinant of $\mathbf{Z}_b$. Hence, this equation can be written in the form

$$\Delta_m = (\det \mathbf{Z}_b)\Delta_n \tag{131}$$

This is a very significant result. Equation (130) states that the loop and node determinants, although they arise from different matrices (which are in general of different orders) are related in a very simple way. In particular, if we take each R, L, and C to be a branch of the network, the two determinants can differ at most by a multiplicative factor ks^p. Thus, for instance, the loop and the node determinants always have the same zeros, except possibly at $s = 0$ and ∞. That is, the finite nonzero natural modes of a network are independent of whether the loop or the node basis is chosen for analysis. In fact, Kirchhoff's rule in this form was stated by him for the branch current system of equations. (Loop currents were invented by Helmholtz about 30 years after Kirchhoff published his rules.) Thus the loop and the branch current systems have the same system determinant.

We have now gone part of the way in evaluating network functions. It remains now to find simple expressions for the cofactors as well. Let us first consider symmetrical cofactors, that is, cofactors of the form Δ_{jj}.

To get a cofactor Δ_{jj} of the node admittance matrix, we have to delete row j and column j. Therefore, the same result is obtained if, in the expression $\mathbf{A}\mathbf{Y}_b\mathbf{A}'$ we delete row j of the first matrix and column j of the last matrix. But column j of $\mathbf{A}'$ is row j of $\mathbf{A}$. Therefore, if we delete row j of $\mathbf{A}$ and denote the resultant matrix by $\mathbf{A}_{-j}$, we get

$$\Delta_{jj} = \det (\mathbf{A}_{-j}\mathbf{Y}_b\mathbf{A}'_{-j}) \tag{132}$$

Let us interpret the matrix $\mathbf{A}_{-j}$. Suppose we short node j to the reference node and write the incidence matrix of the resultant network N_1, using this combined node as reference. Obviously none of the other nodes are affected and so the incidence matrix of the new network N_1 will simply be $\mathbf{A}_{-j}$. Therefore Δ_{jj} of Eq. (132) is simply the node determinant of N_1. Therefore, by Maxwell's rule:

$$\Delta_{jj} = \Sigma \text{ tree admittance products of } N_1 \tag{133}$$

It is useful to interpret trees of N_1 in terms of the original network. Since N_1 has $N_v - 1$ nodes, trees of N_1 have $N_v - 2$ branches. Therefore, these can't be trees of N, which require $N_v - 1$ branches. But they will contain no loops since they don't contain loops in N_1. The only reason they are not trees of N is that they are not connected in N. In other words, they will be in two pieces (one "piece" may be simply an isolated node). The node j and the reference node will be in the two different pieces (otherwise shorting them will produce a loop). Such a structure is called a *2-tree* and in this case a 2-tree (j,r), where r stands for the reference node.

For example, the network N_1 corresponding to the network N of Fig. 17 with node 4 as reference and $j = 1$, is given in Fig. 18. Branch

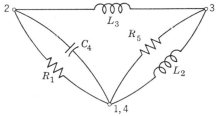

Fig. 18.   Network N_1 corresponding to Fig. 17.

sets 13, 43, 45, 24 are four of the trees of this network. In the original network, these branch sets have the configurations shown in Fig. 19.

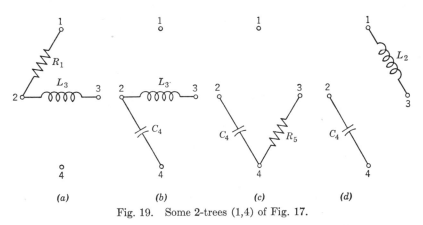

(a)   (b)   (c)   (d)

Fig. 19.   Some 2-trees (1,4) of Fig. 17.

We notice that each of these is a 2-tree with nodes 1 and 4 in different parts. In Fig. 19a, node 4 is isolated. In Fig. 19b and c, node 1 is isolated. In Fig. 19d neither is isolated. Each of these contributes to the right side of Eq. (133). There are four other 2-trees (1,4) in this network which also contribute to Eq. (133). We can, therefore rewrite Maxwell's formula for a symmetrical cofactor as

$$\Delta_{jj} = \sum_{\substack{\text{All} \\ \text{2-trees}}} \text{2-tree } (j,r) \text{ admittance products} \qquad (134)$$

where r is the reference node. This is the desired result.

We adopt a similar procedure to evaluate a symmetrical cofactor of the loop impedance determinant. The cofactor Δ_{jj} of the loop impedance matrix is of interest only when there is a branch b_k in loop j that is in no other loop. Therefore we shall make this assumption. We notice that

$$\Delta_{jj} = \det \mathbf{B}_{-j}\mathbf{Z}_b\mathbf{B}_{-j}' \qquad (135)$$

where $\mathbf{B}_{-j}$ is the matrix obtained when row j of matrix $\mathbf{B}$ is deleted. Deleting row j from the matrix means that loop j in the network is destroyed. Now, to destroy loop j is easy; we merely delete branch b_k from the network. The loop impedance matrix of the derived network, which we will call N_2, will simply be Δ_{jj} of Eq. (135). Applying Kirchhoff's rule to this network, we find the cofactor Δ_{jj} of the loop impedance matrix to be

$$\Delta_{jj} = \Sigma \text{ chord set impedance products of } N_2 \qquad (136)$$

We are now ready to use these results to evaluate driving-point impedance and admittance functions. Let the network N of Fig. 20 be a network of the class under consideration. We shall interpret the source as a voltage source for loop equations and a current source for node equations, for convenience.

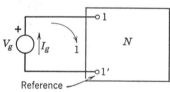

Fig. 20. Driving-point functions.

Taking node equations first, and using $1'$ as the reference node, the driving-point admittance is

$$Y = \frac{\Delta}{\Delta_{11}}\bigg|_y \qquad (137)$$

where the subscript y reminds us that the node admittance determinant is involved. Now, if we disregard the source (current driver) completely, we will get the same node admittance matrix, and so the same determinant and cofactor, as in Eq. (137). Therefore, we may write

$$Y = \frac{\Sigma \text{ tree admittance products of } N}{\Sigma \text{ 2-tree } (1,1') \text{ admittance products of } N} \qquad (138)$$

This is the desired expression for the driving-point admittance.

The situation is different with respect to loop equations. The loop impedance matrix of the total network of Fig. 20 contains one more row and column (corresponding to loop 1) than the loop impedance matrix of N alone. Further, as far as the loop impedance matrix is concerned, the voltage generator is a short circuit. Therefore the loop impedance matrix of Fig. 20 is the same as the loop impedance matrix of N_1 obtained by shorting nodes 1 and 1'. And the cofactor 11 of the loop impedance matrix of Fig. 20 is the same as the loop impedance determinant of N alone. Using Kirchhoff's formula, we can therefore write

$$Z = \frac{\Delta'}{\Delta_{11}'}\bigg|_z = \frac{\Sigma \text{ chord set impedance products of } N_1}{\Sigma \text{ chord set impedance products of } N} \tag{139}$$

(The primed quantities correspond to the total network including the source.) Remembering the 2-tree interpretation given earlier, we can rewrite this as

$$Z = \frac{\Sigma \text{ complements of 2-tree } (1,1') \text{ impedance products}}{\Sigma \text{ chord set impedance products}} \tag{140}$$

where both quantities are computed with respect to N alone, without the generator.

We have now obtained two alternate expressions for the driving-point functions, given in Eqs. (138) and (140), both of which may be referred to as *minimum effort* formulas, since there is no subtraction of terms involved. Let us introduce notation which will shorten these expressions and will also be useful in the further extensions which we will discuss. Define

$$V(Y) = \sum_{\substack{\text{All} \\ \text{trees}}} \text{tree admittance products} \qquad (a)$$

$$W_{i,j}(Y) = \sum_{\substack{\text{All} \\ \text{2-trees}}} \text{2-tree } (i,j) \text{ admittance products} \quad (b)$$

$$\tag{141}$$

The subscripts in $W_{i,j}$ are separated by a comma. This implies that the nodes corresponding to the subscripts fall on separate parts of the network. This interpretation applies even if additional subscripts are included. These expressions take care of Eq. (138). For Eq. (140) we introduce the following convention first given by W. S. Percival. Given a polynomial $V(Y)$, the complementary polynomial $C[V(Y)]$ is obtained by replacing each product in $V(Y)$ by the product of the factors not appearing in this product. Finally $C[V(Z)]$ is obtained by replacing y_j by z_j in $C[V(Y)]$.

With these definitions, Eqs. (138) and (140) can be written

$$Y = \frac{V(Y)}{W_{1,1'}(Y)} \tag{142}$$

$$Z = \frac{C[W_{1,1'}(Z)]}{C[V(Z)]} \tag{143}$$

It remains for us to discuss the unsymmetrical cofactors of the loop and node matrices; that is, determinants of the form Δ_{ij}. Let us first take the node admittance matrix. In this case, with considerations similar to the case of symmetrical cofactors, we get

$$\Delta_{ij} = \det(\mathbf{A}_{-i}\mathbf{Y}_b\mathbf{A}_{-j}') \tag{144}$$

To this we apply the Binet–Cauchy theorem to get

$$\Delta_{ij} = \Sigma \text{ products of corresponding majors of } (\mathbf{A}_{-i}\mathbf{Y}_b) \text{ and } \mathbf{A}_{-j}' \tag{145}$$

We notice as before, that the nonzero majors of $\mathbf{A}_{-i}\mathbf{Y}_b$ correspond to 2-trees (i,r) where r is the reference node. The nonzero majors of $\mathbf{A}_{-j}$ correspond to 2-trees (j,r). Since each factor of the product in Eq. (145) must be nonzero to be of interest, we note that the subnetworks contributing to Δ_{ij} must be both 2-trees (i,r) and 2-trees (j,r). Since a 2-tree has only two parts and r is in one of them, we conclude that i and j must be in the same part. Thus the 2-trees of the type (ij,r) and no others contribute to Δ_{ij}. However, since $\mathbf{A}_{-i}$ and $\mathbf{A}_{-j}$ are different matrices, we have no assurance that the signs of the products will all be positive. This fact is nevertheless true, but we shall not prove it here. Hence, Maxwell's formula for an unsymmetrical cofactor of the node admittance matrix becomes

$$\Delta_{ij} = W_{ij,r}(Y) \tag{146}$$

Let us now use this result to compute a transfer impedance function. Suppose we have the network of Fig. 21 in which we want the transfer

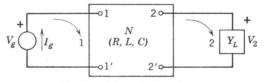

Fig. 21.   Transfer functions.

impedance $Z_{21} = V_2/I_1$ from the generator terminals 1,1' to the load terminals 2,2'. We shall interpret the generator as a current generator for convenience. Then, from the node equations written with $1'$ as the datum node we will get

$$V_2(s) = \frac{\Delta_{12} - \Delta_{12'}}{\Delta} I_1(s) \tag{147}$$

Using Maxwell's formulas for Δ and its unsymmetrical cofactors given in Eqs. (126), (141), and (146), we can write the topological formula for Z_{21} as follows.

$$Z_{21} = \frac{W_{12,1'}(Y) - W_{12',1'}(Y)}{V(Y)} \tag{148}$$

Each of the functions in the numerator and denominator are to be computed for the network N and the load Y_L. This formula is not a *minimum effort* formula. There will, in general, be some cancellation, if $1'$ and $2'$ are different nodes. However we can easily find the terms that cancel and thus convert the expression into a minimum effort formula. We observe that 2-trees of the type $(122',1')$ occur in both $W_{12,1'}$ and $W_{12',1'}$ and will therefore cancel. We observe also that the node $2'$ has to be included, either in one part or the other, in each of the 2-trees in $W_{12,1'}$. Therefore,

$$W_{12,1'}(Y) = W_{122',1'}(Y) + W_{12,1'2'}(Y) \tag{149}$$

Similarly node 2 has to be included, either with nodes $(1,2')$ or with node $1'$ in each 2-tree in $W_{12',1'}$. Therefore,

$$W_{12',1'}(Y) = W_{122',1'}(Y) + W_{12',1'2}(Y) \tag{150}$$

Now when we substitute the last two equations into Eq. (148), we get

$$Z_{21} = \frac{W_{12,1'2'}(Y) - W_{12',1'2}(Y)}{V(Y)} \tag{151}$$

We have now succeeded in obtaining a minimum effort formula since no 2-tree can be included in both terms $W_{12,1'2'}$ and $W_{12',1'2}$. We notice also that Y_L cannot occur in the numerator of Eq. (151) and so the numerator can be computed for N alone.

Let us now turn to the unsymmetrical cofactors of the loop impedance matrix. For this case we will be content just to state the result since even a "reasonableness" argument for this case is quite lengthy. In any case we should intuitively expect the answer to be the dual of the one obtained for the node admittance cofactors, and it is.

In Fig. 21 we choose loops 1 and 2 as shown in the figure. Then, assuming a voltage generator, the transfer admittance can be written

$$Y_{21}(s) = \frac{I_2(s)}{V_1(s)} = \frac{\Delta_{12}}{\Delta}\bigg|_z \qquad (152)$$

We assume that the generator and the load do not lie on any other loops except 1 and 2, respectively. The topological formula for the transfer admittance, which was first given by Kirchhoff, is

$$Y_{21}(s) = \frac{C[W_{12,1'2'}(Z)] - C[W_{12',1'2}(Z)]}{C[W_{1,1'}(Z)]_L} \qquad (153)$$

where the complements in the numerator are computed for the network N alone (not including the generator or Z_L), but the denominator includes Z_L as well.

It is possible to give a geometrical aid in visualizing the 2-trees that are involved in the various terms in Maxwell's and Kirchhoff's formulas for the unsymmetrical cofactors. This was first suggested by Percival and is shown in Fig. 22.

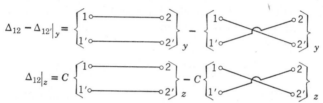

$$\Delta_{12} - \Delta_{12'}\big|_y =$$

$$\Delta_{12}\big|_z = C$$

Fig. 22.   Percival's intuitive representation.

Let us now illustrate some of the ideas we have discussed by means of an example which is simplified by the geometrical aid given in Fig. 22. Let us compute the transfer functions for the lattice network of Fig. 23. Looking at Fig. 22, we can immediately write

$$\Delta_{12} - \Delta_{12'}\big|_y = Y_a Y_b - Y_c Y_d \qquad (154)$$

$$\Delta_{12}\big|_z = Z_c Z_d - Z_a Z_b \qquad (155)$$

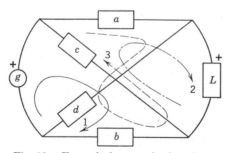

Fig. 23.   Example for transfer functions.

And from Maxwell's and Kirchhoff's formulas for loop and node determinants we can write

$$\Delta_n = Y_a Y_b Y_c + Y_b Y_c Y_d + Y_c Y_d Y_a + Y_d Y_a Y_b + Y_L Y_a Y_b$$

$$+ Y_L Y_a Y_d + Y_L Y_c Y_b + Y_L Y_c Y_d \qquad (a)$$

$$\Delta_m = Z_b Z_d Z_L + Z_b Z_c Z_d + Z_c Z_d Z_L + Z_a Z_b Z_L + Z_a Z_c Z_L$$

$$+ Z_a Z_b Z_c + Z_a Z_b Z_d + Z_a Z_c Z_d \qquad (b)$$

$$(156)$$

The transfer impedance and transfer admittance are now easily found. Furthermore, when the branch impedances are known, it is a simple matter to convert these expressions into rational functions of s.

Let us terminate this section by pointing out that we have barely scratched the surface of this subject here. The same types of considerations can be used to extend these results in several ways. Formulas for other network functions, such as z parameters or y parameters, can be established. The restrictions on mutual inductance and reciprocity can be removed and the pertinent formulas obtained, and so on. For further study, consult the literature.*

In addition to being convenient formulas for evaluating network functions, these topological formulas have important implications in network synthesis. Some of these are suggested as problems. Others we leave to books on network synthesis.

PROBLEMS

9.1 Show that an RC impedance function, in addition to mapping the right half s-plane into the right half Z-plane, also maps the upper half s-plane into the lower half Z-plane; and maps the lower half s-plane into the upper half Z-plane. Use this fact to get an alternative proof that $dZ_{RC}(s)/ds$ is negative real on the real axis.

9.2 Using methods similar to those used in Problem 9.1 show that for an RL impedance function $Z_{RL}(s)$, $dZ_{RL}(s)/ds$ is real positive on the real axis.

9.3 Show that a reactance function $\psi(s)$ is the quotient of an even function to an odd function or vice versa. Hence, show that if $\psi_1(s)$ and $\psi_2(s)$ are reactance functions, $\psi_1(\sqrt{s})/\psi_2(\sqrt{s})$ is a positive real function of s, provided the "positive" branch of $\sqrt{s}$ is chosen.

9.4 Extend Problem 9.3 to show that the quotient of two RC impedances or two RL impedances is a positive real function.

* See:

1. Coates, C. L., "General Topological Formulas for Linear Networks," *Trans. I.R.E.*, vol. CT-5, June, 1958.

2. Mayeda, W., *Topological Formulas for Active Networks*, Rept. No. 8, U.S. Army Contract DA-11-022-ORD-1983, University of Illinois, Jan. 1958.

3. Mason, S. J., "Topological Analysis of Linear Non-Reciprocal Networks," *Proc. I.R.E.*, vol. 45, 1957, pp. 829–838.

9.5 Show that the symmetric matrix of rational functions

$$\begin{bmatrix} z_{11}(s) & z_{12}(s) \\ z_{12}(s) & z_{22}(s) \end{bmatrix}$$

is a positive real matrix if and only if the matrix of real parts

$$\begin{bmatrix} r_{11}(\sigma,\omega) & r_{12}(\sigma,\omega) \\ r_{12}(\sigma,\omega) & r_{22}(\sigma,\omega) \end{bmatrix}$$

is positive definite or semidefinite in $\sigma \geq 0$.

9.6 Let $y_{11} = y_{22}$ and $y_{21} = y_{12}$ be two real rational functions. Suppose the lattice shown in Fig. P9.6 is to have these functions as its short-circuit parameters. Show that the branch impedances Z_a and Z_b will be positive real if

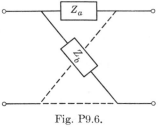

    (a) y_{11} is positive real;
    (b)   the real part condition $(\text{Re } y_{11})^2 - (\text{Re } y_{21})^2 \geq 0$ is satisfied for $\text{Re } s \geq 0$.

If in (b) it is only known that the real part condition is satisfied on the $j\omega$-axis, what additional conditions must be placed on the given functions y_{11} and y_{21} before the theorem will again be true?

Fig. P9.6.

9.7 Show that at a zero of z_{11} or z_{22} on the $j\omega$-axis, z_{12} is imaginary. Hence show that any $j\omega$-axis poles of the open-circuit voltage gain

$$g_{21}(s) = \frac{V_2(s)}{V_1(s)}\bigg|_{I_2=0}$$

are simple and with imaginary residues. Repeat for the short-circuit gain $h_{21}(s)$.

9.8 *Prove:* If a polynomial $p(s)$ is real on the real axis and has no zeros in $\sigma > 0$, then the coefficients of s^k in $p(s)$ are all nonnegative real numbers.

9.9 Suppose that a network having a driving-point impedance $Z_1 = F(s)$ is given. It is desired to find a second network whose driving-point admittance Y_2 is equal to $F(s)$. Such networks are called *inverse*. Discuss the conditions under which the inverse of a given network may be found by the method of duality discussed in Chapter 4.

9.10 For each of the one-ports shown in Fig. P9.10 find the inverse network. Verify that the driving-point admittance of the inverse is the same as the impedance of the given network.

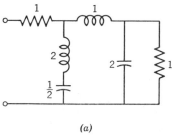

(a)

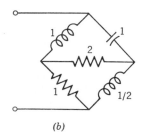

(b)

Fig. P9.10.

9.11 Two positive real functions $F_1(s)$ and $F_2(s)$ are said to be *complementary* if their sum is equal to a positive constant K. Suppose that $F_1(s)$ and K are given. Determine the restrictions on $F_1(s)$ and K such that $F_1(s)$ will have a complementary function. If $F_1(s)$ and $F_2(s)$ are complementary and represent driving-point impedance functions, this means that the series connection of the two corresponding networks has a constant input impedance. In case $F_1(s)$ and $F_2(s)$ are admittance functions, then the parallel connection of the corresponding networks will have a constant input admittance. We refer to such pairs of networks as being complementary.

9.12 Let $Z_1(s)$ be the driving-point impedance function of an RC network and assume that it is regular at the origin. Show that its complementary function $Z_2(s)$ will be an RL impedance function regular at infinity.

9.13 Find complementary networks for each of the networks shown in Fig. P9.13.

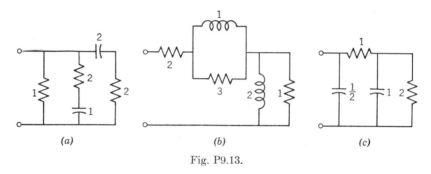

Fig. P9.13.

9.14 Let $\psi(s)$ be a reactance function. Then $\psi(s)$ will have either a zero or a pole at infinity. Suppose it has a pole (if it has a zero there, consider $1/\psi(s)$). If we subtract the principal part of the Laurent expansion at infinity, we will get

$$\psi_1(s) = \psi(s) - k_\infty s$$

$\psi_1(s)$ is also a reactance function, but with a zero at infinity. Take its reciprocal and repeat the above process. Show that this process, when continued, leads to a finite continued, fraction expansion of $\psi(s)$ (about $s = \infty$). Determine a ladder network whose driving-point impedance is represented by this expansion. This result was originally given by Cauer.

9.15 Repeat the preceding problem using $s = 0$ instead of $s = \infty$.

9.16 Through the appropriate transformation show how the results of the preceding two problems can be extended to RC and RL impedance functions.

9.17 Prove that: A is a positive definite symmetric matrix if and only if A^{-1} is positive definite symmetric.

9.18 Prove that a matrix A is positive definite if and only if there exists a nonsingular matrix B such that

$$A = BB'$$

9.19 Prove that if $\mathbf{A}$ is a positive definite symmetric matrix of order n and $\mathbf{B}$ is a matrix of order (r,n) and rank r, then the matrix $\mathbf{BAB}'$ is positive definite symmetric; $\mathbf{A}$ and $\mathbf{B}$ are both real.

9.20 Check whether the following matrices are positive definite.

$$\mathbf{A} = \begin{bmatrix} 2 & 1 \\ 1 & 0 \end{bmatrix} \qquad\qquad \mathbf{B} = \begin{bmatrix} 1 & 0 & \frac{1}{2} & \frac{1}{2} \\ 0 & 2 & 1 & -1 \\ \frac{1}{2} & 1 & 4 & 1 \\ \frac{1}{2} & -1 & 1 & 5 \end{bmatrix}$$

$$\mathbf{C} = \begin{bmatrix} 14 & -2 & 4 & -3 \\ -2 & 5 & 1 & 0 \\ 4 & 1 & 5 & -2 \\ -3 & 0 & -2 & 6 \end{bmatrix} \qquad \mathbf{D} = \begin{bmatrix} 4 & 1 \\ 1 & -1 \end{bmatrix}$$

9.21 It was shown in the text that with real quadratic forms, the matrix can be assumed symmetric; in fact

$$\mathbf{X'AX} = \mathbf{X'A_sX}$$

where $\mathbf{A_s}$ is the symmetric part of $\mathbf{A} : \mathbf{A_s} = \frac{1}{2}(\mathbf{A} + \mathbf{A}')$. Extend this result to show that with complex $\mathbf{X}$, the symmetric part of $\mathbf{A}$ decides the real part of the quadratic form and the skew symmetric part decides the imaginary part. The matrix $\mathbf{A}$ is assumed real.

9.22 In the network shown in Fig. P9.22 all three inductances are mutually coupled. Suppose it is possible to have the following values.

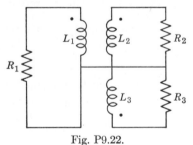

Fig. P9.22.

$$L_1 = L_2 = L_3 = 1$$

$$M_{12} = M_{23} = 0.9$$

$$M_{13} = 0.2$$

(Note that all mutual inductances are less than unity.) Verify that this inductance matrix is not positive definite or semidefinite. With all resistances equal to unity, compute the natural modes of the network and show that it is unstable.

9.23 Generalize the preceding problem to n inductances and prove the following statement.

If a set of n inductances can be found such that the matrix of these inductances is neither positive definite nor semidefinite, then we can construct a passive network with these inductances and some resistances, which is unstable.

9.24 Prove that the inverse of a positive real matrix is also positive real.

9.25 Find the driving-point admittance of the network of Fig. P9.25 using Maxwell's formula.

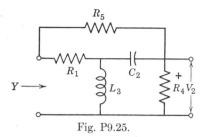

Fig. P9.25.

9.26 Find the transfer voltage ratio V_2/V_1 in the network of Fig. P9.25.

9.27 Find the open-circuit impedance matrix $\mathbf{Z}_{oc}$ of the networks in Fig. P9.27 using topological formulas.

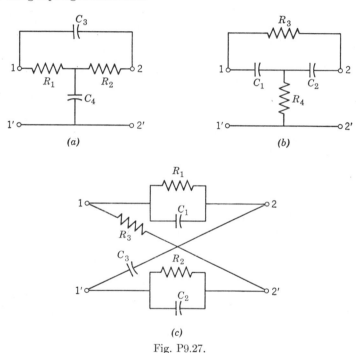

Fig. P9.27.

9.28 *Prove:* The 2-trees that appear in the numerator of $z_{12} = \dfrac{\Delta_{12} - \Delta_{12'}}{\Delta}\bigg|_y$

are precisely those that are common to the numerator of both $z_{11} = \dfrac{\Delta_{11}}{\Delta}\bigg|_y$ and

$z_{22} = \dfrac{\Delta_{22}}{\Delta}\bigg|_y$

9.29 Use the result of Problem 9.28 to prove the following result of Fialkow and Gerst: With reference to the node equations of a network without mutual inductances, let

$$\Delta_{11} = s^m(a_n s^n + a_{n-1}s^{n-1} + \cdots + a_1 s + a_0)$$

$$\Delta_{12} = s^m(b_n s^n + b_{n-1}s^{n-1} + \cdots + b_1 s + b_0)$$

where m is an integer, positive, negative, or zero. Then, $0 \le b_k \le a_k$ for all $k = 0, 1, 2, \cdots, n$.

9.30 Extend Problem 9.29 to prove the further result of Fialkow and Gerst: If N is a two terminal pair network with a common $(1',2')$ terminal which contains no transformers, the voltage ratio transfer function

$$G_{21}(s) = \frac{V_2(s)}{V_1(s)}$$

satisfies $0 \le G_{21}(\sigma) \le 1$ for $0 \le \sigma \le \infty$, where the equality sign can only hold at the extremities of the range ($\sigma = 0, \infty$), unless it holds identically.

9.31 Extend Problem 9.30 to prove: In a general passive two terminal pair network (not necessarily common terminal) the voltage ratio transfer function satisfies:

$$0 \le |G_{21}(\sigma)| \le 1 \qquad \text{for } 0 \le \sigma \le \infty$$

9.32 *Prove:* The number of trees of a graph is

$$n = \det \mathbf{A}\mathbf{A}'$$

where $\mathbf{A}$ is the incidence matrix. (H. M. Trent, *Proc. Nat. Acad. Sci.*, Oct. 1954.)

9.33 Find the transfer impedance function $z_{21}(s)$ of the general ladder network of Fig. P10.9, using Maxwell's formulas. Hence, show that the zeros of transmission of the ladder are the complex frequencies for which the series arms are open circuits (zero admittances) and those for which the shunt arms are short circuits (zero impedances), except for those that cancel with zeros of Δ.

9.34 Find the zeros of transmission of the network of Fig. P9.27c. Show that by suitable choice of parameter values, this network may be made to give any pair of complex conjugate zeros of transmission.

10 · FEEDBACK AND RELATED TOPICS

In our development of network theory up to this point, we have depended solely upon the loop and node systems of equations. As general analytical tools for theoretical developments, loop and node analyses reign supreme. No other tool available at present is as general and simultaneously amenable to theoretical treatment. However from the point of view of the practicing engineer (as opposed to the network theorist) the loop and node systems are just two special methods of analysis. There are several other tools available, some of which are superior as practical tools in special applications. One of these special areas of application of considerable importance is the field of so-called "active networks." By this phrase is conventionally meant networks containing such devices as vacuum tubes, transistors, and conceivably other similar nonreciprocal devices. We should classify the networks just mentioned as "active, nonreciprocal." However the name *active networks* has been used for so long that it has acquired special significance. Hence, we shall continue to call such networks active networks.

Almost all of our earlier discussions, except for Chapter 9, apply to active as well as to reciprocal networks. But we have not, so far, singled out active networks for any special consideration. In this chapter, we shall make slight amends for this lack of special attention by discussing special methods of analysis that find particular application in active networks. Of course these special methods—block diagrams and signal-flow graphs—apply to reciprocal networks as well. But they have their greatest usefulness when applied to active networks, in particular to feedback systems. This chapter, then, will be devoted to the subject of feedback theory, the associated problem of stability, and to some methods of analyzing networks, which are particularly suitable to active networks.

The subject matter which we will discuss in this chapter is of very wide scope. We can do little more than lay the groundwork for a more

extensive treatment.   The topics which we shall treat are capable of extension far beyond the discussion included in this chapter.   The subject is usually presented in books on feedback amplifiers or control systems.   Our purpose in presenting this subject at all is to show the underlying unity of these various fields; to "open up a few doors" and to give a preview of some of the interesting fields to which network analysis leads.   Hence, we will make no attempt at being exhaustive.   Very often we will be satisfied with "reasonableness" arguments rather than formal proofs.

10.1   Block Diagrams and Elementary Concepts of Feedback

One of the objectives of network theory is to educate the engineer's thinking to move from the *component* to the *system* point of view.   Although each element of a network will affect its behavior, the elements in a complicated network are grouped in such a way that each group of elements performs a specific function.   These groups of elements then interact on each other only at their terminals.   The over-all network, or system, is then thought to consist of the interconnection of these groups of elements.

For example, we would be hopelessly lost if we tried to describe the behavior of even a simple radio receiver in terms of the component resistances, inductances, capacitances, and dependent sources.   Some semblance of order will appear if we look upon groups of components which perform a particular function (such as oscillators, amplifiers, demodulators, filters, etc.) as units.

We obtained some concepts in Chapters 6 through 9 which are useful in this direction.   We now characterize networks in terms of describing functions.   We can, for instance, speak of an impedance $(4s^2 + s + 1)/(s^2 + s + 1)$ as a unit, without considering the seven or eight elements that make up the network.   Similarly we can treat a complete transmission network merely as a set of four functions without worrying about the dozens of loops or node pairs that it may contain.*

However even this description of two-ports is too detailed for some purposes.   Specifically, in many active networks, we are interested only in the signal transmitted through the network and not in the details of the currents and voltages at each terminal pair.

For instance, in a simple voltage amplifier we are not concerned about the input (or output) current; we want to know only the voltage ampli-

---

* One is reminded of one of the many cartoons about Thomas J. Watson's sign "Think."   This one shows a small man in a front office with a sign "Think" hanging on the wall.   Somewhere inside is the plush office of the boss with another sign hanging on his wall.   This one says "Think Big."

fication. In such a case we might as well represent the amplifier as in Fig. 1a rather than as in Fig. 1b, which we have been doing until now.

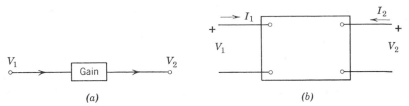

(a)   (b)

Fig. 1. Voltage amplifier description.

Note that Fig. 1a is a single line diagram. We don't even bother showing pairs of terminals, we show merely *ports*, points of entry or exit.

This type of representation is known as a *block diagram*. Each functional unit in a network is represented as a block, the over-all system consisting of the interconnection of the various blocks. The block diagram representation is quite flexible inasmuch as the blocks may be taken to be as large or as small (in complexity, not size) as is desired. As a matter of fact, each element can be taken as a block, but this will obviously seldom serve a useful purpose.

Each block, then, takes an input function and operates on it in some fashion to yield an output function. The input and output quantities are indicated by means of arrows, as shown in Fig. 1a. The operation which the block performs is indicated in the block.

When several functions are to be added algebraically, we use the symbol shown in Fig. 2a. This is referred to as a *summing point*. A

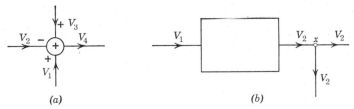

(a)   (b)

Fig. 2. Summing point and pick-off point.

"+" or a "−" sign is placed beside the arrowhead of the entering arrows to indicate the reference. The symbol in Fig. 2a, for instance, represents the equation $V_4 = V_1 - V_2 + V_3$.

A point at which one line in a block diagram separates into several lines, as illustrated by the point x in Fig. 2b, is called a *pick-off point*. Each outgoing line from a pick-off point represents the same function as the incoming line.

Let us illustrate these ideas with an example. Consider the series-parallel connection of two two-ports shown in Fig. 3. A complete descrip-

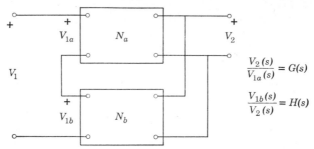

$$\frac{V_2(s)}{V_{1a}(s)} = G(s)$$

$$\frac{V_{1b}(s)}{V_2(s)} = H(s)$$

Fig. 3.   Simple feedback network.

tion of the terminal behavior can be given in terms of the g parameters if we know the g parameters of the individual two-ports. However, we may not be interested in such a complete description; we may want to know only the ratio of the output to input voltage transforms, assuming we know the corresponding ratios of the individual two-ports. If we define these ratios as given in Fig. 3, we can write

$$V_1(s) = V_{1a}(s) + V_{1b}(s) = \frac{V_2(s)}{G(s)} + H(s)V_2(s) \tag{1}$$

Hence

$$\frac{V_2(s)}{V_1(s)} = \frac{G(s)}{1 + G(s)H(s)} \tag{2}$$

One point must be strongly emphasized here. Recall from the discussion in Chapter 8 that, when two-ports are interconnected, we must require that the terminal conditions remain the same after the interconnection as before. It is only under these conditions that the two-port parameters of the interconnected networks can be obtained in terms of those of the individual ones. More descriptively, we say that there should be no "loading" of one two-port on the other.

It is possible to redraw the network of Fig. 3 as a block diagram by noting that $V_{1a} = V_1 - V_{1b}$. This equation can be represented by the summing point in Fig. 4a. The voltage ratios given in Fig. 3 can be

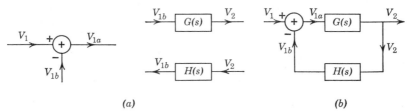

(a)   (b)

Fig. 4.   Block diagram representation of Fig. 3.

represented by the blocks shown in Fig. 4a.   Finally, Fig. 4b results
when these are combined.

Let us consider the form of the block diagram in Fig. 4.   There is a
closed loop with arrows pointing in the same direction around the loop.
This seems to indicate that the output quantity V_2 is able to influence
its own value by virtue of being returned to the input, albeit modified
by the function $H(s)$.   As a matter of fact, this picture provides us with
an intuitive, nonquantitative definition of feedback.   We say that a
network is a *feedback* network if some variable, either the output variable
or an internal one, is used as an input to a part of the network, in such a
way that it is able to affect its own value.   This is not a very useful
definition of feedback since it does not give a quantitative measure.   In
a later section we will spend some time with the mathematical formulation of feedback.

Let us now define some commonly used terms in connection with Fig.
4.   A network such as this is called a *closed-loop* system; specifically a
single-loop system.   The voltage ratio given in Eq. (2) is called the
closed-loop transfer function, while the function $G(s)H(s)$ is called the
open-loop transfer function (an alternative designation will be discussed
in section 10.3).   The function $G(s)$ alone is often called the *forward gain*.

One of the useful features of the block diagram analysis is that it
permits approximations to be readily incorporated, thereby leading to
great simplifications in the analysis.   In fact, in order to achieve the "no
loading" requirement, it is often indispensable to make approximations.

Let us now consider an example which will illustrate these remarks
and which will have the general form of Fig. 3.   A feedback amplifier
network is shown in Fig. 5a.   This is redrawn in Fig. 5b to emphasize
that it fits the pattern of Fig. 3.   Suppose the frequency range of

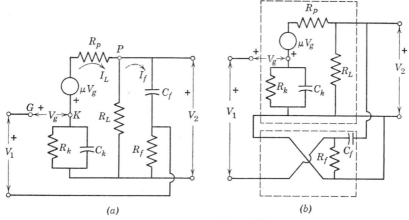

(a)   (b)

Fig. 5.   Feedback amplifier.

interest is such that the break frequency $\omega_k = 1/R_kC_k$ is below this range, so that the parallel R_k–C_k branch can be regarded as a short circuit. Suppose also that the feedback resistance R_f is much larger than the load resistance R_L so that "loading" due to the feedback path can be disregarded. With these assumptions the forward gain $G(s)$ and the feedback ratio $H(s)$ are easily computed from Fig. 5b to be

$$G(s) = \frac{V_2}{V_g} = \frac{-\mu R_L}{R_p + R_L} \qquad (a)$$

$$(3)$$

$$H(s) = \frac{R_f}{R_f + 1/sC_f} = \frac{sR_fC_f}{1 + sR_fC_f} = \frac{as}{1 + as} \qquad (b)$$

With these values of G and H, Fig. 3 represents the amplifier network of Fig. 5.

Let us again emphasize the fact that this idea of representing a network as an interconnection of simple blocks is based on the assumption that the individual block functions remain unchanged when the interconnections are made. This involves an inherent approximation in the block diagram representation.

In using block diagrams as a tool of analysis, we can make use of a few basic rules for manipulations of the diagrams. These rules are so simple that they hardly need any justification. Most of them simply follow from the elementary properties of complex algebra (the associative and commutative laws, etc.). The following are given in Fig. 6.

Rule 1. Associative law of addition and multiplication.
Rule 2. Distributive law.
Rule 3. Removing a block in the feedback loop.
Rule 4. Closed loop to open loop.
Rule 5. Open loop to closed loop.

Some others are suggested as problems at the end of the chapter.

With these basic rules, a given block diagram can be manipulated with considerable ease, and the desired output function calculated. Although we have dealt exclusively with transformed variables, this is not an essential feature of the method. The input and output quantities of a block may be functions of time and may be related through a differential equation. As a matter of fact, it is not even necessary that the blocks represent linear networks; it is possible to use the same procedure if nonlinear elements are also present. For these and other extensions and applications, consult the literature.*

* T. M. Stout, "A Block Diagram Approach to Network Analysis," *Trans. A.I.E.E. (Applications and Industry)*, Vol. 3, 1952, p. 255; T. D. Graybeal, "Block Diagram Network Transformation," *Elec. Eng.*, Vol. 70, 1951, p. 985.

Rule 1.   Associative law of addition and multiplication.

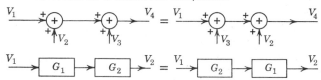

Rule 2.   Distributive law.

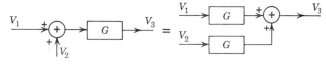

Rule 3.   Removing a block in the feedback loop.

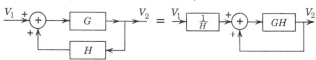

Rule 4.   Closed loop to open loop.

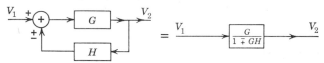

Rule 5.   Open loop to closed loop.

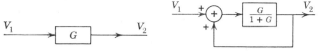

Fig. 6.   Block diagram—basic rules.

10.2   Signal-Flow Graphs

Closely related to the concept of a block diagram, and much more versatile, is the tool of analysis known as a *signal flow graph*, first introduced by S. J. Mason.* Signal-flow graphs retain the intuitive character of block diagrams and at the same time are equivalent to the system of network equations; hence, they are also precise, although many approximations can be readily incorporated.

In this section we shall discuss some of the fundamental ideas in the theory of signal-flow graphs and give their application in network analysis. Such questions as adequacy, linear dependence, order of complexity, etc., will not be answered completely. Our viewpoint will

* S. J. Mason, *Feedback Theory—Some Properties of Signal-Flow Graphs, Proc. IRE*, Vol. 41, Sept., 1953, pp. 1144–1156; also *Proc. IRE*, Vol. 44, July, 1956, pp. 920–926.

be slightly different from that of Mason. We shall discuss signal-flow graphs from the point of view of the *theory of nets*. However, before we enter into the mathematical details, let us observe the intuitive character of a signal-flow graph by actually constructing one for a simple example.

Consider the feedback amplifier of Fig. 5. We shall construct a geometrical representation, not unlike a block diagram, to represent the equations relating the variables. The circles representing summing points in the block diagram will be reduced to mere dots and the blocks will be replaced by line segments, the appropriate function being written alongside. Neither of these details is of fundamental importance.

In Fig. 5a there is an input voltage V_1 and an output voltage V_2, both of which contribute to the grid voltage V_g. These contributions can be represented as in Fig. 7a. The intuitive character of this figure

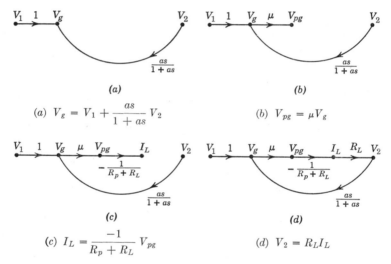

$$(a) \quad V_g = V_1 + \frac{as}{1 + as} V_2 \qquad\qquad (b) \quad V_{pg} = \mu V_g$$

$$(c) \quad I_L = \frac{-1}{R_p + R_L} V_{pg} \qquad\qquad (d) \quad V_2 = R_L I_L$$

Fig. 7. Development of signal flow graph for Fig. 5.

is so evident that there is hardly any need to say any more about it. (We are here merely thinking out loud; the formal development of the subject will follow shortly.) The dependent source voltage V_{pg}, being μ times V_g, can be represented by the additional line shown in Fig. 7b. Let us continue to assume that the parallel R_k–C_k branch can be neglected and that $R_f \gg R_L$, so that there is no loading on R_L. Then, the plate current I_L is given in terms of V_{pg} by

$$I_L = \frac{-1}{R_p + R_L} V_{pg} \qquad\qquad (4)$$

This leads to Fig. 7c. Finally, the output voltage in terms of I_L is simply $V_2 = R_L I_L$; the signal-flow graph then takes the form shown in Fig. 7d. This graph should be compared with the block diagram in Fig. 4 and the similarity noted. Again we find a closed feedback loop around which the arrows all point in the same direction.

Suppose that after constructing this signal flow graph, we decide that the "no loading" approximation is not justified; that is, I_f cannot be neglected in comparison with I_L. All is not lost. The relationship between I_f and V_2 is easily found to be

$$I_f = \frac{V_2}{R_f + (1/sC_f)} = \frac{sC_f}{1 + as} V_2 \tag{5}$$

Hence, to Fig. 7d we add a line from V_2 to a new point labeled I_f, as shown in Fig. 8a. But the relationship between I_L and V_{pg} is no longer

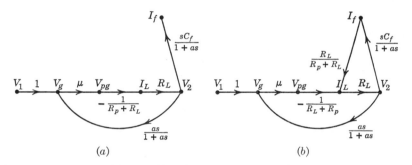

Fig. 8. Completed signal flow graph.

given by Eq. (4), because the current in R_L is now $I_L - I_f$. The new relationship is

$$I_L = -\frac{1}{R_p + R_L} V_{pg} + \frac{R_L}{R_p + R_L} I_f \tag{6}$$

This leads to the final result shown in Fig. 8b. Note that, even though this signal-flow graph represents the "single loop" amplifier of Fig. 5, it has two "feedback" loops. We will have more to say about this later.

The preceding discussion gives us an intuitive idea of the signal-flow graph. Let us turn now to a more formal discussion and formulate our ideas with more precision.

We saw, in section 3.3, that a network can be interpreted as a directed linear graph. If we specify the impedances or admittances of the branches of the network, thus completing the description, we say that the graph is *weighted*. A weighted directed graph is also called a *net*.

The concept of a net has applications in many different fields besides network theory. One of these applications is the signal-flow graph.

A signal-flow graph is a representation of a system of equations as a net. That is, signal-flow graphs have really nothing to do with network theory as such. They are merely a scheme for representing, and solving, a system of simultaneous linear algebraic equations. Since the transformed network equations are linear algebraic equations, signal-flow graphs can also be applied to the representation and solution of network equations. When applied to networks, signal-flow graphs permit our intuitive knowledge to come into play. To emphasize the fact that signal-flow graph analysis is general, and to avoid any narrow implications, we shall use a general notation to establish the theory. Later, we shall apply the theory to networks.

Suppose we have a system of linear algebraic equations, which we can write as

$$\mathbf{AX} = \mathbf{Y} \tag{7}$$

In typical applications the matrix $\mathbf{Y}$ contains transforms of driving functions and the matrix $\mathbf{X}$ contains transforms of response functions. Generally speaking, in communication networks, there is only one driving function or at most a very few driving functions. These can, of course, appear in several of the equations of Eq. (7). Assuming, for simplicity, that there is only one driving function, we can write

$$\mathbf{Y} = \mathbf{K}y_0 \tag{8}$$

where y_0 is the driving function.

Our objective is to solve Eq. (7) for $\mathbf{X}$ so that we will have a set of equations which expresses each variable explicitly. Instead of solving for $\mathbf{X}$ in the usual way, the signal-flow graph formulation makes use of a modified system of equations. These are obtained by adding $\mathbf{X}$ to both sides of Eq. (7) after transposing $\mathbf{Y}$. The result of this algebraic manipulation is

$$\mathbf{X} = -\mathbf{K}y_0 + (\mathbf{A} + \mathbf{U})\mathbf{X} \tag{9}$$

where Eq. (8) has also been used. This can be written alternatively as

$$\mathbf{X} = [-\mathbf{K} \quad (\mathbf{A} + \mathbf{U})] \begin{bmatrix} y_0 \\ \mathbf{X} \end{bmatrix} \tag{10}$$

Note that this is not an explicit solution for the unknowns, since the right-hand side contains $\mathbf{X}$ also. (It is easy to see that additional driving functions will produce little change in this equation. The scalar y_0 will become the matrix $\mathbf{Y}_0$ and $\mathbf{K}$ will have several columns instead of just one column.) We will see, shortly, that we can write network equations directly in the form of Eq. (10) so that none of these manipulations are really important when flow graphs are applied to networks.

Focus attention on Eq. (10) and suppose $\mathbf{X}$ is an nth order column matrix. Then the column matrix on the right side of the equation is of order $n + 1$, and the other matrix on the right is of order $(n, n + 1)$. Let us augment this matrix and make it square by adding a row of zeros. This will define a matrix $\mathbf{C}$ as follows.

$$\mathbf{C} = \begin{bmatrix} 0 & 0 \\ -\mathbf{K} & (\mathbf{A} + \mathbf{U}) \end{bmatrix} \tag{11}$$

This is a square matrix with one more row and column than there are variables in $\mathbf{X}$. (If there are k driving functions instead of one, $\mathbf{C}$ will have k more rows and columns than there are variables in $\mathbf{X}$.)

We now interpret $\mathbf{C}$ as the *connection matrix* of a net as follows. We construct a graph with one node for each row (and column) in $\mathbf{C}$. We label each of these with the symbol for the corresponding variable, thus *weighting* the nodes. Whenever an entry c_{ij} in the matrix $\mathbf{C}$ is nonzero, we draw a directed branch in the graph *from* node j *to* node i and label this branch with the entry c_{ij}, thus weighting the branches.* If $c_{ij} = 0$, we do not draw any branch from j to i. This net, weighted according to the entries of $\mathbf{C}$ is called the *signal-flow graph* of the system of equations represented by Eq. (10).

As an example, suppose the following system of equations is given

$$\begin{bmatrix} 0 & 0 & 2 \\ -2 & 0 & 1 \\ 4 & -1 & -1 \end{bmatrix} \begin{bmatrix} x_1 \\ x_2 \\ x_3 \end{bmatrix} = \begin{bmatrix} y_0 \\ -y_0 \\ 0 \end{bmatrix} \tag{12}$$

Then we can write

$$\mathbf{K} = \begin{bmatrix} 1 \\ -1 \\ 0 \end{bmatrix} ; \ \mathbf{A} = \begin{bmatrix} 0 & 0 & 2 \\ -2 & 0 & 1 \\ 4 & -1 & -1 \end{bmatrix} ; \ \mathbf{A} + \mathbf{U} = \begin{bmatrix} 1 & 0 & 2 \\ -2 & 1 & 1 \\ 4 & -1 & 0 \end{bmatrix} \tag{13}$$

$$\begin{bmatrix} x_1 \\ x_2 \\ x_3 \end{bmatrix} = \begin{bmatrix} -1 & 1 & 0 & -2 \\ 1 & -2 & 1 & 1 \\ 0 & 4 & -1 & 0 \end{bmatrix} \begin{bmatrix} y_0 \\ x_1 \\ x_2 \\ x_3 \end{bmatrix} \tag{14}$$

---

* To avoid this "backwardness" in orientation, the transpose of the matrix, as defined here, is usually called the connection matrix. Then the (i,j) entry corresponds to the branch *from i to j*.

The signal-flow graph of this system of equations will have 4 nodes labeled y_0, x_1, x_2, and x_3, and will take the form of Fig. 9.

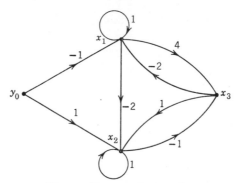

Fig. 9.   Flow graph example.

Let us make a few remarks about the signal-flow graph of Fig. 9 before proceeding. First of all we note that there are no branches entering node y_0, which is natural since the first row of **C** [which is not shown in Eq. (14)] is zero. In giving a physical interpretation for the graph we say that y_0 is a *source node*. By analogy we might say that a node from which no branch *leaves* is a *sink* node. In the conventional theory of signal-flow graphs the existence of such a node is assumed; such a node can always be introduced by adding a trivial equation to the system. (In the present case we could write $x_3 = x_3$.) However, this assumption is unnecessary and so we shall not make it. Another conceptually useful physical interpretation is the following. Let us consider each of the nodes of the signal-flow graph to be points at which *signals* are measurable. Thus the node y_0 is the point at which signal y_0 is present. This signal is *transmitted* along each of the branches *leaving* node y_0. The quantity written alongside the branch is the *transmission* of the branch. Thus $(-1)y_0$ is transmitted from node y_0 to node x_1. The signal present at any node is the *sum* of all the signals coming into the node. Thus the signal at node x_3 is $4x_1 + (-1)x_2$. This signal itself is x_3, so that

$$x_3 = 4x_1 - x_2 \tag{15}$$

which is one of the equations in Eq. (14). Similarly at node x_2 we have $(1)y_0$, $(-2)x_1$, $(1)x_3$. In addition to these, there is a transmission from node x_2 *to itself* as well. Since x_2 is the sum of the incoming signals, we will get

$$x_2 = y_0 - 2x_1 + x_2 + x_3 \tag{16}$$

A loop from a node to itself, such as the loops at x_1 and x_2 in Fig. 9, is called a *self-loop*.

It is from this interpretation that we get the name signal-flow graph. The graph represents the flow of signals from point to point. The points themselves are merely representations of variables. In a network, some of these variables will be currents and others voltages. The interpretation is a physical interpretation of a mathematical model.

The signal-flow graph method of analysis is most useful when we wish to solve the system of equations for one variable only; which is a common situation in many practical problems. Therefore let us make the assumption that we want the solution to, say, x_1. The flow graph method of solving for x_1 corresponds, exactly, to algebraically eliminating all other variables by systematic substitution. In the physical interpretation we find the total transmission from y_0 to x_1 *by removing all other nodes.* We remove the nodes one by one. Every time a node is removed, we take care to see that the total transmissions from y_0 to all other nodes are left invariant by suitably modifying the remaining transmissions. Let us keep both these ideas, the mathematical substitution and the physical concept of node removal, in mind as we proceed.

Let us first consider removing a node at which no self-loop is present. On the mathematical side this corresponds to eliminating a variable x_j when the corresponding diagonal element c_{jj} is zero. In such a case the equation for x_j is

$$x_j = c_{j0}y_0 + \sum_{\substack{k=1 \\ k \neq j}}^{n} c_{jk}x_k \tag{17}$$

To eliminate x_j in this case, all we need to do is to substitute Eq. (17) for x_j into all other equations; and then disregard Eq. (17). For instance, if the original equation for x_p is

$$x_p = c_{p0}y_0 + \sum_{\substack{k=1 \\ k \neq j}}^{n} c_{pk}x_k + c_{pj}x_j \tag{18}$$

we get, on substituting Eq. (17) for x_j,

$$x_p = c_{p0}y_0 + \sum_{\substack{k=1 \\ k \neq j}}^{n} c_{pk}x_k + c_{pj}c_{j0}y_0 + \sum_{\substack{k=1 \\ k \neq j}}^{n} c_{pj}c_{jk}x_k$$

$$= (c_{p0} + c_{pj}c_{j0})y_0 + \sum_{\substack{k=1 \\ k \neq j}}^{n} (c_{pk} + c_{pj}c_{jk})x_k \tag{19}$$

Let us interpret this last equation both in terms of the signal-flow graph and in terms of the connection matrix.

First of all $c_{pj}c_{j0}$ is the transmission from the source node y_0 to the node x_p *through* the intermediate node x_j. So if we add this transmission to the direct transmission c_{p0}, we can eliminate node x_j, keeping the total transmission from y_0 to x_p unaltered. Similarly $c_{pj}c_{jk}$ is the transmission from node x_k to node x_p *through* x_j. So if we add this to the direct transmission c_{pk}, we can eliminate node x_j; leaving the transmission from x_k to x_p unaltered. If we modify every transmission this way, we can remove x_j completely from the graph and all other transmissions remain invariant.

Next let us look at the connection matrix. For convenience let us arrange the variables such that the variable to be eliminated, x_j, is the last variable. Then the connection matrix is

$$\mathbf{C} = \begin{bmatrix} 0 & 0 & \cdots & 0 & 0 & \cdots & 0 & \vdots & 0 \\ c_{10} & c_{11} & \cdots & c_{1,j-1} & c_{1,j+1} & \cdots & c_{1n} & \vdots & c_{1j} \\ c_{20} & c_{21} & \cdots & c_{2,j-1} & c_{2,j+1} & \cdots & c_{2n} & \vdots & c_{2j} \\ \cdot & \cdot & & \cdot & \cdot & & \cdot & \vdots & \cdot \\ c_{j-1,0} & c_{j-1,1} & \cdots & c_{j-1,j-1} & c_{j-1,j+1} & \cdots & c_{j-1,n} & \vdots & c_{j-1\,j} \\ c_{j+1,0} & c_{j+1,1} & \cdots & c_{j+1,j-1} & c_{j+1,j+1} & \cdots & c_{j+1,n} & \vdots & c_{j+1,j} \\ \cdot & \cdot & & \cdot & \cdot & & \cdot & \vdots & \cdot \\ c_{n0} & c_{n1} & \cdots & c_{n,j-1} & c_{n,j+1} & \cdots & c_{n,n} & \vdots & c_{n,j} \\ \hline c_{j0} & c_{j1} & \cdots & c_{j,j-1} & c_{j,j+1} & \cdots & c_{j,n} & \vdots & 0 \end{bmatrix} \tag{20}$$

The dashed line indicates that the last row and column are to be eliminated, and $c_{jj} = 0$ by the assumption of no self-loop at x_j. Now we see that the modification of Eq. (19) corresponds to the following operation on the matrix.

Multiply each entry in the last column by each entry in the last row (not respectively) and add each product to the corresponding entry in the connection matrix. For instance if we take the entry in the pth row of the last column, namely c_{pj}, and multiply it by the entry in the kth column of the last row, namely c_{jk}, we add the result $c_{pj}c_{jk}$ to the (p,k) position of the matrix. Doing this for every element of the last row and column we get

$$\mathbf{C}_1 = \begin{bmatrix} 0 & 0 & \cdots & 0 \\ c_{10} + c_{1j}c_{j0} & c_{11} + c_{1j}c_{j1} & \cdots & c_{1n} + c_{1j}c_{jn} \\ c_{20} + c_{2j}c_{j0} & c_{21} + c_{2j}c_{j1} & \cdots & c_{2n} + c_{2j}c_{jn} \\ \cdot & \cdot & & \cdot \\ c_{n0} + c_{nj}c_{j0} & c_{n1} + c_{nj}c_{j1} & \cdots & c_{nn} + c_{nj}c_{jn} \end{bmatrix} \begin{matrix} 0 \\ c_{1j} \\ c_{2j} \\ \cdots \\ c_{nj} \end{matrix} \tag{21}$$

$$\quad c_{j0} \qquad\qquad c_{j1} \qquad \cdots \qquad c_{jn} \qquad\qquad 0$$

The rule is thus quite simple. In fact by operating on the matrix we can avoid many errors that are likely to creep in if we operate on the graph.

This matrix technique is known as the Aufenkamp–Hohn *node-pulling algorithm* and was introduced by them in connection with a different application of nets. By looking at the matrix procedure we can also observe the need for the assumption that there is no self-loop at x_j. For if $c_{jj} \neq 0$, and we proceed in the same way, we shall lose this information, since c_{jj} does not enter the picture at all.

Now let us consider the case where $c_{jj} \neq 0$. The equation for x_j is now

$$x_j = c_{j0}y_0 + c_{jj}x_j + \sum_{\substack{k=1 \\ k \neq j}}^{n} c_{jk}x_k \qquad (22)$$

If $c_{jj} = 1$, we are obviously in difficulties. Such a condition may arise even when the original system of equations is well behaved. (See the example of Fig. 9 and the corresponding system of Eqs. (12), which are consistent and have a unique solution.) However, if the original system of equations is linearly independent, the system can be rearranged such that the diagonal entries of $\mathbf{A}$ in Eq. (7) are nonzero, so that $c_{jj} \neq 1$ in the modified system of Eq. (10). We shall see that network equations can be written in such a way as to ensure this. Hence, we shall make this assumption. Then we can solve Eq. (22) for x_j, getting

$$x_j = \frac{1}{1 - c_{jj}} \left\{ c_{j0}y_0 + \sum_{\substack{k=1 \\ k \neq j}}^{n} c_{jk}x_k \right\} \qquad (23)$$

Let us interpret this solution. In terms of the flow graph, Eq. (23) corresponds to *dividing* all the *incoming* transmissions at x_j by $(1 - c_{jj})$, where c_{jj} is the self-loop transmission at x_j; and then *removing the self-loop at x_j*. Now the problem reduces to the previous case as there is no longer a self-loop at x_j.

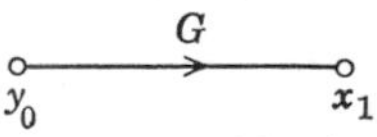

In the connection matrix of Eq. (20) this operation corresponds to *dividing* all entries of the *last row* by $(1 - c_{jj})$ and then replacing the diagonal entry by zero. Once this is done, the Aufenkamp–Hohn node-pulling algorithm can be applied again to remove node x_j.

Fig. 10. Final graph.

By repeated applications of these operations, the signal flow graph can be reduced to a single branch from y_0 to x_1 as shown in Fig. 10. From this figure we can write down the solution for x_1 immediately as

$$x_1 = Gy_0 \qquad (24)$$

where G is called the *graph gain*.

Let us illustrate this graph reduction procedure first with a system of equations before proceeding to network examples. Suppose we have the system of equations

$$
\begin{bmatrix} 2 & 1 & 2 \\ 1 & -1 & -3 \\ 2 & 1 & 1 \end{bmatrix} \begin{bmatrix} x_1 \\ x_2 \\ x_3 \end{bmatrix} = \begin{bmatrix} 1 \\ 0 \\ -1 \end{bmatrix} y_0 \tag{25}
$$

Then we can modify the system as before, getting

$$
\begin{bmatrix} x_1 \\ x_2 \\ x_3 \end{bmatrix} = \begin{bmatrix} -1 & 3 & 1 & 2 \\ 0 & 1 & 0 & -3 \\ 1 & 2 & 1 & 2 \end{bmatrix} \begin{bmatrix} y_0 \\ x_1 \\ x_2 \\ x_3 \end{bmatrix} \tag{26}
$$

The signal-flow graph for this equation is shown in Fig. 11.

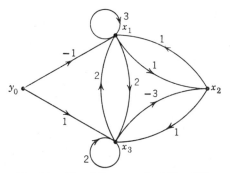

Fig. 11.   Signal-flow graph of Eq. (26).

Suppose that we desire to solve for x_1. Then we go through the following sequence of operations starting with the connection matrix in Eq. (26). The corresponding reductions of the flow graph are illustrated in Fig. 12, the corresponding steps being labeled with the same letter.

(*a*)   Remove self-loop at x_3 by dividing all incoming transmissions by $(1 - c_{33}) = 1 - 2 = -1$. The resulting connection matrix is

$$
\mathbf{C}_1 = \begin{array}{c} y_0 \\ x_1 \\ x_2 \\ \\ x_3 \end{array} \left[\begin{array}{ccc:c} 0 & 0 & 0 & 0 \\ -1 & 3 & 1 & 2 \\ 0 & 1 & 0 & -3 \\ \hdashline -1 & -2 & -1 & 0 \end{array} \right] \tag{27}
$$

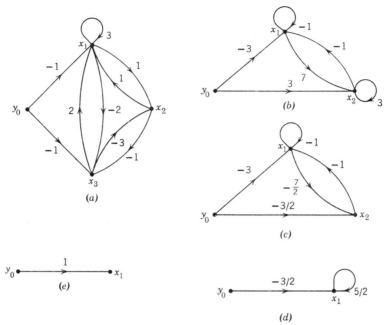

Fig. 12.   Reduction of signal-flow graph.

(b)   Remove node x_3 using the node-pulling algorithm. The resulting connection matrix is

$$\mathbf{C}_2 = \begin{matrix} y_0 \\ x_1 \\ x_2 \end{matrix} \begin{bmatrix} 0 & 0 & 0 \\ -3 & -1 & -1 \\ 3 & 7 & 3 \end{bmatrix} \qquad (28)$$

Notice that in the process a self-loop is created at x_2 with a transmission equal to 3, and notice how the other transmissions are altered.

(c)   Remove self-loop at x_2 by dividing incoming transmissions by $1 - 3 = -2$.

$$\mathbf{C}_3 = \begin{matrix} y_0 \\ x_1 \\ \\ x_2 \end{matrix} \begin{bmatrix} 0 & 0 & \vdots & 0 \\ -3 & -1 & \vdots & -1 \\ \hdashline & & \vdots & \\ -\frac{3}{2} & -\frac{7}{2} & \vdots & 0 \end{bmatrix} \qquad (29)$$

(d)   Remove node x_2.

$$\mathbf{C}_4 = \begin{matrix} y_0 \\ x_1 \end{matrix} \begin{bmatrix} 0 & 0 \\ -\frac{3}{2} & \frac{5}{2} \end{bmatrix} \qquad (30)$$

(e)   Remove self-loop at x_1 by dividing incoming transmissions by $1 - \frac{5}{2} = -\frac{3}{2}$.

$$\mathbf{C}_5 = \begin{matrix} y_0 \\ x_1 \end{matrix} \begin{bmatrix} 0 & 0 \\ 1 & 0 \end{bmatrix} \tag{31}$$

Thus, we find that $x_1 = y_0$. It is clear that the solution can be obtained by working on the matrix only, or the flow graph only.

The preceding discussion constitutes the essentials of the signal-flow graph method of analysis. There are many other manipulations of flow graphs, which are of the nature of "tricks of the trade," which we shall not consider.*

Let us turn now to the problem of applying the signal-flow graph technique to network analysis. What we would like to do is to write down the connection matrix directly, merely by inspection of the network diagram. Alternatively, we want to draw directly the signal-flow diagram, which is simply a representation of the connection matrix. In either case, the first order of business is to choose a set of variables. Different choices of the variables will lead to different flow graphs representing the same network. The choice of variables is guided by many considerations but in any case must include the known quantities and the desired quantities. No matter what variables and equations relating them are chosen, two things must be ensured.

(a)   The system of equations obtained is *adequate* as a description of the network; and

(b)   the system of equations obtained is linearly independent, so that no difficulties are encountered such as a self-loop transmission becoming unity, somewhere in the graph reduction process.

We know that the behavior of a network is expressed in terms of the branch voltages and currents by means of $2N_b$ algebraic equations (transformed). However, N_b of these are simply the branch voltage-current relationships; knowing either the voltage or the current of a branch is enough. Thus, there are N_b equations that must be satisfied simultaneously.

Some choices of the variables and equations will not be very useful if we are to make full use of the signal-flow graph technique. For example, we might simply choose loop currents or node voltages as variables, and represent the loop or node equations as a signal-flow graph. This procedure is certainly valid and needs no comment.

---

* For details see the works of Mason, already cited, and J. G. Truxal, *Control System Synthesis*, McGraw-Hill Book Co., New York, 1955.

Alternatively, we might choose either all the branch currents or all the branch voltages as variables. The equations that we use are (a) KCL at $N_v - 1$ nodes and (b) KVL for $N_b - N_v + 1$ loops, for a total of N_b equations, all expressed in terms of either branch currents or branch voltages. These are the branch current and branch voltage systems of equations that were mentioned in Chapter 4, and here again we know that these systems of equations are both adequate and linearly independent.

After a little experience with signal-flow graphs, it becomes quite simple to choose intuitively a suitable set of variables and equations. However, we will discuss one procedure which is quite a useful one. It is closely related to a system of equations described by Bashkow.*

We first choose a tree of the network. The variables that are chosen are the link currents and tree branch voltages. Therefore, we choose the tree in such a fashion that all the voltage generators are branches for this tree and all the current generators are links for this tree. For concreteness, let us consider the example of Fig. 13.

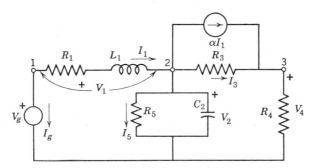

Fig. 13.   Example for constructing a flow graph.

Let us assume that we are interested in the voltage transfer function $G_{21}(s) = V_4(s)/V_g(s)$. We should, therefore, choose V_g and V_4 as two of our variables. Since αI_1 is a current generator and depends on I_1, we should choose I_1 and αI_1 also as variables. Therefore we may choose as the tree, the tree consisting of branches V_g, R_4, and C_2. The variables for the signal-flow graph are then: V_g, V_2, V_4, I_1, I_3, I_5, and αI_1. (There is no real need for αI_1 as a variable, since we have I_1; but nodes in a signal-flow graph are eliminated so easily that a redundant variable is not a serious matter.)

* Bashkow, T. R., "The A-matrix, a New Network Description," *Trans. I.R.E.*, Vol. CT-4, Sept. 1957, pp. 117–119.

The equations that we use are KVL for fundamental loops and KCL for fundamental cut sets. Using KVL for the fundamental loops we can write the chord voltages in terms of the tree branch voltages as follows.

$$V_1(s) = V_g(s) - V_2(s) \qquad (a)$$

$$V_3(s) = V_2(s) - V_4(s) \qquad (b)$$

$$V_5(s) = V_2(s) \qquad (c)$$

$$(32)$$

$$V_\alpha(s) = V_2(s) - V_4(s) \qquad (d)$$

We won't use the equation for $V_\alpha(s)$, since it is unrelated to αI_1. Similarly, using KCL for fundamental cut sets, we can write the tree branch currents as follows.

$$I_2(s) = I_1(s) - \alpha I_1(s) - I_3(s) - I_5(s) \qquad (a)$$

$$I_4(s) = \alpha I_1(s) + I_3(s) \qquad (b) \qquad (33)$$

$$I_g(s) = -I_1(s) \qquad (c)$$

Again, the generator current will not be used.

We now use the v–i relationships to eliminate the unwanted variables. From Eqs. (32) we get

$$I_1(s) = \frac{1}{R_1 + sL_1}\{V_g(s) - V_2(s)\} \qquad (a)$$

$$I_3(s) = \frac{1}{R_3}\{V_2(s) - V_4(s)\} \qquad (b) \qquad (34)$$

$$I_5(s) = \frac{1}{R_5}V_2(s) \qquad (c)$$

Similarly, from Eqs. (33) we get

$$V_2(s) = \frac{1}{sC_2}\{I_1(s) - \alpha I_1(s) - I_3(s) - I_5(s)\} \qquad (a)$$

$$(35)$$

$$V_4(s) = R_4\{\alpha I_1(s) + I_3(s)\} \qquad (b)$$

With a little experience, we could write down these final equations (34) and (35) by inspection; or equivalently, we could draw the signal-flow graph by inspection. The signal-flow graph for these equations is given in Fig. 14 and the associated connection matrix is given in Eq. (36).

$$
\begin{array}{c}
\begin{array}{ccccccc}
V_g & V_2 & V_4 & I_1 & I_3 & I_5 & \alpha I_1
\end{array} \\
\begin{array}{c}
V_g \\
V_2 \\
V_4 \\
I_1 \\
I_3 \\
I_5 \\
\alpha I_1
\end{array}
\left[
\begin{array}{ccccccc}
0 & 0 & 0 & 0 & 0 & 0 & 0 \\
0 & 0 & 0 & 1/sC_2 & -1/sC_2 & -1/sC_2 & -1/sC_2 \\
0 & 0 & 0 & 0 & R_4 & 0 & R_4 \\
1/(R_1+sL_1) & -1/(R_1+sL_1) & 0 & 0 & 0 & 0 & 0 \\
0 & 1/R_3 & -1/R_3 & 0 & 0 & 0 & 0 \\
0 & 1/R_5 & 0 & 0 & 0 & 0 & 0 \\
0 & 0 & 0 & \alpha & 0 & 0 & 0
\end{array}
\right]
\end{array}
$$

$$(36)$$

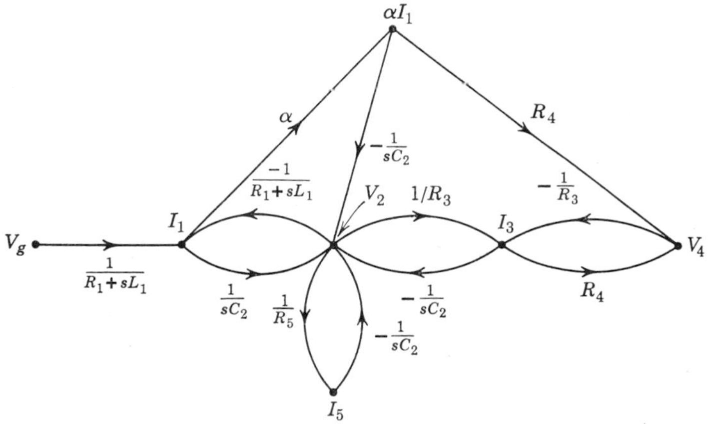

Fig. 14. Signal-flow graph of network example in Fig. 13.

Notice that the signal-flow graph is quite different from the circuit diagram. One can always go from the circuit diagram to a signal-flow graph; in fact, to many signal-flow graphs. But in general, the reverse is not always possible. For a given, arbitrary, signal-flow graph, there may or may not exist a network, and, if one exists, we have no general means of finding it (other than trial and error). We may also note that there are many loops in Fig. 14 in which all the branches are similarly oriented. For instance, we have the oriented loops: $(I_1, \alpha I_1, V_2, I_1)$, (I_1, V_2, I_1), (V_2, I_5, V_2), etc. Each of these is called a *feedback loop*. They do not correspond to an intuitive conception of a feedback loop; but that is only because our intuitive conception cannot be made precise, and still agree with an intuitive conception of feedback.

The two variables αI_1 and I_5 can be eliminated immediately, giving us a simpler graph shown in Fig. 15, with the following connection matrix.

$$\mathbf{C} = \begin{array}{c} V_g \\ V_2 \\ V_4 \\ I_1 \\ I_3 \end{array} \begin{bmatrix} 0 & 0 & 0 & 0 & 0 \\ 0 & -1/sC_2R_5 & 0 & (1-\alpha)/sC_2 & -1/sC_2 \\ 0 & 0 & 0 & \alpha R_4 & R_4 \\ 1/(R_1+sL_1) & -1/(R_1+sL_1) & 0 & 0 & 0 \\ 0 & 1/R_3 & -1/R_3 & 0 & 0 \end{bmatrix}$$

(37)

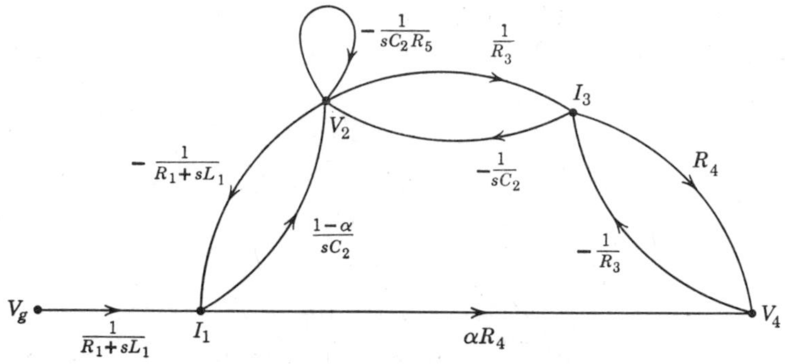

Fig. 15.   Reduced signal-flow graph.

We may now eliminate the variables V_2, I_1, I_3 to get the desired solution. The details will be left to you.

It is possible to look upon the signal-flow graph as presenting a physical picture of the flow of signals through the network. This may sometimes be of help in visualizing the operation of the network. However, remember that more than one signal-flow graph can be obtained for the same network, each one of which will give a somewhat different picture of the "signal flow." This leads to the conjecture that intuitive ideas about the flow of signals through a network do not necessarily correspond to the truth. Different patterns of signal flow can be set up for the same network, each of which will lead to the same answer for the graph gain.

There is no more and no less information in the signal-flow graph than there is in the equations represented by the graph. Interpretations can also be attached to the equations, as well as to the flow graph. It is true, however, that a majority of engineers are able to visualize the behavior of a network more easily by means of a geometrical diagram than through a set of equations, and for this reason the flow graph technique will be appealing.

The graph reduction process which we described can be systematized, and a single formula derived for the graph gain G, which is defined in

Eq. (21). This was originally done by Mason. We will state the result here without proof. The graph gain is given by

$$G = \frac{1}{\Delta} \sum_{\substack{\text{All} \\ \text{forward} \\ \text{paths}}} G_k \Delta_k \tag{38}$$

in which G_k is the gain (transmission) of the kth *forward path* (or direct path) from the input to the output, and

$$\Delta = 1 - \sum_m P_{m1} + \sum_m P_{m2} - \sum_m P_{m3} + \cdots \tag{39}$$

where P_{m1} is the *loop gain* (the product of all the transmissions around a loop) of the mth feedback loop;

P_{m2} is the product of the loop gains of the mth set of two *non-touching* feedback loops; that is, feedback loops that have neither a node nor a branch in common;

P_{m3} is the product of the loop gains of the mth set of three non-touching feedback loops, etc.

The quantity Δ_k in Eq. (38) is the value of Δ for that part of the graph not touching the kth forward path.

Although we have not proved this formula, let us illustrate its use by computing the graph gain for the signal-flow graph of Fig. 14. Let us first compute the P_{mi}'s. The feedback loops in the graph are $(I_1, \alpha I_1, V_4, I_3, V_2, I_1)$, $(I_1, \alpha I_1, V_2, I_1)$, (I_1, V_2, I_1), (V_2, I_5, V_2), (V_2, I_3, V_2), (I_3, V_4, I_3). The loop gains can be calculated from Fig. 14 by inspection. Hence, for P_{m1} we get

$$\Sigma P_{m1} = -\frac{\alpha R_4}{R_3 s C_2 (R_1 + sL_1)} + \frac{\alpha}{s C_2 (R_1 + sL_1)}$$

$$-\frac{1}{s C_2 (R_1 + sL_1)} - \frac{1}{s C_2 R_5} - \frac{1}{s C_2 R_3} - \frac{R_4}{R_3}$$

$$= -\frac{\alpha R_4 R_5 + (1 - \alpha) R_3 R_5 + (R_1 + sL_1)(R_3 + R_5 + s C_2 R_4 R_5)}{s C_2 R_3 R_5 (R_1 + sL_1)} \tag{40}$$

To compute P_{m2} we must find all the sets of two nontouching feedback loops. From Fig. 14 we find these to be

(a) $(I_1, \alpha I_1, V_2, I_1)$ and (I_3, V_4, I_3)
(b) (I_1, V_2, I_1) and (I_3, V_4, I_3)
(c) (V_2, I_5, V_2) and (I_3, V_4, I_3)

From the loop gains already computed, we find

$$\Sigma P_{m2} = -\frac{R_4}{R_3}\left\{\frac{\alpha}{sC_2(R_1+sL_1)} - \frac{1}{sC_2(R_1+sL_1)} - \frac{1}{sC_2R_5}\right\}$$

$$= \frac{R_4}{sC_2R_3}\left(\frac{1-\alpha}{R_1+sL_1} + \frac{1}{R_5}\right) \tag{41}$$

We observe that there are no sets of three, or more, loops that do not touch each other, so Δ is obtained by substituting the last two equations into Eq. (39). The result will be

$$\Delta = 1 + \frac{\alpha R_4 R_5 + (1-\alpha)R_3 R_5 + (R_1+sL_1)(R_3+R_5+sC_2R_4R_5)}{sC_2R_3R_5(R_1+sL_1)}$$

$$+ \frac{R_4R_5(1-\alpha) + R_4(R_1+sL_1)}{sC_2R_3R_5(R_1+sL_1)}$$

$$= \frac{(R_1+sL_1)[(R_3+R_4+R_5+sC_2R_5(R_3+R_4)] + R_5[R_4+R_3(1-\alpha)]}{sC_2R_3R_5(R_1+sL_1)} \tag{42}$$

Notice that $\alpha R_4 R_5$ cancels in the numerator. This fact demonstrates that Mason's graph gain formula is not a *minimum effort* formula (i.e., one in which no unnecessary computations are made) as the topological formulas given in Chapter 9 are.

The next step is to calculate the forward gains G_k. There are three forward paths to be considered.

(a) $(V_g, I_1, \alpha I_1, V_4)$
(b) $(V_g, I_1, V_2, I_3, V_4)$
(c) $(V_g, I_1, \alpha I_1, V_2, I_3, V_4)$

The corresponding forward gains are easily found from Fig. 14 to be

$$G_1 = \frac{\alpha R_4}{R_1 + sL_1} \tag{a}$$

$$G_2 = \frac{R_4}{sC_2R_3(R_1+sL_1)} \tag{b} \tag{43}$$

$$G_3 = \frac{\alpha R_4}{sC_2R_3(R_1+sL_1)} \tag{c}$$

Finally, it remains to calculate the values of Δ_k corresponding to these three paths. For the first forward path, the part of the graph that does not touch the path consists of nodes (V_2, I_3, V_5) and the two loops formed by these.   Hence, we get

$$\Delta_1 = 1 - \Sigma P_{m1} = 1 + \frac{1}{sC_2R_5} + \frac{1}{sC_2R_3} \tag{44}$$

(Note that P_{m1} here is not the same as that of Eq. (40); it is pertinent to the part of the graph under consideration here.)   For the other forward paths, there are no nontouching feedback loops.   Therefore

$$\Delta_2 = \Delta_3 = 1 \tag{45}$$

The numerator of Eq. (38) can now be formed, to give

$$\Sigma G_k \Delta_k = \frac{\alpha R_4 (sC_2R_3R_5 + R_3 + R_5)}{(R_1 + sL_1)sC_2R_3R_5}$$

$$+ \frac{R_4}{sC_2R_3(R_1 + sL_1)} - \frac{\alpha R_4}{sC_2R_3(R_1 + sL_1)}$$

$$= \frac{\alpha R_4 (sC_2R_3R_5 + R_3) + R_4R_5}{sC_2R_3R_5(R_1 + sL_1)} \tag{46}$$

(Once again there is a cancellation.)   Finally, the desired graph gain is given by

$$G(s) = \frac{V_4(s)}{V_g(s)}$$

$$= \frac{R_4(sC_2R_3R_5 + R_3) + R_4R_5}{(R_1+sL_1)[R_3+R_4+R_5+sC_2R_5(R_3+R_4)]+R_5[R_4+R_3(1-\alpha)]} \tag{47}$$

You may verify this result by performing the reduction of the flow graph, starting with Fig. 15.

10.3   Feedback and Stability—The Nyquist Criterion

In the first section of this chapter we briefly discussed the intuitive concept of feedback.   We are now ready to expand this idea and to give it some analytical meaning.   Although the idea of feedback is not restricted to either reciprocal or active nonreciprocal networks, it has relevance mostly for active networks.   Another important problem that presents itself in the consideration of active networks is that of stability.   This topic is intimately related with feedback.   Hence, in this section we will study some aspects of feedback and stability. Again we shall not attempt to be exhaustive. Specifically, we shall treat only those aspects of the subject which tie in most closely with our earlier studies in this book.

In a linear lumped system, as we saw in Chapter 2, stability is decided by the location in the complex plane of the natural modes of the system. If there are any natural modes in the right half plane, the system is unstable. The natural modes of the system are the zeros of the system determinant. The (conceptually) simplest way to find out whether the determinant has any zeros in the right half plane is to find the zeros. However, with polynomials of high order, this is no mean task, and so we resort to other methods. We shall discuss two methods of determining stability, due to Hurwitz and Nyquist.

In this, and in the discussion of the rest of the section, we will assume that *each R, L,* and *C* is considered a branch of the network. With such an assumption, the system determinant (loop or node or other) is given by

$$\Delta(s) = \frac{1}{s^p} (a_n s^n + a_{n-1} s^{n-1} + \cdots + a_1 s + a_0) \tag{48}$$

where p is a non-negative integer. We would like to know whether or not the polynomial in this expression has any zeros in the right half plane. A polynomial with real coefficients with no zero in the right half plane was defined in Chapter 9 as a Hurwitz polynomial. There we discussed certain necessary conditions of a Hurwitz polynomial, such as the fact that all coefficients must be present and must be positive.

We will now state a theorem that can be used as a test of the Hurwitz character of a polynomial. Let us first write a polynomial as the sum of its *even* and *odd* parts. That is,

$$P(s) = m(s) + n(s) \tag{49}$$

where m contains all the even powers of s and n contains all the odd powers. *If $P(s)$ is a Hurwitz polynomial, then the ratio m/n, or its reciprocal, is a reactance function.* Conversely, *if the ratio of the even and odd parts of a polynomial $P(s)$ is found to be a reactance function, then $P(s)$ will differ from a Hurwitz polynomial by at most a multiplicative even polynomial.* We shall not prove this theorem here.*

In using this theorem to test a given polynomial $P(s)$, the simplest procedure is to form the ratio of the even and odd parts and expand the result in a continued fraction. This will take the form

---

* For a proof, see N. Balabanian, *Network Synthesis*, Prentice-Hall, 1958.

$$\frac{m(s)}{n(s)} = b_1 s + \cfrac{1}{b_2 s + \cfrac{1}{b_3 s + \cfrac{1}{\begin{matrix} \cdot \\ \cdot \\ \cdot \\ + \cfrac{1}{b_k s} \end{matrix}}}} \tag{50}$$

m/n will be a reactance function if and only if the coefficients b_1, b_2, $\cdots$, b_k are all positive, except that b_1 may be zero. (See Problem 9.14.) Note that if $m(s)$ and $n(s)$ have any common even factors, these will cancel in the ratio and will not affect the b coefficients. We refer to this procedure as the *Hurwitz test for stability*.

Let us illustrate the Hurwitz test with an example. Let

$$P(s) = 2s^4 + 5s^3 + 6s^2 + 3s + 1 \tag{51}$$

Then

$$m(s) = 2s^4 + 6s^2 + 1 \tag{a}$$
$$\tag{52}$$
$$n(s) = 5s^3 + 3s \tag{b}$$

To expand the ratio m/n in a continued fraction, we divide the denominator into the numerator, as by long division, stopping after the first quotient. Then we invert and divide again, stopping after the first term. Again we invert and continue in this fashion until the function is exhausted. The work can be arranged as follows.

$$5s^3 + 3s \overline{)2s^4 + 6s^2 + 1} \left(\tfrac{2}{5}s\right.$$
$$\underline{2s^4 + \tfrac{6}{5}s^2}$$

$$\tfrac{24}{5}s^2 + 1 \overline{)5s^3 + 3s} \left(\tfrac{25}{24}s\right.$$
$$\underline{5s^3 + \tfrac{25}{24}s}$$

$$\tfrac{47}{24}s \overline{)\tfrac{24}{25}s^2 + 1} \left(\tfrac{576}{1175}s\right.$$
$$\underline{\tfrac{24}{25}s^2}$$

$$1 \overline{)\tfrac{47}{24}s} \left(\tfrac{47}{24}s\right.$$
$$\underline{\tfrac{47}{24}s}$$

$$0$$

Hence, the continued fraction is

$$\frac{2s^4 + 6s^2 + 1}{5s^3 + 3s} = \frac{2}{5}s + \cfrac{1}{\frac{25}{24}s + \cfrac{1}{\frac{576}{1175}s + \cfrac{1}{\frac{47}{24}s}}} \tag{53}$$

The polynomial is thus Hurwitz and has no zeros in the right half plane.

The Hurwitz test is a relatively simple test. However, in order to use the test, we require that the network determinant $\Delta(s)$ be calculated as a function of s. This is not always an easy job. It would be useful to have a method for stability testing which uses experimental data, or only approximate curves based on asymptotic or corner plots. Such a technique is the *Nyquist criterion*, which we shall now take up in some detail.

Since our interest is in the determinant, we select some function that involves the determinant. For instance, we may select a transfer function

$$G(s) = \frac{\Delta_{12}(s)}{\Delta(s)} \tag{54}$$

Since $\Delta(s)$ is in the denominator, we would like to find out whether $G(s)$ has any poles in the right half plane. Nyquist's test uses the principle of the argument to decide this issue. Since the region of interest is the right half plane, we choose a contour that "encloses" the right half plane, as shown in Fig. 16.

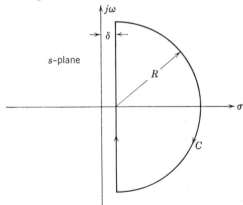

Fig. 16.   Contour for Nyquist's test.

Here we can make the distance δ between the $j\omega$-axis and the contour arbitrarily small, and the radius R arbitrarily large. In the limit the contour becomes the $j\omega$-axis. In order to use the principle of the argument, we must require that there be no poles on the contour C. Hence, if we wish to let δ become zero, we must require that $G(s)$ have no poles on the $j\omega$-axis. Similarly, if we wish to let the radius R go to infinity, we must require that $G(s)$ be regular at infinity. From here on we will assume that these conditions are satisfied.

Let us consider the mapping of the contour by the function G; that is, the locus of the point $G(s)$ as s traverses the contour of Fig. 16. This may be a figure such as the one shown in Fig. 17a. Since G is a network

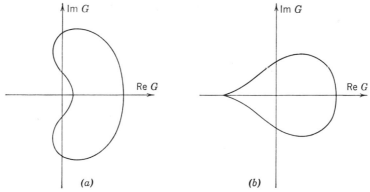

Fig. 17.   Map of the contour of Fig. 16.

function, it is real on the real axis and so the map is symmetric with respect to the real axis. Let N_0 and N_p be the number of zeros and number of poles of $G(s)$, respectively, which lie inside the contour C. Now the argument principle states that

$$\Delta_C \arg G(s) = 2\pi(N_0 - N_p) \qquad (55)$$

That is, the change in the argument of $G(s)$ as s traverses the contour C in the positive direction is 2π times the number of zeros minus the number of poles of $G(s)$ within C (counting multiplicity).

Let us see what the nature of the locus of $G(s)$ must be if this change of angle is to be nonzero. It is quite evident that the locus must go round the origin in the G-plane if there is to be any change in the argument. This is the case in Fig. 17b. In Fig. 17a, there is no change in the argument as we traverse the locus once. In other words, the locus must *enclose* the origin in the G-plane if there is a net change in the angle of $G(s)$ over the contour C. If C is traversed in the positive (counterclockwise) direction, positive (counterclockwise) enclosures of the origin in the G-plane correspond to a positive value of $N_0 - N_p$ in Eq. (55).

Thus, if the $G(s)$ locus does not enclose the origin, we can conclude that $G(s)$ has *as many poles as zeros in the right half plane.* But we really want to know whether it has any poles in the right half plane. Therefore, for this test to be useful, we must know, by some other means, that $G(s)$ has no zeros in the right half plane; i.e., that $G(s)$ is a minimum-phase function. This is by no means an easy task. However, there is no need to abandon our procedure because we have met some difficulty. What we can do is to find another function involving the network determinant and some other factor, this factor being such that its zero locations are known to us.

Such a function is the *return difference.* Let us digress for a moment to introduce this concept. Consider the signal-flow graph of the system under consideration. We first set all the sources in the graph (corresponding to independent generators in the network) to zero. As we have observed earlier, this corresponds to short circuiting the voltage generators and open circuiting the current generators. We focus attention on one of the transmissions of the graph. As far as the definition of return difference is concerned, this may be any transmission. But for the application of interest, we will focus attention on the transmission of a dependent source, such as μ or g_m or α. Implied in this statement is the assumption that we draw the graph such that the desired transmission appears only once, and alone, in the signal-flow graph. It is always possible to modify the network equations (by suitable linear combinations and introduction of auxiliary variables) such that this assumption is satisfied, except when this transmission is a mutual inductance. Now we cut this branch in two, inserting a source node on the "forward" side and a sink node on the "return" side, as shown in Fig. 18b. We have labeled the branch transmission with the

Fig. 18.   Definition of return difference.

neutral symbol k. The unit transmission in Fig. 18b is introduced merely to permit the sink to appear as a separate node.

We now let y_0 be a unit signal, and compute the returned signal x_0. Interpreting k as a unilateral transmission, this signal at x_0 will tell us how much of the input signal y_0 is "fed back" to the input. For this reason we define $(-x_0/y_0)(=-x_0)$ as the *return ratio,* symbolized conventionally as T. The negative sign is introduced to conform with standard reference conventions in feedback amplifier theory.

The *return difference* F is defined as the difference between the input and returned signals, when the input is unity. Thus

$$F = 1 - x_0 = 1 + T \tag{56}$$

The return difference thus defined is called the return *difference for zero reference* because we have cut the transmission path k completely. There are other conditions that are also useful in feedback theory but the zero reference quantity suffices for our present purposes. A mathematical description and measure of feedback is thus provided by the return difference. If there is no feedback, then the return ratio will be zero and the return difference will equal unity.

To get back to the question of stability, we have to establish first that the quantity F has something to do with the system determinant. In fact, we can show that if k appears as a coefficient in the loop (or node) equations, then

$$F(k) = \frac{\Delta}{\Delta^0} \tag{57}$$

where Δ is the loop (or node) determinant and Δ^0 is the value of the determinant when $k = 0$. Before establishing the reasonableness of this expression, let us observe that k must appear in its natural form and not as $1/k$ in the equations. We choose the loop or node basis depending on this fact. (If k appears in natural form in both—as μ would, for example—we may choose either basis.)

To establish the validity of Eq. (57), consider the system of equations represented by the signal-flow graph, before any branch is cut. Writing these in conventional form, we have

$$\mathbf{AX} = \mathbf{Y} \tag{58}$$

Remember that the element k is to appear in only one of the equations. Referring to Fig. 18a, the equation for node x_b will be

$$x_b = kx_a + \sum_{i \neq a} a_{bi}x_i + a_{b0}y_0 \tag{59}$$

where k does not appear in any of the transmissions a_{bi}. When written in the form of Eq. (58), this equation will be

$$-kx_a - \sum_{i \neq a} a_{bi}x_i + x_b = a_{b0}y_0 \tag{60}$$

Therefore we can express the determinant of the matrix $\mathbf{A}$ as

$$\det \mathbf{A} = \Delta^0 - k\Delta^0{}_{ba} = \Delta \tag{61}$$

where

$$\Delta^0 = \det \mathbf{A} \text{ with } k = 0 \tag{62}$$

and

$$\Delta^0{}_{ba} = \text{co-factor } (b,a) \text{ with } k = 0 \tag{63}$$

$$= \Delta_{ba}$$

The second line of Eq. (63) follows from the fact that k does not appear in Δ_{ba}. (Equation (61) can be obtained by expanding Δ along the bth row and then collecting all the terms except the one containing k.)

Now consider the case where the branch k is cut. We can represent this situation in the equations as follows. We first replace the right side of Eq. (58) by zero. Then we add k to the right side in the bth row, corresponding to the insertion of the unit signal in the forward path of Fig. 18b. (In this figure the unit signal multiplied by k appears in the equation for x_b.) Finally we delete kx_a from the left side of the bth equation. Now the returned signal is x_a. Solving for x_a in this modified system, we get

$$x_a = k\frac{\Delta_{ba}}{\Delta^0} \tag{64}$$

where Δ^0 is the new system determinant which obviously is the same as in Eq. (62). The return difference is then

$$F = 1 - x_a = 1 - k\frac{\Delta_{ba}}{\Delta^0} = \frac{\Delta^0 - k\Delta_{ba}}{\Delta^0} \tag{65}$$

Or, using Eq. (61),

$$F = \frac{\Delta}{\Delta^0} \tag{66}$$

This derivation was with respect to the system of equations represented by the signal-flow graph—not the loop or node systems. To show that Eq. (66) is invariant to a change of basis of analysis we make the following observations. The natural modes of the system are always given by the zeros of the system determinant and are independent of the basis of analysis. Therefore the determinants of every system of network equations have the same zeros (with possibly different behaviors at $s = 0$). With our assumption that each R, L, C is a branch, the determinants have no finite poles except possibly at $s = 0$. Thus the different determinants obtained can only differ by multiplicative factors of the type Ks^n where K is a constant. Such factors cancel between numerator and denominator of the right side of Eq. (66), leaving it invariant to a change of basis (as long as we write equations such that $\Delta(s) = 0$ is the characteristic equation).

Let us return from this digression to a consideration of the Nyquist locus. The mapping function is the return difference function for the transmission k, which we will denote by $F_k(s)$. Thus,

$$F_k(s) = \frac{\Delta(s)}{\Delta^0(s)} \tag{67}$$

Now if this map is going to tell us anything about the zeros of $\Delta(s)$ in the right half plane, we must know that $F_k(s)$ has no poles in the right half plane; or if it has any poles there, we must know how many. There is one case in which we can definitely say that F_k has no poles in the right half plane. This is the case in which setting $k = 0$ makes the network *passive*, i.e., if k represents the *only active element* (that is, dependent source) in the network, then we can say for sure that $\Delta^0(s)$ has no zeros in the right half plane. In this case the stability of the system is deducible from the character of the F-locus. For emphasis, let us summarize this result.

Let k represent the transmission of the only active element in a network and let $F_k(s)$, defined by Eq. (67), be the return difference for k. Assuming $F_k(s)$ is regular everywhere on the $j\omega$-axis including $s = 0$ and ∞, the network will be stable if and only if the locus of $F_k(j\omega)$ for $-\infty < \omega < \infty$ does not enclose the origin in the F_k-plane.

In case $F_k(s)$ is regular on the $j\omega$-axis except at $s = 0$, we can do some "patchwork" on the locus. We can find the loci for $-\infty < \omega < -\epsilon$ and $\epsilon < \omega < \infty$, where $\epsilon > 0$, and complete the locus by estimating the behavior of $F(s)$ near $s = 0$ from the first term of the Laurent expansion.

The assumption that k is the only active element can be relaxed to include all single-loop systems by observing that if the transmissions of any one of the active elements is reduced to zero, the loop transmission becomes zero. As a matter of fact, this behavior can be made the definition of a single-loop system. Hence, stability for any single-loop system is determined in the same way as for a system with a single active element.

Instead of using the return difference $F(s)$ in Nyquist's stability criterion, the return ratio $T(s)$ is almost always used. These two quantities differ only by unity. The origin in the F-plane corresponds to the point -1 in the T-plane. Thus, the stability criterion in terms of $T(s)$ will be the same, except that instead of encirclements of the origin, we must talk about encirclements of the point -1.

Nyquist's criterion can be extended to multiple-loop feedback systems also. This involves plotting several Nyquist diagrams, with different numbers of active elements "alive" in each case. We will not discuss this extension here.*

Let us turn again to the special case of a single-loop feedback system. The block diagram and signal-flow diagram are shown in Fig. 19.

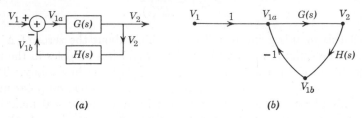

(a)   (b)

Fig. 19.   Single loop system.

Suppose we find the return ratio for the branch $G(s)$. To do this we break the branch at the left hand end and insert a unit signal. Clearly, the returned signal will be $-G(s)H(s)$. The return difference will then be $1 - (-GH) = 1 + G(s)H(s)$. A glance back at section 10.1 will show that GH is precisely what we there called the open-loop transfer function. Thus, the concepts of return ratio T and open-loop function for a single-loop system are identical. One point should be emphasized, however. Our ability to draw the block diagram in this simple form involves approximations. On the other hand, for calculating the return difference (of the μ of a tube, say), approximations *may* be made to simplify computation, but they *need* not be.

Thus, one way in which the Nyquist criterion can be used, is to place a given network in the form of Fig. 19, from which $G(s)$ and $H(s)$ can be calculated relatively simply. A plot of $G(j\omega)H(j\omega) = T(j\omega)$ then gives the desired information.

Let us now illustrate the Nyquist stability criterion by means of an example. We shall go through this example in some detail and show how approximations can be incorporated in the procedure.

Consider the three stage RC coupled amplifier with frequency sensitive feedback shown in Fig. 20. In this example we shall try to show the advantage of the Nyquist criterion by not computing $\Delta(s)$. Instead we shall estimate the return ratio $T(s)$ by making use of a number of approximations. This network is a simplified model of a vacuum tube network in which many of the interelectrode capacitances have been neglected to simplify the example.

Since this is a single-loop system, we need compute only one return

---

* See the Bode and Truxall references already cited.

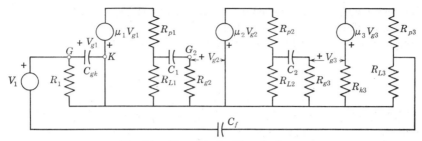

Fig. 20.   Example for Nyquist locus.

ratio, say for μ_1. Our interest lies entirely on the $j\omega$-axis; hence, we can deal with steady-state phasors instead of Laplace transforms. Remembering the signal-flow graph definition of the return ratio, we must cut the branch of the graph having transmission μ_1 and apply a unit signal at the right hand node of the pair of nodes thus formed. The signal applied at the other node to which branch μ_1 is connected is then simply μ_1. We should now interpret this step in terms of the actual network rather than the signal-flow graph. If we were to assume a unit voltage V_{g1}, then the voltage of the first dependent source would be simply μ_1. Thus, the condition shown in Fig. 21 is the appropriate one

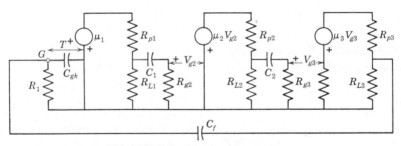

Fig. 21.   Return ratio computation.

for computing the return ratio. Here, the external sources are removed and the first dependent source is assumed to be an independent source having a phasor voltage μ_1.

Notice that the reference for T is chosen to conform with the definition that it is the negative of the returned signal at the node x_a in Fig. 18b. It is easy to see how this interpretation can be used for experimental measurement of $T(j\omega)$ on the network of which this example is a model.

In order to construct the Nyquist diagram, let us split the frequency range $0 \leq \omega < \infty$ into a number of bands and use suitable approximations in each band. At very low frequencies, the returned signal will be very small due to the coupling capacitances C_1, C_2, and C_f. The influence of C_{gk} can be neglected in this range. There are three RC coupling networks in the loop transmission. Let us use the notation

$$R_e = \frac{R_L R_g}{R_L + R_g} \qquad (68)$$

with suitable subscripts for each of the coupling networks. Then, the voltage ratio of each stage will be

$$\frac{-\mu R_e C s}{(R_e + R_p)Cs + (R_p + R_L)/(R_g + R_L)} \qquad (69)$$

with appropriate subscripts. Hence, in this range the return ratio will be given by

$$T(s) = \frac{\mu_1 R_{e1} C_1 s}{(R_{e1} + R_{p1})C_1 s + (R_{p1} + R_{L1})/(R_{g2} + R_{L1})}$$

$$\times \frac{\mu_2 R_{e2} C_2 s}{(R_{e2} + R_{p2})C_2 s + (R_{p2} + R_{L2})/(R_{g3} + R_{L2})}$$

$$\times \frac{\mu_3 R_{e3} C_f s}{(R_{e3} + R_{p3})C_f s + (R_{p3} + R_{L3})/(R_1 + R_{L3})} \qquad (70)$$

(The negative signs disappear because of the reference for T.) The asymptotic phase of each of the factors in Eq. (70) as $\omega \to 0$ will be $\pi/2$ radians. Thus, the total asymptotic phase of $T(j\omega)$ will be $3\pi/2$ radians, the magnitude approaching zero. Hence, the low-frequency portion of the locus of $T(j\omega)$ looks like the curve in Fig. 22.

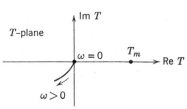

Fig. 22. Low-frequency behavior of $T(j\omega)$.

Let us assume that the break frequency of $R_1 C_{gk}$ is considerably higher than the break frequencies of the three RC coupling networks.

Thus, there will be a *midband* frequency range in which the behavior of the network in Fig. 21 can be approximated by that shown in Fig. 23.

For this network T is computed quite easily. Alternatively, the desired expression can be obtained from Eq. (70) by neglecting the constant terms in the denominators compared with the frequency-dependent terms. In either case the result will be

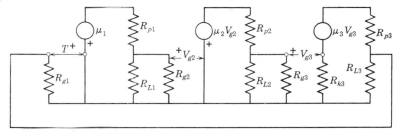

Fig. 23.   Midband approximation.

$$T = \mu_1\mu_2\mu_3 \frac{R_{e1}}{R_{p1} + R_{e1}} \frac{R_{e2}}{R_{p2} + R_{e2}} \frac{R_{e3}}{R_{p3} + R_{e3}} = T_m \qquad (71)$$

This is obviously a real positive number. Thus the midband T-locus is on the positive real axis. The point T_m is marked on Fig. 22.

At high frequencies Fig. 23 can still be used, except that the effect of C_{gk} must now be included. Since C_{gk} is in parallel with R_{e3}, the third factor in Eq. (71) should be modified and replaced by the following.

$$\frac{R_{e3}}{R_{e3} + R_p + j\omega C_{gk}R_{e3}R_{p3}} \qquad (72)$$

Hence, the angle of T will asymptotically approach $-\pi/2$. The high end of the $T(j\omega)$ locus therefore takes the form shown in Fig. 24.

We can now estimate the $T(j\omega)$ locus for $0 \leq \omega < \infty$ to have roughly the shape shown in Fig. 25. To improve the approximation, we should estimate a few points on the curve, using what we know about RC networks. Suppose for simplicity, that the three significant break frequencies of the interstage circuits are either identical, or widely

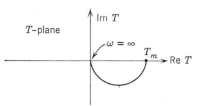

Fig. 24.   High-frequency behavior of $T(j\omega)$.

separated. In the first case, we know that at the common break frequency, each circuit contributes an angle of 45° and a 3 db attenuation. This point, marked ω_3 in Fig. 24, must be 9 db below T_m in gain. Similarly, we can find the frequency at which each circuit contributes a 60° angle. This is the frequency at which each of the denominator factors in Eq. (70) contributes 30°, which is easily found to be approximately $\omega_2 = 0.58\omega_3$. At this frequency the logarithmic magnitude of each factor will be down about 4 db. Therefore the logarithmic magnitude of $T(j\omega_2)$ will be down 12 db from that of T_m. The frequency ω_2

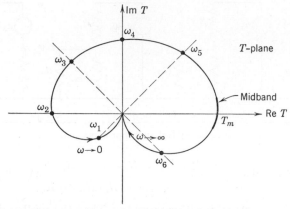

Fig. 25.   Approximate T-locus for example.

is marked in Fig. 25 at the point where the locus crosses the negative
real axis.   The other points ω_1, ω_4, ω_5, ω_6 are similarly computed.   For
example ω_6 is the break frequency of C_{gk}–R_{e3}.

Once the locus for the positive range of ω is known, the diagram can
be completed by symmetry about the real axis.   The complete locus for
the example is shown in Fig. 26.

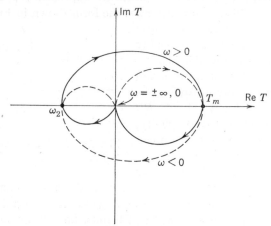

Fig. 26.   Complete T-locus.

It is evident that the stability of the system is determined by the
value of $|T(j\omega_2)|$.   If this magnitude is greater than 1, the system is
unstable.   In such a case the system can be made stable by modifying
some of the element values.   Even if the point $(-1,0)$ is not enclosed

by the T locus, the proximity of the curve to this point gives a measure of the "relative stability"; that is, it gives an indication of the closeness of a pole to the $j\omega$-axis.

This idea can be expressed in a somewhat more quantitative way by defining stability margins, the *gain margin*, and the *phase margin*. As a matter of fact, consideration of the Nyquist locus leads to many other concepts which are useful in system design. However, we shall arbitrarily terminate the discussion at this point, leaving such extensions to advanced books on feedback theory. We hope enough has been said to interest you in further study of stability.

10.4 Root Locus

Let us here continue to restrict ourselves to single-loop feedback systems. We have seen that the Nyquist locus gives us a fairly rapid method of determining system stability, and even relative stability. We stated that an unstable network could be made stable by modifying some of the network parameters. It is obvious that the poles of the system function will change as a network parameter is modified. Since the poles are the natural frequencies, which determine the transient response of the network, it would be very useful to know their variation when a network element is varied. The *root locus method* is a technique which provides this information. Since the concept of a root locus is related with many of the concepts which we have considered earlier, we will devote some time to a discussion of the method in this section.

The block diagram and signal-flow graph of a single-loop feedback system are shown in Fig. 19. The voltage transfer function (closed loop) can be written

$$\frac{V_2(s)}{V_1(s)} = \frac{G(s)}{1 + G(s)H(s)} = \frac{G(s)}{1 + T(s)} \tag{73}$$

We have already seen that the open-loop transfer function GH is the same as the return ratio $T(s)$. By expressing $G(s)$ and $H(s)$ as rational functions in s, it is easy to see that all the poles of the transfer function are the points at which

$$T(s) = -1 \tag{74}$$

The locus of the solutions of Eq. (74) as some network parameter is varied, is called the *root locus*. Although this general definition applies to the variation of any network parameter, the name *root locus* is usually applied to the case where the parameter involved is the *gain constant K*. This is the constant multiplying factor when $T(s)$ is written as a rational function as follows.

$$T(s) = K \frac{\prod_j (s - s_{0j})}{\prod_j (s - s_{pj})} \tag{75}$$

The reason for this specialization is not far to seek, since the gain constant is a very important factor in determining the amount of feedback, and the advantages resulting from it.

The root locus, as K varies from 0 to ∞, has a very simple geometric interpretation. By examining Eq. (74) we see that whenever the angle of $T(s)$ is equal to π, there will be some value of K for which the equation will be satisfied. Thus, the root locus consists of merely those lines in the s-plane along which the normalized return ratio $T_n(s) = T(s)/K$ takes on negative real values. Or, to put it in the language of conformal mapping, the root locus is a map in the s-plane of the negative real axis of the T_n-plane, under the function which is the inverse of $T_n(s)$. The points corresponding to $K = 0$ are inverse images of $T_n = \infty$ and the points corresponding to $K = \infty$ are inverse images of $T_n = 0$.

Evidently the function inverse to $T_n(s)$ will be multi-valued if $T_n(s)$ has more than one pole and one zero. In general, then, there will be more than one curve in the root locus. We refer to each of these as a *branch* of the locus.

The utility of the root locus is enhanced if it is possible to sketch the locus rapidly. This can be done once the poles and zeros of the return ratio are known. Let us now discuss some of the general features of the root locus. In terms of the normalized return ratio, the locus is the set of points satisfying

$$T_n(s) = -1/K \tag{76}$$

If we interpret the locus to start when $K = 0$ and to end when K is infinite, then we see that the branches of the locus start from the poles of $T_n(s)$ and end at the zeros. It is clear that there will be as many branches as $T_n(s)$ has poles or zeros. (Counting zeros at infinity and multiplicities, a rational function always has as many zeros as it has poles.)

Branches of the locus that fall on the negative real axis are easily found. Quadratic factors in $T_n(s)$ of the form $s^2 + as + b$ due to conjugate poles or zeros will be real and positive when s is negative real, and hence will not contribute to the angle of $T_n(s)$. All factors due to real poles or zeros will have the form $s + a$. Each such factor will contribute zero angle if s lies to the right of $-a$ on the real axis and an angle $\pm \pi$ if s lies to the left of $-a$. Thus, all parts of the negative real axis which lie to the left of an odd number of critical points (zeros and poles) will be parts of the locus.

It is a simple matter to calculate the angle with respect to the real axis at which a root locus leaves a pole or approaches a zero. Consider, for example, a pole of order n of $T_n(s)$. The dominant term in the Laurent expansion will determine the behavior of the root locus near the pole. Let s_{pj} be an nth order pole of $T_n(s)$. Then, the dominant term in the Laurent expansion will be

$$\frac{a_{-n}}{(s - s_{pj})^n}$$

If we write

$$s - s_{pj} = re^{j\theta}; \qquad a_{-n} = \rho e^{j\beta} \tag{77}$$

Then the angle of the dominant term will be

$$\arg \frac{a_{-n}}{(s - s_{pj})^n} = \beta - n\theta \tag{78}$$

If s is to lie on the locus, this angle should be equal to π. Hence,

$$\theta = \frac{\beta - \pi}{n} \tag{79}$$

This is the desired result. The angle β is easily calculated from $T_n(s)$. It is

$$\beta = \arg (s - s_{pj})^n T_n(s)\big|_{s=s_{pj}} \tag{80}$$

This step is easily performed graphically if the poles and zeros of $T_n(s)$ are located on the complex plane. The angles of the lines from each of the critical points to the pole s_{pj} are measured. Their algebraic sum (positive for zeros, negative for poles), suitably modified for multiple poles or zeros, is the desired angle.

Similarly we can compute the angle at which the locus approaches a zero. In this case the dominant term is the first nonzero term in the Taylor series expansion. For a zero of order n at s_{0j}, we find that the angle of approach θ is

$$\theta = \frac{\pi - \alpha}{n} \tag{81}$$

where

$$\alpha = \arg \frac{T_n(s)}{(s - s_{0j})^n}\bigg|_{s_{0j}} \tag{82}$$

We can also see from the dominant terms, that there are as many branches leaving a pole (or arriving at a zero) as the order of the pole (or zero). These branches intersect at the pole (or zero) with equal angles between them. We have given one of these angles; the others are obtained by adding $2\pi k/n$, $k = 1, 2, \cdots, n - 1$ to this angle.

What has been stated about the number of loci applies also if T_n has an nth order multiple zero at infinity. Let us write

$$T_n(s) = \frac{s^m + a_1 s^{m-1} + \cdots + a_m}{s^{n+m} + b_1 s^{n+m-1} + \cdots + b_{n+m}} \tag{83}$$

Then, the asymptotic behavior of $T_n(s)$ as $s \to \infty$ will be given by

$$T_n(s) \xrightarrow[s \to \infty]{} 1/s^n \tag{84}$$

In this case the angle α is zero. Hence, the angles at which the asymptotes approach infinity are given by

$$\theta = (2k + 1)\pi/n; \qquad k = 0, 1, 2, \cdots, n - 1 \tag{85}$$

This, of course, does not tell us the positions of the asymptotes; it gives only the angles. At first sight it might appear that the asymptotes all radiate from the origin. However, this is not the case. As a first step in finding the positions of the asymptotes, let us take the reciprocal of $T_n(s)$ in Eq. (83) and divide the denominator into the numerator, stopping when the remainder is a proper fraction. The result will be

$$\frac{1}{T_n(s)} = s^n + A_1 s^{n-1} + A_2 s^{n-2} + \cdots + A_n + \frac{B_1 s^{m-1} + \cdots + B_m}{s^m + a_1 s^{m-1} + \cdots + a_m} \tag{86}$$

where $A_1 = b_1 - a_1$.

The remainder term in this expression goes to zero as $s \to \infty$, so it will have no effect on the asymptotic behavior of $1/T_n(s)$. Thus, for large values of $|s|$ the locus will be given approximately by

$$\frac{1}{T_n(s)} \doteq s^n + A_1 s^{n-1} + \cdots + A_n = -K \tag{87}$$

Let us suppose that the asymptotes radiate from some point on the real axis; designate this point s_0. For any value of K, a point on an asymptote can be described by

$$(s - s_0) = K\epsilon^{j\theta} = K\epsilon^{j(2k+1)\pi/n} = (-K)^{1/n} \tag{88}$$

A point $s = s_0 + (-K)^{1/n}$ which lies on the asymptote must satisfy the equation of the locus in the limit as K (and s) approach infinity. Hence, let us substitute Eq. (88) into Eq. (87) for the locus (eventually expecting to take the limit as $K \to \infty$). After substituting the value of

s into Eq. (87), let us expand each term by the binomial theorem, and then collect terms involving the same power of K. The result will be

$$[s_0 + (-K)^{1/n}]^n + A_1[s_0 + (-K)^{1/n}]^{n-1} + \cdots + A_n = -K$$

$$-K + ns_0(-K)^{1-1/n} + \cdots + A_1(-K)^{1-1/n}$$

$$+ (n-1)s_0A_1(-K)^{1-2/n} + \cdots + A_2(-K)^{1-2/n} + \cdots + A_n = -K$$

$$(-K)^{1-1/n} \left\{ (A_1 + ns_0) + \left[n(n-1)\frac{s_0^2}{2} + (n-1)s_0A_1 + A_2 \right] K^{-1/n} \right.$$

$$\left. + \text{ higher powers of } K^{-1/n} \right\} = 0 \quad (89)$$

Now let us take the limit as $K \to \infty$. Each term in the square brackets except the first will go to zero because of the factors $K^{-1/n}$. In order for Eq. (89) to hold in the limit, then, we must require that

$$s_0 = -\frac{A_1}{n} = -\frac{b_1 - a_1}{n} \quad (90)$$

But, returning to Eq. (83) shows that b_1 is the negative sum of the poles of $T_n(s)$ and a_1 is the negative sum of its finite zeros. Hence, the *asymptotic center* of the root locus can be expressed in terms of $T_n(s)$ as

$$s_0 = \frac{\Sigma s_{pj} - \Sigma s_{0j}}{n} \quad (91)$$

where n is the order of the zero of $T_n(s)$ at infinity.

Before considering other general properties of the locus, let us illustrate the preceding discussion with a simple example. Consider the normalized return ratio

$$T_n(s) = \frac{1}{(s + \frac{1}{2})(s + 2)(s + 3)} \quad (92)$$

All of the poles are negative real and there is a triple zero at infinity. The branches of the locus that lie on the negative real axis are immediately determined to lie between $-\frac{1}{2}$ and -2, and between -3 and $-\infty$. There are three infinite asymptotes; hence the angle between them is 120°. One of the asymptotes is the negative real axis. From Eq. (91) we find that the asymptotes intersect at

$$s_0 = \frac{-\frac{1}{2} - 2 - 3}{3} = -\frac{11}{6} \quad (93)$$

This amount of information is shown in Fig. 27a. The branches of the locus which go to infinity asymptotically can now be crudely sketched in.   Knowledge of two specific points will greatly facilitate this sketch. One of these is the point at which the locus crosses the $j\omega$-axis and enters the right half plane.   This is an important point; the value of K corresponding to this point is the largest possible value for a stable network. Larger values of K lead to instability, since poles of the transfer function will then lie in the right half plane.

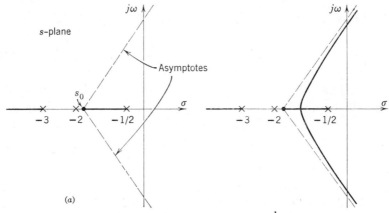

Fig. 27.   Root locus for $T_n(s) = \dfrac{1}{(s + 1/2)(s + 2)(s + 3)}$.

In the present case, this point is relatively easy to find.   The return difference corresponding to $T_n(s)$ given in Eq. (92) is

$$F(s) = 1 + T(s) = 1 + \frac{K}{(s+\frac{1}{2})(s+2)(s+3)} = \frac{s^3+\frac{11}{2}s^2+\frac{17}{2}s+3+K}{(s+\frac{1}{2})(s+2)(s+3)}$$

(94)

The problem is to find the value of K for which the numerator on the right side will just cease being a Hurwitz polynomial.   This is the value of K which will cause $F(s)$ to have a pair of zeros on the $j\omega$-axis.   If a polynomial has a pair of zeros on the $j\omega$-axis, say at $s = \pm j\omega_0$, it must have a factor $s^2 + \omega_0^2$.   This factor must be a factor both of the even part and the odd part.   Let us, then, write the even and odd parts of the numerator of $F(s)$ separately.

$$n = s(s^2 + \tfrac{17}{2}) \qquad\qquad (a)$$
$$m = \tfrac{11}{2}[s^2 + \tfrac{2}{11}(3 + K)] \qquad (b)$$

(95)

Since the quadratic factors are to be the same, this immediately gives us the values of K and ω_0.   They are

$$\omega_0 = \sqrt{\tfrac{17}{2}}$$

$$K = \tfrac{175}{4} \tag{96}$$

Alternatively, the Hurwitz test can be applied to determine the largest value of K for which the numerator polynomial of $F(s)$ will be Hurwitz.

The other important point on the root locus is the point in Fig. 27b at which branches of the locus appear to cross. Recall that the root locus is the map of the negative real axis of the T_n-plane into the s-plane under the transformation which is the inverse of $T_n(s)$; let us label this $s = f(T_n)$. Hence, to locate the crossover points, we need to locate those branch points of $f(T_n)$ which lie on the negative real axis in the T_n-plane.

This task is simplified by the use of a theorem from function theory, which states that if a function $T_n(s)$ has an nth order saddle point * at $s = s_b$, then the inverse function $f(T_n)$ will have an nth order branch point at the corresponding point $T_n(s_b)$. Thus, to find the saddle points of $T_n(s)$, we must differentiate it and find the zeros of the derivative. In order to determine which of these correspond to negative real branch points, we must evaluate $T_n(s)$ at these points.

To illustrate this procedure, let us return to Eq. (92). We first differentiate $T_n(s)$ to get

$$\frac{dT_n(s)}{ds} = \frac{3s^2 + 6s + \tfrac{5}{2}}{[(s + \tfrac{1}{2})(s + 2)(s + 3)]^2} \tag{97}$$

The finite zeros of this expression are found to lie approximately at $s = -2.56$ and $s = -1.107$. The first of these is not on the root locus and hence does not correspond to a negative real branch point. The point $s = -1.107$ is on the root locus and corresponds to a value of approximately $T_n(-1.107) = -0.975$, which is indeed negative real. Hence, $s = -1.107$ is the crossover point. Since $K = -1/T_n$ on the root locus, we have incidentally found the value of K corresponding to a particular point on the locus.

It should be noted that the branches of the root locus do not actually cross at the saddle point; they change their direction abruptly. Thus, the locus of Fig. 27b near the saddle point actually behaves in the manner illustrated in Fig. 28. (Or alternatively, the branch of the locus coming from the right may turn upward while the branch coming from the left may turn downward.)

There are other properties of the root locus which can be used to facilitate sketching of the locus, but we shall be content to stop here.

* An nth order saddle point of a function $T_n(s)$ is a value of s at which the first n derivatives of the function vanish, and the $(n + 1)$th derivative is nonzero.

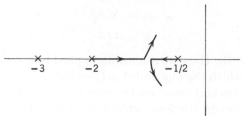

Fig. 28.　The root locus in the vicinity of a saddle point.

After a rough sketch of the locus is obtained, the accuracy of any desired portion of it can be increased by more careful plotting.

Let us now briefly consider some of the things that can be accomplished by working with the root locus. Turn again to the example illustrated in Fig. 27. The Hurwitz test tells us the maximum value of K that can be used for stability. However, the closer the poles of the closed-loop transfer function to the $j\omega$-axis, the more violent will be the transient response of the system. The pole which lies on the branch of the locus to the left of $s = -3$ contributes little to the transient response compared to the other two poles.

Qualitatively, then, it appears that to get a less violent transient response we should attempt to move the branches of the locus which correspond to complex poles toward the left. One way to do this is to move the poles of $T_n(s)$ farther from the origin. This can be done if $T_n(s)$, is multiplied by a function which has zeros at one or more poles of $T_n(s)$ and poles at the desired points. As an example, suppose we multiply $T_n(s)$ by

$$G_1(s) = \frac{s + \frac{1}{2}}{s + 4} \tag{98}$$

In terms of the system this amounts to cascading with $G(s)$ a network having $G_1(s)$ as its transfer function. (This is known as a lead network in control system language.) The new return ratio will be

$$T_{n1} = T_n(s)G_1(s) = \frac{1}{(s + 2)(s + 3)(s + 4)} \tag{99}$$

The zero of $G_1(s)$ cancels the pole of $T_n(s)$ closest to the origin. The root locus will now take the form sketched in Fig. 29. Now the branches of the locus have been moved farther away from the origin. A much larger value of K is allowable ($K = 210$) before the system becomes unstable. From another point of view, a given value of K will lead to a transfer function with much greater relative stability and less violent transient response.

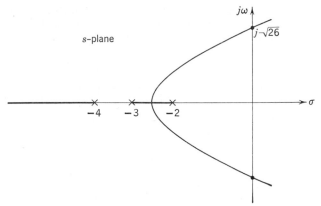

Fig. 29.   Improved root locus.

In closing this chapter, let us repeat that only the fundamental concepts of the several subjects we have treated have been introduced. Much of the detail and many interesting ramifications of stability and feedback theory which deserve consideration have been omitted. We hope that this chapter has whetted your appetite and aroused your interest sufficiently that you will seek further study of feedback theory and control systems in more advanced texts.

PROBLEMS

10.1   Prove the following block diagram identities.

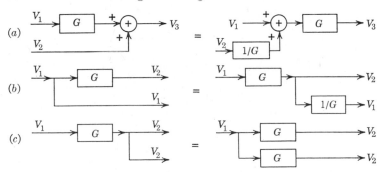

(d)   Parallel Combination:

Fig. P10.1.

10.2 Draw a block diagram for the networks of Fig. P10.2 with *one block for each element*. Reduce the block diagram using known identities to find the desired transfer functions.

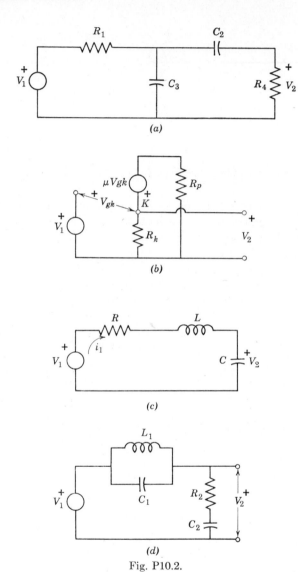

Fig. P10.2.

10.3 For the amplifier network shown in Fig. P10.3a draw a block diagram in the form shown in Fig. P10.3b.

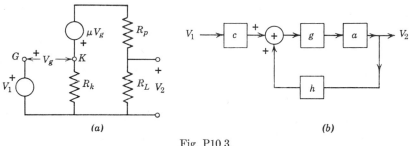

(a)   (b)

Fig. P10.3.

10.4 Draw a functional block diagram for the network of Fig. P10.4 which gives an intuitive picture of the essential operation.

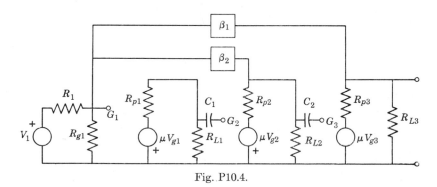

Fig. P10.4.

10.5 Solve the following system of equations for x_1 using signal-flow graphs. Also find x_1 by Cramer's rule (both as a check and to illustrate the amount of work involved).

$$\begin{bmatrix} 2 & 1 & -1 & 3 \\ 4 & 1 & 0 & -1 \\ 1 & 0 & 1 & 2 \\ -4 & -7 & 2 & 3 \end{bmatrix} \begin{bmatrix} x_1 \\ x_2 \\ x_3 \\ x_4 \end{bmatrix} = \begin{bmatrix} 2 \\ 1 \\ 0 \\ 0 \end{bmatrix}$$

10.6 Complete the network example started in Fig. 13 and find V_4/V_g, (i) by reducing the flow graph alone, (ii) by operating on the connection matrix alone and (iii) by using node equations. Compare with the solution given in Eq. (47).

10.7 Set up a signal-flow graph for the network of Fig. P10.7, to find the transfer function $Y_{21}(s) = I_2/V_1$. Find this function by reducing the example. Also, apply Mason's formula (38) to the original graph, and compare the answers obtained.

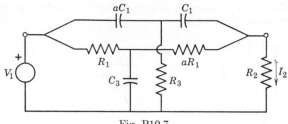

Fig. P10.7.

10.8 Solve Problem 10.2 by signal-flow graphs.

10.9 Find the voltage ratio V_2/V_1 for the general ladder network of Fig. P10.9 by first setting up the signal-flow graph. From the signal-flow graph show that the transmission zeros occur at series branch poles or shunt branch zeros.

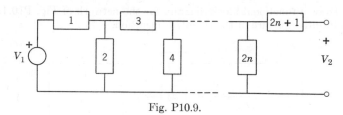

Fig. P10.9.

10.10 Find the gain V_2/V_1 for the "pseudo-tuned" amplifier of Fig. P10.10, using signal-flow graphs. Find the poles and zeros of V_2/V_1 and plot them in the complex plane. Sketch the frequency response (magnitude only) curve. (Normalize the frequency and impedance to make the numbers more manageable.)

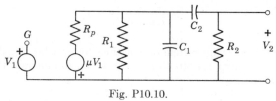

Fig. P10.10.

$\mu = 10$, $R_p = 10,000$ ohms, $R_1 = 250,000$ ohms, $R_2 = 2$ megohms, $C_1 = 0.0015$ μf, $C_2 = 0.01$ μf.

10.11 State the rules in signal-flow graph terminology which are analogous to the rules given for block diagrams in the text and in Problem 10.1.

10.12 Check whether the following polynomials represent stable systems by the Hurwitz test.

(a) $4s^3 + 7s^2 + 7s + 2$ (b) $2s^3 + s^2 - 5s + 2$
(c) $s^3 + 3s^2 + 4s + 2$ (d) $s^4 + 3s^3 + 2s^2 + s + 1$
(e) $3s^3 + 5s^2 + 4s + 6$ (f) $2s^4 + 4s^3 + 7s^2 + 7s + 3$
(g) $s^6 + 7s^5 + 7s^4 + 5s^3 + 4s^2 + s + 1$
(h) $2s^5 + 4s^4 + 3s^3 + 3s^2 + 4s + 2$

10.13 In the network of Fig. 20 in the text let the values of the components be such that the break-frequencies of the three interstage networks are

$$\omega_a = 100, \qquad \omega_b = 1000, \qquad \omega_c = 100,000$$

Sketch the Nyquist locus carefully for this case. Find the maximum value that T_m can be, if the network is to be stable.

10.14 Sketch the Nyquist locus for the network of Fig. P10.14. Find values of $R_f L_f$ for which the network is stable. What is the maximum value of α under this condition, if the network is to remain stable for small variations of parameter values (R_e, G_e, R_f, L_f in particular) from the design value?

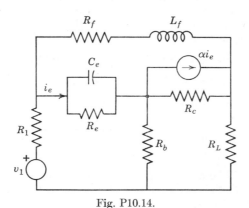

Fig. P10.14.

10.15 Sketch the Nyquist locus for the network of Fig. P10.15 and give the condition for stability.

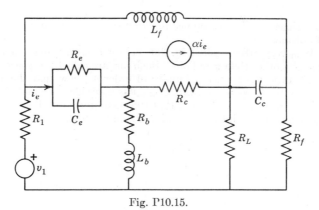

Fig. P10.15.

10.16 Draw a block diagram and signal-flow graph for the network given in Fig. P5.14. By reducing these diagrams, calculate the transfer voltage ratio.

10.17 Sketch the root locus for each of the following return ratio functions.

(a) $T_n(s) = \dfrac{1}{s(s+1)(s+2)}$ 	(b) $T_n(s) = \dfrac{s+1}{s^2+3s+3}$

(c) $T_n(s) = \dfrac{s+3}{s(s+2)(s^2+2s+2)}$ 	(d) $T_n(s) = \dfrac{(s+1)(s+3)}{s^2+4s+4}$

(e) $T_n(s) = \dfrac{(s+1)(s+3)}{s(s^2+4s+4)}$ 	(f) $T_n(s) = \dfrac{1}{s(s+2)(s^2+2s+10)}$

10.18 It is desired to prove the Hurwitz theorem stated on page 426. In the first place, to prove that if $P(s) = m(s) + n(s)$ is Hurwitz, then m/n is a reactance function, note that the factors of a Hurwitz polynomial are of the form $(s^2 + as + b)$ or $(s + c)$, where a, b, and c are real and positive. Write

$$P(s) = (s^2 + as + b)P_1(s) = (s^2 + as + b)(m_1 + n_1)$$

$$= [(s^2 + b)m_1 + asn_1] + [(s^2 + b)n_1 + asm_1]$$

Then, the ratio of the even and odd parts is

$$\frac{m}{n} = \frac{(s^2+b)m_1 + asn_1}{(s^2+b)n_1 + asm_1} = \frac{1}{\dfrac{n_1}{m_1} + \dfrac{as}{s^2+b}} + \frac{1}{\dfrac{s^2+b}{as} + \dfrac{m_1}{n_1}}$$

Show that m/n will be a reactance function provided m_1/n_1 is also. Repeat this procedure, with $P_1 = m_1 + n_1$ until all the factors of $P(s)$, both quadratic and linear, are exhausted.

In the second place, if $P(s) = m(s) + n(s)$ and m/n is a reactance function then $P(s)$ is a Hurwitz polynomial (except for a possible even factor). The zeros of $P(s)$ occur when

$$P(s) = m + n = n\left(\frac{m}{n} + 1\right) = 0$$

Prove that, since m/n is a reactance function, $m/n = -1$ cannot occur in the right half s-plane.

10.19 It is very often desired to plot loci for constant angle of the return ratio, for angles other than π radians. Such loci are called the *phase-angle loci*. If the return ratio has a zero at infinity of order n, show that the asymptote approached by the locus for constant angle θ is a straight line making an angle $-\theta/n$ with the real axis. Show also that the asymptotes for all angles intersect on the real axis at the point given by Eq. (91) in the text.

11 · IMAGE PARAMETERS AND FILTER THEORY

When discussing methods of describing the external behavior of two-ports in Chapter 8, we postponed the discussion of image parameters. One reason for doing this was our desire to follow the presentation of the formalism of image parameters with a treatment of the subject in which image parameters have had their greatest use, filter theory. In this respect we will again depart slightly from the main stream of thought in this book in that filter *theory* cannot be completely divorced from filter *design*. However, we will attempt to emphasize the basic analysis involved and will keep design or synthesis considerations to a minimum.

There are several possible sources of confusion in discussions of image parameter theory. For one thing, there is a whole new vocabulary associated with image parameter theory that has to be learned. Also there is so much algebraic manipulation involved that the overall philosophy of the discussion may become blurred. These difficulties become compounded when we try to compress the theory into the space of one chapter. In this chapter we shall try to minimize the confusion by confining our attention to the basic essentials of the theory and keeping the special vocabulary to a minimum. There is not much that can be done with the algebraic manipulation. (Wherever these are straightforward we shall leave them out.) Along these lines, let us first give a bird's eye view of the discussion, in the hope of establishing the philosophy of the whole chapter.

We first define the image parameters and relate them to the more familiar two-port parameters introduced in Chapter 8, namely $ABCD$, z, and y parameters.

In section 11.2 we restrict ourselves to the most important class of networks in filter theory, namely lossless two-ports. In this case we find that the image parameters exhibit very special properties, being purely real or imaginary on the $j\omega$-axis. We find further, that two of the parameters suffice to describe the two-port, the third being derivable from these.   This important result, due to Bode, is proved here.   From this result we conclude that one image impedance and the transmission zeros virtually decide the network.

We then define the concept of a filter and discuss the locations of the poles and zeros of the image parameters of a lossless low-pass filter. We find that the poles and zeros of z_{11} and y_{11} are related in a very special fashion.

Next we turn to the question of filter realization.   That is, given one image impedance and the zeros of transmission, we seek a network that is a tandem combination of simple two-ports, with the given image impedance and zeros of transmission.   The familiar constant-K and m-derived Tee and Pi sections are introduced as elementary two-ports realizing zeros of transmission on the $j\omega$-axis.   The lattice is then introduced as a section for realizing zeros of transmission off the $j\omega$-axis. We also relate the lattice to the Tee and Pi sections, as well as to a general symmetric two-port.   The realization of the given image impedance is also taken up, by bringing in the terminating sections.

In section 11.5 of the chapter we consider, very briefly, the other important problem of filter design, namely, the problem of approximating a given ideal characteristic by a realizable one.   We state Cauer's solution for the Tchebyscheff approximation without proof, introducing the Jacobian elliptic functions for this purpose.

In the last section, the frequency transformations that convert a low-pass filter into a high-pass or band-pass filter are described.

11.1   Image Parameters

The image parameter system for the description of the behavior of two-ports grew out of the study of propagation of waves in uniform media.   Probably the most familiar example of this to us is transmission line theory.   The propagation of the wave is affected by the properties of the line.   These properties are described in terms of two quantities; the characteristic impedance and the propagation constant.

The earliest analysis of communications systems was in terms of wave propagation.   Even when lumped networks were involved, thoughts on the subject followed along the lines of propagation and reflection of waves.   However, unlike the uniform transmission line, many lumped networks are not symmetrical and, hence, require more than two parameters to describe their behavior.   Again historically, the image parameter system has been used only in the case of reciprocal networks.   Even though it is possible to extend the system to include nonreciprocal networks, we will not attempt to achieve this generality.   In this chapter, then, we are restricted to linear, lumped, reciprocal, and time-invariant networks.

In all the other systems of describing two-port behavior discussed in Chapter 8 (except for the scattering parameters which are also based on a wave propagation analysis), the parameters of the system are defined as properties of the two-port itself and the definitions do not involve the terminations. This is not the case for the image parameters. Consider the two-port with its terminations shown in Fig. 1. The terminals are

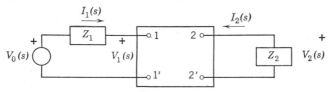

Fig. 1.   Terminated two-port.

numbered in the usual way. We define two *image impedances* as follows. The image impedance at end two, labeled Z_{02}, is that impedance which, when connected at terminals (2,2′) of the two-port, causes the input impedance at the terminals (1,1′) to be equal to an impedance Z_{01}. This impedance, called the image impedance at end 1, is that impedance which, when connected at terminals (1,1′), causes the driving-point impedance at the terminals (2,2′) to be equal to Z_{02}. The image impedances thus have a sort of mutual relationship. From these definitions it is clear that, for a symmetrical network, the two image impedances are equal. In such a case we will label their common value Z_0. Thus, Z_0 coincides with the concept of characteristic impedance.

It is a simple matter to determine expressions for the image impedances in terms of other two-port parameters. Perhaps the simplest procedure is to start with the chain parameter equations which, for the usual references shown in Fig. 1, are

$$V_1 = AV_2 - BI_2 \qquad (a)$$
$$I_1 = CV_2 - DI_2 \qquad (b) \tag{1}$$

If we consider the terminating impedance Z_2 in Fig. 1 to be the image impedance Z_{02}, then $V_2 = -Z_{02}I_2$. We now take the ratio of the two equations and note that, by definition, $V_1/I_1 = Z_{01}$ for this termination. Hence, it follows that

$$Z_{01} = \frac{AZ_{02} + B}{CZ_{02} + D} \tag{2}$$

In a similar way, suppose the impedance Z_1 in Fig. 1 is equal to Z_{01}. Then $V_1 = -Z_{01}I_1$ (assuming the source is removed). We now consider the inverse of equations (1) and compute the ratio V_2/I_2. [This can be done directly with Eq. (1) if desired.] By definition this ratio is

Z_{02}. The result of this step will be

$$Z_{02} = \frac{DZ_{01} + B}{CZ_{01} + A} \tag{3}$$

It now remains to solve the last two equations simultaneously. This step, as well as many of the other expressions we will establish in this section, will involve some algebraic manipulations whose details we will leave for you to work out. In the present case the result will be

$$Z_{01} = \sqrt{\frac{AB}{CD}} \qquad (a)$$
$$\tag{4}$$
$$Z_{02} = \sqrt{\frac{BD}{AC}} \qquad (b)$$

These equations express the image impedances in terms of the chain parameters. For our later use let us express the image impedances in terms of the open-circuit and short-circuit parameters. (See Chapter 8 for these relationships.) We easily find these expressions to be

$$Z_{01} = \sqrt{\frac{z_{11}}{y_{11}}} \qquad (a)$$
$$\tag{5}$$
$$Z_{02} = \sqrt{\frac{z_{22}}{y_{22}}} \qquad (b)$$

Note that in the case of symmetrical networks $z_{11} = z_{22}$ and $y_{11} = y_{22}$ so that the two image impedances become identical.

In these expressions for the image impedances we find something very disconcerting, since they are irrational functions. We know that the driving-point impedances of lumped networks must be rational functions. Hence, we conclude that *image impedances are not driving-point functions of lumped networks*. That is, there is no lumped network which we can use as the terminating impedance Z_2 in Fig. 1 such that the driving-point impedance at the input end is equal to the image impedance Z_{01}. This fact, however, does not detract from the usefulness of the image parameters for the description of two-port behavior.

Even though the image impedances are irrational, we still require that they be positive real if the two-port is assumed passive. This is easily done by choosing the proper Riemann surface for the square root. We choose the branch of each square root in Eq. (5) to be the "positive" one; that is, the branch of the function on which the square root of a real positive number is real positive.* [We met a similar situation in Eq. (123) of Chapter 7.]

The image impedances alone do not constitute a complete set of parameters for describing two-port behavior. Each of the image impedances refers to a single pair of terminals. We need another parameter which will involve transmission through the network. Suppose the network is terminated at end two in its image impedance. Let us calculate the voltage and current transfer ratios starting with the chain parameter equations. The result will be

$$\frac{V_2}{V_1} = \sqrt{\frac{D}{A}}\,(\sqrt{AD} - \sqrt{BC}\,) \qquad (a)$$

$$\tag{6}$$

$$\frac{I_2}{I_1} = \sqrt{\frac{A}{D}}\,(\sqrt{AD} - \sqrt{BC}\,) \qquad (b)$$

We see that these two functions differ from each other but they have certain common features. Note that in the case of symmetrical networks, $A = D$ and the two functions become identical. Suppose we multiply these two functions together. We then get

$$\frac{V_2 I_2}{V_1 I_1} = (\sqrt{AD} - \sqrt{BC}\,)^2 = \epsilon^{-2\theta} = \epsilon^{-2(\alpha + j\beta)} \qquad (7)$$

Note that this equation defines β only to within a $k\pi$ ambiguity.† This result is the same whether the network is symmetrical or not.

On the right-hand side we have expressed the function in an exponential form. The quantity $\theta = \alpha + j\beta$ is called the *image transfer* or *propagation function*. Its real part α is called the *image attenuation* or *loss function*. Note the inconsistencies with the former notation in the book. Previously we used the symbol α for the gain function, whereas here it is the negative of gain. The only reason for this is to comply with the usage in image parameter theory. For passive networks it is perhaps more natural to think of loss rather than gain as being a positive quantity.

---

* Actually each pole and each zero of z_{11} and y_{11} (or z_{22} and y_{22} for Z_{02}) is a branch point of Z_{01}, except for coincident poles and zeros. Therefore there will be many sheets in the Riemann surface. For each square root that appears, we take the positive sheet. In the low-pass filter case to be considered later there will be only two sheets.

† This ambiguity, which physically corresponds to an ambiguity in the output (or input) terminals, runs through image parameter theory. It is perhaps due to a lack of emphasis on the phase function in classical filter theory.

Return now to the voltage and current ratios in Eqs. (6). These can be written in terms of the propagation function. From Eqs. (4) and (5) we see that

$$\sqrt{\frac{D}{A}} = \sqrt{\frac{Z_{02}}{Z_{01}}} = \sqrt{\frac{z_{22}}{z_{11}}} \tag{8}$$

Hence, the voltage and current transfer ratios can be written

$$\frac{V_2}{V_1} = \sqrt{\frac{Z_{02}}{Z_{01}}}\, \epsilon^{-\theta} \tag{a}$$

$$\frac{I_2}{I_1} = \sqrt{\frac{Z_{01}}{Z_{02}}}\, \epsilon^{-\theta} \tag{b}$$

(9)

The propagation function is related to the chain parameters according to Eq. (7). For future reference we will express it in terms of the z and y parameters. Let us first use Eq. (7) in the definition of hyperbolic functions. We get

$$\epsilon^{-\theta} = \sqrt{AD} - \sqrt{BC} \tag{a}$$

$$\cosh \theta = \frac{\epsilon^{\theta} + \epsilon^{-\theta}}{2} = \sqrt{AD} \tag{b}$$

$$\sinh \theta = \frac{\epsilon^{\theta} - \epsilon^{-\theta}}{2} = \sqrt{BC} \tag{c}$$

$$\tanh \theta = \frac{\sinh \theta}{\cosh \theta} = \sqrt{\frac{BC}{AD}} \tag{d}$$

(10)

If we now substitute into the last equation the relationships between the chain parameters and the z and y parameters, we will get the following expression.

$$\tanh \theta = \frac{1}{\sqrt{z_{11}y_{11}}} = \frac{1}{\sqrt{z_{22}y_{22}}} \tag{11}$$

This equation and Eqs. (5), together, relate the image parameters to a mixed set of z and y parameters. They will prove very useful in the discussion of filters.

Note that the voltage and current ratios are related to the image parameters in the simple manner expressed by Eqs. (9) only when the two-port is properly terminated (i.e., terminated in its image impedance). According to the wave propagation picture, when the terminations Z_1 and Z_2 in Fig. 1 are different from the respective image impedances, reflections will occur. The *image reflection coefficients* at the ends of the two-port are defined as

$$\rho_1 = \frac{Z_1 - Z_{01}}{Z_1 + Z_{01}} \qquad (a)$$

$$\rho_2 = \frac{Z_2 - Z_{02}}{Z_2 + Z_{02}} \qquad (b)$$

$$(12)$$

These quantities give a measure of how widely the terminations differ from the image impedances. We called these the *image* reflection coefficients because the *actual* reflection coefficients will depend on the values of the terminating impedances relative to the actual driving-point impedances obtained with the actual terminations. We will leave to you as a problem the job of calculating these reflection coefficients in terms of the image reflection coefficients.

If the terminations Z_1 and Z_2 are different from the image impedances, the question arises as to how widely the voltage ratio will differ from its value given in terms of the image parameters in Eq. (9). To answer this question, turn to Eq. (1) and note that $I_2 = -V_2/Z_2$. Hence, this equation can be written

$$\frac{V_2}{V_1} = \frac{1}{A + B/Z_2} \qquad (13)$$

It remains to express the chain parameters in terms of the image parameters and to substitute into this equation. This is easily done by combining Eqs. (4) and (10). The result is

$$A = \sqrt{\frac{Z_{01}}{Z_{02}}} \cosh \theta; \qquad B = \sqrt{Z_{01} Z_{02}} \sinh \theta$$

$$(14)$$

$$C = \frac{1}{\sqrt{Z_{01} Z_{02}}} \sinh \theta; \qquad D = \sqrt{\frac{Z_{02}}{Z_{01}}} \cosh \theta$$

The final step is to substitute A and B from here into the previous equation. The result is

$$\frac{V_2}{V_1} = \sqrt{\frac{Z_{02}}{Z_{01}}} \frac{1}{\cosh \theta + (Z_{02}/Z_2) \sinh \theta}$$

$$= \sqrt{\frac{Z_{02}}{Z_{01}}} \, \epsilon^{-\theta} \, \frac{2 Z_2}{Z_2 + Z_{02}} \frac{1}{1 + \rho_2 \epsilon^{-2\theta}} \qquad (15)$$

The last form is obtained after considerable algebraic manipulation by using the definition of the reflection coefficient in Eq. (12).

On comparing this expression with Eq. (9) we see that the voltage ratio has been modified by two additional factors each of which reduces to unity when the terminating impedance matches the corresponding image impedance. The contribution of these two factors to the voltage ratio will depend on the amount of mismatch.

This expression does not indicate the effect on the transmission due to mismatch at the input terminals. This should be clear from Fig. 1; the impedance Z_1 has no effect on the voltage ratio V_2/V_1. However, it does affect the ratio of output voltage to source voltage, V_2/V_0. This ratio can be computed by noting that

$$V_0 = V_1 + I_1 Z_1 \qquad (16)$$

We now substitute for V_1 and I_1 from Eqs. (1) and again use $I_2 = -V_2/Z_2$. Finally, we replace the chain parameters by the image parameters from Eqs. (14). After considerable manipulation, the result can be expressed as

$$\frac{V_2}{V_0} = \frac{1}{2} \sqrt{\frac{Z_{02}}{Z_{01}}} \, \epsilon^{-\theta} \left[\frac{\left(\dfrac{2Z_{01}}{Z_1 + Z_{01}}\right)\left(\dfrac{2Z_2}{Z_2 + Z_{02}}\right)}{1 - \rho_1 \rho_2 \epsilon^{-2\theta}} \right] \qquad (17)$$

(The factor $\frac{1}{2}$ would be there even under matched conditions since then V_1 would be $V_0/2$.) In the present case the voltage ratio has been modified by the factors in the brackets. The two factors in the numerator are called the *sending end* and *receiving end reflection factors*. Each of them reduces to unity whenever the pertinent impedance is equal to its corresponding image impedance. The factor in the denominator is referred to as the *interaction factor*, since it involves both sending end and receiving end quantities. This factor reduces to unity whenever either of the terminal impedances matches its image impedance.

Note that the interaction factor and the reflection factors are somewhat compensatory. But the magnitude of the interaction factor is usually closer to unity than that of the reflection factors.

Very often it is desired to express this voltage ratio relative to the value it would have if the two-port were completely removed and Z_1 connected directly to Z_2. This step simply introduces a factor $(Z_1 + Z_2)/Z_2$ on the right-hand side of Eq. (17). The resulting voltage ratio is called the *insertion ratio*. There is nothing fundamentally significant in this step. We will be content to stop with Eq. (17).

11.2   Image Parameters of Lossless Networks

Let us now restrict ourselves to networks in which resistance is absent. The special properties attained by the image parameters in this case are interesting and important in filter theory.

In the first place, *for lossless networks, the image impedances and tanh θ are either real or imaginary for all values of $s = j\omega$.* This is easily seen by looking at Eqs. (5) and (11). For lossless networks z_{11}, z_{22}, y_{11}, and y_{22} are all reactance functions; that is, they are imaginary for imaginary values of s. A product or ratio of such functions will therefore be real, either positive or negative, and the square root of a real number is either real or imaginary.

But that is not all. *When one image impedance is real, the other one is also, and tanh θ is then imaginary.* Similarly, *when one image impedance is imaginary, the other one is also, and tanh θ is then real.* (We are still talking about the $j\omega$-axis.) This is also established by considering the same equations. Suppose $Z_{01}(j\omega)$ is real. Looking at Eq. (5, a) this means that $z_{11}(j\omega)$ and $y_{11}(j\omega)$ are of the same sign. (By this we mean that both of these are positive imaginary or both are negative imaginary.) This, in turn, shows that tanh θ is imaginary, from the first part of Eq. (11). The second part of this equation then requires that $z_{22}(j\omega)$ and $y_{22}(j\omega)$ also be of the same sign, which, in turn, causes $Z_{02}(j\omega)$ to be real, from Eq. (5, b). The same reasoning proves the second part of the statement.

As a second result we will show that *one image impedance and the propagation function are enough to determine the behavior of a lossless two-port,* except for the possibility of an ideal transformer in cascade at the opposite end.* This result was first proved by Bode. For reciprocal two-ports three parameters are generally required to describe the external behavior. This theorem states that in case the two-port is lossless, two parameters suffice.

Let us assume that Z_{01} and tanh θ are known. From Eqs. (5) and (11) we can write

$$z_{11} = \frac{Z_{01}}{\tanh \theta} \qquad (a)$$

$$(18)$$

$$\frac{1}{y_{11}} = Z_{01} \tanh \theta \qquad (b)$$

Thus, knowledge of Z_{01} and tanh θ implies knowledge of z_{11} and y_{11}. We can here remark parenthetically that the statement of the theorem can be changed to read: *the open-circuit driving-point impedance and short-circuit driving-point admittance at one end of a lossless two-port completely determine the external behavior of the two-port,* except for the possibility of an ideal transformer at the opposite end. When stated in this way, the theorem takes on an added dimension. It states that the

---

* In this argument we allow the ideal transformer to have a positive or negative turns ratio, thus absorbing the ambiguity in phase.

transmission properties of a lossless two-port are known as soon as short-circuit and open-circuit driving-point functions *at one end* of the two-port are known.

Let us now return to the task of proving the theorem. To do this it will be enough to show that a knowledge of one image impedance and $\tanh \theta$ determines the other image impedance as well, to within a multiplicative constant. Alternatively, we should show that any set of two-port parameters is completely determined from a knowledge of Z_{01} and $\tanh \theta$. We shall use the z parameters as a criterion. Note that z_{11} is already determined according to Eq. (18). It remains to determine z_{12} and z_{22}.

As a first step, using Eq. (11) again, we can express $1 - \tanh^2 \theta$ in terms of z_{11} and y_{11}. Then we can replace y_{11} by its equivalent in terms of the z parameters. The result can be written

$$\frac{z_{12}{}^2}{z_{11}z_{22}} = 1 - \frac{1}{z_{11}y_{11}} \qquad (a)$$

$$\frac{z_{12}{}^2}{z_{11}z_{22}} = 1 - \tanh^2 \theta \qquad (b)$$

$$(19)$$

The right-hand side of the last expression is presumed given. Also known are z_{11} and y_{11} from Eqs. (18).

Let us now recall some facts about the z parameters of lossless two-ports. The poles and zeros of z_{11} and z_{22} are on the $j\omega$-axis, as well as the poles of z_{12}. The zeros of z_{12} need not lie on the $j\omega$-axis. The poles of z_{12} are shared by z_{11} and z_{22}, but each of these latter may have *private* poles, or both of them may share a pole not shared by z_{12}. (These may be called *semi-private* poles.)

With these facts tucked away, note that the zeros of z_{12} will, by-and-large, be the zeros on the right side of Eq. (19, *b*), except for special conditions that must be investigated. The zeros of $1 - \tanh^2 \theta$ may be of either odd or even multiplicity. Let us assume that they are either simple or double; if the multiplicity is higher, the changes in the arguments to follow will be evident.

Consider first the double zeros of $1 - \tanh^2 \theta$. A double zero can occur in one of two ways: either it is a zero of z_{12} or it is a semi-private pole of z_{11} and z_{22}. Remember that z_{11} is known from Eq. (18). Hence, it is immediately determined whether any of the double zeros of $1 - \tanh^2 \theta$ are poles of z_{11}. Those which are not, are simple zeros of z_{12}.

Next we come to the simple zeros of $1 - \tanh^2 \theta$. This case is somewhat more complicated. Considering the left side of Eq. (19) we see that a simple zero can occur if z_{12} has a common zero with z_{11} or with

z_{22} (not with both). It can also occur if z_{11} or z_{22} have private poles. We must establish for each simple zero of $1 - \tanh^2 \theta$ which one of these alternatives apply. To do this, consider Eq. (19, a). Suppose $s = j\omega_0$ is a simple zero of $1 - \tanh^2 \theta$ and it is a common zero of z_{12} and z_{22}. At this point we must then require that $z_{11}(j\omega_0) = 1/y_{11}(j\omega_0)$. Since we know both z_{11} and y_{11} from Eqs. (18), it is a simple matter to calculate their values at the simple zeros of $1 - \tanh^2 \theta$ and to determine whether or not this condition is satisfied.

Next suppose $s = j\omega$, is a simple zero of $1 - \tanh^2 \theta$ and it is a common zero of z_{12} and z_{11}, but not of z_{22}. Then, in order for the right side of Eq. (19, a) to be zero at $s = j\omega$, we must require that y_{11} have a pole there. Again, since we know y_{11}, it is a simple matter to determine if any of its poles coincide with simple zeros of $1 - \tanh^2 \theta$.

Finally, if a simple zero of $1 - \tanh^2 \theta$ is not a pole of y_{11} and if at this point z_{11} is not equal to $1/y_{11}$, then this point must be a private pole of either z_{11} or z_{22}. Again, since we know the poles of z_{11}, we can determine which it is. We have now completely determined all the poles of the z parameters, and the zeros of z_{12}. We have also determined the zeros that z_{22} has in common with z_{12}. The remaining zeros of z_{22} consist of all those poles of $1 - \tanh^2 \theta$ which are not zeros of z_{11}.

A quick glance at Eq. (19) again will show that the right-hand side will remain unaffected if z_{12} is multiplied by a constant n and z_{22} is multiplied by the square of that constant. This corresponds to an ideal $1:n$ transformer at the output terminals as shown in Fig. 2.

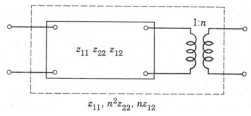

Fig. 2.   Modification of z parameters by ideal transformer.

We have seen that the zeros of the function $1 - \tanh^2 \theta$ are either zeros of z_{12} or private poles of z_{11} or z_{22} (or both). In any of these cases there will be no output voltage across the load impedance Z_2 in Fig. 1 at these points for any finite value of source voltage. We refer to these points as the *transmission zeros* of the network.

Another consideration is evident from the preceding discussion. Since simple zeros of $1 - \tanh^2 \theta$ are zeros or poles of a reactance function, they must lie on the $j\omega$-axis. On the other hand, double zeros of $1 -$

$\tanh^2 \theta$ may lie on the $j\omega$-axis, but they may also lie anywhere else in the complex plane since there is no restriction on the permissible locations of zeros of z_{12} of a lossless network. However, the zeros must occur in quadrantal symmetry. That is complex zeros must come in quadruplets symmetrically located with respect to both axes and real zeros must come in pairs, a negative real zero being paired off with its positive real image. We also note that all zeros of $1 - \tanh^2 \theta$ which are not on the $j\omega$-axis must be of even multiplicity, since these are necessarily zeros of z_{12}.

11.3   Image Parameter Filter Theory

The greatest application that the image parameters have found has been in filter theory. The viewpoint in the early considerations was again one of wave propagation, and filters were called *wave* filters. Qualitatively a filter can be defined as a frequency selective network. However, this is an inadequate definition since any network containing at least one reactive element, being frequency selective in some way or other, will qualify as a filter by this definition. What we should do is to define a filter as a two-port whose network function magnitude behaves in a specified way along the $j\omega$-axis. We know that the magnitude should be large and constant over one or more bands of frequency and small (preferably zero) over the rest of the $j\omega$-axis.

Which network function should we use in prescribing filter behavior? The theory that is obtained when the definition of a filter is based on the image parameters is aptly called *image parameter filter theory*. This is the theory we will develop in this chapter.

Let us, therefore, make the following definition. *A filter is a two-port whose image attenuation function is zero over one or more intervals on the $j\omega$-axis, called the pass bands, and nonzero at all other intervals on the axis, called the stop bands.* Over the range in which $\alpha = 0$, the function $\tanh \theta$ is imaginary. A glance at Eq. (11) will show that if z_{11} and y_{11} are arbitrary positive real functions, it is not possible for $\tanh \theta$ to behave in this way over a finite band of frequencies. Such a behavior is possible only for lossless networks; hence, we will restrict ourselves to such networks.

We will also restrict ourselves on the number of j-axis intervals over which $\alpha = 0$. Although the theory can be generalized to include multiple-pass-band filters, we will here treat only those that have a single pass band on the positive $j\omega$-axis. These will include *low-pass* filters, which have $\omega = 0$ in the pass band; *high-pass* filters, which have $\omega = \infty$ in the pass band; and *band-pass* filters, for which both the origin and infinity are in the stop band.

In the last section we found that, in the case of lossless networks, tanh θ, and the image impedances are either real or imaginary. By the definition of a filter we now see that these functions behave in the following way.

TABLE 1

	Z_{01} and Z_{02}	tanh θ	z_{11} and y_{11}
Pass band	Real	Imaginary	Same sign
Stop band	Imaginary	Real	Opposite sign

(We have included the behavior of z_{11} and y_{11} for future reference.) The behavior of the image impedances and of tanh θ abruptly changes from real to imaginary (or vice-versa) at the boundaries between the pass band and stop band. These points are called the *cut-off frequencies*.

In the stop band, tanh θ is to be real. This is possible only if $\theta = \alpha + jk\pi$, for integral values of k. That is, the image phase must be integral multiples of π in the stop band. Hence, in the stop band

$$\tanh \theta = \tanh (\alpha + jk\pi) = \tanh \alpha \qquad (20)$$

Since we would like the image attenuation to be positive in the stop band, the last equation implies that not only is tanh θ real, it is also positive there.

For an *ideal* filter, in addition to zero image attenuation in the pass band, we would like infinite attenuation in the stop band. When α is infinite, tanh α is unity. This means that for an ideal filter tanh $\alpha =$ tanh θ is identically equal to unity in the stop band

In the most usual case in which a filter is used, the impedances Z_1 and Z_2 in Fig. 1 are simply resistances R_1 and R_2, as in Fig. 3. Thus, it is required that the image impedances be equal to R_1 and R_2, respectively.

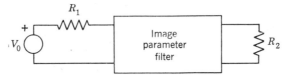

Fig. 3.   Filter and its termination.

Since the image impedances are not even real in the stop band, it is impossible to meet this requirement in that frequency range. But if the filter is ideal, there is no need to worry about mismatches in the stop band, since the image attenuation is infinite there anyway. Ideally, then, it is enough to require that the image impedances be real and constant over the pass band. Let us normalize all impedances by considering R_1 to be unity. Then for an ideal filter the image impedance Z_{01} is to be identically unity in the pass band.

Let us now consider the detailed functional forms which the image impedances and tanh θ will take. Since the network is lossless both z_{11} and y_{11} will be reactance functions. Hence, according to Eq. (77) of Chapter 9, we can write

$$z_{11}(s) = \frac{K_1(1 + s^2/\omega_{a1}{}^2)(1 + s^2/\omega_{a3}{}^2) \cdots}{s(1 + s^2/\omega_{a2}{}^2)(1 + s^2/\omega_{a4}{}^2) \cdots} \tag{21}$$

$$y_{11}(s) = \frac{K_2(1 + s^2/\omega_{b1}{}^2)(1 + s^2/\omega_{b3}{}^2) \cdots}{s(1 + s^2/\omega_{b2}{}^2)(1 + s^2/\omega_{b4}{}^2) \cdots} \tag{22}$$

Note that the zeros and poles of z_{11} have been given the subscript a whereas those of y_{11} have been given the subscript b. In both cases odd subscripts imply zeros and even ones poles. Here, both z_{11} and y_{11} have a pole at the origin, although either one may have a zero there. As we shall see, the present case corresponds to a low-pass filter. Let us now substitute these expressions into Eqs. (5) and (11). Since the second image impedance is determined once we know one of them and tanh θ, let us consider only Z_{01} in the following discussion. Thus,

$$Z_{01}{}^2 = \frac{z_{11}}{y_{11}} = \frac{K_1}{K_2} \frac{(1 + s^2/\omega_{a1}{}^2) \cdots (1 + s^2/\omega_{b2}{}^2) \cdots}{(1 + s^2/\omega_{a2}{}^2) \cdots (1 + s^2/\omega_{b1}{}^2) \cdots} \tag{23}$$

$$\tanh^2 \theta = \frac{1}{z_{11}y_{11}} = \frac{1}{K_1 K_2} \frac{s^2(1 + s^2/\omega_{a2}{}^2) \cdots (1 + s^2/\omega_{b2}{}^2) \cdots}{(1 + s^2/\omega_{a1}{}^2) \cdots (1 + s^2/\omega_{b1}{}^2) \cdots} \tag{24}$$

Suppose we consider imaginary values of s and let $s = j\omega$ increase from zero to infinity. Consider any one of the factors $1 + s^2/\omega_i{}^2$ (with subscript a or b). When $s = j\omega_i$ this factor will go through zero. Hence, $\tanh^2 \theta$ will change sign as many times as there are factors in the numerator and denominator. But according to Table 1, a pass band will exist whenever $\tanh^2 \theta$ is negative and a stop band will exist when it is positive. Hence, there will be many pass bands and stop bands. If we wish to restrict ourselves to single-pass-band filters, we must require that the poles and zeros of z_{11} and y_{11} be appropriately located.

Suppose that y_{11} has a pole at a zero of z_{11} or a zero at a pole of z_{11}. This factor will then cancel in their product, and will not appear at all in $\tanh^2 \theta$. However, it will appear as a double zero or a double pole of $Z_{01}{}^2$. In neither case will there be a change of sign as ω varies through that particular point. Similarly, if y_{11} has a common pole or a common zero with z_{11}, then $\tanh^2 \theta$ will have a double pole or a double zero there, and the factor will not appear in $Z_{01}{}^2$. Again there will be no sign change. However, we require that there be a change of sign of both $Z_{01}{}^2$ and $\tanh^2 \theta$ at the cut-off frequencies. Hence, we require these "coincidences" of zeros and/or poles of z_{11} and y_{11}, except at one pole or zero for low-pass and high-pass filters, and two poles or zeros for band-pass filters.

For the sake of simplicity let us restrict ourselves to a consideration of low-pass filters only. As we shall see later, this is no real restriction since, by means of a suitable transformation, we can reduce the treatment of band-pass and high-pass filters to the low-pass case. For a low-pass filter the origin must be in the pass band and, hence, $\tanh^2 \theta$ must be negative in the vicinity of $\omega = 0$. In Eq. (24) each of the factors $(1 + s^2/\omega_i{}^2)$ will be positive when $s = j\omega$ increases from zero. The factor $s^2 = -\omega^2$ must therefore be present in order to make $\tanh^2 \theta$ negative near $\omega = 0$. Remember that $s = 0$ is a pole of both z_{11} and y_{11}. Hence, because of the alternation property of poles and zeros of reactance functions, the next critical point of both z_{11} and of y_{11} must be a zero ($s = j\omega_{a1}$ and $s = j\omega_{b1}$, respectively, in the notation used here). If the pass band is to extend beyond these frequencies, these frequencies must coincide.

By the same reasoning, all the poles of z_{11} which are to lie in the pass band must coincide with poles of y_{11} and all zeros of z_{11} which are to lie in the pass band must coincide with zeros of y_{11}. Finally, one of these critical points will not find itself a mate and so will become a cut-off frequency. Notice that all of these factors which appear as double zeros or double poles of $\tanh^2 \theta$ do not appear at all in $Z_{01}{}^2$ due to cancellation. The cut-off factor, however, will appear in both $Z_{01}{}^2$ and $\tanh^2 \theta$ as a simple factor. It may be either a pole or a zero in each of these functions.

The cut-off factor will cause $\tanh^2 \theta$ and $Z_{01}{}^2$ to change sign. Beyond the cut-off frequency $\tanh^2 \theta$ must remain positive. This again requires coincidence of some of the factors of z_{11} and y_{11}. However, since the cut-off factor has broken the rhythm, the coincidence of poles and zeros will be out of step. In the stop band, then, the poles of z_{11} must coincide with the zeros of y_{11}, and vice versa. These factors will then appear as double poles or zeros of $Z_{01}{}^2$ and will not appear at all in $\tanh^2 \theta$.

As an example consider the pole-zero patterns shown in Fig. 4. Poles are shown by crosses and zeros by circles as usual. The poles and zeros of z_{11} are matched with the poles and zeros of y_{11}, respectively, up until ω_4. At $s = j\omega_4$, z_{11} has a pole which is not mated. It thus becomes a cut-off frequency. Below this frequency Z_{01} has no poles or zeros, whereas $\tanh \theta$ does. Above this frequency the poles and zeros of z_{11} are again paired with those of y_{11}, but this time poles with zeros, and zeros

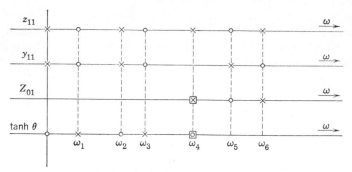

Fig. 4. Pole-zero patterns.

with poles. Now it is tanh θ from which these poles and zeros are missing. The cut-off factor, in the form $\sqrt{1 + s^2/\omega_4{}^2}$, appears in both Z_{01} and tanh θ; in the denominator of the first and the numerator of the second. In the diagram, the cut-off frequency is indicated by a square around the cross or circle. The functional forms of Z_{01} and tanh θ will be

$$Z_{01} = \frac{K_1(1 + s^2/\omega_5{}^2)}{\sqrt{1 + s^2/\omega_4{}^2}(1 + s^2/\omega_6{}^2)} \tag{25}$$

$$\tanh \theta = \frac{K_2 s(1 + s^2/\omega_2{}^2)\sqrt{1 + s^2/\omega_4{}^2}}{(1 + s^2/\omega_1{}^2)(1 + s^2/\omega_3{}^2)} \tag{26}$$

One point is brought out from these expressions and from the figures. Except for the irrational cut-off factor, the poles and zeros of z_{11} and y_{11} which appear in Z_{01} are all different from those that appear in tanh θ. We refer to those that appear in Z_{01} as *impedance controlling factors* or *frequencies* and those that appear in tanh θ as *propagation function controlling factors* or *frequencies*.

We may note a peculiarity in these control factors. We are really interested in the behavior of Z_{01} in the pass band; namely, we want it to be real and nearly constant there. However, we find that the control frequencies of Z_{01} are not in this region, but in the stop band, where Z_{01} is purely reactive. Similarly, we are interested in the behavior of tanh θ in the stop band. But its control frequencies are in the pass band, where tanh θ is pure imaginary.

To get an even clearer picture of the variation of Z_{01} and tanh θ let us plot these expressions for $s = j\omega$. Each of these quantities changes from real to imaginary, or vice versa, at the cut-off frequencies. Thus, when they are imaginary, we will plot the function divided by j. Figure 5

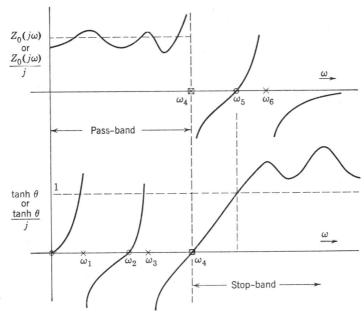

Fig. 5.   Plots of Z_{01} and $\tanh \theta$ against frequency.

shows the result. In the pass band Z_{01} is real. Its variation in this band will depend on the relative spacing of the impedance controlling frequencies, which lie in the stop band. If we want to control the variation of Z_{01} in the pass band, which we do, then we must choose the controlling frequencies appropriately. We shall discuss this point in somewhat greater detail in a later section. Similar statements apply to the variation of $\tanh \theta$ in the stop band.

Let us now consider the image impedance at the second end of the two-port. As we showed in the previous section, Z_{02} is completely determined except for a constant multiplier, from a knowledge of Z_{01} and $\tanh \theta$. Let us now see how to do this. From Eqs. (8) and (19) the following expression can be simply derived

$$\frac{Z_{02}}{Z_{01}} (1 - \tanh^2 \theta) = \left(\frac{z_{12}}{z_{11}}\right)^2 \tag{27}$$

When $s = j\omega$ the right-hand side of this equation is real and positive for all ω. Hence, the left-hand side must be also. Each of the factors Z_{02}/Z_{01} and $1 - \tanh^2 \theta$ is an even rational function and hence real when $s = j\omega$. We must, therefore, require that when one is positive or negative, the other one be also; if one factor should change sign, the other should do so as well.

In the pass band both Z_{01} and Z_{02} and, hence, also their ratio, are positive. The factor $1 - \tanh^2 \theta$ will also be positive, since $\tanh \theta$ is imaginary in the pass band. Now consider the cut-off frequency. As ω goes through the cut-off frequency, $\tanh \theta$ becomes real and the sign of $1 - \tanh^2 \theta$ will depend on the value of $\tanh^2 \theta$ relative to unity. This, in turn, will depend on the location of the cut-off factor in $\tanh \theta$. If the cut-off factor appears in the numerator of $\tanh \theta$, as in the example given in Eq. (26) and portrayed by Fig. 4, then just beyond the cut-off $1 - \tanh^2 \theta$ will still be positive. (See Fig. 5.)

The cut-off factor, which appears in both image impedances, will appear in their ratio only if it is in the numerator of one of them and in the denominator of the other. If it is in the numerator of both or the denominator of both, it will cancel in their ratio. In this case the sign of Z_{02}/Z_{01} will not change as ω goes through the cut-off frequency. Hence, in case the cut-off factor appears in the numerator of $\tanh \theta$, it must appear either in the numerator of both impedances or in the denominator of both. Since we know where it appears in Z_{01}, we now also know where it appears in Z_{02}.

Now suppose the cut-off factor appears in the denominator of $\tanh \theta$. Then, instead of going through zero at the cut-off frequency, the value of $\tanh \theta$ will go "through" infinity. The value of $1 - \tanh^2 \theta$ will then be negative in the immediate vicinity of the cut-off frequency. Hence, we must require that the value of Z_{02}/Z_{01} also change sign and become negative at the cut-off frequency. This will happen if the cut-off factor appears in the ratio, which, in turn, will happen if the factor is in the numerator of one image impedance and in the denominator of the other. Since we know where it is in Z_{01}, this determines where it should be in Z_{02}. The above discussion is summarized in Table 2.

TABLE 2

POSSIBLE LOCATIONS OF CUT-OFF FACTOR $\sqrt{1 + s^2/\omega_c^2}$ IN TANH θ, Z_{01}, AND Z_{02}

$\tanh \theta$	Z_{01}	Z_{02}
Numerator	Numerator Denominator	Numerator Denominator
Denominator	Numerator Denominator	Denominator Numerator

Beyond the cut-off frequency, in the stop band, the factor $1 - \tanh^2 \theta$ will change sign at any odd order zero of the equation $1 - \tanh^2 \theta = 0$.

We have already named these points the transmission zeros. Hence, we must require that any odd-order transmission zeros on the $j\omega$-axis appear as simple factors in the numerator or denominator of the ratio Z_{02}/Z_{01}. Hence, such a factor must appear in Z_{02} if it is not in Z_{01}. If it is in Z_{01}, it cannot appear in Z_{02}.

Nowhere else in the entire stop band will $1 - \tanh^2 \theta$ change sign. Hence, neither should the ratio Z_{02}/Z_{01}. This means that any zero or pole of Z_{01} not accounted for in the preceding paragraph (and these are all in the stop band) must be zeros or poles of Z_{02} also. In this way they will either be double zeros or poles of the ratio, or they will cancel. In either case the sign of Z_{02}/Z_{01} will not change. There is still some haziness as to which are poles of Z_{02} and which are zeros. This question is settled by the requirement of the alternation of poles and zeros. In particular, if all the zeros of Z_{01} are simple transmission zeros, then Z_{02} will be a very simple function.*

As an example let us determine Z_{02} for the case given by Eqs. (25) and (26). In the first place, the cut-off factor appears in the numerator of $\tanh \theta$ and in the denominator of Z_{01}. Hence, by Table 2 it must appear in the denominator of Z_{02} also. From Fig. 5 we see that there is only one point at which $\tanh \theta$ (and therefore $\tanh^2 \theta$) equals one. This frequency is a zero of Z_{01} so it cannot be a zero or pole of Z_{02}. The only other finite critical point of Z_{01} is at $s = j\omega_6$ and this must also be a critical point of Z_{02}. Also Z_{01} has a zero at infinity and so Z_{02} must have a pole at infinity. From all these considerations Z_{02} must have the following form

$$Z_{02} = \frac{K_3(1 + s^2/\omega_6{}^2)}{\sqrt{1 + s^2/\omega_4{}^2}} \tag{28}$$

The constant K_3 is not determined by this process.

In the above discussion a point needs clarification. We defined the transmission zeros to be the values of s at which $\tanh^2 \theta = 1$. But, if $\tanh^2 \theta = 1$, it must follow that $\tanh \theta$ is either plus one or minus one. How can we rule out the last possibility? Note that, because of the irrational factor, $\tanh \theta$ is a double valued function of s. If we stay on a single sheet of the Riemann surface we can make the function single-valued. The branch points are the cut-off frequencies, and we choose the branch cut to be the pass band, the part of the $j\omega$-axis joining the cut-off frequencies. The branch of $\tanh \theta$ that we choose must be the one which leads to positive values of the image attenuation function α in the stop band and, hence, to positive values of $\tanh \theta$.

---

* We shall use the fact that Z_{02} contains just the cut-off factor in such a case, to simplify filter designs.

Remember that $\tanh^2 \theta$ is a rational function with double poles and zeros except for one simple one representing the cut-off frequency. It is real and negative throughout the pass band and all of its poles and zeros lie there. A plot of this function against ω for the example given in Eq. (26) is shown in Fig. 6. Both negative and positive values of ω are in-

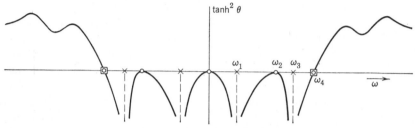

Fig. 6.   Plot of $\tanh^2 \theta(j\omega)$.

cluded. Throughout the pass band the value of $\tanh^2 \theta$ is negative and varies between $-\infty$ and zero. It takes on all negative values eight times in this range, exactly as many times as $\tanh^2 \theta$ has zeros or poles (each double one being counted twice, of course). This result is general and applies no matter how many poles and zeros $\tanh \theta$ may have.

It is a well-known fact that a rational function can take on a given value only as many times as it has poles or zeros. This means that $\tanh^2 \theta$ cannot take on any negative value anywhere else in the entire complex plane except on the pass band, which we have taken as the branch cut for $\tanh \theta$. This means that $\tanh \theta$ cannot have a purely imaginary value anywhere else except on the branch cut; thus the real part of $\tanh \theta$ cannot be zero except on the branch cut. However, $\tanh \theta$ is a continuous function on each sheet of the Riemann surface. If the real part of $\tanh \theta$ cannot be zero anywhere but on the branch cut, it follows from the continuity that the real part cannot change sign on a given sheet. Now the value of $\tanh \theta$ is real and positive in the stop band on the sheet which we have chosen. Hence, the real part of $\tanh \theta$ must be positive everywhere on this sheet. In particular, all the points at which $\tanh \theta = +1$ will lie on this sheet.

The preceding discussion shows that by a suitable choice of the branch of $\tanh \theta$, the points at which $\tanh^2 \theta = 1$ are also the points at which $\tanh \theta = 1$.

A possible method of filter design is now available to us. We choose realizable expressions for Z_{01} and $\tanh \theta$ based on some desired performance criteria (of which we will say more later). This permits us to calculate Z_{02} within a constant multiplier. Alternatively, we can calculate the z parameters or y parameters. We then have a complete set of parameters (aside from multiplying constants) which specify the behavior of the desired two-port. Our job is to find this two-port. When formulated in this manner, the image parameter method of filter synthesis is not different from network synthesis in general. We cannot here go into this aspect any further.

Let us now turn to an alternative approach. We have seen how a knowledge of one image impedance and of the function $\tanh \theta$ serves to determine the second image impedance. In this procedure the simple roots of $\tanh^2 \theta = 1$ play a prominent part. Let us now inquire into the significance of the roots of $\tanh^2 \theta = 1$, both simple and double.

In the first place we shall prove the following theorem. *The function* $\tanh \theta$ *is uniquely determined from a knowledge of the cut-off frequencies and the roots of* $\tanh^2 \theta = 1$ (including multiplicity of multiple roots). That is to say, only one possible $\tanh \theta$ function having the appropriate functional form can be found which will have the given cut-offs and transmission zeros. We will prove this theorem by contradiction.

Suppose $\tanh^2 \theta = 1$ has n roots and let there be two $\tanh \theta$ functions that satisfy the given conditions. Let us write

$$F_1 = \tanh^2 \theta_1 \qquad (a)$$

$$F_2 = \tanh^2 \theta_2 \qquad (b)$$

$$(29)$$

Both of these must be rational functions each of which has only one pair of j-axis poles or zeros which are simple (corresponding to the cut-off frequency), the remaining poles and zeros being double. The order of each function must be n, since $\tanh^2 \theta = 1$ has n roots. (By the order of a rational function is meant the highest degree of the numerator or the denominator, whichever is higher.) Now consider the functions

$$G_1 = \sqrt{F_1 F_2} \qquad (a)$$

$$G_2 = \sqrt{F_1/F_2} \qquad (b)$$

$$(30)$$

These will be rational functions, since all the poles and zeros of F_1 and F_2 are double, except for the cut-off factor. The cut-off factor can be either in the numerator or the denominator of F_1 and F_2. In any case, this factor must cancel from either G_1 or G_2, whereas it appears to the second power in the other one. Thus, both G_1 and G_2 will be rational functions. The order of one of them will be n, and that of the other, in which the cut-off factor cancels, will be $n - 1$. However, each of them must be equal to unity at the given n roots of $\tanh^2 \theta$, because both F_1 and F_2 are unity there. (This implies a proper choice of Riemann surface.)

But a rational function cannot take on a given value (unity in this case) more often than its order, unless it is identically equal to that value. Hence, either $G_1 = 1$ or $G_2 = 1$. This means that either $F_1 = F_2$ or $F_1 = 1/F_2$.

To summarize, we assumed two possible tanh θ functions having the same cut-off frequency and transmission zeros and we found that these two are either the same or they are reciprocals. To show that they cannot be reciprocals, look at Eq. (19). From a knowledge of the z parameters of lossless two-ports, note that the left-hand side must be real and positive for real positive values of s, hence, the same must be true for $1 - \tanh^2 \theta$. This means $\tanh^2 \theta$ must be less than unity for these values of s. Since F_1 and F_2 are two possible $\tanh^2 \theta$ functions, they must both be less than unity for real positive values of s. But this is impossible if $F_2 = 1/F_1$. This completes the proof.

The theorem which we have just discussed is very useful. It implies that no matter how we are able to do so, if we can in some manner obtain a tanh θ function which has specified cut-off frequencies and transmission zeros, this is the only possible such function. Let us now consider a method whereby tanh θ can be generated.

Consider the two networks in cascade shown in Fig. 7. The image impedances at the junction are assumed to be equal. The propagation

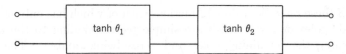

Fig. 7.   Cascade connection of filter components.

functions of the networks are θ_1 and θ_2, respectively. Since there is no internal reflection, the over-all transfer function θ is the sum of θ_1 and θ_2. Hence, we can write

$$\tanh \theta = \tanh (\theta_1 + \theta_2) = \frac{\tanh \theta_1 + \tanh \theta_2}{1 + \tanh \theta_1 \tanh \theta_2} \tag{31}$$

The right side expresses the hyperbolic tangent of a sum of two quantities in terms of the hyperbolic tangents of the individual quantities.

From this equation we see that in order for tanh θ to be equal to unity, we must have either $\tanh \theta_1 = 1$ or $\tanh \theta_2 = 1$. That is, the transmission zeros of two cascaded networks will be the totality of the transmission zeros of the individual networks, assuming the image impedances at the junction are equal. The same result can obviously be extended to more than two cascaded networks.

Let us now change our point of view and consider the over-all network in Fig. 7 to be a symmetrical network, structurally as well as electrically. The propagation functions of the two halves will then be equal; $\theta_1 = \theta_2 = \theta/2$. In this case Eq. (31) becomes

$$\tanh \theta = \frac{2 \tanh \theta/2}{1 + \tanh^2 \theta/2} \tag{32}$$

Now let us form $1 - \tanh \theta$ using this expression. We get

$$1 - \tanh \theta = \frac{(1 - \tanh \theta/2)^2}{1 + \tanh^2 \theta/2} \tag{33}$$

From this equation we see that if $1 - \tanh \theta/2$ has a simple zero, then $1 - \tanh \theta$ will have a double zero. The multiplicity of the zeros of $1 - \tanh \theta$ for a symmetrical network are all even. If a symmetrical network is bisected, the double transmission zeros become simple transmission zeros of each half. The function $\tanh \theta/2$ is called the *index function*.

The preceding discussion suggests an alternative approach to the filter synthesis problem. Suppose one image impedance Z_{01} and the transmission zeros are specified. The filter is realized as a cascade connection of sections as shown in Fig. 8 with image impedance match at each inter-

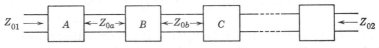

Fig. 8. Composite filter.

connection. Each of the sections realizes one pair of conjugate transmission zeros, either simple or double. The first one has Z_{01} as one of its image impedances, the second image impedance, Z_{0a}, being dictated by Z_{01} and the transmission zeros realized by this section. The second section has Z_{0a} as one of its image impedances, its second image impedance, Z_{0b}, being dictated by Z_{0a} and the transmission zeros, and so on. The final image impedance Z_{02} must of course be whatever is dictated by the given Z_{01} and the given transmission zeros.

In this approach we have assumed that it is possible to find filter sections which will realize a simple or double transmission zero while having an arbitrary image impedance at one end. For the contemplated procedure to be successful, we must find such sections.

11.4 Component Filter Sections

We shall now be concerned with finding certain simple two-ports which will realize a pair of conjugate imaginary transmission zeros, a pair of positive and negative real ones or a quadruplet of complex ones. The latter two varieties must be double, of course, while the imaginary ones may be simple or double. The simple transmission zeros must also be critical points of one or the other image impedance.

Long before the general theory we have been discussing in this chapter was developed, Zobel developed a filter theory based on the symmetrical Tee and Pi shown in Fig. 9. If the series and shunt branches are inverse

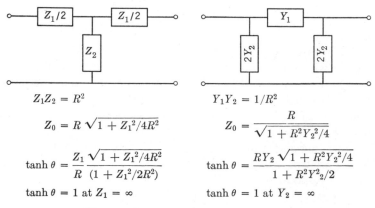

$$Z_1 Z_2 = R^2 \qquad\qquad Y_1 Y_2 = 1/R^2$$

$$Z_0 = R \sqrt{1 + Z_1^2/4R^2} \qquad\qquad Z_0 = \frac{R}{\sqrt{1 + R^2 Y_2^2/4}}$$

$$\tanh \theta = \frac{Z_1 \sqrt{1 + Z_1^2/4R^2}}{R \ (1 + Z_1^2/2R^2)} \qquad\qquad \tanh \theta = \frac{R Y_2 \sqrt{1 + R^2 Y_2^2/4}}{1 + R^2 Y^2{}_2/2}$$

$$\tanh \theta = 1 \text{ at } Z_1 = \infty \qquad\qquad \tanh \theta = 1 \text{ at } Y_2 = \infty$$

Fig. 9.   Constant-K Tee and Pi sections.

with respect to a constant, that is, $Z_1 Z_2 = R^2$, the resulting networks are called *constant-K*. (Note that the labeling on the branches is for convenience only.) The corresponding image parameters are also given in the figure.

The concept of a dual network introduced in Chapter 4 can be used to find these inverse networks. If we know the network realizing the function Z_1 of Fig. 9a or Y_1 of Fig. 9b, and this network is planar in the one terminal-pair sense (that is, the network remains planar on adding a generator between the input terminals), then we can construct its dual and modify the R's, L's, and reciprocal C's by the factor R^2 to get the desired inverse network. However even if the network realizing Z_1 or Y_1 is nonplanar, it will have an inverse network. The class of inverse networks is larger than the class of dual networks. In the present case, Z_1 or Y_1 will be Foster realizations of reactance functions and will therefore certainly be planar. The inverse can therefore be found by duality.

For the special case of a low-pass filter, these networks take the form shown in Fig. 10. Note that the characteristic impedances of the low-pass constant-K Tee and Pi are themselves inverse with respect to R^2. We refer to these as a *Tee-type* and a *Pi-type constant-K image impedance*,

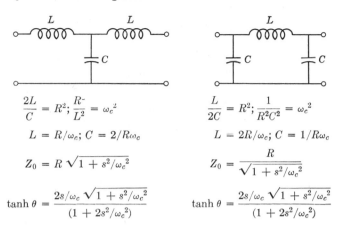

$$\frac{2L}{C} = R^2; \frac{R^-}{L^2} = \omega_c{}^2$$

$$L = R/\omega_c; \ C = 2/R\omega_c$$

$$Z_0 = R\sqrt{1 + s^2/\omega_c{}^2}$$

$$\tanh\theta = \frac{2s/\omega_c\sqrt{1 + s^2/\omega_c{}^2}}{(1 + 2s^2/\omega_c{}^2)}$$

$$\frac{L}{2C} = R^2; \frac{1}{R^2C^2} = \omega_c{}^2$$

$$L = 2R/\omega_c; \ C = 1/R\omega_c$$

$$Z_0 = \frac{R}{\sqrt{1 + s^2/\omega_c{}^2}}$$

$$\tanh\theta = \frac{2s/\omega_c\sqrt{1 + s^2/\omega_c{}^2}}{(1 + 2s^2/\omega_c{}^2)}$$

Fig. 10.   Low-pass constant-K sections.

respectively.* The $\tanh\theta$ functions of the two are identical for the same cut-off frequency. The only transmission zero is at infinity.

Consider the Tee section of Fig. 10. If the capacitance is replaced by a series tuned circuit, this will produce a transmission zero at the resonant frequency of the branch. However, if such a section is to be cascaded with a constant-K section, we must choose the elements in such a way that the image impedance remains the same as the constant-K image impedance. The procedure followed by Zobel in arriving at the element values starting from the symmetrical Tee in Fig. 9 is as follows. Let primes designate the new branch impedances and let $Z_1' = mZ_1$, where m is a constant. Now equate the image impedance of the primed Tee with that of the original Tee. This leads to the following new shunt-branch impedance

$$Z_2' = \frac{1 - m^2}{4m} Z_1 + \frac{Z_2}{m} \tag{34}$$

The new Tee for the low-pass case is shown in Fig. 11. Zobel called this process m-derivation and the new network an *m-derived* network. Clearly, in order to be realizable, m must be a positive number less than one. The original Tee is called the *prototype* and corresponds to $m = 1$. By direct computation we find that $\tanh\theta = 1$ has a double root on the $j\omega$-axis at the point s_∞ given by

* In the literature these are also called midseries type and midshunt type. These names arose from a consideration of a transmission system as a uniform ladder structure. The Tee and Pi sections could be formed by breaking into the structure in the middle of a series branch or in the middle of a shunt branch.

$$s_\infty{}^2 = -\frac{\omega_c{}^2}{1 - m^2}$$

$$\omega_\infty = \frac{\omega_c}{\sqrt{1 - m^2}} \; ; \qquad m = \sqrt{1 - \frac{\omega_c{}^2}{\omega_\infty{}^2}} \tag{35}$$

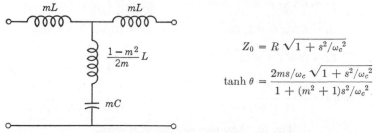

$$Z_0 = R \sqrt{1 + s^2/\omega_c{}^2}$$

$$\tanh \theta = \frac{2ms/\omega_c \sqrt{1 + s^2/\omega_c{}^2}}{1 + (m^2 + 1)s^2/\omega_c{}^2}$$

Fig. 11.   *m*-derived low-pass Tee section.

If we bisect the *m*-derived section, the half section, shown in Fig. 12, will have a simple transmission zero at the same frequency. Now, however, the far end image impedance will be different. Direct computation gives the value of Z_{02} shown in the figure. Note that this agrees with the result we would get if we were to calculate Z_{02} from Z_{01} and the transmission zero. We see that Z_{02} is not simply a constant-K image impedance; it has a control factor.

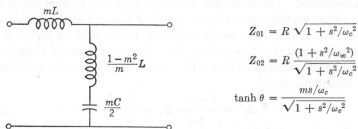

$$Z_{01} = R \sqrt{1 + s^2/\omega_c{}^2}$$

$$Z_{02} = R \frac{(1 + s^2/\omega_\infty{}^2)}{\sqrt{1 + s^2/\omega_c{}^2}}$$

$$\tanh \theta = \frac{ms/\omega_c}{\sqrt{1 + s^2/\omega_c{}^2}}$$

Fig. 12.   *m*-derived low-pass half Tee section.

The *m*-derivation procedure can be carried out starting from a Pi prototype as well. Starting from the Pi network in Fig. 9, let primes designate the new branch admittances and let $Y_2' = mY_2$. We now compute the image impedance in terms of the branch impedances and then equate the image impedance of the primed Pi with that of the original one. This leads to the following new series admittance.

$$Y_1' = \frac{Y_1}{m} + \frac{1 - m^2}{4m} Y_2 \tag{36}$$

The m-derived low-pass Pi section with Fig. 10b as a prototype is shown in Fig. 13. The image impedance is a constant-K Pi type, of course. By direct computation we find that tanh θ is the same for the m-derived Pi as for the m-derived Tee. Hence, Eq. (35) which relates the value of m to the transmission zero will apply in this case as well.

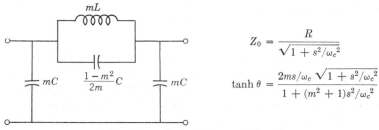

$$Z_0 = \frac{R}{\sqrt{1 + s^2/\omega_c^2}}$$

$$\tanh \theta = \frac{2ms/\omega_c \sqrt{1 + s^2/\omega_c^2}}{1 + (m^2 + 1)s^2/\omega_c^2}$$

Fig. 13. m-derived low-pass Pi section.

Let us now bisect the m-derived Pi section. The half section, shown in Fig. 14, will have simple transmission zeros where the whole section has double zeros. The half section is unsymmetrical and so the far end image impedance will be different. Direct computation gives the value of Z_{02} and tanh θ given in the figure.

The elementary filter sections we have considered so far still leave a number of gaps in our proposed synthesis technique. In the first place,

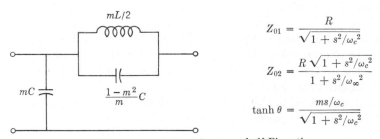

$$Z_{01} = \frac{R}{\sqrt{1 + s^2/\omega_c^2}}$$

$$Z_{02} = \frac{R\sqrt{1 + s^2/\omega_c^2}}{1 + s^2/\omega_\infty^2}$$

$$\tanh \theta = \frac{ms/\omega_c}{\sqrt{1 + s^2/\omega_c^2}}$$

Fig. 14. m-derived low-pass half Pi section.

we have been able to account for single and double transmission zeros on the $j\omega$-axis only. Secondly, the image impedances of these sections have the cut-off factor only and no control factors. It is possible to show that a lossless ladder network cannot have transmission zeros anywhere but on the $j\omega$-axis. Hence, we need not even consider a ladder network to realize complex or real transmission zeros.

Let us now consider a symmetrical lattice network as shown in Fig. 15. By direct computation of z_{11} and y_{11} we find the image parameters to be

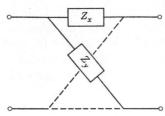

$$\tanh \theta = \frac{2\sqrt{Z_x Z_y}}{Z_y + Z_x} = \frac{2\sqrt{Z_x/Z_y}}{1 + Z_x/Z_y} \qquad (37)$$

$$\tanh \frac{\theta}{2} = \sqrt{Z_x/Z_y} \qquad (a)$$

$$(38)$$

Fig. 15.   Lattice network.

$$Z_0 = \sqrt{Z_x Z_y} \qquad (b)$$

The second expression follows by comparing the preceding equation with Eq. (32). These expressions are very interesting. Let us compare them with Eqs. (5) and (11) which give the image parameters for an arbitrary symmetric network (we should set $z_{11} = z_{22}$ and $y_{11} = y_{22}$ in these expressions). We see that, if we set

$$Z_x = 1/y_{11} \qquad (a)$$

$$Z_y = z_{11} \qquad (b)$$

$$(39)$$

then the image parameters of the lattice will be the same as those of an arbitrary symmetrical network. All the previous results pertaining to the image parameters will apply to the lattice, except that we must use $\tanh \theta/2$ instead of $\tanh \theta$. There is one exception to this statement and this pertains to the multiplicity of the complex zeros of $1 - \tanh^2 \theta$. The fact that these must be of even order was established from Eq. (19). We cannot simply substitute $\tanh \theta/2$ for $\tanh \theta$ in this expression. The restrictions on the multiplicity of transmission zeros still applies to $1 - \tanh \theta$ and not to $1 - \tanh \theta/2$. Hence, the zeros of $1 - \tanh \theta/2$ need not be of even order. In any case, no matter what the multiplicity of the zeros of $1 - \tanh \theta/2$, the zeros of $1 - \tanh \theta$ will have twice their multiplicity, as shown by Eq. (33).

Let us now invert Eqs. (38) and solve for the lattice branch impedances in terms of the image parameters. The result is

$$Z_x = Z_0 \tanh \theta/2 \qquad (a)$$

$$Z_y = \frac{Z_0}{\tanh \theta/2} \qquad (b)$$

$$(40)$$

From these expressions it is easy to see that if Z_0 and $\tanh \theta/2$ are given and have the forms satisfying the conditions of realizability, then Z_x and Z_y will be reactance functions.

Recall that we are still seeking filter sections which will provide transmission zeros off the $j\omega$-axis and which will have arbitrary image impedances. Let us first consider the question of transmission zeros.

Suppose a lattice with branch impedances Z_x and Z_y has its series branch impedance multiplied by a constant m and its cross-arm impedance divided by the same constant, as shown in Fig. 16. According to Eqs. (38) the image impedance of the new lattice is the same as that of the original lattice, but the index function is multiplied by m. This lattice can be called an m-derived lattice. The simplest index function for a low-pass filter will have the cut-off factor only and no control factors. Let us write

$$\tanh \theta/2 = \frac{ms/\omega_c}{\sqrt{1 + s^2/\omega_c^2}} \quad (41)$$

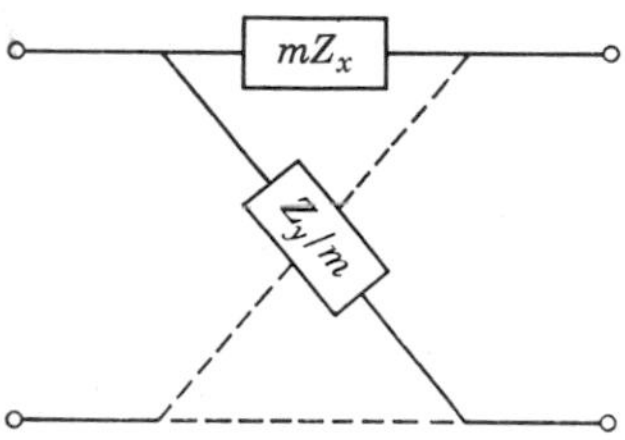

Fig. 16. m-derived lattice.

and assume that an m-derived lattice is to have this function. The function $1 - \tanh^2 \theta/2$ will be of second order in s^2. If we designate the zeros of this function by s_∞, then we find that

$$s_\infty = \pm \frac{\omega_c}{\sqrt{m^2 - 1}} \quad (a)$$

$$(42)$$

$$m = \sqrt{1 + \omega_c^2/s_\infty^2} \quad (b)$$

Note that, if $s_\infty = \pm j\omega_\infty$, then the value of m is real and less than one. This is, then, the same as an m-derived Tee section. However, suppose s_∞ is real; that is, there are a pair of real transmission zeros, one positive and one negative, which is permissible. Then m will again be real but this time greater than one. This case does not have its counterpart in the m-derived Tee section.

As a final possibility, suppose s_∞ is complex. This is not really possible since complex transmission zeros must come in quadruplets. But let us overlook this defect in the argument and proceed, in the hope that the difficulty can be overcome. If s_∞ is complex, then m will also be complex. This will require that the branches in the lattice of Fig. 16 have complex element values—an unbearable thought. This lattice gives only a pair of complex zeros. Suppose we think of another lattice which gives the complementary pair of transmission zeros. The cascade connection of these will then supply the whole quadruplet.

On this line of thought, consider the cascade connection of two lattices having a common image impedance at the junction, and having propagation functions θ_1 and θ_2 shown in Fig. 17. The over-all propagation function will be $\theta = \theta_1 + \theta_2$. Let us now consider a single lattice which is to be the equivalent of this cascade connection. We shall compute the

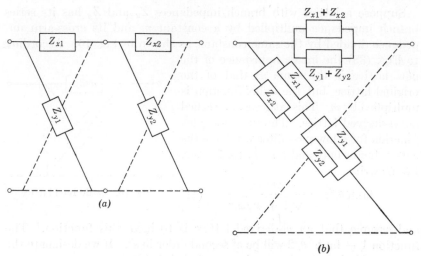

Fig. 17.   Cascade connection of lattices.

branch impedances; if they are realizable, the equivalence will exist. Denoting the branch impedances of the single lattice by Z_x and Z_y, we can write

$$Z_x = Z_0 \tanh \frac{\theta}{2} = Z_0 \tanh \frac{\theta_1 + \theta_2}{2} = Z_0 \frac{\tanh \theta_1/2 + \tanh \theta_2/2}{1 + (\tanh \theta_1/2) \tanh \theta_2/2}$$

$$= \cfrac{1}{\cfrac{1}{Z_0 \tanh \theta_1/2 + Z_0 \tanh \theta_2/2} + \cfrac{1}{\cfrac{Z_0}{\tanh \theta_1/2} + \cfrac{Z_0}{\tanh \theta_2/2}}}$$

$$= \frac{1}{1/(Z_{x1} + Z_{x2}) + 1/(Z_{y1} + Z_{y2})} \tag{43}$$

In arriving at the final result we used Eq. (40). In a similar way the cross arm impedance of the over-all lattice can be calculated. The circuit representation is shown in Fig. 17b. These branches will certainly be realizable if the original branches are.

Let us now assume that two m-derived lattices having the same prototype are cascaded in this fashion as shown in Fig. 18. The two values of m are denoted by m_1 and m_2. Using the result we just established, the single-lattice equivalent will take the form shown in the second part of the figure. Now suppose that m_1 and m_2 are complex conjugates with a

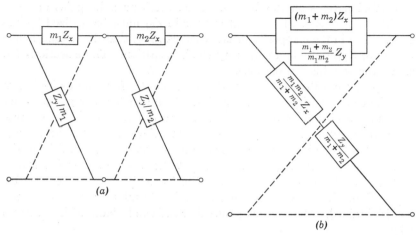

Fig. 18. Cascaded m-derived lattices.

positive real part. The branches of this lattice will then be realizable assuming the branches of the prototype lattice are.

If we inquire into the transmission zeros corresponding to a pair of conjugate values of m, we find from Eqs. (42) that they form a quadruplet having the desired symmetry. Thus, our difficulties are overcome. We have found that a symmetrical lattice will realize either a pair of real transmission zeros or a pair of conjugate imaginary zeros, or a quadruplet of complex transmission zeros.

The question of arbitrary image impedance with any number of control factors remains. From Eqs. (38) or (40) we see that $\tanh \theta/2$ will be unaffected if identical factors $(1 + s^2/\omega_i{}^2)$ are introduced as poles or zeros of both Z_x and Z_y. But such a factor will become a pole or zero of Z_0. In this way, a lattice having the simple index function given in Eq. (41) can be made to have an image impedance with any number of poles and zeros.

Let us now summarize the preceding discussion. The starting point is one image impedance Z_{01} and the transmission zeros. If all these zeros are of even multiplicity, then Z_{01} will be the same as Z_{02} and the network will be symmetrical. Each pair of real or imaginary transmission zeros can be realized by an m-derived lattice like that of Fig. 16 with a real value of m; $m > 1$ for the real zeros and $m < 1$ for the j-axis zeros. The image impedance of each of these lattices will be the same as the given image impedance. Each quadruplet of zeros is realized by a lattice having the form of Fig. 18b.

The only remaining case to investigate is the possibility of simple transmission zeros on the $j\omega$-axis. Such zeros must be poles or zeros of either Z_{01} or Z_{02}. Those that appear in Z_{01} must be realized by the first section in the composite filter, whereas those that don't (and hence belong to Z_{02}) must be realized by the last section. These sections are called the terminating sections.

Suppose we realize a lattice with the given Z_{01} function as its image impedance and with an index function which equals unity at the given simple transmission zeros which also appear in Z_{01}. For the lattice as a whole these are double zeros of $1 - \tanh \theta$. If we can bisect this lattice, half of it will still have the same transmission zeros and it will have Z_{01} as its image impedance at one end. At the other end the image impedance will be dictated by Z_{01} and the transmission zeros realized by the section. In this way the unsymmetrical terminating section at one end is obtained. The section at the other end can be handled in the same way.

We have now demonstrated that the cascade realization of the composite filter can always be obtained, provided that the lattice which is to supply the terminating sections can be bisected. At this point it will be worth while to turn back to problem 8.14 in which a theorem called Bartlett's bisection theorem was discussed. Note that the theorem involves networks that are structurally as well as electrically symmetrical, and which are planar at the line of symmetry. The lattice does not satisfy this last condition.* However, if we can find another symmetrical network which is equivalent to the lattice in the two-port sense, and which can be bisected, our troubles will be over. Let us now briefly consider the possibility of two-port equivalents of a lattice.

In the first place, suppose that the branches of a lattice have a common series impedance as shown in Fig. 19a. Let us contemplate finding the

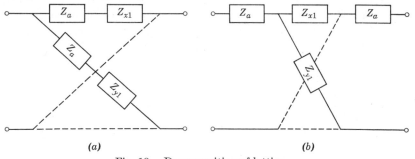

(a)   (b)

Fig. 19.   Decomposition of lattice.

* Bartlett's theorem can be applied to a lattice also if we are willing to add an ideal transformer.

Tee equivalent of the lattice. We find the series branch impedance of the Tee to be $Z_a + Z_{x1}$ and the shunt branch impedance to be $(Z_{y1} - Z_{x1})/2$. Because of the subtraction involved in the shunt branch impedance, this may not be realizable. However, suppose we leave Z_a in the series branches the way it stands and contemplate converting the remaining Tee, consisting of Z_{x1} in the series branches and $(Z_{y1} - Z_{x1})/2$ in the shunt branch back into a lattice. The result will take the form shown in Fig. 19b. This takes us part of the way to the solution of our problem.

As a second step, suppose that the branches of the lattice have a common shunt admittance, as shown in Fig. 20a. By taking the Pi equivalent and converting a portion of this back into a lattice, we obtain the network in Fig. 20b.

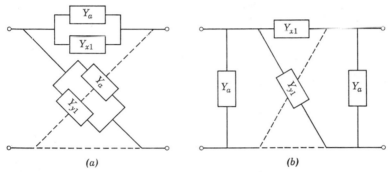

(a) (b)

Fig. 20. Lattice decomposition.

It may be possible in some cases that these two steps can be applied alternately, first one then the other, until the lattice is completely decomposed. The resulting structure will be a symmetrical ladder, which can certainly be bisected. Now we know that the transmission zeros of a lossless ladder network necessarily lie on the $j\omega$-axis. Hence, this decomposition will be possible only if the transmission zeros of the original lattice all lie on the $j\omega$-axis. But this is exactly the case for the lattice which is to provide the terminating sections. Hence, we should expect our contemplated procedure to apply.[*]

Let us now consider some simple low-pass lattices that can provide transmission zeros anywhere in the complex plane. Figure 21 shows a low-pass m-derived lattice. By direct computation, we find the image impedance and the index function to be

---

[*] It is possible to obtain more general two-port equivalents of a lattice which come into play when the transmission zeros are not all on the $j\omega$-axis. For a more complete discussion, see N. Balabanian, *Network Synthesis*, Prentice Hall, 1958, Englewood Cliffs, N. J., pp. 172 and 255.

$$Z_0 = R\sqrt{1 + s^2/\omega_c^2} \qquad (a)$$

$$\tanh \frac{\theta}{2} = \frac{ms/\omega_c}{\sqrt{1 + s^2/\omega_c^2}} \qquad (b)$$

$$(44)$$

where $R = \sqrt{L/C}$ and $\omega_c^2 = 1/LC$. By using Eq. (32) we can compute $\tanh \theta$ for this lattice. We get

$$\tanh \theta = \frac{2 \tanh \theta/2}{1 + \tanh^2 \theta/2} = \frac{2ms/\omega_c \sqrt{1 + s^2/\omega_c}}{1 + (m^2 + 1)s^2/\omega_c} \qquad (45)$$

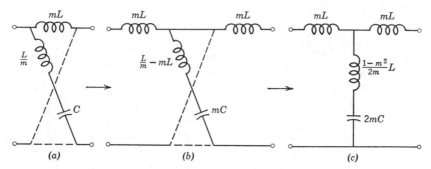

Fig. 21.   Low-pass m-derived lattice and its decomposition.

If we now compare these expressions with those given in Fig. 11 for the image parameters of an m-derived Tee section, we see that they are identical, except for a factor 2 in the definitions of R^2 and ω_c^2. They would be exactly the same if we would use $2C$ instead of C in the cross arm of the lattice. However, in the case of the lattice m is not restricted to be less than 1.

The same result can be demonstrated by noting that the two branch impedances of the lattice have a common pole at infinity. If we use the equivalence shown in Fig. 19, we will get the result shown in Fig. 21, parts (b) and (c). Of course, in order for the shunt branch inductance to be positive, we must require $m < 1$.

The equivalence between the m-derived lattice and the m-derived Tee section for $m < 1$ is now clearly portrayed. However, the lattice is a more general network in that m is not restricted to be less than one. It should nevertheless be real in Fig. 21.

Now let us consider the cascade connection of two m-derived low-pass lattices with complex conjugate values of m; m_1, and m_2. The lattices are again the same as that of Fig. 21a. Let us write

$$m_1 = r + ji = |m| \epsilon^{j\phi}$$

$$m_2 = r - ji = |m| \epsilon^{-j\phi} \tag{46}$$

Then the single lattice equivalent illustrated by Fig. 18 will take the form shown in Fig. 22. This lattice will realize a quadruplet of trans-

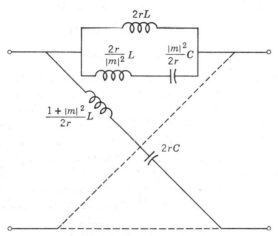

Fig. 22. Low-pass m-derived lattice realizing a quadruplet of transmission zeros.

mission zeros given by Eq. (42) in terms of the two conjugate values of m. By direct calculation we will find the index function of this lattice to be

$$\tanh \frac{\theta}{2} = \frac{2rs/\omega_c \sqrt{1 + s^2/\omega_c^2}}{1 + (1 + |m|^2)s^2/\omega_c^2} \tag{47}$$

The image impedance, of course, is the same as that given in Eq. (44).

Finally, let us carry through a numerical example of a filter design starting from a knowledge of (1) the cut-off frequency ω_c, (2) the image impedance Z_{01} at one end, (3) the desired transmission zeros and (4) the design resistance R. Actually, R and ω_c will enter into consideration only when element values are to be determined. Most of the procedure is carried through with impedances normalized with respect to R and with frequency normalized with respect to ω_c by using the transformation $p = s/\omega_c$.

The following information is given. It is desired to have double transmission zeros at $p = \pm j2$ and simple transmission zeros at $p = \pm j\frac{5}{4}$. Z_{01} (normalized) is to be

$$Z_{01} = \frac{\sqrt{1 + p^2}}{(1 + 16p^2/25)} \tag{48}$$

Thus, Z_{01} has only one impedance controlling frequency which is the same as the simple transmission zero. The values of m corresponding to the given transmission zeros are obtained from Eq. (35) by writing the normalized value of ω_∞ as $x_\infty = \omega_\infty/\omega_c$. Thus

$$x_\infty = 2; \qquad m = 0.866 \qquad (a)$$
$$x_\infty = \tfrac{5}{4}; \qquad m = 0.6 \qquad (b) \tag{49}$$

Since there are two pairs of transmission zeros, we can contemplate the composite filter to consist of the cascade connection of two sections. One of these must realize the simple pair of transmission zeros and must have the given Z_{01} as its image impedance at one end. The other section must realize the double pair of transmission zeros; its image impedance will be the same as that at the second end of the first section.

Let us first consider the unsymmetrical section which will realize the simple zeros at $p = \pm j\tfrac{5}{4}$. The tanh θ function must have only the cut-off factor since otherwise tanh $\theta = 1$ will have more than 2 roots. Thus,

$$\tanh \theta = 0.6p/\sqrt{1 + p^2} \tag{50}$$

We see that this expression equals unity when $p = \pm j\tfrac{5}{4}$. Hence, from the uniqueness theorem it is the only possible function. The image impedance at the second end can now be easily found. According to Table 2, the cut-off factor must appear in the denominator of Z_{02}. Furthermore, the impedance controlling factor appearing in Z_{01} must not appear in Z_{02}, since it represents a simple transmission zero. Hence, Z_{02} will be simply

$$Z_{02} = 1/\sqrt{1 + p^2} \tag{51}$$

which is a Pi type constant-K image impedance.

The general procedure for realizing the unsymmetrical section is to consider the tanh θ function given in Eq. (50) to be the tanh $\theta/2$ function of a symmetrical lattice having an image impedance given by Z_{01}. The lattice branch impedances are given by Eqs. (40). After finding the lattice, we replace it by an equivalent symmetrical ladder. We then bisect the ladder, giving us the desired unsymmetrical section. However, for the case under consideration, we have already considered an unsymmetrical section which will fill the bill. This is the m-derived half Pi section shown in Fig. 14. The image impedances and tanh θ given in the figure (suitably normalized) are identical with the ones under consideration here, except that Z_{01} and Z_{02} are interchanged. Hence, the filter now takes the form shown in Fig. 23. Remember that the symbols L and C appearing in Fig. 14 refer to the branches of the prototype Pi section in Fig. 10. The values appearing in Fig. 23 are obtained by using the values of L and C from the prototype in terms of the design resistance R and the cut-off frequency ω_c.

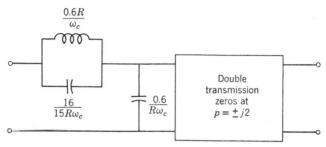

Fig. 23. Partial realization of filter.

Now let us turn to the section which will realize the double transmission zeros at $p = \pm j2$. This will be a symmetrical two-port with an image impedance equal to Z_{02} as given in Eq. (51). Let us find $\tanh \theta$. One way to proceed is to note that, since the section is symmetrical, half of it must have simple transmission zeros at $p = \pm j2$. Hence, $\tanh \theta/2$ must have the form of Eq. (50) but with a multiplier $m = 0.866$ instead of 0.6. We then use Eq. (32) to find $\tanh \theta$. The result of this operation will be

$$\tanh \theta = \frac{2 \tanh \theta/2}{1 + \tanh^2 \theta/2} = \frac{(2\sqrt{3}p/2)/\sqrt{1 + p^2}}{1 + 3p^2/[4(1 + p^2)]}$$

$$= \frac{\sqrt{3}p\sqrt{1 + p^2}}{1 + 7p^2/4} \qquad (52)$$

As a check, we find that this reduces to unity when $p = \pm j2$. By the uniqueness theorem it is the only possible $\tanh \theta$ function.

An alternate way of obtaining the same result is to note that $1 - \tanh^2 \theta$ must have the factor $(p^2 + 4)^2$. In order for $1 - \tanh^2 \theta$ to have the correct order, $\tanh \theta$ must have one controlling factor besides the cut-off factor. Hence, it must have the form

$$\tanh \theta = \frac{Kp\sqrt{1 + p^2}}{1 + ap^2} \qquad (53)$$

We now form $1 - \tanh^2 \theta$ and set the numerator equal to $(p^2 + 4)^2$.

We will get

$$p^4 + \frac{2a - K^2}{a^2 - K^2} p^2 + \frac{1}{a^2 - K^2} = p^4 + 8p^2 + 16 \qquad (54)$$

Solving this for a and K makes Eq. (53) identical with Eq. (52).

Again, we can always fall back on a lattice realization of this symmetrical section. However, again because of the simplicity of the case, we have already examined a section which meets the requirements. This is the m-derived Pi section shown in Fig. 13. If we substitute $m = \sqrt{3}/2$ in the tanh θ function given in the figure, we get Eq. (52). Substituting $m = \sqrt{3}/2$ and values of L and C in terms of R and ω_c our filter finally takes the form shown in Fig. 24. The two parallel capaci-

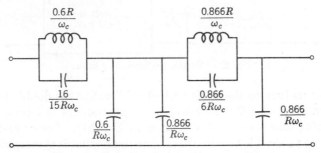

Fig. 24.   Complete design of low-pass filter.

tances can, of course, be combined into a single one. Note that the design resistance and the cut-off frequency are arbitrary; our synthesis is valid no matter what they are.

The procedure we have just described is not the only way to obtain a filter synthesis. Knowing the transmission zeros, we can form the tanh θ function for the entire filter. The easiest way to do this is to think in terms of cascaded sections. The tanh θ of each section is easily found from the transmission zeros which it is to realize. For the two sections we obtained above these are given by Eqs. (50) and (52). They can then be combined by the use of Eq. (31). In the present case the result will be

$$\tanh \theta = \frac{2.332p(1 + 1.191p^2)}{(1 + 2.789p^2)\sqrt{1 + p^2}} \qquad (55)$$

The image impedance at the other end of the filter can now be determined. From the pertinent considerations, we find that it will be given by Eq. (51), as it should. We now have a complete set of image parameters. From these we can calculate the open-circuit or the short-circuit parameters, if we so desire. Of course, for all of this work to be worth anything, we must have one or more synthesis procedures available that can be used when z or y parameters are prescribed. Furthermore, the resulting networks should have advantages over the one which we have already obtained; advantages which outweigh any increase in the computational work. We will leave the further exploitation of this topic to the books on network synthesis.

As a conclusion for this section let us outline the basic philosophy of the realization technique. The purpose is to begin with a realizable Z_{01} and zeros of transmission, and to end with a network. We realize the network as a cascade connection of simple two-ports, as in Fig. 8. At each interconnection the image impedances are made equal. This step has two consequences. First of all, the zeros of transmission of the over-all network consist of all the zeros of transmission of the individual two-ports. Secondly, the image impedance of the over-all network at end 1 is the same as the input image impedance of the terminating section at end 1. Similarly, the image impedance at end 2 depends only on the terminating section at end 2. (It is of course, decided by the given Z_{01} and zeros of transmission.) We make use of this fact in the following way to make all the intermediate sections simple. For the terminating section we begin with a symmetrical balanced lattice that has the given image impedance, but a very simple index function. We achieve this effect by making Z_x and Z_y have many common poles and zeros. [See Eq. (37).] The only requirements on the index function of this lattice are that it must contain the cut-off factor and become equal to unity at the odd-order zeros of transmission on the $j\omega$-axis which are also critical frequencies of Z_{01}. Since Z_x and Z_y have many common poles and zeros, and the zeros of transmission are on the $j\omega$-axis, a symmetrical ladder equivalent can be found for this lattice. Now we bisect this equivalent and obtain one terminating half section. This "bisecting" has two consequences. First of all, the transmission zeros come to the correct order. Secondly the image impedance at the second end is no longer the complicated function Z_{01} but a simple constant-K function, either Tee or Pi. This allows all the intermediate sections to have the same simple image impedance, and hence to be simple two-ports.

Each intermediate network is chosen to be symmetrical. Its image impedances are simply the constant-K type image impedances found from the terminating half section. Each of these networks realizes one set of transmission zeros—either a pair of conjugate zeros on the $j\omega$-axis, or a pair of real zeros, or a quadruplet of complex zeros—each zero being double. For zeros of transmission on the $j\omega$-axis we can use the m-derived Tee or Pi network (whether it is Tee or Pi is decided by the constant-K impedance obtained from the terminating section). For the other zeros we have considered only lattices. It is possible to obtain unbalanced (common-terminal) sections for the complex zeros as well (but not for the real pair), but classical filter theory does not make use of these sections for a special reason. As we shall see in the next section, the ideal filter characteristics can be approximated satisfactorily using only transmission zeros on the $j\omega$-axis. Thus no other sections (besides the m-derived Tee and Pi) are required for the interior part of the filter (i.e., excluding the terminating half sections). The design of the m-derived sections has been reduced to formulas, and so is immediately accomplished.

11.5   Determination of the Image Parameters

Up to this point we have carried on the discussion under the assumption that the image parameters, at least Z_{01} and $\tanh \theta$, are given. However, the starting point in any filter problem is not from known image parameters. What is specified is a desirable behavior of the image impedance and the attenuation function in the pass band and stop band, respectively. We must then find suitable functions for the image impedances and $\tanh \theta$ in such a way that the ideal filter behavior is approximated in some manner. Remember that by ideal filter behavior we mean that the normalized image impedances should be identically equal to unity in the pass band, and $\tanh \theta$ should be identically equal to unity in the stop band. This behavior is, of course, impossible. The requirements of each particular application will dictate how wide a discrepancy between the actual behavior and the ideal behavior can be tolerated.

For the sake of convenience, let us normalize the frequency variable with respect to the cut-off frequency ω_c; that is, $p = y + jx = s/\omega_c$. The normalized frequency corresponding to the cut-off will then be $x_c = 1$. Now consider the diagram of Fig. 25. The abscissa is x and the

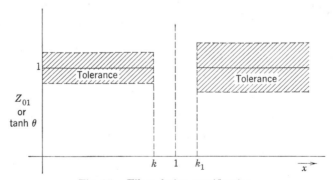

Fig. 25.   Filter design specification.

ordinate is Z_{01} or tanh θ. The nominal pass band extends from $x = 0$ to $x = 1$. The design specifications can be stated in terms of the tolerances on the variations of Z_{01} and tanh θ in the pertinent frequency ranges, and in terms of the quantities k and k_1 which specify the extent of these ranges within which the variations of the pertinent function is kept within its tolerance. It now remains to choose the number and locations of the poles and zeros of Z_{01} and tanh θ in order to satisfy the design requirements. This portion of an over-all design or synthesis is referred to as the *approximation* problem. Note that the determination of Z_{01} is independent of the determination of tanh θ. However, in their respective frequency bands (pass band for Z_{01} and stop band for tanh θ) these two functions are to exhibit similar behavior. In fact, it will be enough to consider the x-axis interval from zero to one, if we plot tanh θ against the variable $1/x$.

Any convenient procedure can be used to solve the approximation problem. In Chapter 7 two desirable forms of a transfer function magnitude were mentioned, the monotonic maximally flat response and the oscillatory equal-ripple response.

Let us here consider an equal-ripple approximation of Z_{01} and tanh θ as illustrated in Fig. 26. The function tanh θ is plotted against $1/x$ as a

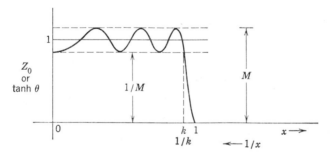

Fig. 26.   Equal-ripple approximation.

variable and the point k_1 in Fig. 25 becomes $1/k$. All the peak deviations above unity are equal as are those below unity, their geometric mean being one. The tolerance is then $M - 1$, where M is defined in the figure.

Instead of specifying the tolerable maximum deviation of Z_{01} in the pass band from its ideal value, it is possible to state this specification in an equivalent form in terms of the reflection coefficient. Thus, with $Z_1 = R_1 = 1$, the reflection coefficient given in Eq. (12) becomes

$$\rho_1 = \frac{1 - Z_{01}}{1 + Z_{01}} \tag{56}$$

Clearly, a tolerance on Z_{01} can be simply translated into a tolerance on ρ_1, and vice-versa. Ideally, the reflection coefficient should be zero in the pass band. In a particular problem we can specify the peak deviation from zero which can be tolerated. This, then, specifies the maximum deviation of Z_{01} from unity.

If Z_{01} is approximated in the pass band in the manner indicated in Fig. 26, we shall find that the value of the reflection coefficient corresponding to the positive peaks of Z_{01} will be equal, but of opposite sign, to its value corresponding to the negative peaks. In this way the reflection coefficient will be approximated in an equal ripple manner also.

Let ρ_m be the maximum tolerable pass band reflection coefficient. This can be related to the peak value of Z_{01} by noting that $\rho_1 = \rho_m$ when $Z_{01} = 1/M$. Thus, solving Eq. (56) for M with these values substituted, we get

$$M = \frac{1 + \rho_m}{1 - \rho_m} \tag{57}$$

Let us now consider the attenuation in the stop band. Ideally, we want infinite attenuation throughout this band. However, in a given problem we will be content if the attenuation never falls below a specified value, say α_0. In order to tie this in with our previous discussion, we should relate the minimum stop band attenuation with the tolerance on $\tanh \theta$. Remember that in the stop band, $\tanh \theta = \tanh \alpha$, since β is an integral multiple of π radians. If we now express $\tanh \alpha$ in terms of exponentials and solve for α, we obtain

$$\alpha = \frac{1}{2} \ln \left| \frac{\tanh \theta + 1}{\tanh \theta - 1} \right| \tag{58}$$

Substituting either of the peak deviations M or $1/M$ for $\tanh \theta$ in this expression will lead to the same value of α, the stop-band minimum. In this way we can relate the minimum stop-band attenuation with the peak deviations of $\tanh \theta$. Thus

$$\alpha_0 = \frac{1}{2} \ln \left(\frac{M + 1}{M - 1} \right) \tag{a}$$

$$M = \coth \alpha_0 \tag{b}$$

$$\tag{59}$$

(The absolute value signs are not needed, since M is greater than one.)

The question that now remains is how to determine the number and locations of the poles and zeros of Z_{01} and of $\tanh \theta$ in order that an equal-ripple approximation is obtained for each function, when the maximum pass band reflection coefficient ρ_m and minimum stop band loss α_0 are specified. This problem was first solved by Cauer in 1931. We cannot go into the details here since it would take us far afield. We will be satisfied to summarize the results here, only for continuity of the discussion.

The answer to our question is sought by first making a transformation of variable as follows

$$x = k \operatorname{sn} u \tag{60}$$

where

$$u = \int_0^\phi \frac{dz}{\sqrt{1 - k^2 \sin^2 z}} \tag{61}$$

The function u is called an *elliptic integral* of the first kind. It is a function of the upper limit ϕ and of the parameter k.

The value of u when ϕ is equal to $\pi/2$ is designated K and is called the *complete elliptic integral*. Thus

$$K = \int_0^{\pi/2} \frac{dz}{\sqrt{1 - k^2 \sin^2 z}} \tag{62}$$

The value of the complete elliptic integral is thus dependent only on the parameter k. These values are tabulated and are readily available.

The function sn u is the *Jacobian elliptic sine function*. It is related to an ordinary sine by

$$\sin \phi = \operatorname{sn} u \tag{63}$$

It is, thus, a periodic function; one period corresponds to a variation of ϕ over 2π radians, which corresponds to $4K$. The complete elliptic integral is thus a quarter period of the elliptic sine function. The parameter k is called the *modulus* of the elliptic sine function. The elliptic sine function sn u is also tabulated.

Let us now return to our problem. The general forms for Z_{01} and tanh θ for a low-pass filter with frequency normalized to the cut-off value are

$$Z_{01} = \frac{K_1(1 + p^2/x_1^2) \cdots (1 + p^2/x_n^2)}{\sqrt{1 + p^2}(1 + p^2/x_2^2) \cdots (1 + p^2/x_{n-1}^2)} \tag{64}$$

$$\tanh \theta = \frac{K_2 p(1 + p^2/x_b^2) \cdots (1 + p^2/x_{n-1}^2)\sqrt{1 + p^2}}{(1 + p^2/x_a^2) \cdots (1 + p^2/x_n^2)} \tag{65}$$

where $p = s/\omega_c$ and $x_i = \omega_i/\omega_c$. We have used numeral subscripts for the critical points of Z_{01} and literal subscripts for those of tanh θ. The number of critical frequencies n need not be the same in both cases.

For the equal ripple approximation Cauer found expressions for the critical frequencies of Z_{01} and $\tanh \theta$. He also found expressions for the points at which the peak deviations occur and the points at which Z_{01} and $\tanh \theta$ equal unity. In the case of $\tanh \theta$, these latter are the points of infinite attenuation.

Critical frequencies of tanh θ

$$x_i = \operatorname{sn}\left(\frac{n + 1 - i}{n} K\right) ; \qquad i = 1, 2, \cdots, n \tag{66}$$

Frequencies of peak deviation

$$x = \cfrac{1}{k \operatorname{sn} \cfrac{iK}{n}} ; \qquad i = 0, 1, \cdots, n \tag{67}$$

Frequencies at which tanh θ = 1; infinite attenuation

$$x_{\infty i} = \cfrac{1}{k \operatorname{sn}\left(\cfrac{2i - 1}{2n} K\right)} ; \qquad i = 1, 2, \cdots, n \tag{68}$$

The infinity in the last subscript refers to infinite attenuation. In the case of Z_{01}, the corresponding points are obtained by taking the reciprocals of these three expressions.

Let us make a remark on these solutions which illustrates a different point of view that may be helpful. For the function $\tanh \theta$, we want that $\tanh \theta$ should not differ from 1 by too much in the frequency range $1/k < x < \infty$. We would like to locate its critical frequencies in the range $0 \le x < 1$ suitably, to achieve this result. The location of critical frequencies on the x-axis, to achieve the desired behavior of $\tanh \theta$, turns out to be nonuniform. However if we transform the x-axis, using the elliptic sine function as in Eq. (60), with the number k as modulus, the spacing of the critical frequencies becomes uniform on the u-axis, over the interval $K(k)/n \le u \le K(k)$; where $K(k)$ is the complete elliptic integral. Thus the critical frequencies are easily located on the u-axis.

Perhaps the transformation (60) itself can use a word of explanation. Suppose we have a given value of x in the interval $(0,1)$ and we wish to find the corresponding u. We first find ϕ such that $x = \sin \phi$ $(0 \le \phi \le \pi/2)$. Then we substitute this ϕ in the integral (61), using the given value of k — the same k as in Fig. 26. The value of the integral is the desired u. On the other hand if we start with a u in the interval $0 \le u \le K(k)$, we proceed as follows to find x. We first find a ϕ such that the given u is equal to the value of the integral in (61) for this ϕ and the given k. Then $x = \sin \phi$.

Note from Fig. 26 that the points at which $\tanh \theta = 1$ are simple points; that is, these points will be simple transmission zeros. It would be desirable to have double zeros as well, in order to account for a symmetrical filter or for symmetrical sections of a composite filter. This desire can be fulfilled by treating the function $\tanh \theta/2$ instead of $\tanh \theta$. Remember that, for a symmetrical network, $\tanh \theta/2$ will have the same form as $\tanh \theta$ for an arbitrary network. If $\tanh \theta/2 = 1$ has simple roots, $\tanh \theta$ will have double roots. Even when unsymmetrical sections of a composite filter are under consideration, we can deal with $\tanh \theta/2$. If we eventually design a symmetrical section with this information, we then bisect it and retain only half. From now on, therefore, we will deal with the function $\tanh \theta/2$ instead of $\tanh \theta$. Any previous discussion concerning $\tanh \theta$ will be assumed to pertain to $\tanh \theta/2$.

Another interesting fact about Cauer's procedure is that all the transmission zeros occur on the $j\omega$-axis. Hence, the design can always be obtained as a ladder network.

Another question still remains to be answered: from a given ρ_m or α_0, how do we determine the number n of impedance controlling factors or of propagation function controlling factors? This question can be answered with the help of Eq. (67) which gives the frequencies at which the peak deviations occur. There are two parameters in this expression, the modulus k and the order n. For a given value of n we can use this expression to calculate the peak deviations as a function of k. If we do this for a number of values of n we will be able to plot a family of curves of peak deviations (which can be expressed as ρ_m or α_0) versus the modulus k with n as a parameter. In Fig. 27 charts of ρ_m and α_0 are presented as a function of k with n as a parameter. Since values near $k = 1$ are the desired ones, the scale near this point is expanded by defining $k = \sin \gamma$ and plotting α_0 and ρ_m against γ.

Let us now contemplate the procedure for synthesizing a low-pass filter which is to operate between equal resistive terminations. We will consider a symmetrical filter. What is given is the maximum tolerable reflection coefficient ρ_m in a band of frequencies from 0 to ω_1, and the minimum permissible attenuation α_0 in another band from ω_2 to ∞, with $\omega_2 > \omega_1$. In order for these points to correspond to k and $1/k$, respectively, on the normalized scale, we choose $\omega_c = \sqrt{\omega_1 \omega_2}$. Then, $k = \omega_1/\omega_c = \sqrt{\omega_1/\omega_2}$. With k now known we can find the number of control factors in Z_0 from Fig. 27 for the given value of ρ_m, and then find the critical frequencies from Eq. (65).

We intend that the filter will be a cascade connection of sections. In our previously described procedure for a symmetrical filter, each of the cascaded sections will have the same image impedance as the given

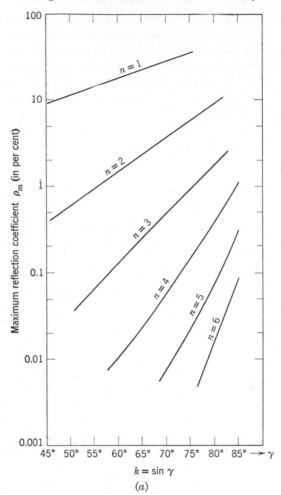

Fig. 27. Maximum reflection coefficient and minimum attenuation plotted against k with the number of sections as parameter.

one. Since this has several poles and zeros besides the cut-off factor, each section will be relatively extensive. Suppose that instead of this, we find the symmetrical section which has the given image impedance and has double transmission zeros at each of the poles and zeros of this impedance. When bisected, each half of this symmetrical network, will have simple transmission zeros at the same points. Hence, the image impedance at the other end will be simply a constant-K type, either Tee or Pi. The desired filter is to have one of these half sections at each end, thus providing the correct image impedances. Any number of additional

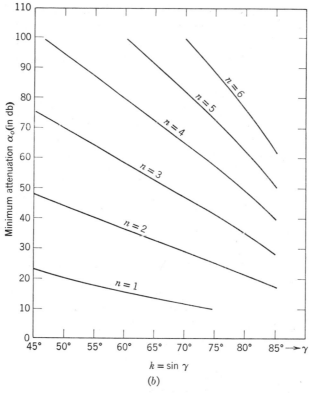

Fig. 27.   (*continued*)

symmetrical sections can now be cascaded between the two ends, each of which has a constant-K image impedance and provides a double transmission zero.   These will have relatively few elements and will take the form of m-derived sections.

We are now ready to consider the stop band behavior in which a minimum attenuation α_0 is specified.   The terminating sections, of course, will provide some attenuation.   The value of the minimum attenuation provided by these sections can be found from Fig. 27b for the values of k and n used in determining Z_0.   If this is equal to or greater than the specified α_0, the job is complete; the terminating sections which provide the required behavior of the image impedance serve to provide for the required attenuation as well.   Usually, this will not be true.   Then we subtract from α_0 the minimum attenuation provided by the terminating sections.   The remainder is the minimum that must be provided by the "attenuating" sections in the interior of the filter.   We enter Fig. 27b with this value of α and find n corresponding to the given k.   Then we use Eq. (68) to find the frequencies of infinite attenuation. These are related to the m parameters through Eq. (35), remembering that $x_\infty = \omega_\infty/\omega_c$. For each value of x_∞ an m-derived section is readily designed. With this procedure it appears that the terminating sections are the only ones that require individual attention. The interior attenuating sections simply require substituting numbers into formulas.

The Cauer synthesis method which we have briefly described is a powerful synthesis technique. However, it solves only one type of problem. Very often it is not required to maintain a high value of attenuation throughout the stop band; the attenuation is required to be high just beyond the cut-off but towards very high frequencies lower attenuation can be tolerated. If our synthesis procedure maintains high attenuation where it isn't required, we are paying for something we don't even want to buy.

In addition, the Cauer procedure takes no cognizance of the image phase in the pass band. If there are requirements on the behavior of the phase, then some other procedure must be devised to locate the critical points of Z_0 and $\tanh \theta$ appropriately.

We should also mention that when the filter requirements are relatively simple, the general procedure need not be employed. We have seen in Figs. 12 and 14 that half an m-derived section has an image impedance at one end which has one impedance controlling factor. This corresponds to $n = 2$ in Fig. 27a. If we can stand the combination of tolerance and coverage which this will provide for Z_0, then we can use two m-derived half sections as terminations. Any number of interior attenuating sections can still be used to satisfy stop band requirements.

11.6   Frequency Transformations

In the preceding sections of this chapter we dealt exclusively with low-pass filters. As a matter of fact, the approximation and most of the realization are handled with a normalized frequency variable $p = y + jx = s/\omega_c$ such that when $s = \pm j\omega_c$, $p = jx = \pm j1$. If we wish to deal with other types of filters, such as high-pass and band-pass, it is not necessary to repeat all of the analysis with filter sections and functional forms appropriate to the new frequency ranges. If we can find a transformation which will map the desired portions of the $j\omega$-axis onto the interval of the jx-axis (normalized low pass) from -1 to 1, then we can solve the filter problem as a low-pass problem, and subsequently transform back to the desired range.

As an example, consider the transformation

$$p = \omega_c/s; \qquad x = -\omega_c/\omega \tag{69}$$

This relationship transforms the positive $j\omega$-axis from ω_c to infinity into the negative x axis from -1 to 0, and the negative $j\omega$-axis from $-\omega_c$ to $-\infty$ into the range $0 < x < 1$. It is a *low-pass to high-pass* transformation.

Suppose now that a high-pass filter is required, satisfying certain pass-band and stop-band requirements. With the use of Eq. (69) these requirements are translated into requirements for a normalized low-pass filter. This filter is then synthesized and element values are found on a normalized low-pass basis. What we must do now is to modify the branch impedances in such a way that the value of each branch impedance at a value of p is the same as the value of the modified branch impedance at the corresponding value of s. In this way, any network function, image impedance, attenuation function, or any other one, will have the same value on the $j\omega$-axis as it has on the jx-axis.

Let us designate element values in the normalized low-pass case with a subscript 0 and those in the high-pass case with a subscript h. Then, in view of the transformation in Eq. (69), we will require

$$L_0 p = L_0 \frac{\omega_c}{s} = \frac{1}{C_h s} \qquad (a)$$

$$\frac{1}{C_0 p} = \frac{s}{C_0 \omega_c} = L_h s \qquad (b)$$

$$(70)$$

This means that in the normalized low-pass filter, we replace each inductance with a capacitance and each capacitance with an inductance, the corresponding values being

$$C_h = 1/L_0 \omega_c \qquad (a)$$

$$L_h = 1/C_0 \omega_c \qquad (b)$$

$$(71)$$

The high-pass filter synthesis is then complete.

Another common filter is the band-pass filter. Here the pass band is the frequency interval between two cut-off frequencies ω_{c1} and ω_{c2} (and also the image of this interval on the negative $j\omega$-axis). Consider the transformation

$$p = \frac{\omega_0}{w} \left(\frac{s}{\omega_0} + \frac{\omega_0}{s} \right) \qquad (72)$$

where ω_0 is the geometric mean between the two cut-offs and w is the bandwidth. That is

$$\omega_0^2 = \omega_{c1} \omega_{c2} \qquad (a)$$

$$w = \omega_{c2} - \omega_{c1} \qquad (b)$$

$$(73)$$

Figure 28 shows the corresponding portions of the two imaginary axes. This transformation is called a *low-pass to band-pass* transformation.

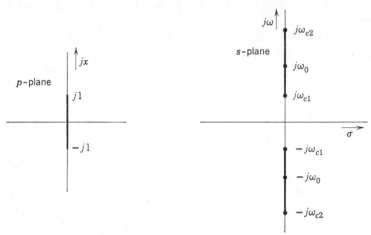

Fig. 28.   Low-pass to band-pass transformation.

To synthesize a band-pass filter, we again start from a normalized low-pass filter. Each branch of this filter must be so modified that its impedance remains the same, for any value of s, as the original one for the corresponding value of p. Let us use the subscript b to designate band-pass quantities. Then

$$L_0 p = \frac{L_0}{w} s + \frac{L_0 \omega_0{}^2}{ws} = L_{b1} s + \frac{1}{C_{b1} s} \qquad (a)$$

$$\frac{1}{C_0 p} = \frac{1}{(C_0 s/w) + (C_0 \omega_0{}^2/ws)} = \frac{1}{C_{b2} s + (1/L_{b2} s)} \quad (b) \tag{74}$$

Hence, each inductance in the normalized low-pass filter should be replaced by a series-resonant circuit whose element values are

$$L_{b1} = L_0/w \qquad (a)$$

$$C_{b1} = w/L_0 \omega_0{}^2 \qquad (b) \tag{75}$$

Similarly, each capacitance should be replaced by a parallel-resonant circuit whose element values are

$$L_{b2} = \frac{w}{C_0 \omega_0{}^2} \qquad (a)$$

$$C_{b2} = \frac{C_0}{w} \qquad (b) \tag{76}$$

As examples of this transformation, Fig. 29 shows m-derived high-pass and band-pass Tee sections obtained by making the changes in the elements called for by Eqs. (71), (75), and (76).

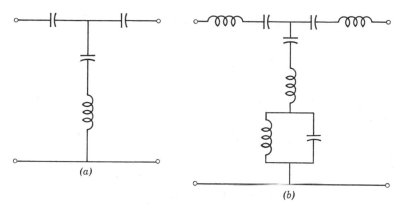

(a)

(b)

Fig. 29. High-pass and band-pass m-derived Tee sections.

This same concept can be applied to find other types of filters as well, including multiple-pass-band filters of which the band-elimination type is a special case. All that is required is to find transformations that will map the desired intervals on the $j\omega$-axis onto the range $-1 \leq x \leq 1$ in the p-plane.

One fact that we should note in the low-pass to band-pass transformation (72) is that any two points on the ω-axis that have ω_0 for a geometric mean correspond to conjugate values of p. That is, if

$$\omega_1\omega_2 = \omega_0{}^2 \qquad (a)$$

so that $\hspace{6cm} (77)$

$$\omega_1/\omega_0 = \omega_0/\omega_2 \qquad (b)$$

then

$$p_1 = \frac{\omega_0}{w}\left(\frac{j\omega_1}{\omega_0} + \frac{\omega_0}{j\omega_1}\right) \qquad (a)$$

$$p_2 = \frac{\omega_0}{w}\left(\frac{j\omega_2}{\omega_0} + \frac{\omega_0}{j\omega_2}\right) \qquad (78)$$

$$= -\frac{\omega_0}{w}\left(\frac{\omega_0}{j\omega_1} + \frac{j\omega_1}{\omega_0}\right) = -p_1 \qquad (b)$$

Thus if both ω_1 and ω_2 are in the pass band the values of the image impedance at these two points will be the same. If they are in the stop band, the values of the attenuation at these two points will be the same. Thus if we use a log ω scale, the filter characteristics will be symmetrical about the point $\log \omega_0$. Only band-pass filters possessing this type of symmetry can be realized by first starting with a low-pass filter.

PROBLEMS

11.1 Obtain the relationship between the actual reflection coefficient and the image reflection coefficient.

11.2 Carry out the details of the derivation of Eqs. (15) and (17) in the text.

11.3 The *insertion ratio* was defined at the end of section 11.1. The logarithmic magnitude of the reciprocal of this quantity, measured in db, is called the *insertion loss*. Find the relation between insertion loss and image loss.

11.4 Compute the image parameters of the following networks. (Make use of their relationship to the other sets of parameters and short cuts, instead of using the definitions.) (*a*) Equalizer network of Fig. 8.41, (*b*) Bridged Tee network of Fig. 8.43, (*c*) Twin Tee network of Fig. 8.46, and (*d*) Lattice network of Fig. P8.5.

11.5 Compute $Z_{01}(j\omega)$, the image attenuation $\alpha(\omega)$, and $\tanh \theta(j\omega)$ for the low-pass filter used with a conventional detector, as shown in Fig. P11.5. Find the poles and zeros of Z_{01} and $\tanh \theta(s)$, and find the cut-off frequency, if there is one. Sketch the variations of these functions in the frequency ranges of interest.

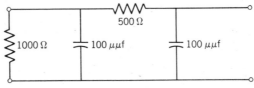

Fig. P11.5.

11.6 Repeat Problem 11.5 for the power supply filter of Fig. 8.35.

11.7 Using Z_{01} and $\tanh \theta$ derived in Problem 11.6, compute Z_{02}. Verify by direct computation of Z_{02} from the network.

11.8 Design a low-pass (ladder) filter to operate between 600 ohm terminations, for the following specifications. The input impedance should not vary from the 600 ohm level by more than 10 percent, over the frequency range 0 to 10,000 cycles per second. Beyond 12 kc/s, the attenuation should be at least 30 db. Compute the insertion loss of the final filter obtained, and sketch its variation up to 20 kc/s.

11.9 The following combinations of $Z_{01}(s)$ and the zeros of transmission are given. Find $Z_{02}(s)$ and $\tanh \theta(s)$. (Assume s is a normalized variable.)

(*a*) $Z_{01}(s) = \dfrac{\sqrt{1 + s^2}}{(1 + 4s^2/9)}$, double transmission zeros at $s = \pm j2$.

(*b*) Same Z_{01} and double transmission zeros, but with simple transmission zeros at $s = \pm j\frac{3}{2}$ in addition.

(*c*) $Z_{01}(s) = \dfrac{(1 + 4s^2/9)}{\sqrt{1 + s^2(1 + s^2/4)}}$, simple transmission zeros at $s = \pm j\frac{3}{2}, \pm j2$.

(*d*) Same Z_{01} as part (*c*), double transmission zeros at $s = \pm j\frac{5}{4}$.

11.10 Find the networks realizing the image parameters given in Problem 11.9.

APPENDIX

THEORY OF FUNCTIONS
OF A COMPLEX VARIABLE
AND LAPLACE TRANSFORMS

Even to attempt an appendix on two such extensive topics as the theory of functions and Laplace transforms may appear presumptuous. It is impossible to treat these topics with any semblance of precision and completeness in an appendix that is any shorter than the rest of the text. And when we try to keep the appendix shorter than the average chapter, the task is indeed hopeless. (The only meaningful "appendix" for this text is a pair of books, one on each of the subjects of the present title, tucked inside the back cover.)

Why, then, should we write this condensed treatment of function theory and Laplace transforms and call it an appendix? Our purpose here is twofold. First we would like to provide a handy reference for those who are familiar with the subject through an earlier encounter, but would like to refresh their memories on specific points as they go through the main text. Secondly we would like to provide a "skeleton" on which an instructor can base an introduction to the rest of the text. The material in the appendix is assumed as a prerequisite in the main body of the text; but the coverage provided in the appendix is inadequate for self-study.

We shall give the material in the appendix almost entirely in summary form. We shall not attempt to provide any motivation, and only very rarely shall we prove any results. However we shall state the important results precisely, for reference purposes.

A.1 Analytic Functions

We assume familiarity with the algebra of complex numbers (addition, subtraction, multiplication, and division), and the representation of complex numbers as points on a plane. We also assume familiarity with the elements of the theory of functions of a real variable.

Let $s = \sigma + j\omega$ denote a complex variable. We say that another complex variable $W = U + jX$ is a *function* of the complex variable s, if to each value of s (in some set), there corresponds a value of W or a set of values of W. We write $W = F(s)$, where F is the rule that associates the values of W with values of s. If to each value of s (in the set) there is only one value of W, we say that W is a *single-valued* function of s; otherwise it is *multi-valued*.

Continuity for a function of a complex variable is formally defined in the same way as for functions of a real variable. Namely, $F(s)$ is *continuous* at s_0 if it is defined in a neighborhood of s_0 and

$$\lim_{s \to s_0} F(s) = F(s_0) = W_0 \tag{1}$$

We may interpret this statement in the complex plane as follows. Let $\varepsilon > 0$ be a given number. We consider a circular neighborhood of $F(s_0)$ as in Fig. 1, where all the points within the circle of radius ε around

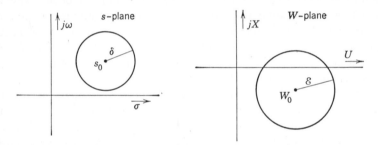

Fig. 1.   Neighborhoods in the s-plane and W-plane.

$F(s_0)$ belong to this neighborhood. Now Eq. (1) is equivalent to the following claim. We can find a small enough neighborhood of s_0, of radius $\delta > 0$, such that the values of $F(s)$ at all points in this neighborhood fall within the circle of radius ε about $F(s_0)$.

Differentiability in the complex plane is also defined by the same formal relation as on the real line, but is conceptually of much greater significance.

$F(s)$ is *differentiable* at s_0, with the derivative $F'(s_0)$, provided

$$F'(s_0) = \lim_{s \to s_0} \frac{F(s) - F(s_0)}{s - s_0} \tag{2}$$

exists and is finite.

Implicit in this definition is the assumption that s may approach s_0 in any direction, or may spiral into it, or follow any other path. The limit in Eq. (2) must exist (and be unique) independently of how s approaches s_0. It is this fact that makes differentiability in the complex plane a very strong requirement. In consequence, differentiable functions of a complex variable are extremely "well-behaved," as contrasted with real functions, which can be "pathological."

It can be shown (this is only one of many "it can be shown's" that we shall meet in this appendix) that the usual rules for derivatives of sums, products, quotients, etc., carry over from the real case, with no changes. So does the chain rule for the function of a function; and all the familiar functions have the same derivatives as on the real line, except that the variable is now complex. We summarize these results below.

Let $F_1(s)$ and $F_2(s)$ be two differentiable functions. Then

$$\frac{d}{ds}[F_1(s) + F_2(s)] = \frac{d}{ds}F_1(s) + \frac{d}{ds}F_2(s) \tag{3}$$

$$\frac{d}{ds}[F_1(s)F_2(s)] = F_1(s)\frac{d}{ds}F_2(s) + \left[\frac{d}{ds}F_1(s)\right]F_2(s) \tag{4}$$

$$\frac{d}{ds}\frac{F_1(s)}{F_2(s)} = \frac{F_2(s)\cdot dF_1(s)/ds - F_1(s)\cdot dF_2(s)/ds}{F_2{}^2(s)}; \quad F_2(s) \neq 0 \tag{5}$$

$$\frac{d}{ds}F_1[F_2(s)] = \frac{dF_1}{dF_2}\frac{dF_2(s)}{ds} \tag{6}$$

$$\frac{d}{ds}(s^n) = ns^{n-1} \tag{7}$$

If a function F of a complex variable is differentiable at the point s_0 *and at all points in a neighborhood of s_0*, we say that $F(s)$ is *regular* at s_0.

Notice that the statement "$F(s)$ is regular at s_0" is a very much stronger statement than "$F(s)$ is differentiable at s_0." A function $F(s)$ that has *at least one regular point* (i.e., a point at which the function is regular) in the complex plane, is called an *analytic function*. A point s_0 at which the analytic function $F(s)$ is *not regular* is a *singular point* of the function. $F(s)$ is said to have a singularity at s_0. In particular, a point at which the derivative does not exist is a singular point.

Although the requirement of regularity is a very strong condition and therefore the class of analytic functions is a "very small" subset of the set of all functions, almost all functions that we meet in physical applications are analytic functions. An example of a nonanalytic function is $|s|^2$. This function has a derivative at $s = 0$ and nowhere else. Hence it has no regular points. The function s^* $(= \sigma - j\omega)$ is another simple example of a nonanalytic function. The function $F(s) = 1/(s - 1)$ is a simple example of an analytic function. Its *region of regularity* consists of the whole plane exclusive of the point $s = 1$. The point $s = 1$ is a singular point of this function.

The singularities of an analytic function are extremely important, as we shall see. For the present we can only distinguish between two kinds of singularities. The point s_0 is an *isolated singularity* of $F(s)$, if s_0 is a singular point, but there is a neighborhood of s_0 in which all other points (except s_0) are regular points. If no such neighborhood exists, s_0 is a *nonisolated essential singularity*. Thus in every neighborhood of a non-isolated singularity there is at least one other singular point of the function. Hence a nonisolated singularity is a *limit point* (or *point of accumulation*) of singularities; and conversely.

Rational functions (quotients of polynomials) are examples of functions that have only isolated singularities. To give an example of a function that has nonisolated singularities, we have to use trigonometric functions that we have not defined yet. Nevertheless, an example of a nonisolated singularity is the point $s = 0$ for the function

$$F(s) = \frac{1}{\sin 1/s} \tag{8}$$

The denominator becomes zero whenever

$$s = \frac{1}{k\pi} \tag{9}$$

and so these points are singular points of $F(s)$. The origin is a limit point of these singularities.

The famous French mathematician Augustine Cauchy (who originated about half of complex function theory) gave the following necessary and sufficient condition for the differentiability of a function of a complex variable. The function

$$F(s) = U(\sigma,\omega) + jX(\sigma,\omega)$$

is differentiable at s_0 if and only if the partial derivatives $\partial U/\partial\sigma$, $\partial U/\partial\omega$, $\partial X/\partial\sigma$, and $\partial X/\partial\omega$ exist and are continuous at (σ_0,ω_0) and satisfy the equations

$$\partial U/\partial\sigma = \partial X/\partial\omega \qquad (a)$$

$$\partial X/\partial\sigma = -\partial U/\partial\omega \qquad (b)$$

$$\tag{10}$$

at this point.

The necessity is proved by letting s approach s_0 in Eq. (2) by first letting σ approach σ_0 and then letting ω approach ω_0 for one computation, and reversing the order for another computation. Equating the two derivatives so obtained leads to Eq. (10). The sufficiency is proved by using the concept of the total differential of a function of two variables and the definition of the derivative.

The equations in (10) are known as the *Cauchy–Riemann equations* honoring the German mathematician Bernhard Riemann (who made these equations fundamental to the theory of analytic functions) in addition to Cauchy. We can use the Cauchy–Riemann equations as a test for the regularity of a function as follows.

If the four partial derivatives are continuous in a region of the complex plane and if they satisfy the Cauchy–Riemann equations at every point of this region, then $F(s)$ is regular in the region.

Notice that this condition involves the neighborhood about s_0 just as the definition of the regularity of a function does. The proof of the result again depends on the concept of a differential for a function of two variables.

By differentiating one of the two equations in (10) with respect to σ and the other with respect to ω, and combining, we may observe the important fact that the real and imaginary parts of an analytic function satisfy Laplace's equation in two dimensions, within the region of regularity. That is,

$$\partial^2 U/\partial\sigma^2 + \partial^2 U/\partial\omega^2 = 0 \qquad (a)$$
$$\partial^2 X/\partial\sigma^2 + \partial^2 X/\partial\omega^2 = 0 \qquad (b)$$

$$(11)$$

Thus the real and imaginary parts of an analytic function are *harmonic functions*. The converse of this statement is also true. Every harmonic function (in two dimensions) is the real part of an analytic function, and the imaginary part of another analytic function. This fact makes analytic functions of considerable interest in two dimensional potential theory.

A.2 Mapping

We are all used to representing functions of a real variable as graphs. However with functions of a complex variable, a "graph" would require four dimensions, two for the variable and two for the function. Hence it is impossible to draw a graph for an analytic function. However we can still use the concept of geometrical representations with analytic functions to give us a better understanding of these functions. We use two planes, an s-plane for the variable and a W-plane for the function as we did in Fig. 1. This way we get four co-ordinate axes.

To draw a complete picture, telling what the value of the function is at each point in the s-plane, is futile, since this merely results in a smear. Therefore, we choose certain representative lines in the s-plane; and show in the W-plane the functional values of $F(s)$ at points on these lines. Single-valued functions $F(s)$ will give us smooth lines in the W-plane, as a result. As an example, we have a representative sketch of the function $F(s) = s^2$ in Fig. 2. Here we have taken some lines along which either σ

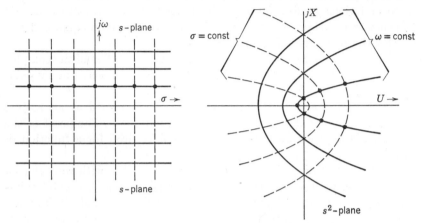

Fig. 2.   Representation of the mapping $F(s) = s^2$.

or ω is constant as representative lines. The corresponding lines in the s^2-plane are all parabolas. The two sets of parabolas, corresponding to $\sigma = $ const. and $\omega = $ const., are orthogonal families. If we had chosen other representative lines in the s-plane, we would have obtained other types of curves in the s^2-plane.

We refer to this graphical concept as a *mapping*. The s-plane is said to be *mapped into* the F-plane; the F-plane is a map of the s-plane. The lines in the F-plane are *images* of the lines in the s-plane, under the function $F(s)$. We also refer to $F(s)$ as a *transformation*. The function $F(s)$ transforms points in the s-plane into points in the F-plane. The concept of a mapping by an analytic function is a very useful one.

The fact that the parabolas of Fig. 2 constitute an orthogonal family is no accident. The reason is that the original lines in the s-plane intersect at right angles, and an analytic function preserves angles, except when the derivative does not exist or is zero. Let us make a definition before establishing this fact. A *conformal transformation* F is one in which the angle of intersection of two image curves in the F-plane is the same (both in magnitude and in sense) as the angle of intersection of the two corresponding curves in the s-plane.

The mapping by an analytic function is conformal at all points at which the function is regular and the derivative is nonzero.

To prove this result we take two smooth curves C_1 and C_2 in the s-plane, which intersect at s_0. Let s be an arbitrary point on C_1. Let us introduce polar co-ordinates about s_0, by defining

$$s - s_0 = re^{j\theta_1} \qquad (12)$$

Then as s approaches s_0, the angle θ_1 approaches the angle α_1, which is the angle of the tangent to C_1 at s_0. By the definition of the derivative

$$\lim_{s \to s_0} \frac{F(s) - F(s_0)}{s - s_0} = F'(s_0) \qquad (13)$$

Since this derivative exists, we may take the limit along C_1. Since the derivative is nonzero, we may write

$$F'(s_0) = \rho e^{j\beta} \qquad (14)$$

Then from Eq. (13)

$$\lim_{s \to s_0} \left| \frac{F(s) - F(s_0)}{s - s_0} \right| = \rho \qquad (a)$$

and $\qquad\qquad\qquad\qquad\qquad\qquad\qquad\qquad\qquad\qquad (15)$

$$\lim_{s \to s_0} \{ \arg [F(s) - F(s_0)] - \arg (s - s_0) \} = \beta \qquad (b)$$

Eq. (15b) can be rewritten

$$\lim_{s \to s_0} \arg [F(s) - F(s_0)] = \beta + \lim_{s \to s_0} \arg (s - s_0) = \beta + \alpha_1 \qquad (16)$$

The point $F(s)$ is on the curve C_1' which is the image of C_1 under the mapping $F(s)$. Thus the left side of Eq. (16) is the angle of the tangent to C_1' at $F(s_0)$. Thus from Eq. (16), the curve C_1' has a definite tangent at $F(s_0)$, making an angle $\beta + \alpha_1$ with the positive real axis. An identical argument gives the angle of the tangent to C_2' at $F(s_0)$ to be $\beta + \alpha_2$. Thus the angle between the two tangents, taken from C_1' to C_2' is $(\alpha_2 - \alpha_1)$ which is the same (in magnitude and sign) as the angle between the curves C_1 and C_2 at s_0 measured from C_1 to C_2.

Incidentally, we see from Eq. (15a) that the *local magnification*, that is the increase in linear distance near s_0, is independent of direction and is given by the magnitude of the derivative. Thus, locally, the mapping by an analytic function (when $F'(s_0) \neq 0$) produces a linear magnification $|F'(s_0)|$ and a rotation $\arg F'(s_0)$; thus preserving shapes of small figures.

An auxiliary consequence is that the images of smooth curves are also smooth curves; that is, they cannot have corners.

We have not yet defined some point-set-topological concepts about regions and curves that are really needed to clarify our earlier discussions.

Let us proceed to rectify this omission, although we cannot be completely precise without introducing very complex ideas, which we do not propose to do. Therefore we shall take a few concepts such as path, continuous curve, etc., to be intuitively obvious.

A *simple arc* is a continuous path in the complex plane which has no crossover or multiple points. A *simple closed curve* is a path in the complex plane which if cut at any one point becomes a simple arc. If the end points of a simple arc are joined, we form a simple closed curve.

An *open region* is a set of points in the complex plane each of which has a neighborhood all of whose points belong to the set. The region "inside" a simple closed curve, not counting the curve itself, is an example. If we add the points on the boundary of an open set to the open set itself, the combined region is called a *closed region*. An open or closed region is said to be *connected* if any two points in the region can be connected by a line all points on which are in the region.

In the preceding paragraph the word "inside" was put in quotation marks. Although we have a strong intuitive feeling that the inside of a closed curve is well defined, nevertheless this requires a proof. The *Jordan curve theorem* gives the desired result. It states that *every simple closed curve divides the complex plane into two regions, an "inside" and an "outside," the curve itself being the boundary of these two regions.* If we start at some point on the curve and traverse it in a counterclockwise sense, the region to the left of the curve will be called the inside, that to the right, the outside.

If we do not permit a closed curve to pass through infinity, then the "inside" region, as just defined, will be *bounded*; that is, all points in the region will satisfy the condition $|s| \leq M$, where M is a fixed positive number. On the other hand, if the closed curve goes through infinity, then neither the inside nor the outside is bounded.

The question arises as to what is meant by a closed curve passing through infinity. The path consisting of the imaginary axis, for example, is such a curve. But this may appear to be a simple arc rather than a closed curve. The *Riemann sphere* will serve to clarify this point.

Consider a sphere placed on the complex plane with its "south pole" at the origin, as illustrated in Fig. 3. Now consider joining by a straight line every point in the plane to the "north pole" of the sphere. These lines will all intersect the sphere, thus setting up a one-to-one correspondence between the points in the plane and those on the sphere. Every point in the finite plane will have its counterpart on the sphere. As we go farther and farther away from the origin of the plane in any direction, the point of intersection of the lines with the sphere will approach closer and closer to the north pole. Thus, the north pole corresponds to in-

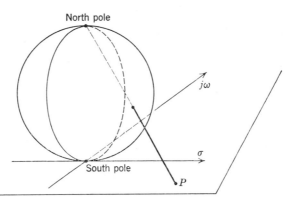

Fig. 3.   The Riemann sphere.

finity. On the sphere infinity appears to be a unique point. Both the real and the imaginary axes become great circles on the sphere, and a great circle appears like a simple closed curve.

The concept of the Riemann sphere serves another purpose; it permits us to look upon "infinity" as a single point, whenever this is convenient. We refer to infinity as the *point at infinity*.

Very often we wish to talk about the behavior of a function at the point infinity. A convention in mathematics is that no statement containing the word "infinity" is to be considered meaningful, unless the whole statement can be defined without using this word. This convention is introduced to avoid many inconsistencies that would otherwise arise. The behavior of a function at the point infinity is defined as follows.

That behavior is assigned to the function $F(s)$ at $s = \infty$, as is exhibited by the function

$$G(s) = F(1/s)$$

at $s = 0$. For example the function $F(s) = 1/s$ is regular at $s = \infty$, since $G(s) = F(1/s) = s$ is regular at $s = 0$. Similarly the function $F(s) = as^2 + bs$ is not regular at infinity since $G(s) = a/s^2 + b/s$ has a singularity at $s = 0$.

By a similar artifice we can also talk about the value of a function at a point in the complex plane being ∞, if we are careful. By this statement we mean that the reciprocal of the function is zero at this point.

A.3   Integration

The definite integral of a function of a complex variable is defined in a manner similar to the definition of real integration. In the case of real variables the definite integral can be interpreted as an area. For complex variables such a geometrical interpretation is not possible. In Fig. 4 two points P_1 and P_2 are connected by a simple arc C. The path is divided into intervals by the points s_k; the chords * joining these points are labeled $\Delta_k s$. Suppose we multiply each of the chords by the value of a function $F(s)$ evaluated at some point $s_k{}^*$ of the interval, and then add all these products. Now we let the number of intervals increase

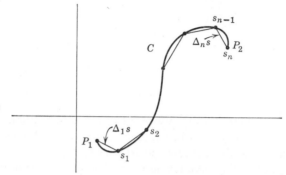

Fig. 4.   The definite integral.

with a simultaneous decrease in the lengths of the chords. We define the definite integral of $F(s)$ as the limit of this sum as the number of intervals goes to infinity while the length of each chord goes to zero. More precisely

$$\int_{C\,P_1}^{P_2} F(s)\,ds = \lim_{\substack{n\to\infty \\ \max|\Delta_k s|\to 0}} \sum_{k=1}^{n} F(s_k{}^*)\Delta_k s \tag{17}$$

provided the limit on the right exists.

Note that in addition to the lower and upper limits P_1 and P_2, we have indicated that in going from P_1 to P_2 we shall follow the path C. It is conceivable that a different answer will be obtained if a different path is followed. It would not be necessary to write the limits on the integration symbol if we were to always show the path of integration on a suitable diagram together with the direction along the path. Because the path, or contour, is inseparable from the definition of an integral, we refer to it as a *contour integral*.

To determine the conditions under which the definite integral in Eq. (17) exists, it is possible to express this integral as a combination of real integrals. With $F(s) = U + jX$, and after some manipulation, Eq. (17) becomes

---

* Here the chords are taken to be expressed as complex numbers. Thus $\Delta_k s = s_k - s_{k-1}$.

$$\int_C F(s)\,ds = \int_C U\,d\sigma - \int_C X\,d\omega + j\left[\int_C U\,d\omega + \int_C X\,d\sigma\right] \qquad (18)$$

Each of the integrals on the right is a real line integral; if these integrals exist, then the contour integral will exist. From our knowledge of real integrals we know that continuity of the integrand is a sufficient condition for the existence of a real line integral. It follows that *the contour integral of a function $F(s)$ along a curve C exists if $F(s)$ is continuous on the curve.*

The question still remains as to the conditions under which the integral between two points is independent of the path joining those points. Consider Fig. 5 which shows two points P_1 and P_2 joined by two simple

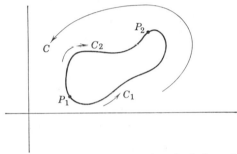

Fig. 5. Conditions for the value of an integral to be independent of the path of integration.

paths C_1 and C_2. Note that the directions of these paths are both from P_1 to P_2. The combined path formed by C_1 and the negative of C_2 forms a simple closed curve, which we will label $C = C_1 - C_2$. If the integral of a function $F(s)$ along path C_1 is to equal the integral along path C_2, then the integral along the combined path C must be equal to zero, and conversely. The inquiry into conditions under which an integral is independent of path is now reduced to an inquiry into conditions under which a contour integral along a simple closed curve is equal to zero. The question is answered by the following theorem which is known as *Cauchy's integral theorem.*

Let $F(s)$ be a function which is regular everywhere on a simple closed curve C and inside the curve. Then,

$$\int_C F(s)\,ds = 0 \qquad (19)$$

This is a very powerful and important theorem but we shall omit its proof.

A word is in order about the *connectivity* of a region in the complex plane. Suppose we connect any two arbitrary points P_1 and P_2 which lie in a region by two arbitrary simple arcs C_1 and C_2 also lying in the region. The region is said to be *simply-connected* if it is possible to slide one of these arcs along (distortion of the arc is permitted in this process) until it coincides with the other, without ever passing out of the region. Cauchy's theorem is proved ab initio for just such a region. The hatched region between the two closed curves in Fig. 6 is called *doubly connected*.

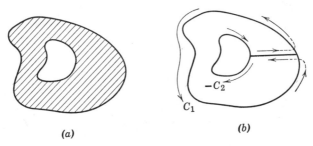

(a)   (b)

Fig. 6.   A doubly-connected region.

Such a region can be reduced to a simply connected region by the artifice of "digging a canal" between the two closed curves. The region now is bounded by the composite curve whose outline is shown by the arrows in Fig. 6b.

Suppose that a function $F(s)$ is regular in the hatched region shown in Fig. 6a including the boundaries. Cauchy's theorem can be applied here to the composite curve consisting of the inner and outer curves and the "canal." The canal is traversed twice, but in opposite directions, so that its contribution to the complete contour integral is zero. If we denote the outside and inside curves by C_1 and C_2, respectively, both in the counterclockwise direction, then Cauchy's theorem will lead to the result that

$$\int_{C_1} F(s)\ ds = \int_{C_2} F(s)\ ds \tag{20}$$

As a matter of fact, if we choose any other closed path between the inner and outer ones in Fig. 6, the same reasoning will tell us that the integral around this path in the counterclockwise direction will be equal to each of the integrals in Eq. (20).

This reasoning leads us to conclude that the value of a contour integral around a simple closed curve will not change if the contour is distorted, so long as it always stays inside a region of regularity.

Turn again to Fig. 5. The points P_1 and P_2 are in a simply connected region R throughout which a function $F(s)$ is single-valued and regular. Let P_1 be a fixed point which we will label s_0, and P_2 a variable point which we will label s. We have stated that the integral from s_0 to s is independent of the path of integration so long as the paths remain in the region of regularity. Hence, we can define the function $G(s)$ as

$$G(s) = \int_{s_0}^{s} F(z)\, dz \qquad (21)$$

where z is a dummy variable of integration. This function is a single-valued function of the upper limit s for all paths in the region of regularity. It is easy to show that $G(s)$ is regular in R and that its derivative is $F(s)$. We call it the *anti-derivative* of $F(s)$. (For each s_0 we get a different anti-derivative.)

Actually it is not necessary to assume that $F(s)$ is regular in the region. Instead it is sufficient to assume that $F(s)$ is *continuous* in R and that its closed contour integral for all possible simple closed curves in R is zero. However, Morera's theorem, which we will discuss later, states that a function satisfying these conditions is regular.

In evaluating a definite integral in real variables we often look for an anti-derivative of the integrand. The same procedure is valid for complex variables. That is, if an anti-derivative of $F(s)$ is $G(s)$, then

$$\int_{s_1}^{s_2} F(s)\, ds = G(s_2) - G(s_1) \qquad (22)$$

Let us now consider a simple closed curve C within and on the boundary of which a single-valued function $F(s)$ is regular. It is possible to express the value of the function at any point s_0 inside the curve in terms of its values along the contour C. This expression is

$$F(s_0) = \frac{1}{2\pi j} \int_C \frac{F(s)}{s - s_0}\, ds \qquad (23)$$

It is referred to as *Cauchy's integral formula* (as distinct from Cauchy's theorem). This result can be proved by noting that in the integral involved the contour C can be replaced by a circular contour C' around the point s_0 without changing its value, according to the discussion centering around Eq. (20). The purely algebraic step of adding and subtracting $F(s_0)$ in the integrand then permits writing

$$\int_{C'} \frac{F(s)}{s - s_0}\, ds = \int_{C'} \frac{F(s_0)}{s - s_0} + \int_{C'} \frac{F(s) - F(s_0)}{s - s_0}\, ds \qquad (24)$$

The last integral on the right can be shown to be zero. It remains to evaluate the first integral on the right.

Let us write $s - s_0 = re^{j\theta}$; then $ds = jre^{j\theta}\, d\theta$, since the contour C' is a circular one and only θ varies. Then

$$\int_{C'} \frac{ds}{s - s_0} = \int_0^{2\pi} j\, d\theta = 2\pi j \tag{25}$$

The desired expression now follows immediately upon substituting this result into Eq. (24).

Cauchy's integral formula sheds much light on the properties of analytic functions. We see that the value of an analytic function which is regular in a region is determined at any point in the region by its values on the boundary. Note that the point s_0 is *any point whatsoever* inside the region of regularity. We should really label it with the general variable s, which would then require that in Eq. (23) we relabel the variable s—which merely represents points on the boundary and is thus a dummy variable—with some other symbol. For clarity, we will rewrite Eq. (23) as

$$F(s) = \frac{1}{2\pi j} \int_C \frac{F(z)}{z - s}\, dz \tag{26}$$

Here s represents any point inside a contour C in which $F(s)$ is regular, and z refers to points on the contour.

Another very important fact about analytic functions can be determined from Cauchy's integral formula. Let us try to find the nth order derivative of an analytic function $F(s)$. For the first and second derivatives we can use the definition of a derivative directly on Eq. (26), without getting bogged down in a great mass of algebra. The result will be

$$F'(s) = \frac{1}{2\pi j} \int_C \frac{F(z)}{(z - s)^2}\, dz \tag{a}$$

$$F''(s) = \frac{2}{2\pi j} \int_C \frac{F(z)}{(z - s)^3}\, dz \tag{b}$$

(27)

The form of these expressions, which seems to indicate that we simply differentiate with respect to s under the integral sign, suggests the following expression for the nth derivative.

$$F^{(n)}(s) = \frac{n!}{2\pi j} \int_C \frac{F(z)}{(z - s)^{n+1}}\, dz \tag{28}$$

This result can be corroborated by the use of mathematical induction.

An extremely important implication of the points we have just been discussing is the following. *If a single-valued function $F(s)$ is regular at a point, it follows that the function will have derivatives of all orders at that point.* This same statement cannot be made for a function of a real variable.

Having seen that the derivative of an analytic function is itself analytic and has the same region of regularity, we can now make a statement which appears to be the converse of Cauchy's theorem. *Let $F(s)$ be a function which is continuous in a region R and whose closed contour integral around all possible paths in the region is zero.* These conditions ensure that $F(s)$ has an anti-derivative $G(s)$ which is regular in the region R. But the derivative of $G(s)$ is $F(s)$; consequently $F(s)$ *is also regular in R.* This result is known as *Morera's theorem.*

Cauchy's formula leads to some other very interesting results. However, we shall demonstrate these same results from the viewpoint of mapping. Let $W = F(s)$ be an analytic function which is regular within and on a curve C in the s-plane; let this region, including the curve C, be R. The map of the curve C may take one of the forms shown in Fig. 7.

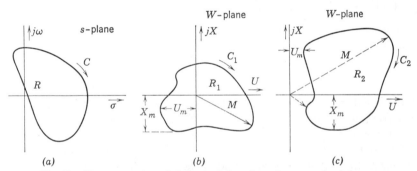

Fig. 7.   Demonstration of the principles of maximum and minimum.

Note that the maps of the region R cannot extend to infinity, since infinity in the W-plane corresponds to a singular point in the s-plane, and there are no singular points in R. Both maps of the curve C have been shown as simple closed curves for simplicity; they need not, and usually will not, be. In the map shown in part (b) the origin of the W-plane is inside the region. This corresponds to the possibility that $F(s)$ has a zero in the region R. The origin is not included inside the map of region R shown in part (c).

In either of these cases, it is clear from the figures that the point in R_1 or R_2 which lies farthest from the origin of the W-plane lies on the boundary of the region, which is the map of curve C. Similarly, if $F(s)$ does not have a zero in region R, then the point in R_2 which lies closest to the origin of the W-plane lies on the boundary, as illustrated in part (c) of the figure. It is also clear from the figure that the minimum values in region R_2 of the real part of W, and the imaginary part, lie on the boundary. The last statement is also true when $F(s)$ has a zero in the region, as part (b) of the figure illustrates. But in this case the smallest value of the magnitude, which is zero, lies inside the region and not on the boundary. We shall summarize these results as follows.

Let a closed curve C and its interior constitute a region R in the s-plane and let $W = F(s) = U + jX$ be regular in R. The largest value reached by the magnitude $|F(s)|$, the real part U and the imaginary part X in region R occurs for some point or points on the boundary. Likewise, the minimum values reached by the real part and the imaginary part in R occur on the boundary. The last is also true for the magnitude if $F(s)$ has no zero in region R. The statements concerning the magnitude are referred to as the *maximum modulus theorem* and the *minimum modulus theorem*. Similar designations can be applied to the other cases by replacing "modulus" by "real part" and "imaginary part."

A.4   Infinite Series

Let $f_1(s)$, $f_2(s)$, $\cdots$ be an infinite sequence of functions and consider the sum of the first n of these.

$$S_n(s) = \sum_{j=1}^{n} f_j(s) \tag{29}$$

This is called a *partial sum* of the corresponding infinite series. Now consider the sequence of partial sums S_1, S_2, $\cdots$, S_n. We say that this sequence *converges* in a region of the complex plane if there is a function $F(s)$ from whose value at a given point the value of the partial sum S_n differs as little as we please, provided that we take n large enough. The function $F(s)$ is called the *limit function* of the sequence. More precisely, we say that the sequence converges in a region R if, given any positive number ε, there exists an integer N_j and a function $F(s)$ such that at any point s_j in the region

$$|S_n(s_j) - F(s_j)| < \varepsilon \tag{30}$$

for all values of n greater than N_j. The value of the integer N_j will depend on the number ε and on the point s_j.

We say that the sequence is *uniformly convergent* in a closed region if the same integer N can be used in the role of N_j for all points in the region instead of having this integer depend on the point in question. (N still depends on ε.)

The infinite series is said to converge (or converge uniformly) to the function $F(s)$ if the sequence of partial sums converges (or converges uniformly). An infinite series is said to *converge absolutely* if the series formed by taking the absolute value of each term itself converges. Absolute convergence is a stronger kind of convergence. It can be shown that *if a series converges absolutely in a region R, it also converges in the region.*

We will now state a number of theorems about sequences of functions without giving proofs.*

Theorem 1. *If a sequence of continuous functions $S_n(s)$ is uniformly convergent in a region R, then the limit function of the sequence is continuous in the same region R.*

Theorem 2. *If a sequence of continuous functions $S_n(s)$ converges uniformly to a limit function $F(s)$ in a region R, then the integral of $F(s)$ along any simple arc C in the region R can be obtained by first finding the integral along C of a member $S_n(s)$ of the sequence and then taking the limit as $n \to \infty$.* That is

$$\int_C F(s)\, ds = \int_C [\lim_{n\to\infty} S_n(s)]\, ds = \lim_{n\to\infty} \int_C S_n(s)\, ds \qquad (31)$$

Theorem 3. *If a sequence of analytic functions $S_n(s)$ are regular in a region R and if they converge uniformly in R to a limit function $F(s)$, then $F(s)$ is regular in the region R.*

Theorem 4. *If the members of a sequence of analytic functions $S_n(s)$ are regular in a region R and if the sequence converges uniformly in R to a limit function $F(s)$, then the sequence of derivatives $S_n'(s)$ converges uniformly to the derivative of $F(s)$ for all interior points in R.* Repeated applications of the theorem shows that the sequence of kth order derivatives $S_n^{(k)}(s)$ converges uniformly to $F^{(k)}(s)$.

These theorems can be used to establish many important properties of infinite series, by letting the sequence of functions $S_n(s)$ represent the partial sums of a series. Let us consider an important special case of infinite series.

We will define a *power series* as follows.

$$F(s) = \sum_{n=0}^{\infty} a_n(s - s_0)^n \qquad (32)$$

* All of these theorems have to do with conditions under which two limit operations can be interchanged. They are of the general character

$$\lim_{x\to a} \lim_{y\to b} f(x,y) = \lim_{y\to b} \lim_{x\to a} f(x,y)$$

This interchange is permissible if both limits (separately) exist and one of them (say $x \to a$) exists uniformly with respect to the other variable.

The partial sums of a power series are polynomials in $(s - s_0)$; hence, they are regular in the entire finite complex plane (this implies that they are continuous as well). If we can now determine the region of uniform convergence, we can use Theorems 1 through 4 to deduce properties of the limit function.

Suppose that a power series converges for some point $s = s_1$. It is easy to show that the series will converge absolutely (and hence, it will also converge) at any point inside the circle with center at s_0 and radius $|s_1 - s_0|$. The *largest* circle with center at s_0 within which the series converges is called the *circle of convergence*, the radius of the circle being the *radius of convergence*. It follows that a power series *diverges* (does not converge) at any point outside its circle of convergence. For if it does converge at such a point s_2, it must converge everywhere inside the circle of radius $|s_2 - s_0|$, which means the original circle was not its circle of convergence.

Let R_0 be the radius of convergence of a power series and suppose that R_1 is strictly less than R_0. Then, it can be shown that the given series is uniformly convergent in the closed region bounded by the circle of radius $R_1 < R_0$ with center at s_0.

Suppose now that a power series converges to a function $F(s)$ in a circle of radius R_0. This means that the sequence of partial sums $S_n(s)$ will have $F(s)$ as a limit function. Since $S_n(s)$ is a continuous function, it follows from Theorem 1 that $F(s)$ is also continuous everywhere inside the circle. Furthermore, since the partial sums are regular in the region of uniform convergence, it follows from Theorem 3 that $F(s)$ is regular in the region. Thus, *a power series represents an analytic function which is regular inside its circle of convergence.*

Two other important conclusions about power series follow from Theorems 2 and 4. According to Theorem 2, since the partial sums of a power series satisfy the conditions of the theorem, *a power series which converges to $F(s)$ can be integrated term-by-term and the resulting series will converge to the integral of $F(s)$ for every path inside the circle of convergence.* Similarly, according to Theorem 4, *a power series may be differentiated term-by-term and the resulting series will converge to the derivative of $F(s)$ everywhere inside the circle of convergence.* The circles of convergence of both the integrated series and the differentiated series are the same as that of the original series.

We saw that a power series converges to an analytic function which is regular within the circle of convergence. The converse of this statement, which is more interesting, is also true. Every analytic function can be represented as a power series about any regular point s_0. The desired result is *Taylor's theorem*, which states: *Let $F(s)$ be regular everywhere in a* *circle of radius R_0 about a regular point s_0. Then $F(s)$ can be represented as*

$$F(s) = \sum_{n=0}^{\infty} a_n(s - s_0)^n \tag{33}$$

where the coefficients are given by

$$a_n = \frac{1}{n!} F^{(n)}(s_0) \tag{34}$$

The circle of convergence of the power series is the largest circle about s_0 in which $F(s)$ is defined or is definable as a regular function.

This series is referred to as a *Taylor series*. The theorem is proved by starting with Cauchy's integral formula given in Eq. (23) and expanding $(z - s)^{-1}$ as a finite number of terms in inverse powers of $(z - s_0)$ (after adding and subtracting s_0 to the denominator of the integrand), together with a remainder term. Use of the integral formulas for the derivatives of an analytic function given in Eq. (28) leads to a polynomial in $(s - s_0)$ plus a remainder term. The proof is completed by noting that the remainder term vanishes as the order of the polynomial in $(s - s_0)$ approaches infinity.

An important consequence of Taylor's theorem is that the circle of convergence of any power series passes through a singular point of the analytic function represented by it. For, by Taylor's theorem the radius of convergence is the distance from the point s_0 to the nearest singular point.

To find the power series representation of a function, it is not necessary to use the formulas given in Taylor's theorem. But independent of the method used to find the power series representation, we will end up with Taylor's series, with the coefficients satisfying Taylor's formula. This fact is established through the following *Identity Theorem for Power Series.* *If the two power series*

$$\sum_{n=0}^{\infty} a_n(s - s_0)^n \text{ and } \sum_{n=0}^{\infty} b_n(s - s_0)^n$$

have positive radii of convergence and if their sums coincide for an infinite number of distinct points having the limit point s_0, then $a_n = b_n$ for all n. That is, they are identical.

In particular the conditions of the theorem are satisfied if the two series agree in a neighborhood of s_0 or along a line segment (no matter how small) containing s_0. This result is proved by induction on n. Thus, the representation of an analytic function by a power series about a given regular point s_0 is unique.

We have seen that a power series representation can be found for an analytic function in the neighborhood of a regular point with a region of convergence which extends to the nearest singular point of the function. The question arises whether it is possible to find other infinite series representations for an analytic function which converge in other regions.

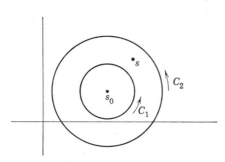

Consider the annular region between the two concentric circles C_1 and C_2 with center at s_0 shown in Fig. 8. A function $F(s)$ is regular on C_1, C_2, and the region between them. The point s_0 may be a regular point or a singular point of $F(s)$. Also there may be other singular points of $F(s)$ inside the inner circle. The annular region can be made simply connected by the device of "digging a canal" as discussed in a previous

Fig. 8. Region of convergence of a Laurent series.

section. If we now apply Cauchy's integral formula, we get

$$F(s) = \frac{1}{2\pi j} \int_{C_2} \frac{F(z)}{z - s} \, dz - \frac{1}{2\pi j} \int_{C_1} \frac{F(z)}{z - s} \, dz \qquad (35)$$

where s is a point in the interior of the annular region and z represents points on the contours of the two circles. For the quantity $(z - s)^{-1}$ we can write

$$\frac{1}{z - s} = \frac{1}{z - s_0} \sum_{k=0}^{n} \left(\frac{s - s_0}{z - s_0}\right)^k + \frac{1}{z - s} \left(\frac{s - s_0}{z - s_0}\right)^{n+1} \qquad (36)$$

$$\frac{1}{z - s} = -\frac{1}{s - s_0} \sum_{k=0}^{n} \left(\frac{z - s_0}{s - s_0}\right)^k + \frac{1}{z - s} \left(\frac{z - s_0}{s - s_0}\right)^{n+1} \qquad (37)$$

These can be checked by noting that the expression

$$\frac{1}{1 - w} = \sum_{k=0}^{n} w^k + \frac{w^{n+1}}{1 - w} \qquad (38)$$

is an identity for all values of w except $w = 1$. Equation (36) is obtained by adding and subtracting s_0 in the denominator on the left and then writing it in the form of Eq. (38) with

$$w = \frac{s - s_0}{z - s_0} \qquad (39)$$

Similarly for Eq. (37) except that w is now

$$w = \frac{z - s_0}{s - s_0} \tag{40}$$

Now let us use Eq. (36) in the first integral in Eq. (35), and Eq. (37) in the second integral. Each integral will give a finite number of terms plus a remainder term. It can be shown, as in the proof of Taylor's theorem, that the remainder terms vanish as $n \to \infty$. The final result is

$$F(s) = \sum_{k=0}^{\infty} a_k (s - s_0)^k + \sum_{k=1}^{\infty} a_{-k} (s - s_0)^{-k} \tag{41}$$

or

$$F(s) = \sum_{k=-\infty}^{\infty} a_k (s - s_0)^k \tag{42}$$

where a_k in the last expression is given by

$$a_k = \frac{1}{2\pi j} \int_C \frac{F(z)}{(z - s_0)^{k+1}} \, dz \tag{43}$$

The contour C is any closed contour in the annular region between C_1 and C_2.

The series we have just obtained is called a *Laurent series*. It is characterized by having negative powers as well as positive powers. Its region of convergence is an annular region as contrasted with the region of convergence of a Taylor series which is a circle.* For a given function $F(s)$ and a point of expansion s_0 there can be more than one Laurent series with different regions of convergence. The point of expansion can be a regular point or a singular point. As in the case of a Taylor series it is not necessary to use the formula in order to determine the coefficients in any particular case. But the identity theorem for Laurent series, which follows the statement of the residue theorem in the next section, tells us that no matter how the Laurent series of a function may be obtained, it must be unique, for a given region of convergence.

Let us now consider the particular case of a Laurent expansion of a function $F(s)$ about a point s_0 which is a singular point. The inner circle in Fig. 8 is to enclose no other singularities (this implies the singularity is isolated). Hence, we should expect the Laurent series to tell us something about the nature of the singularity at s_0. Remember that the

---

* This property of Laurent series can be interpreted as saying that the series of positive powers in $(s - s_0)$ converges everywhere inside C_2 of Fig. 8, and the series of negative powers converges everywhere outside of C_1, the two converging simultaneously in the annular region between C_1 and C_2.

Laurent series consists of two parts, the positive powers and the negative powers. Let us define the *regular part* $F_r(s)$ of the Laurent expansion as the series of positive powers and the constant, and the *principal part* $F_p(s)$ as the series of negative powers. If there were no principal part, the Laurent series would reduce to a Taylor series and s_0 would be a regular point. Thus, the principal part of the Laurent series contains the clue regarding the nature of the singularity at s_0.

To describe the singularity at s_0, we make the following definitions. We say $F(s)$ has a *pole of order n* at s_0 if the highest negative power in the principal part is n. (A pole of order 1 is also called a *simple* pole.) On the other hand, if the principal part has an infinite number of terms, the singularity at s_0 is called an *isolated essential singularity*. (The word "isolated" is often omitted.)

One of the results that we noted previously is that a power series defines an analytic function which is regular inside its circle of convergence. We shall now use this fact to define some specific functions. Up until now we have explicitly mentioned rational functions. But in the case of real variables we know the importance of such functions as exponentials, trigonometric and hyperbolic functions, and others. However, we have no basis for taking over the definitions of such functions from real variables. The tangent of a complex variable, for instance, can not be defined as the ratio of two sides of a triangle.

We use the above-quoted property of power series to *define* an exponential function as follows.

$$\epsilon^s = 1 + s + \frac{s^2}{2!} + \frac{s^3}{3!} + \cdots = \sum_{k=0}^{\infty} \frac{s^n}{n!}$$

$$= \epsilon^{\sigma}(\cos \omega + j \sin \omega) \qquad (44)$$

The last form is obtained by inserting $s = \sigma + j\omega$ in the series, expanding the powers of s, collecting terms and finally identifying the real power series representing ϵ^{σ}, $\cos \omega$, and $\sin \omega$. We are not completely free in choosing a defining series for ϵ^s because it must reduce to the correct series when s is real.

To determine the radius of convergence of the defining series we can resort to various tests for the convergence of series (which we have not discussed). Alternatively, since the series represents an analytic function, we can use the Cauchy–Riemann equations. In the latter case we find that there are no singular points in the entire finite plane, since the Cauchy–Riemann equations are satisfied everywhere. Hence, the series converges everywhere. (The same result is of course obtained by testing the series for convergence.)

We can now follow the same procedure and define other transcendental functions in terms of series. However, it is simpler to define the trigonometric and hyperbolic functions in terms of the exponential. By definition, then,

$$\sin s = \frac{\epsilon^{js} - \epsilon^{-js}}{2j} \; ; \qquad \cos s = \frac{\epsilon^{js} + \epsilon^{-js}}{2}$$

$$\tan s = \frac{\sin s}{\cos s} \tag{45}$$

$$\sinh s = \frac{\epsilon^{s} - \epsilon^{-s}}{2} \; ; \qquad \cosh s = \frac{\epsilon^{s} + \epsilon^{-s}}{2}$$

$$\tanh s = \frac{\sinh s}{\cosh s} \tag{46}$$

Note that, based on the behavior of the exponential, we see that the sines and cosines, both trigonometric and hyperbolic, are regular for all finite values of s. The singular points of $\tan s$ occur when $\cos s = 0$, namely for an infinite number of real values of s at the points $s = (2k - 1)\pi/2$, for all integral values of k. Similarly the singular points of $\tanh s$ occur when $\cosh s = 0$, namely at an infinite number of imaginary values of s at the points $s = j(2k - 1)\pi/2$, for all integral values of k.

The trigonometric and hyperbolic functions of a complex variable satisfy practically all of the identities satisfied by the corresponding real functions.

A.5 Multi-Valued Functions

In real function theory we define a number of "inverse" functions. These functions can be extended into the complex plane as analytic functions. As we know, most of these functions (the nth root, inverse sine, etc.) are multi-valued on the real line. We may therefore expect similar behavior in the complex plane. Let us begin by extending the concept of the logarithm. We define

$$G(s) = \log F(s) \qquad (a)$$

if and only if

$$F(s) = \epsilon^{G(s)} \qquad (b) \tag{47}$$

(In this appendix we shall conform to the mathematical convention of writing log for the logarithm to the base ϵ.) Since we know the meaning of Eq. (47b), we also know the meaning of Eq. (47a). Let us first observe that if $G(s)$ satisfies Eq. (47b), so does $G(s) + j2k\pi$. For,

$$\epsilon^{G(s)+j2k\pi} = \epsilon^{G(s)} \epsilon^{j2k\pi} = \epsilon^{G(s)} \tag{48}$$

(We are using several results about the exponential function which we have not established in the complex plane, but which can be proved very easily.) Thus Eq. (47a) does not define a unique functional value for $G(s)$. However, we can show that any two values satisfying Eq. (47b) can at most differ by $j2k\pi$. (Do this.) Thus although the function log $F(s)$ is multi-valued, its values are related by the simple additive constants $j2k\pi$. We shall find a formula for one of these multiple values by writing

$$F(s) = |F(s)| \epsilon^{j \text{ Arg } F(s)} \tag{49}$$

where Arg $F(s)$ is the principal value of the argument defined by

$$-\pi < \text{Arg } F(s) \leq \pi \tag{50}$$

Using the real logarithm for $|F(s)|$ we can write

$$F(s) = \epsilon^{\log|F(s)|} \epsilon^{j \text{ Arg } F(s)}$$

$$= \epsilon^{[\log|F(s)|+j \text{ Arg } F(s)]} \tag{51}$$

Therefore from the definition of the logarithm, *one of the values* of this function is

$$\text{Log } F(s) = \log|F(s)| + j \text{ Arg } F(s) \tag{52}$$

This particular value, which is *unique* by virtue of Eq. (50) is known as the *principal value* of the logarithm function. We signify this conventionally by writing a capital "*L*" in Log $F(s)$; similarly Arg $F(s)$ always means the principal value given in Eq. (50). Thus we can write, for all values of the log function,

$$\log F(s) = \text{Log } F(s) + j2k\pi$$

$$= \log|F(s)| + j[\text{Arg } F(s) + 2k\pi] \tag{53}$$

where k is an integer—positive, negative, or zero.

Thus, there are an infinite number of values for the logarithm function, one for each value of k. Because of this difficulty, we might try to simplify life by using only the principal value, Log $F(s)$. Let us first consider the behavior of the function Log s in the complex plane before considering Log $F(s)$. Log s is a well-defined function.

$$\text{Log } s = \text{Log } r + j\theta \tag{54}$$

where

$$s = r\epsilon^{j\theta} \tag{55}$$

We notice that the angle θ is undefined at $s = 0$. Therefore this equation does not define Log s at $s = 0$. But no matter how we define Log 0, Log s will not be continuous at $s = 0$, since the imaginary part of Log s

takes on all values from $-\pi$ to π in any neighborhood of $s = 0$. There-fore $s = 0$ is a singular point of Log s. When we restrict ourselves to the principal value, Log s is also discontinuous at any point on the nega-tive real axis; for, the imaginary part of Log s here is π, but there are points arbitrarily close to it at which the imaginary part is very nearly $-\pi$. Thus Log s is not regular at any point on the negative real axis, including $s = 0, \infty$. (The behavior at ∞ is identical to the behavior at 0, since Log $1/s = -$Log s, as you can verify.)

However, if we consider the complex plane to be "cut" along the nega-tive real axis, as illustrated in Fig. 9, preventing us from going from one

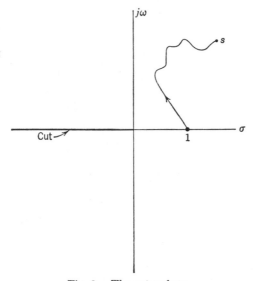

Fig. 9.   The cut s-plane.

side of it to the other, Log s is regular in the rest of the complex plane. In fact, we have

$$\frac{d}{ds} \text{Log } s = \frac{1}{s} \tag{56}$$

at all other points of this "cut" plane. Thus, Log s is an anti-derivative of $1/s$. In fact we can show that

$$\text{Log } s = \int_1^s \frac{dz}{z} \tag{57}$$

provided the path of integration does not go through the "cut" negative real axis.

Similar remarks apply to the other values of the logarithm function.

The restriction to principal values is unnecessary. The only thing we need to do is to restrict the imaginary part of $\log s$ to some 2π range. For Eq. (57) to apply, we have to add a suitable multiple of $j2\pi$ to the right side. It is not even necessary that the cut be along the negative real axis. We may cut the plane along any radius vector by defining

$$\theta_1 < \arg F(s) \leq 2\pi + \theta_1 \qquad (58)$$

Even this is unnecessary. Any simple path from $s = 0$ to $s = \infty$ will do.

Thus by suitable restrictions, we can make the function $\log s$ single-valued and regular in any neighborhood. The only exceptional points are $s = 0, \infty$. No matter what artifice we employ, we cannot make $\log s$ regular and single-valued in a deleted neighborhood of $s = 0, \infty$. (Since these points are singular points, we have to delete them from the neighborhood, if we hope to make the function regular.) Thus, these two singular points are different in character, from the ones we have met so far. Therefore we give them a different name. They are called *branch points*. Precisely, a branch point is defined as follows.

The point s_0 is a *branch point* of the function $F(s)$ if s_0 is an isolated singular point and there is no deleted neighborhood of s_0 in which $F(s)$ is defined or is definable as a single-valued regular function.

We now see that the plane has to be cut along a simple path from one branch point of $\log s$ to the other branch point. Each value of $\log s$ so obtained is called a *branch of the function*. Thus Log s is a branch of $\log s$.

Riemann introduced an artifice that allows us to consider the complete log function and treat it as a single-valued function. This important concept is known as the *Riemann surface*. It is quite difficult to define this term precisely, and we shall not attempt it. Instead let us describe a few Riemann surfaces. For the function $\log s$, the Riemann surface has the following structure. We consider the s-plane to consist of an infinite number of identical planes. One of these is the plane in which $\arg s$ is restricted to its principal value. There are an infinite number of *sheets* above this and another infinity below. All of these planes are cut along the negative real axis. All of these have the same origin and ∞, so that the sheets are all joined together at these points. Each sheet is also joined to the ones immediately above and below, along the negative real axis. The upper edge of the negative real axis of each sheet is joined to the lower edge of the negative real axis of the sheet immediately above it. The whole Riemann surface looks somewhat like an endless spiral ramp.

Let us consider $\log s$ on such a surface. On each sheet

$$\log s = \log|s| + j(\text{Arg } s + 2k\pi) \qquad (59)$$

where k is a *fixed integer*. The integer k increases by 1 as we go to the sheet immediately above; and decreases by 1 as we go to the sheet immediately below. On this Riemann surface therefore, $\log s$ is a single-valued regular function with two singular points, $s = 0, \infty$.

We can now return to the function $\log F(s)$. We are considering $\log F(s)$ as a function of s. In the F-plane, the branch cut goes from $F(s) = 0$ to $F(s) = \infty$. Let us consider only the simplest case where $F(s)$ is rational. The other cases are somewhat more complicated. The branch points in the s-plane are the zeros and poles of $F(s)$. Each branch cut goes from a zero to a pole. The number of branch cuts at a zero or a pole is equal to the multiplicity. The branch cuts are chosen not to intersect except at branch points.

As another example of the concept of the Riemann surface, let us consider the inverse of the function

$$F(s) = s^2 \tag{60}$$

The inverse of this function is called the *square root*, written

$$G(s) = s^{\frac{1}{2}} = \sqrt{s} \tag{61}$$

(Formally we define powers of s other than integral powers as

$$s^\alpha = \epsilon^{\alpha \log s} \tag{62}$$

where α may be any complex number.) As in the real case, the square root is a double-valued function. The two values G_1 and G_2 are related by

$$G_1(s) = -G_2(s) = G_2(s)\epsilon^{j\pi} \tag{63}$$

We may make this function single-valued by restricting the angle of s as before. That is,

$$-\pi < \text{Arg } s \leq \pi \tag{64}$$

and defining the "positive square root" as

$$G_1(s) = \sqrt{|s|}\, \epsilon^{\frac{1}{2}j\, \text{Arg } s} \tag{65}$$

where $\sqrt{|s|}$ is a real positive number.

Again we find that $G_1(s)$ is not continuous on the negative real axis, including $s = 0, \infty$. The points $s = 0, \infty$ are seen to be branch points of this function $G(s)$. The Riemann surface concept may be introduced as follows. We need two sheets of the Riemann surface, both cut along the negative real axis. To make $G(s)$ continuous and regular on this surface, we "cross-connect" the two sheets along the negative real axis. The upper edge of the negative real axis of *each sheet* is connected to the lower edge of the negative real axis of the *other sheet*. (Obviously, it is useless to attempt to draw a picture of this in three dimensions.) On this Riemann surface, $G(s)$ is regular and single-valued except at $s = 0$, ∞.

We see that the branch points of the function log s are somewhat different from the branch points of $s^{\frac{1}{2}}$. In one case we have an infinite number of branches and in the other case, we have only a finite number. Therefore we sometimes distinguish between these, by calling the former a *logarithmic singularity* (or a logarithmic branch point) and the other an *algebraic singularity* (or an algebraic branch point).

We can extend this discussion to other algebraic irrational functions,

$$F(s) = \left\{ \frac{as^2 + bs + c}{ds + e} \right\}^{\frac{1}{3}} \tag{66}$$

for example, in an obvious way.

We have seen that the singularities of an analytic function are extremely important. In fact, we can *classify* analytic functions according to the type and locations of its singular points. This we shall do in the following brief discussion.

The simplest case is that of an analytic function possessing no singularities at all, either in the finite plane or at ∞. In this case, a theorem known as Liouville's theorem tells us that the function is simply a constant. The next case one might consider is that of a function which has no finite singularities. That is, the only possible singularity is at $s = \infty$. The exponential function is an example of this class. A function that has no singularities in the finite s-plane is known as an *entire* (or *integral*) function. If the singularity at ∞ is a pole, we see from the Laurent expansion about ∞, that this function is a *polynomial* (also called *entire rational* or *integral rational*). If the singularity at ∞ is an essential singularity the function is an *entire transcendental* function. The functions ϵ^s, sin s, cos s, etc., belong to this category.

The quotient of two entire functions is a *meromorphic function*. The only singularities of a meromorphic function in the finite plane are the points at which the entire function in the denominator goes to zero. Thus a meromorphic function can have only poles in the finite part of the s-plane. Again the behavior at infinity divides this class into two subclasses. If the point ∞ is either a regular point or a pole, then it can be shown that the function has only a finite number of poles (using a theorem known as the Bolzano–Weierstrass theorem). Then by using the partial fraction expansion, to be given in section 7, we can show that this function is a *rational function*—that is, a quotient of two polynomials. Conversely, every rational function is a meromorphic function with at most a pole at $s = \infty$. An example of a nonrational meromorphic function is tan s or cosec s.

All of these functions are single-valued functions. The multi-valued functions can be classified according to the number of branch points and the number of branches at each branch point. A function with a finite number of branch points and a finite number of branches is an *algebraic irrational* function. We saw examples of these. The logarithm function can be used to construct examples for infinite number of branches. The function log s has a finite number of branch points but an infinite number of branches. The function log sin s has an infinite number of branch points and an infinite number of branches, whereas the function $\sqrt{\sin s}$ has an infinite number of branch points with a finite number of branches at each branch point. These three classes have no special names associated with them.

A.6   The Residue Theorem

Cauchy's theorem tells us about the value of a closed contour integral of a function when the function is regular inside the contour. We now have the information required to determine the value of a closed contour integral when the contour includes one or more singular points of the function. For this purpose turn to the formula for the coefficients of a Laurent series given in Eq. (43) and consider the coefficient of the first inverse power term, $k = -1$. This is

$$a_{-1} = \frac{1}{2\pi j} \int_C F(z)\,dz \qquad (67)$$

This is an extremely important result. It states that if a function is integrated around a closed contour inside which the function has one singular point, the value of the integral will be $2\pi j$ times the coefficient of the first negative power term in the Laurent series. None of the other terms in the series contribute anything; they all "wash out." We call this coefficient the *residue*. Note that the function is regular on the contour.

If the contour in question encloses more than one singular point (but a finite number), we can enclose each singular point in a smaller contour of its own within the boundaries of the main contour. By "digging canals" in the usual way, we find the value of the integral around the original contour to be equal to the sum of the integrals around the smaller contours, all taken counterclockwise. Now we consider a Laurent series about each of the singular points such that no other singular points are enclosed. According to the preceding paragraph, the value of the integral about each small contour is equal to $2\pi j$ times the corresponding residue. Hence, the integral around the original contour is equal to $2\pi j$ times the sum of the residues at all of the singular points inside the contour. That is,

$$\int_C F(s)\, ds = 2\pi j \, \Sigma \text{ residues at enclosed singularities} \qquad (68)$$

This statement is referred to as the *residue theorem*. To find the value of a closed contour integral, then, all we need to do is to calculate the residues at all of the singular points in a manner independent of the formula for the coefficients of the Laurent series.

Consider a function $F(s)$ which has a pole of order n at s_0. If the Laurent series about s_0 is multiplied by $(s - s_0)^n$, the result will be

$$(s - s_0)^n F(s) = a_{-n} + a_{-n+1}(s - s_0) + \cdots + a_{-1}(s - s_0)^{n-1}$$
$$+ a_0(s - s_0)^n + \cdots \quad (69)$$

The function on the left is regular at s_0 and the series on the right is the Taylor series representing it in the neighborhood of s_0. Hence, using the formula for the Taylor coefficients we get

$$a_{-1} = \frac{1}{(n-1)!} \frac{d^{n-1}}{ds^{n-1}} [(s - s_0)^n F(s)]\big|_{s=s_0} \qquad (70)$$

For a simple pole this reduces to the following simple form

$$a_{-1} = (s - s_0)F(s)\big|_{s=s_0} \qquad (71)$$

In the case of poles, at least, we now have an independent way of finding residues.

There are alternate ways of expressing the residue at a simple pole, which are useful in computations. If the given function is expressed as

$$F(s) = G(s)/H(s) \qquad (72)$$

where s_0 is a simple pole of $F(s)$, in the nontrivial case $H(s)$ has a simple zero at s_0 and $G(s)$ is regular and nonzero at s_0. In this case we may write

$$\text{Residue of } F(s) \text{ at } s_0 = \lim_{s \to s_0} (s - s_0)F(s) = \frac{\lim\limits_{s \to s_0} G(s)}{\lim\limits_{s \to s_0} H(s)/(s - s_0)} \qquad (73)$$

since $G(s)$ is regular at s_0. Thus, the limit in the numerator is simply $G(s_0)$. For the limit in the denominator, we subtract $H(s_0)$ from $H(s)$, which is permissible since $H(s_0) = 0$, getting

$$\text{Residue of } F(s) \text{ at } s_0 = \frac{G(s_0)}{\lim\limits_{s \to s_0} [H(s) - H(s_0)]/(s - s_0)} = \frac{G(s_0)}{H'(s_0)} \qquad (74)$$

since the limit of the difference quotient is by definition the derivative. If on the other hand, we write

$$F(s) = 1/G(s) \tag{75}$$

(this is a different function G from the one in Eq. (72)), and follow through the same argument, we conclude that

$$\text{Residue of } F(s) \text{ at } s_0 = 1/G'(s_0) \tag{76}$$

Thus the residue at a simple pole is the reciprocal of the derivative of the reciprocal function.

One of the important applications of the residue theorem is the identity theorem for Laurent series.

If the two Laurent series

$$\sum_{n=-\infty}^{\infty} a_n(s - s_0)^n \quad \text{and} \quad \sum_{n=-\infty}^{\infty} b_n(s - s_0)^n$$

have a common region of convergence $R_1 < |s - s_0| < R_2$, *and represent the same function in this region, then*

$$a_n = b_n \quad \text{all } n, -\infty < n < \infty$$

Since the two series represent the same function,

$$\sum_{n=-\infty}^{\infty} a_n(s - s_0)^n = \sum_{n=-\infty}^{\infty} b_n(s - s_0)^n, \quad R_1 < |s - s_0| < R_2 \tag{77}$$

Since the positive and negative series are power series, they converge uniformly for $|s - s_0| \leq R_2 - \varepsilon$, $(\varepsilon > 0)$, and $|s - s_0| \geq R_1 + \varepsilon$, respectively. Therefore in the annular region $R_1 + \varepsilon \leq |s - s_0| \leq R_2 - \varepsilon$, the Laurent series are uniformly convergent. We now multiply both sides of Eq. (77) by $(s - s_0)^{k-1}$, where k is an integer—positive, negative, or zero—and integrate along a circular path C lying in the region of uniform convergence and enclosing s_0. By the residue theorem we get

$$a_{-k} = b_{-k} \quad \text{all } k, -\infty < k < \infty$$

which proves the result.

The residue theorem (which, incidentally, includes Cauchy's theorem) provides a means for evaluating many real definite integrals which cannot be evaluated by other means. We choose a function of s which reduces to the given real integrand when s is real, and we choose a closed contour which includes as part of it the desired interval in the definite integral. Now if we can find the residues at the singularities of the integrand which might lie inside the chosen contour, and if we can independently calculate the contribution to the closed contour integral of the parts of the path other than the desired interval, the value of the desired integral can be found.

In evaluating such integrals two circumstances often arise. In the first place it may happen that the integrand has a simple pole on the path of integration. In order to apply the residue theorem the function must be regular on the closed contour. This situation is remedied by distorting or indenting the contour by a small semicircular arc as shown in Fig. 10. The new contour is of course different from the old one. How-

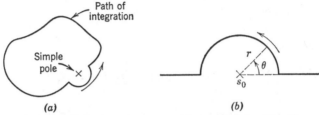

Fig. 10.   Distortion of contour of integration around pole.

ever, we eventually let the radius of the semicircle approach zero. It remains to calculate the contribution of the semicircle to the closed contour integral.

Consider the semicircular path shown in Fig. 10b around a simple pole at s_0. The Laurent expansion of $F(s)$ about s_0 has the form

$$F(s) = \frac{a_{-1}}{s - s_0} + \sum_{n=0}^{\infty} a_n(s - s_0)^n \qquad (78)$$

Note that the direction of the path is counterclockwise around the pole when we are to indent the contour in such a way that the pole is inside. We can also indent the contour to exclude the pole. Then the value obtained will be the negative of that obtained here. The series in this equation can be integrated term-by-term; let $(s - s_0) = re^{j\theta}$ and let C represent the semicircle. On the semicircle θ varies from 0 to π. The integral of $F(s)$ on the semicircle becomes

$$\int_C F(s)\, ds = \int_0^\pi \frac{a_{-1}}{re^{j\theta}}\, jre^{j\theta}\, d\theta + \sum_n a_n \int_0^\pi r^n \epsilon^{jn\theta}\, jre^{j\theta}\, d\theta$$

$$= j\pi a_{-1} + \sum_n \frac{a_n r^{n+1}}{n + 1}\, (\epsilon^{j(n+1)\pi} - 1) \qquad (79)$$

The first term is seen to be independent of the radius r of the semicircle. As we let r approach zero, each term in the summation will vanish.

Hence,

$$\int_{\text{Semicircle}} F(s)\,ds = j\pi a_{-1} \tag{80}$$

That is, the integral around half a circle about a simple pole will have one half the value of an integral around a complete circle. In fact, by the same reasoning, if the contour is a fraction k of a circular arc, the contribution will be $k(2\pi j a_{-1})$.

The second circumstance that often arises is the need to evaluate an integral with infinite limits, such as

$$I = \int_{-\infty}^{\infty} f(\omega)\,d\omega \tag{81}$$

Such an integral is called an *improper integral*. The notation means

$$I = \lim_{R_0 \to \infty} \int_{-R_0}^{R_0} f(\omega)\,d\omega \tag{82}$$

The value obtained by going to negative and positive infinity in a symmetrical fashion is called the *principal value* of the integral.

This type of integral can be evaluated by choosing a contour consisting of the imaginary axis from $-R_0$ to R_0 and a large semicircle in the right-half or left-half plane, such as the one shown in Fig. 11. The integrand must be a function $F(s)$ which reduces to the given integrand on the imaginary axis. Use of the residue theorem will now permit the evaluation of the desired integral provided that the integral along the semicircular arc tends to a limit as $R_0 \to \infty$, and this limit can be found. It would be best if there were no contribution from this arc. Let $F(s)$ be the integrand of the contour integral. It can be shown that if $sF(s)$ on the arc approaches zero uniformly * as the radius of the circle ap-

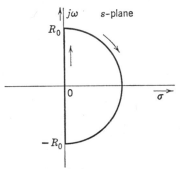

Fig. 11. Contour for evaluating infinite integrals.

---

* That is, the limit is approached at the same rate for all angles of s within this range. The range is $|\text{Arg } s| \le \pi/2$ for a semicircle in the right-half plane and $|\text{Arg } s| \ge \pi/2$ for a semicircle in the left-half plane. In the ε-δ language, the magnitude of the difference between $sF(s)$ and the limit (in this case 0), can be made less than ε, so long as $|s| > N(\varepsilon)$, where $N(\varepsilon)$ is independent of Arg s in the appropriate range.

proaches infinity, then there will be no contribution from the infinite arc. For example, if $F(s)$ is a ratio of two polynomials, the degree of the denominator must exceed that of the numerator by 2 or more.

Let t be a real variable and suppose the integrand has the form

$$F(s) = G(s)\epsilon^{st} \tag{83}$$

Then it can be shown that for $t > 0$ the infinite arc in the left-half plane will not contribute to the integral, nor will the arc to the right for $t < 0$, provided that $G(s)$ vanishes uniformly as the radius of the semicircle approaches infinity. This result is called *Jordan's lemma*. The presence of the exponential loosens the restriction on the remaining part of the integrand. Thus, if $G(s)$ is a ratio of two polynomials, it is enough that the degree of the denominator exceed that of the numerator by one (or more).

As an example of the evaluation of integrals consider

$$I = \int_0^\infty \frac{\sin \omega t}{\omega}\, d\omega \tag{84}$$

Substituting the definition of a sine function in terms of exponentials, this becomes

$$I = \int_0^\infty \frac{\epsilon^{j\omega t}}{2j\omega}\, d\omega + \int_0^\infty \frac{-\epsilon^{-j\omega t}}{2j\omega}\, d\omega \tag{85}$$

In the second integral if we replace ω by $-\omega$, the integrand will become identical with that of the first integral, whereas the limits will become $-\infty$ to zero. The two integrals can then be combined to yield

$$I = \frac{1}{2j} \int_{-\infty}^\infty \frac{\epsilon^{j\omega t}}{\omega}\, d\omega \tag{86}$$

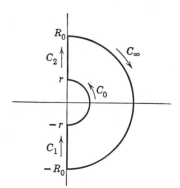

Now consider the integral

$$\int_C \frac{\epsilon^{st}}{s}\, ds \tag{87}$$

where the contour C is the closed contour shown in Fig. 12. The integrand has a simple pole on the original contour so that we indent the contour around the pole as shown. The complete contour consists of

Fig. 12. Path of integration for the evaluation of an integral.

two portions of the $j\omega$-axis and two semicircles, the radius of one of which will approach zero while the other will approach infinity. Since the integrand is regular everywhere inside the contour, the closed contour integral will vanish. We can write

$$\int_C \frac{\epsilon^{st}}{s} ds = 0 = \int_{-R_0}^{-r} \frac{\epsilon^{j\omega t}}{\omega} d\omega + \int_{C_0} \frac{\epsilon^{st}}{s} ds + \int_r^{R_0} \frac{\epsilon^{j\omega t}}{\omega} d\omega + \int_{C_\infty} \frac{\epsilon^{st}}{s} ds \quad (88)$$

The integrand satisfies Jordan's lemma so that the last integral in this equation will vanish. The value of the integral on C_0 is $-j\pi$ times the residue of the integrand at $s = 0$, according to Eq. (80). (To account for the sign keep in mind the direction of the path.) To calculate the residue we use Eq. (71) and find it to be unity. Hence,

$$\int_{C_0} \frac{\epsilon^{st}}{s} ds = -j\pi \quad (89)$$

We can now write Eq. (88) as

$$\lim_{\substack{r \to 0 \\ R_0 \to \infty}} \left\{ \int_{-R_0}^{-r} \frac{\epsilon^{j\omega t}}{\omega} d\omega + \int_r^{R_0} \frac{\epsilon^{j\omega t}}{\omega} d\omega \right\} = j\pi \quad (90)$$

But by the improper integral in Eq. (86) we mean precisely the left side of the last equation. Hence, finally

$$I = \int_0^\infty \frac{\sin \omega t}{\omega} d\omega = \frac{1}{2j} j\pi = \frac{\pi}{2} \quad (91)$$

As another application of the Residue theorem we shall now prove a very useful theorem called the "argument principle." Let $F(s)$ be an analytic function which is regular in a region R except possibly for poles. We would like to evaluate the integral

$$\int_C \frac{F'(s)}{F(s)} ds \quad (92)$$

around a closed contour C in region R in the counterclockwise direction, where the prime denotes differentiation. There should be no poles or zeros of $F(s)$ on the contour C.

Suppose $F(s)$ has a zero of order n at a point s_1 in R. Then we can write

$$F(s) = (s - s_1)^n F_1(s)$$

$$F'(s) = n(s - s_1)^{n-1} F_1(s) + (s - s_1)^n F_1'(s)$$

$$\frac{F'(s)}{F(s)} = \frac{n}{s - s_1} + \frac{F_1'(s)}{F_1(s)} \quad (93)$$

We see that this function has a simple pole at the zero of $F(s)$ with a residue n. The function $F_1(s)$ can now be treated in the same way and the process repeated until all the zeros of the original function $F(s)$ have been put into evidence. Each zero will lead to a term like the first one on the right side of Eq. (93).

Now suppose that $F(s)$ has a pole of order m at a point s_2 in R. Then we can write

$$F(s) = \frac{F_2(s)}{(s - s_2)^m}$$

$$F'(s) = \frac{(s - s_2)F_2'(s) - mF_2(s)}{(s - s_2)^{m+1}}$$

$$\frac{F'(s)}{F(s)} = -\frac{m}{s - s_2} + \frac{F_2'(s)}{F_2(s)} \tag{94}$$

The desired function is seen to have a simple pole at the pole of $F(s)$ with a residue which is the negative of its order. Again the same process can be repeated and each pole of $F(s)$ will lead to a term like the first one on the right side of the last equation. The only singularities of $F'(s)/F(s)$ in the region R will lie at the zeros and the poles of $F(s)$. Hence, by the residue theorem, the value of the desired contour integral will be

$$\int_C \frac{F'(s)}{F(s)} ds = 2\pi j[\Sigma\, n_j - \Sigma\, m_j] \tag{95}$$

where the n_j are the orders of the zeros of $F(s)$ in R and the m_j are the orders of the poles.

Note however that

$$\frac{F'(s)}{F(s)} = \frac{d}{ds} \log F(s) \tag{96}$$

Hence, we can evaluate the contour integral by means of the antiderivative of $F'(s)/F(s)$, which is $\log s$. In going around the contour C we mean to start at a point and return to the same point. Note that the multi-valued function $\log F(s)$ will have the same real part after returning to the starting point. Hence, the value of the integral will be j times the increase in angle of $F(s)$ as s traverses the contour C in the counterclockwise direction. This should equal the right side of Eq. (95). If we now divide by 2π, the result should be the number of times the locus of the contour C in the F-plane goes around its origin counterclockwise (increase in angle divided by 2π is the number of counterclockwise encirclements of the origin).

Let us now state the principle of the argument. *If a function $F(s)$ has no singular points within a contour C except for poles and it has neither* *zeros nor poles on C, then the number of times the locus of the curve C in the F-plane encircles its origin in the counterclockwise direction is equal to the number of zeros minus the number of poles of F(s) inside C. Each zero and pole is to be counted according to its multiplicity.*

Before concluding this section, let us consider another contour integration problem, whose solution we use in Chapter 7, although it is not connected to the residue theorem. This is the problem of integrating a function partway around a logarithmic singularity.

Let us therefore consider the integral

$$\int_P \log F(s) \, ds$$

where the path P is an arc of a circle around a zero or a pole of $F(s)$, as shown in Fig. 10b. Let $F(s)$ have a zero (or a pole) of order k at s_0. Then we may write

$$F(s) = (s - s_0)^k F_1(s) \qquad (a)$$

$$\log F(s) = k \log (s - s_0) + \log F_1(s) \qquad (b)$$

$$(97)$$

If s_0 is a pole, we let k be a negative integer in these expressions, thus including a zero of order k and a pole of order $-k$ simultaneously in the discussion. As we let the radius of the circle approach zero, $\log F_1(s)$ will not contribute anything to the integral, since it is regular at s_0. Thus it is sufficient to consider

$$\int_P \log (s - s_0) \, ds$$

if we wish to take the limit, as we do.

On the arc of radius r, we may estimate:

$$\left| \int_P \log (s - s_0) \, ds \right| \le r\theta \, |\log r| + r\theta^2 = \theta \, |r \log r| + r\theta^2 \qquad (98)$$

where θ is the angle subtended by the arc at the center. Now it is a well-known result that

$$\lim_{r \to 0} r \log r = 0 \qquad (99)$$

Hence,

$$\lim_{r \to 0} \int_P \log F(s) \, ds = 0 \qquad (100)$$

which is the result we wish to establish. In words, we have shown that a logarithmic singularity lying on a path of integration does not contribute anything to the integral.

A.7 Partial-Fraction Expansions

The Laurent expansion of a function about a singular point describes a function in an annular region about that singular point. The fact that the function may have other singular points is completely submerged and there is no evidence as to any other singular points. It would be useful to have a representation of the function which would put into evidence all of its singular points.

Suppose a function $F(s)$ has isolated singularities at a finite number n of points in the finite plane. It may also have a singularity at infinity. Let us consider expanding $F(s)$ in a Laurent expansion about one of the singular points, say s_1. The result will be

$$F(s) = F_{p1}(s) + F_{r1}(s) \tag{101}$$

where the subscripts refer to the principal part and the regular part.

Now consider $F_{r1}(s)$, which is simply the original function $F(s)$ from which has been subtracted the principal part of the Laurent series about one of its singularities. This function is regular at s_1 but has all the other singularities of $F(s)$. Let us expand it in a Laurent series about one of the other singularities, s_2.

$$F_{r1}(s) = F(s) - F_{p1}(s) = F_{p2}(s) + F_{r2}(s) \tag{102}$$

The function $F_{p1}(s)$ is regular at the singularity s_2; hence, it will not contribute anything to the principal part $F_{p2}(s)$. This means that the principal part $F_{p2}(s)$ will be the same whether we expand $F_{r1}(s)$ or the original function $F(s)$.

We now repeat this process with $F_{r2}(s)$, and keep repeating with each singularity. At each step we subtract the principal part of the Laurent expansion until all the singular points are exhausted. The regular part of the last Laurent expansion will have no other singularities in the finite plane. Hence, it must be an entire function. In this fashion we have succeeded in obtaining a representation of $F(s)$ which has the form

$$F(s) = \sum_{k=1}^{n} F_{pk}(s) + F_r(s) \tag{103}$$

Each of the terms in the summation is the principal part of the Laurent series of $F(s)$ expanded about one of its singularities. The last term is an entire function. If $F(s)$ is regular at infinity, this term will be a constant. If $F(s)$ has a pole of order n at infinity, this term will be a polynomial of degree n. Finally, if $F(s)$ has an essential singularity at infinity, this term will be an infinite power series. The representation of an analytic function given in Eq. (103) is called a *partial-fraction expansion*.

Suppose a function has an infinite number of poles and no essential singularities in the finite plane (this makes it a meromorphic function). In such cases also a partial-fraction expansion can be found. However, the summation of principal parts in Eq. (104) will be an infinite series and may not converge in general. Nevertheless, it is always possible to so modify the terms that the series converges. But now the form of the expansion is changed. Of course, in some cases such a modification is not necessary, but the statement of the conditions when this is true is not a simple one, and we will not pursue the subject any further. (This expansion is known as the Mittag–Leffler expansion.)

A.8   Analytic Continuation

Near the beginning of this appendix we defined an analytic function as one that is differentiable everywhere in a neighborhood, however small, of a point. Later, from the Taylor expansion of an analytic function about a point s_0 at which the function is regular, we saw that knowledge of all the derivatives of an analytic function at a point permits us to represent the function everywhere in a circle about the point, a circle which extends up to the closest singularity of the function. We stated that once a power series representation of a function about a point is obtained, no matter by what procedure, this series is unique. We can state this result in a different way as follows. *If two functions are regular in a region R and if they coincide in some neighborhood, no matter how small, of a point s_0 in R, then the two functions are equal everywhere in R.* This theorem is called the *identity theorem for analytic functions*. (In fact the two functions need coincide only on a segment of path no matter how small; or even only on an infinite number of distinct points having a limit point at s_0.)

Now let us consider two functions $F_1(s)$ and $F_2(s)$ which are respectively regular in overlapping regions R_1 and R_2, the common region being R_0, as shown in Fig. 13. (The regions need not be circular as shown here.) The two functions $F_1(s)$ and $F_2(s)$ determine each other uniquely. This follows from the identity theorem since only one function can be regular in R_1 (or R_2) and have the same values in R_0.

Suppose we were starting with the function $F_1(s)$ in R_1 and could find a function $F_2(s)$ in R_2 having the property just described. We would say that $F_1(s)$ had been *analytically continued* beyond its original region into region R_2. But we might just as well consider $F_2(s)$ to be the original one and $F_1(s)$ its *analytic continuation* into region R_1. For

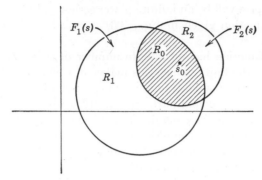

Fig. 13.   Common region of definition of two functions.

this reason we say that each of them is but a *partial representation* or an *element* of a single function $F(s)$ which is regular in both R_1 and R_2.

Consider now the problem of starting with one element $F_1(s)$ of a function, which is in the form of a power series, and determining its analytic continuation outside its original circle of convergence. Figure 13 can again be used. Suppose we choose a point s_0 in region R_1. From the given element $F_1(s)$ we can evaluate all the derivatives at s_0 and form a new power series about s_0. This series will certainly converge in R_1, the original region of convergence of $F_1(s)$, and may also converge in a circle which extends beyond the original circle, as the illustration in Fig. 13 shows. The series then defines another element $F_2(s)$ of the function of which $F_1(s)$ is also an element. We can now choose another point within the new region R_2, but not common with R_1, and again calculate a new series which may converge in a circle extending beyond the boundaries of R_2.

This procedure can now be repeated. The only circumstance that will prevent any one circle from extending beyond the preceding one is the existence of a singular point on the circumference of the first circle which lies on the radius of the first circle drawn through the center chosen for the second one. But this can be rectified by choosing a different point for the center of the second circle, *unless every point on the first circle happens to be a singular point.* This is a possible occurrence but it is not common. If such is the case, the original function is said to have a *natural boundary* beyond which it cannot be analytically continued.

Barring a natural boundary, then, an element can be analytically continued into the whole plane by this process of overlapping circles. The only points that will be excluded from the interiors of any of the circles will be the singular points. The sequence of functions defined in the circles will all be elements of a single function. It is now clear why an analytic function was defined as it was.

The process we have described has very little practical value since we would not ever contemplate the actual construction of all the elements of a function in this manner. However, it has very great significance in providing insight into the fundamental behavior of functions.

In the process of constructing (in imagination, at least) the overlapping circles, suppose one of them overlaps one of the earlier ones (thus forming a closed chain). The question will arise whether the functional values given by the latest function will be the same as those given by the previous one in the common region of the two circles. If these values are not the same, then the function defined by this set of elements will be *multi-valued*.

Let us now consider another aspect of analytic continuation. Suppose a function is defined along a simple arc which lies in a region R. It may be possible to find a function which is regular in R and coincides with this one on the simple arc. This function is also called the analytic continuation of the original one. The simple arc may be, for example, part or all of the $j\omega$-axis. If we define, as an example, a function to have the value $1 + j\omega$ for the interval $1 \leq \omega \leq 2$, its analytic continuation is $1 + s$. There is no other function which is regular in the region containing the given interval on the $j\omega$-axis and which coincides with the given function in that interval.

A.9 Laplace Transforms: Definition and Convergence Properties

The concept of transforming a function can be approached from the idea of making a change of variable in order to simplify the solution of a problem. Thus, if we have a problem involving the variable x, we substitute some other expression for x in terms of a new variable, for example, $x = \sin \theta$, with the anticipation that the problem has a simpler formulation and solution in terms of the new variable θ. After obtaining the solution in terms of the new variable, we use the opposite of the previous change and thus have the solution of the original problem.

A more complicated "change of variable," or transformation, is often necessary. If we have a function $f(t)$ of the variable t, we define an *integral transform of $f(t)$* as

$$\text{Integral transform of } f(t) = \int_a^b f(t)K(t,s)\, dt \qquad (104)$$

The function $K(t,s)$, which is a function of two variables, is called the *kernel* of the transformation. Note that the integral transform no longer depends on t; it is a function of the variable s on which the kernel depends. The type of transform that is obtained and the types of problem in which it is useful depend on two things: the kernel and the limits of integration. For the particular choice of the kernel $K(s,t) = \epsilon^{-st}$ and the limits 0 and infinity, the transform is called a *Laplace transform* and is denoted by $\mathcal{L}\{f(t)\}$. Thus,

$$\mathcal{L}\{f(t)\} = \int_0^\infty f(t)\epsilon^{-st}\,dt \tag{105}$$

The Laplace transform of $f(t)$ is thus a function of the complex variable s. We denote the Laplace transform of $f(t)$ by $F(s)$.

Because it is defined as an integral, the Laplace transform is a *linear functional*. That is, if $f_1(t)$ and $f_2(t)$ have Laplace transforms $F_1(s)$ and $F_2(s)$, and k_1, k_2 are constants,

$$\mathcal{L}\{k_1 f_1(t) + k_2 f_2(t)\} = k_1 F_1(s) + k_2 F_2(s) \tag{106}$$

Since the defining equation contains an integral with infinite limits, one of the first questions to be answered concerns the existence of Laplace transforms. A simple example of a function that does not have a Laplace transform is ϵ^{ϵ^t}. Let us therefore state a few theorems (a few of which we shall also prove) concerning the convergence of the Laplace integral. Since s appears as a significant parameter in Eq. (105) we may expect the convergence to depend upon the particular value of s. In general the integral converges for some values of s and diverges for others.

In all of the theorems to follow, we shall consider only integrable functions $f(t)$ without specifically saying so each time. As a first theorem, consider the following.

If the function $f(t)$ is bounded for all $t \geq 0$, then the Laplace integral converges absolutely for $Re(s) > 0$.

To prove the theorem, note that the condition on $f(t)$ means $|f(t)| < M$ for all $t \geq 0$, where M is a positive number. Then, for $\sigma > 0$ we will get

$$\int_0^T |\epsilon^{-st} f(t)|\,dt < M \int_0^T \epsilon^{-\sigma t}\,dt = (M/\sigma)(1 - \epsilon^{-\sigma T}) \tag{107}$$

In the limit, as T approaches infinity, the right-hand side approaches M/σ. Hence,

$$\int_0^\infty |\epsilon^{-st} f(t)|\,dt < M/\sigma; \qquad \sigma > 0 \tag{108}$$

The familiar sine and cosine functions, and other periodic functions such as the square wave, satisfy the conditions of the theorem. Before commenting on this theorem, let us consider one more theorem.

If the Laplace integral converges for some $s_0 = \sigma_0 + j\omega_0$, then it converges for all s with $\sigma > \sigma_0$.

Let

$$\int_0^\infty \epsilon^{-s_0 t} f(t) \, dt = k_0 \qquad (109)$$

where k_0 is a constant, since s_0 is a fixed complex number. Let us define the auxiliary function

$$\int_0^\tau \epsilon^{-s_0 t} f(t) \, dt = g(\tau) \qquad (110)$$

Then $g(\tau)$ has a limit as τ goes to ∞, namely k_0. Hence, $g(\tau)$ is bounded for all τ. Next, we shall write the Laplace integral as below and integrate by parts to get:

$$\int_0^T \epsilon^{-st} f(t) \, dt = \int_0^T \epsilon^{-(s-s_0)t} \epsilon^{-s_0 t} f(t) \, dt$$

$$= \epsilon^{-(s-s_0)t} g(t) \Big|_0^T - \int_0^T - (s - s_0) \epsilon^{-(s-s_0)t} g(t) \, dt \quad (111)$$

Or

$$\int_0^T \epsilon^{-st} f(t) \, dt = \epsilon^{-(s-s_0)T} g(T) - g(0) + (s - s_0) \int_0^T \epsilon^{-(s-s_0)t} g(t) \, dt \qquad (112)$$

Now $g(0) = 0$, $g(\infty) = k_0$, and if $\sigma > \sigma_0$, $\epsilon^{-(s-s_0)T} g(T)$ approaches 0 as T approaches ∞. Also, by the preceding theorem, the last integral in Eq. (112) converges absolutely for $\sigma > \sigma_0$, as T approaches ∞. Thus the result is proved. In fact,

$$\int_0^\infty \epsilon^{-st} f(t) \, dt = (s - s_0) \int_0^\infty \epsilon^{-(s-s_0)t} g(t) \, dt, \qquad (\sigma > \sigma_0) \quad (113)$$

This result can be strengthened to show that the Laplace integral converges *absolutely* for $\sigma > \sigma_0$, if it converges for σ_0. However, we shall not need this result in the general case. For functions of exponential order (to be defined shortly) we can prove this result with greater ease.

Thus the *region of convergence* of the Laplace integral is a *half-plane*. For by this theorem, whenever the integral converges for some point in the s-plane, it converges at all points to the right. Thus we can define an *abscissa of convergence* σ_c such that the Laplace integral converges for all s with $\sigma > \sigma_c$ and diverges for all s with $\sigma < \sigma_c$. The stronger result, which we have not proved, says that the region of convergence is also the region of absolute convergence. The behavior of the Laplace integral is, thus, somewhat analogous to the behavior of power series. The function $f(t)$ plays the role of the coefficients of the power series and the function ϵ^{-st} plays the part of $(s - s_0)^n$. Just as a power series may have any behavior on the circle of convergence, the Laplace integral may also have any behavior on the abscissa of convergence. The only difference concerns the existence of a singular point on the circle of convergence, which we shall examine a little later.

With infinite series, we have many tests for convergence. All of these have analogs in Laplace transforms. We shall be content to state just two of these. The analog of the ratio test is the following.

If $|f(t)| \leq M\epsilon^{ct}$ for some constant M and some number c, for all t (or only for t greater than some T_0), then the Laplace integral converges absolutely for $\sigma > c$.

We see this result immediately since

$$\int_0^\infty |\epsilon^{-st}f(t)|\, dt \leq M \int_0^\infty \epsilon^{-\sigma t}\epsilon^{ct}\, dt = M/(\sigma - c), \qquad \text{for } \sigma > c \quad (114)$$

We thus have a sufficient criterion for the existence of the Laplace integral. Functions satisfying the inequality

$$|f(t)| \leq M\epsilon^{ct} \qquad \text{for some } M \text{ and for } t > T \qquad (115)$$

are called functions of *exponential order*. The *order* of the function is the smallest number σ_0 such that the inequality (115) is satisfied by any

$$c = \sigma_0 + \varepsilon, \qquad \varepsilon > 0 \qquad (116)$$

and by no $c = \sigma_0 - \varepsilon$. In this case we have established that the Laplace integral converges absolutely for $\sigma > \sigma_0$ and diverges for $\sigma < \sigma_0$.

Many functions that are not of exponential order have Laplace transforms. However, we can state the following necessary and sufficient condition which shows that the integral of a transformable function is of exponential order.

The function $f(t)$ is transformable, with the abscissa of convergence $\sigma_0 > 0$ if and only if the function

$$g(t) = \int_0^t f(x)\, dx \qquad (117)$$

satisfies

$$|g(t)| \leq M\epsilon^{ct} \qquad (118)$$

for any $c = \sigma_0 + \varepsilon$.

The proof of this result depends on the Stieltjes integral and so we cannot give it here. We can use this theorem to get an analog for the Cauchy root test for power series.

Let $g(t)$ be the function defined in Eq. (117). If

$$\lim_{t\to\infty} \frac{\log |g(t)|}{t} = c \neq 0 \qquad (119)$$

then the abscissa of convergence of the Laplace integral of $f(t)$ is c.   The integral converges for $\sigma > c$ and diverges for $\sigma < c$.   If $c = 0$, the test is inconclusive.

In the case of power series, the regions of convergence, absolute convergence, and uniform convergence coincide.   We have stated that in the case of the Laplace integral the regions of convergence and absolute convergence coincide, both of them being half-planes.   Therefore we may ask whether the region of uniform convergence also coincides with the region of convergence.   The answer to this question is in the negative in the general case.   The region of uniform convergence is described in the following theorem, which we shall not prove.

If the Laplace integral converges for $s = \sigma_0$, then it converges uniformly in the sector

$$|\arg\,(s - \sigma_0)| \leq (\pi/2) - \varepsilon \qquad \text{for every } \varepsilon > 0 \qquad (120)$$

This region is shown in Fig. 14.   We may take σ_0 to be the abscissa of convergence σ_c, if the integral converges at this point.   Otherwise σ_0 is a point arbitrarily close to σ_c and to the right.

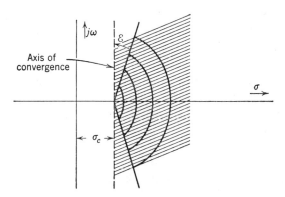

Fig. 14.   Regions of convergence and uniform convergence of Laplace integral.

In the case of functions of exponential order however, the region of uniform convergence coincides with the region of convergence.   That is, we may take $\varepsilon = 0$ in the theorem above.

For functions of exponential order, the region of uniform convergence is the half-plane

$$\sigma \geq \sigma_c + \delta, \qquad (\delta > 0)$$

where σ_c is the abscissa of convergence.

The proof of this result is quite similar to the proof given earlier for absolute convergence and so is omitted.

Thus the convergence behavior of the Laplace integral for functions of exponential order is identical with the behavior of power series.

A.10   Analytic Properties of the Laplace Transform

Using the power series analogy again, a power series defines an analytic function within the circle of convergence. We may therefore wonder whether the analogy extends this far. The answer to this question is in the affirmative, as stated by the following theorem.

If the integral

$$F(s) = \int_0^\infty \epsilon^{-st} f(t) \, dt \tag{121}$$

converges for $\sigma > \sigma_c$, then the function $F(s)$ defined by the integral is regular in the half-plane $\sigma > \sigma_c$. In fact, the derivative of $F(s)$ is given by

$$dF(s)/ds = \int_0^\infty \epsilon^{-st}(-t) f(t) \, dt \qquad (a)$$

and in general $\tag{122}$

$$F^{(n)}(s) = \int_0^\infty \epsilon^{-st}(-t)^n f(t) \, dt \qquad (b)$$

Given any point s with $\sigma > \sigma_c$, we can surround this point with a circle that is entirely within the region of uniform convergence, since ε in (120) is arbitrary. Now, because of the uniform convergence, the limit operations of integration and differentiation can be interchanged. Hence,

$$\frac{d}{ds} F(s) = \frac{d}{ds} \int_0^\infty \epsilon^{-st} f(t) \, dt$$

$$= \int_0^\infty \frac{\partial}{\partial s} \epsilon^{-st} f(t) \, dt \tag{123}$$

This leads to Eq. (122a). The convergence of Eq. (122a) is easily established for functions of exponential order. For the general case, we integrate by parts.

Thus the Laplace integral defines a regular function within the half plane of convergence. However, although the function $F(s)$ is *defined* by the integral only in the half plane of convergence, we can use the technique of *analytic continuation* to extend the function across the abscissa of convergence whenever it may be continuable. [In practice this is merely a formality, the "analytic continuation" being merely an extension of the formula for $F(s)$.] It is this more general analytic function that is referred to as the *Laplace transform*. If $F(s)$ is the Laplace transform of $f(t)$ we refer to $f(t)$ as the *determining function* and $F(s)$ as the *generating function*.

In this more general concept of a Laplace transform, the generating function will, in general, have singularities. They will have to lie in the half-plane $\sigma \leq \sigma_c$ or at ∞. Here we may revert to the power series analogy again. The function defined by a power series always has a singular point on the circle of convergence. We may ask whether $F(s)$ has a finite singular point on the abscissa of convergence σ_c. Here the analogy breaks down. In general there may be no singular point on $\sigma = \sigma_c$. The following example is given by Doetsch.

$$f(t) = -\pi\epsilon^t \sin(\pi\epsilon^t) \tag{124}$$

For this function the abscissa of convergence is zero. However, its transform satisfies the difference equation

$$F(s) = 1 - \frac{s(s+1)}{2} F(s+2) \tag{125}$$

so that $F(s)$ is an entire function.

However in certain special cases, the transform has a singular point on $s = \sigma_c + j\omega$. For instance if $f(t)$ is ultimately nonnegative, then it can be shown that the real point on the abscissa of convergence is a singular point. This result is too specialized to be of interest to us and so we omit its proof. The important result as far as we are concerned is that the Laplace transform is an analytic function which is regular in the half plane of convergence of the defining integral. The general Laplace transform is the function obtained by analytically continuing the original function.

One of the important analytic properties of the Laplace transform is its behavior at ∞. Concerning this we have the following theorem.

If the determining function $f(t)$ is a real or complex valued function of t and the Laplace integral converges at s_0, then as s approaches ∞ from within the sector
$$|\arg(s - s_0)| \leq (\pi/2) - \delta \qquad \text{with } \delta > 0$$

the generating function $F(s)$ approaches 0.

The proof of this result proceeds as follows. We begin with a given $\varepsilon > 0$. Since $f(t)$ is an integrable function and therefore bounded for all t, we can find a T_1 so small that for $\sigma > 0$,

$$\left| \int_0^{T_1} \epsilon^{-st} f(t)\, dt \right| < \int_0^{T_1} |f(t)|\, dt < \varepsilon/3 \tag{126}$$

Since the Laplace integral is uniformly convergent in this sector, we can find T_2 so large that $T_2 > T_1$ and

$$\left| \int_{T_2}^{\infty} \epsilon^{-st} f(t) \, dt \right| < \varepsilon/3 \tag{127}$$

for all s in this sector. These two conditions fix T_1 and T_2 and, therefore, the value of the integral

$$\int_{T_1}^{T_2} |f(t)| \, dt = M \tag{128}$$

Finally, we find σ_1 so large that

$$\epsilon^{-\sigma_1 T_2} < \varepsilon/3M$$

so that

$$\left| \int_{T_1}^{T_2} \epsilon^{-st} f(t) \, dt \right| < \varepsilon/3, \qquad (\sigma > \sigma_1) \tag{129}$$

Since s approaches ∞ in the sector $|\arg (s - s_0)| \le \pi/2 - \delta$, its real part has to exceed σ_1 eventually. If we put together the three conditions (126), (127), and (129) and restrict s by

$$|\arg (s - s_0)| \le \frac{\pi}{2} - \delta, \qquad \sigma > \sigma_1$$

we get

$$\left| \int_{0}^{\infty} \epsilon^{-st} f(t) \, dt \right| = |F(s)| < \varepsilon \tag{130}$$

so that

$$\lim_{\substack{s \to \infty \\ |\arg s| \le \pi/2 - \delta}} F(s) = 0 \tag{131}$$

Thus the behavior at ∞ is quite restricted. The point $s = \infty$ cannot be a pole for example. If $F(s)$ is regular at ∞, then it must have a zero there; $F(\infty)$ cannot be a nonzero constant. Thus, for example, *if $F(s)$ is a rational function, the degree of the denominator polynomial must be strictly greater than the degree of the numerator polynomial.* However $F(s)$ may have an essential singularity or a branch point at ∞. (These conditions apply only to real or complex valued determining functions, and not to *distributions* like the impulses of various orders.)

While we are talking about the general behavior, we may ask one more general question about the Laplace transform, namely its *uniqueness*. This question is of particular importance as we would like, eventually, to find the determining function from its Laplace transform. In order to state the answer to this question without getting involved in concepts of null functions, "zero measure" and "almost everywhere," we shall agree to *normalize* the function $f(t)$ by defining

$$f(0) = \tfrac{1}{2}f(0+) \qquad (a)$$
$$f(t) = \tfrac{1}{2}[f(t+) + f(t-)] \qquad (b)$$
$$\text{(132)}$$

where the $+$ and $-$ indicate as usual the right- and left-hand limits. Implicit here is the assumption that these limits exist, which we shall assume.

There cannot exist two different normalized determining functions $f_1(t)$ and $f_2(t)$ having the same Laplace transform $F(s)$.

The proof of this result is too complicated to be given here. If we do not normalize the functions, we can only conclude that the two functions $f_1(t)$ and $f_2(t)$ differ at most by a null function.

A.11 Operations on the Determining and Generating Functions

In the application to network theory, we are interested in the results of performing various algebraic and analytic operations in both the t- and s-domains. In this section we will summarize these results.

The simplest of these operations is the algebraic operation of linear combination, which we have dealt with already. The generating function corresponding to a linear combination of determining functions is the same linear combination of the corresponding generating functions. That is

$$\mathcal{L}\left\{ \sum_{i=1}^{n} k_i f_i(t) \right\} = \sum_{i=1}^{n} k_i \mathcal{L}\{f_i(t)\} \qquad (133)$$

This linearity is quite useful in both direct and inverse Laplace transformations.

The other algebraic operation, multiplication in either domain, leads to quite complicated results. The results obtained are quite similar to those in infinite series. For example, if we have two power series with a common region of convergence,

$$F_1(s) = \sum_{n=0}^{\infty} a_n s^n \qquad (a)$$
$$F_2(s) = \sum_{n=0}^{\infty} b_n s^n \qquad (b)$$
$$\text{(134)}$$

then the product of the two is again a power series.

$$F_1(s)F_2(s) = \sum_{n=0}^{\infty} c_n s^n \qquad (a)$$

where

$$c_n = \sum_{k=0}^{n} a_{n-k} b_k = \sum_{k=0}^{n} a_k b_{n-k} \qquad (b)$$
$$\text{(135)}$$

The product series converges in the common region of convergence of the two individual series. The sums in Eq. (135b) are known as *convolution sums*. We get a similar result in Laplace transforms.

If

$$F_1(s) = \int_0^\infty \epsilon^{-st} f_1(t)\, dt \qquad (a)$$

and $\qquad\qquad\qquad\qquad\qquad\qquad\qquad\qquad\qquad\qquad$ (136)

$$F_2(s) = \int_0^\infty \epsilon^{-st} f_2(t)\, dt \qquad (b)$$

have finite abscissae of convergence σ_1 and σ_2, then the product $F_1(s)F_2(s)$ is also a Laplace transform

$$F_1(s)F_2(s) = \int_0^\infty \epsilon^{-st} g(t)\, dt \qquad (a)$$

where $\qquad\qquad\qquad\qquad\qquad\qquad\qquad\qquad\qquad\qquad$ (137)

$$g(t) = \int_0^t f_1(x) f_2(t-x)\, dx = \int_0^t f_1(t-x) f_2(x)\, dx \quad (b)$$

with an abscissa of convergence equal to the larger of σ_1, σ_2.

If $F_1(s)$ and $F_2(s)$ are Laplace transforms of $f_1(t)$ and $f_2(t)$, with abscissae of convergence σ_1 and σ_2, the Laplace transform of the product $f_1(t)f_2(t)$ is given by

$$\mathcal{L}\{f_1(t)f_2(t)\} = \int_s^\infty F_1(z) F_2(s-z)\, dz \qquad (138)$$

where the path of integration is in the sector defined by $|\arg s| \le (\pi/2) - \varepsilon$ and the abscissa of convergence is $\sigma_1 + \sigma_2$.

The first of these two results is of considerable interest in network theory and is proved in Chapter 6. The second result is not of particular interest to us; we shall omit its proof. The integrals in Eqs. (137b) and (138) are known as *convolution integrals*, the first being a real convolution and the second a complex convolution.

Next we shall consider the analytic operations of differentiation and integration in both domains. These correspond, as we shall see, to multiplication or division by s or t. Differentiation in the s-domain has already been considered; let us repeat the result here:

If

$$\mathcal{L}\{f(t)\} = F(s) \qquad (a)$$

then $\qquad\qquad\qquad\qquad\qquad\qquad\qquad\qquad\qquad\qquad$ (139)

$$\mathcal{L}\{t^n f(t)\} = (-1)^n \cdot F^{(n)}(s) \qquad (b)$$

the abscissae of convergence being the same.

As might be expected, the inverse operations, division by t and integration in s, correspond. The negative sign is missing however.

If

$$\mathcal{L}\{f(t)\} = F(s) \qquad (a)$$

then $\qquad\qquad\qquad\qquad\qquad\qquad\qquad\qquad\qquad\qquad$ (140)

$$\mathcal{L}\left\{\frac{f(t)}{t}\right\} = \int_s^\infty F(z)\, dz \qquad (b)$$

where the abscissae of convergence are the same and the path of integration is restricted to the sector of uniform convergence.

This result is proved by integrating by parts in the s-domain, noting that $F(s)$ approaches 0 as s approaches ∞. More important operations than the preceding ones, as far as the application to network theory is concerned, are differentiation and integration in the t-domain. These are found to be sort of dual to the ones above.

Let $f(t)$ be differentiable (and therefore continuous) for $t > 0$, and let the derivative $f'(t)$ be transformable. Then $f(t)$ is also transformable and with the same abscissa of convergence. Further

$$\mathcal{L}\{f'(t)\} = sF(s) - f(0+) \qquad (a)$$

where $\qquad\qquad\qquad\qquad\qquad\qquad\qquad\qquad\qquad\qquad$

$$F(s) = \mathcal{L}\{f(t)\} \qquad (b) \qquad (141)$$

and

$$f(0+) = \lim_{\substack{t \to 0 \\ t > 0}} f(t) \qquad (c)$$

Since $f'(t)$ is transformable, it follows that $f(t)$ is of exponential order and therefore transformable. The rest follows on integrating

$$\int_0^T \epsilon^{-st} f'(t)\, dt$$

by parts and taking the limit as T goes to ∞.

Let $f(t)$ be an integrable and transformable function. Let

$$g(t) = \int_0^t f(x)\, dx \qquad (142)$$

Then $g(t)$ is also transformable and with the same abscissa of convergence. Further

$$G(s) = \frac{1}{s} F(s) \qquad (143)$$

where $G(s)$ and $F(s)$ are Laplace transforms of $g(t)$ and $f(t)$ respectively.

The first part follows as before. Equation (143) follows from Eq. (141a) on observing that $g(0+) = 0$ by Eq. (142).

These results can easily be extended to higher order derivatives and integrals of $f(t)$ by repeated applications of these theorems.

Two other limit operations are of considerable interest in estimating the behavior of the transient response of linear systems. In the first one, we seek to relate the value of $f(t)$ at $t = 0$ to a specific value of $F(s)$. The definition of the Laplace transform gives us only a relationship between the values of $f(t)$ on the whole of the real positive t-axis and the behavior of $F(s)$ in a complex half-plane. The desired relationship is the following.

If $\mathcal{L}\{f(t)\} = F(s)$ *with a finite abscissa of convergence, and if* $f'(t)$ *is transformable, then*

$$f(0+) = \lim_{s \to \infty} sF(s) \qquad (144)$$

where the limit on the right is to be taken in the sector

$$|\arg s| \leq (\pi/2) - \varepsilon$$

This is called the *initial value theorem*.

To prove this result we start with the derivative formula

$$\mathcal{L}\{f'(t)\} = sF(s) - f(0+) \qquad (145)$$

and take the limit as s goes to ∞ in the sector specified. Since $\mathcal{L}\{f'(t)\}$ is a Laplace transform, it goes to zero as s goes to ∞ in this sector. The result is Eq. (144).

We might analogously expect to get the final value $f(\infty)$ by taking the limit of Eq. (145) as s approaches 0. We run into difficulties here. For,

$$\lim_{s \to 0} sF(s) = f(0+) + \lim_{s \to 0} \int_0^\infty f'(t) \epsilon^{-st} \, dt \qquad (146)$$

where the limits are to be taken with $|\arg s| \leq (\pi/2) - \varepsilon$.

It is first of all not clear that the last limit exists. If it does, we don't see what it might be. If we can interchange the limit and the integral, however, we will get

$$\int_0^\infty \lim_{s \to 0} f'(t) \epsilon^{-st} \, dt = \int_0^\infty f'(t) \, dt = f(\infty) - f(0) \qquad (147)$$

If we assume uniform convergence of the Laplace integral for $f'(t)$ in a region including $s = 0$, then this interchange can be made. In such a case, however, the abscissae of convergence of both $f'(t)$ and $f(t)$ must be negative. This is possible only if $f(t)$ approaches 0 as s approaches ∞. That is,

$$f(\infty) = 0 \qquad (148)$$

But in this instance the whole theorem will be devoid of content. Hence, in order to establish the theorem, the interchange of the limit and the integral must be justified by finer criteria than uniform convergence; which takes the proof of the theorem "outside the scope of this text." The desired theorem can be stated as follows.

If $f(t)$ and $f'(t)$ are Laplace transformable, and if $sF(s)$ is regular on the jω-axis and in the right half plane, then

$$\lim_{t \to \infty} f(t) = \lim_{s \to 0+} sF(s) \tag{149}$$

where the limit on the right is to be taken along the positive real axis. This result is known as the *final value theorem*.

The last two operations that we shall consider are multiplication of $f(t)$ or $F(s)$ by an exponential function. Let us first consider multiplication of $F(s)$ by ϵ^{-as} where a is a real number. We have

$$\epsilon^{-as}F(s) = \epsilon^{-as} \int_0^\infty \epsilon^{-st}f(t) \, dt$$

$$= \int_0^\infty \epsilon^{-s(t+a)}f(t) \, dt \tag{150}$$

If we make the substitution $x = t + a$, and then change the dummy variable of integration back to t, we will get

$$\epsilon^{-as}F(s) = \int_a^\infty \epsilon^{-st}f(t - a) \, dt \tag{151}$$

If we assume that $f(t)$ vanishes for $t < 0$, then $f(t - a)$ will vanish for $t < a$ and the lower limit of the integral can be replaced by zero. To indicate that $f(t - a)$ is zero for $t < a$ we can write it in the form $f(t - a)u(t - a)$. The function $u(x)$ is the unit step, defined as zero for negative x and unity for positive x. This leads to the following result.

If $\mathcal{L}[f(t)] = F(s)$ and a is real, then

$$\mathcal{L}[f(t - a)u(t - a)] = \epsilon^{-as}F(s) \tag{152}$$

with the same abscissa of convergence.

This result is called the *real shifting* or *translation theorem* since $f(t - a)$ is obtained by shifting $f(t)$ to the right by a units.

The operation of multiplying $f(t)$ by ϵ^{at} leads to a similar result. This is called the *complex shifting theorem*.

If $\mathcal{L}[f(t)] = F(s)$ with abscissa of convergence σ_c, then

$$\mathcal{L}[\epsilon^{at}f(t)] = F(s + a) \tag{153}$$

with the abscissa of convergence $\sigma_c + Re(a)$.

This theorem follows directly from the definition of the Laplace transform.

A.12   The Complex Inversion Integral

We now consider the problem of finding the determining function $f(t)$ from a knowledge of the generating function $F(s)$. Since the uniqueness theorem tells us that two essentially different functions $f(t)$ cannot lead to the same function $F(s)$, we can expect to find an inverse transformation that will give us $f(t)$. We might (intuitively) expect that the inverse transformation will also be an integral, this time a complex integral in the s-domain. It must involve some kernel function of s and t, since we must end up with a function of t. Such is indeed the case, as stated by the following theorem. *Let* $\mathcal{L}\{f(t)\} = F(s)$, *with an abscissa of convergence* σ_c. *Then,*

$$\frac{1}{2\pi j} \int_{c-j\infty}^{c+j\infty} F(s)\,\epsilon^{st}\,ds = \begin{cases} 0 & t < 0 \\ \frac{1}{2}f(0+) & t = 0 \\ \frac{1}{2}[f(t+) + f(t-)] & t > 0 \end{cases} \qquad (154)$$

where $c \geq 0,\ c > \sigma_c$. This is known as the *inversion integral*.

The proof of this important theorem involves a knowledge of the Fourier integral theorem and several results from the theory of Lebesgue integration. Usually, we understand the normalization implied and write

$$\frac{1}{2\pi j} \int_{c-j\infty}^{c+j\infty} F(s)\,\epsilon^{st}\,ds = f(t)u(t) \qquad (155)$$

or simply

$$\frac{1}{2\pi j} \int_{c-j\infty}^{c+j\infty} F(s)\,\epsilon^{st}\,ds = f(t) \qquad (156)$$

the assumption $f(t) = 0$ for $t < 0$ being understood.

When the function $F(s)$ alone is given, we do not generally know σ_c. However we do know that $F(s)$ is regular for $\sigma > \sigma_c$. Hence, in such a case, we take the path of integration to be a vertical line to the right of all the singular points of $F(s)$. Such a path is known as a *Bromwich path* after the famous mathematician T. J. I'A. Bromwich who made many significant contributions to the theory of Laplace transformation. The abbreviation Br is used on the integral sign, instead of the limits, to signify this contour.

We saw in section A.6 that the residue theorem can often be used to evaluate integrals of this type. In order to use the residue theorem, we have to close the contour. Let us consider the two closed paths shown in Fig. 15. If the integrand $F(s)\epsilon^{st}$ satisfies Jordan's lemma on either of the semicircular arcs, we can evaluate the integral by the residue theorem. If Jordan's lemma is satisfied on the arc to the right, i.e., if

$$\lim_{s \to \infty} sF(s)\epsilon^{st} = 0, \qquad |\arg s| \leq \pi/2$$

(which will be true, for instance, if $t < 0$), the integral on C_1 of Fig. 15 is zero. Since, in addition, the closed contour integral is zero because no singularities are enclosed, the inversion integral yields zero.

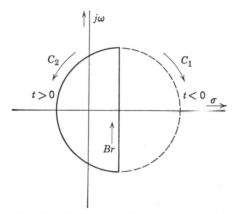

Fig. 15.   Evaluation of inversion integral.

If Jordan's lemma is satisfied on the semicircular arc to the left, which is much more often the case, the integral on the closed contour C_2 is $2\pi j$ times the sum of the residues of $F(s)\epsilon^{st}$ at the enclosed singular points. Including also the $1/2\pi j$ in Eq. (155), we get the following result.

If $F(s) \to 0$ as $s \to \infty$, uniformly in the sector $|\arg s| \geq \pi/2$, then

$$f(t) = \Sigma \text{ residues of } F(s)\epsilon^{st} \text{ at finite singularities of } F(s)$$

This is an extremely useful result. For simple functions, rational functions for example, we can evaluate $f(t)$ very easily by this theorem. For a rational function to be a Laplace transform, the degree of the denominator polynomial must exceed the degree of the numerator polynomial by the condition of Eq. (131). Thus, this inversion by residues is always applicable to rational functions.

In our brief discussion of the Laplace transform, we have had to omit many of the proofs and several results that are of considerable importance. However, we have at least stated all the results that have been used in the main text. Those who would like a more thorough treatment are referred to the standard texts listed in the bibliography. We will conclude our discussion with a very short table of transform pairs, which will be adequate for the present application.

TABLE OF TRANSFORM PAIRS

	$f(t)$	$F(s) = \mathcal{L}f(t)$
1	df/dt	$sF(s) - f(0+)$
2	$\displaystyle\int_0^t f(x)\, dx$	$\dfrac{1}{s}F(s)$
3	$-tf(t)$	$\dfrac{dF(s)}{ds}$
4	$\dfrac{1}{t}f(t)$	$\displaystyle\int_s^\infty F(z)\, dz$
5	$\epsilon^{-at}f(t)$	$F(s + a)$
6	$f(t - a)u(t - a)$	$\epsilon^{-as}F(s)$
7	$f(t/a)$	$aF(as)$
8	$u(t)$	$1/s$
9	t^n	$n!/s^{n+1}$
10	ϵ^{-at}	$1/(s + a)$
11	$\sin \omega t$	$\omega/(s^2 + \omega^2)$
12	$\cos \omega t$	$s/(s^2 + \omega^2)$

BIBLIOGRAPHY

This bibliography is not intended to be exhaustive but the entries listed constitute the major references for the subjects treated in this text.

1. Mathematical Background

Complex Variables

Churchill, R. V., *Introduction to Complex Variables and Applications*, McGraw-Hill Book Co., New York, 1948.

Knopp, K., *Theory of Functions*, Dover Publications, New York, Vol. I, 1945.

LePage, W. R., *Complex Variables in Linear Systems Analysis*, McGraw-Hill Book Co., New York, 1959.

Titchmarsh, E. C., *Theory of Functions*, Oxford University Press, Oxford, England, 1932.

Laplace Transformation

Churchill, R. V., *Modern Operational Mathematics in Engineering*, McGraw-Hill Book Co., New York, 1951.

Doetsch, G., *Handbuch der Laplace Transformation*, Birkhauser, Basel, Vol. I, 1950. (Rigorous proofs of all the results on Laplace transforms used in this text are to be found in this reference.)

Widder, D. V., *Laplace Transform*, Princeton University Press, Princeton, 1941.

Algebra

Aitken, A. C., *Determinants and Matrices*, Oliver and Boyd Ltd., London, 1942.

Birkhoff, G., and MacLane, S., *A Survey of Modern Algebra*, Macmillan, New York, 1955.

Bocher, M., *Introduction to Higher Algebra*, The Macmillan Co., New York, 1931.

Hohn, F. E., *Elementary Matrix Algebra*, The Macmillan Co., New York, 1958.

Perlis, S., *Theory of Matrices*, Addison-Wesley Press Inc., Cambridge, Mass., 1952.

2. Topology of Networks

Ingram, W. H., and Cramlet, C. M., "On the Foundations of Electrical Network Theory," *Journal of Mathematics and Physics*, Vol. 23, No. 3 (1944), pp. 134–155.

Kirchhoff, G., "On the Solution of the Equations Obtained from the Investigation of the Linear Distribution of Galvanic Currents," Translated by J. B. O'Toole, *Trans. I.R.E.*, Vol. CT-5 (March, 1958), pp. 4–7.

Kuratowski, C., "Sur le Problème des Courbes Gauches en Topologie," *Fundamenta Mathematica*, Vol. 15 (1930), pp. 271–283.

Seshu, S., *Theory of Linear Graphs with Applications in Electrical Engineering*, Department of Electrical Engineering, Syracuse University, 1958.

Whitney, H., "Non-separable and Planar Graphs," *Trans. Amer. Math. Soc.*, Vol. 34 (1932), pp. 339–362.

3. Network Response and Time-Frequency Relationships

Bayard, M., "Relations entre les Parties Réèles et Imaginaires des Impédances et Détermination des Impédances en Fonction de l'une des Parties," *Rev. Gen. Elec.*, 37 (1935), pp. 659–664.

Bode, H. W., *Network Analysis and Feedback Amplifier Design*, Van Nostrand Book Co., New Jersey, 1945.

Carson, J. R., *Electric Circuit Theory and Operational Calculus*, McGraw-Hill Book Co., New York, 1920.

Goldman, S., *Transformation Calculus and Electric Transients*, Prentice-Hall Inc., New York, 1949.

Guillemin, E. A., *The Mathematics of Circuit Analysis*, John Wiley and Sons, New York, 1949.

Lee, Y. W., "Synthesis of Electric Networks by Means of the Fourier Transforms of Laguerre's Functions," *Journal of Mathematics and Physics*, II (1932), pp. 83–113.

Waidelich, D. L., (1) "Steady State Operational Calculus," *Communications*, Vol. 22 (October, 1942), pp. 14–18.

———, (2) "Steady State Operational Calculus," *Proc. I.R.E.*, Vol. 34 (February, 1946), pp. 78–83.

4. Two-Port Parameters

Carlin, H. J., "The Scattering Matrix in Network Theory," *Trans. I.R.E.*, Vol. CT-3 (June, 1956), pp. 88–96.

Guillemin, E. A., *Communication Networks*, Vol. II, John Wiley and Sons, New York, 1935.

5. Network Functions

Balabanian, N., *Network Synthesis*, Prentice-Hall, Englewood Cliffs, 1958.

Brune, O., "On the Synthesis of a Two Terminal Network Whose Driving Point Impedance Is a Prescribed Function of Frequency," *Jour. Math. Phys.*, Vol. 10 (1931), pp. 191–236.

Cauer, W., (1) "Die Verwicklichung von Wechselstrom Widerstanden vorgeschriebener Frequenzabhangigkeit," *Archiv fur Electrotechnik*, Vol. 17, No. 4 (1926), pp. 355–388.

———, (2) *Synthesis of Communications Networks*, McGraw-Hill Book Co., translation of 2nd German Edition, 1958.

Darlington, S., "Synthesis of Reactance 4-poles," *Jour. Math. and Phys.*, Vol. 18 (1939), pp. 257–353.

Foster, R. M., "A Reactance Theorem," *Bell System Tech. Jour.*, Vol. 3 (1924), pp. 259–267.

Guillemin, E. A., *Synthesis of Passive Networks*, John Wiley and Sons, New York, 1957.

Richards, P. I., "On a Special Class of Functions with a Positive Real Part in a Half Plane," *Duke Math. Jour.*, Vol. 14 (1947), pp. 777–786.

6. Potential Analog

Darlington, S., "The Potential Analog Method of Network Synthesis," *BSTJ*, Vol. 30 (April, 1951), pp. 315–365.

Huggins, W. H., The Potential Analogue in Network Synthesis and Analysis, Air Force Cambridge Research Center, Report E5066, 1951.

Klinkhamer, J. F., "Empirical Determination of Wave Filter Transfer Functions with Specified Properties," Philips Research Reports, *3*, 1948, pp. 66 and 378.

Tuttle, D. F., *Network Synthesis*, John Wiley and Sons, New York, 1958.

7. Block Diagrams and Signal-Flow Graphs

Graybeal, T. D., "Block Diagram Network Transformation," *Elec. Engg.*, Vol. 70 (1951), p. 785.

Mason, S. J., (1) "Feedback Theory—Some Properties of Signal Flow Graphs," *Proc. I.R.E.*, Vol. 41 (1953), pp. 1144–1156.

———, (2) "Feedback Theory—Further Properties of Signal Flow Graphs," *Proc. I.R.E.*, Vol. 44 (1956), pp. 920–926.

Stout, T. M., (1) "A Block Diagram Approach to Network Analysis," *Trans. AIEE* (Applications and Industry), Vol. 3 (1952), p. 255.

———, (2) "Block Diagram Solution for Vacuum Tube Circuits," *Comm. and Electronics*, Vol. 9 (1953), p. 561.

Truxal, J. G., *Control System Synthesis*, McGraw-Hill Book Co., New York, 1955.

8. Stability

Black, H. S., "Stabilized Feedback Amplifiers," *BSTJ*, Vol. 13 (1934), pp. 1–18.

Bode, H. W., *Network Analysis and Feedback Amplifier Design*, loc. cit.

Hurwitz, A., "Ueber die Bedingungen unter Welchen eine Gleichung nur Wurzeln mit Negativen Reelen Teilen besitzt," *Math. Ann.*, Vol. 46 (1895), p. 273.

Nyquist, H., "Regeneration Theory," *BSTJ*, Vol. 11 (1932), pp. 126–147.

Routh, E. J., *Dynamics of a System of Rigid Bodies*, Macmillan, London, 1930.

9. Topological Formulas

Coates, C. L., "General Topological Formulas for Linear Network Functions," *Trans. IRE*, Vol. CT-5 (March, 1958), pp. 42–54.

Kirchhoff, G., loc. cit.

Maxwell, J. C., *Electricity and Magnetism*, Clarendon Press, Oxford, Vol. I, 1892, pp. 403–410.

Mayeda, W., and Seshu, S., "Topological Formulas for Network Functions," Engg. Expt. Station, University of Illinois, Bull. No. 446, Nov., 1957.

Mayeda, W., "Topological Formulas for Active Networks," Rept. No. 8, U. S. Army Contract No. DA-11-022-ORD-1983, University of Illinois, 1958.

Percival, W. S., (1) "The Solution of Passive Electrical Networks by Means of Mathematical Trees," *Jour. I.E.E.* (London), Vol. 100 (May, 1953), pp. 143–150.

———, (2) "The Graphs of Active Networks," *Proc. I.E.E.*, Vol. 102, part C (1955), pp. 270–278.

Reza, F. M., "Some Topological Considerations in Network Theory," *Trans. I.R.E.*, Vol. CT-5 (March, 1958), pp. 30–42.

10. Image Parameter Theory

Bode, H. W., "A General Theory of Electric Wave Filters," *Jour. Math. and Phys.*, Vol. 13 (1934), pp. 275–362.

Bode, H. W., *Network Analysis and Feedback Amplifier Design*, loc. cit.

Guillemin, E. A., *Communication Networks*, Vol. II, loc. cit.

Reed, M. B., *Electric Network Synthesis*, Prentice-Hall Inc., Englewood Cliffs, 1955.

11. General

Bashkow, T. R., "The A-matrix, a New Network Description," *Trans. I.R.E.*, Vol. CT-4 (Sept., 1957), pp. 117–119.

Guillemin, E. A., *Introductory Circuit Theory*, John Wiley and Sons, New York, 1953.

Halperin, Introduction to the Theory of Distributions, Canadian Math. Congress, University of Toronto Press, 1952.

LePage, W. R., and Seely, S., *General Network Analysis*, McGraw-Hill Book Co., New York, 1952.

Reza, F., and Seely, S., *Modern Network Analysis*, McGraw-Hill Book Co., New York, 1959.

Ryder, J. D., *Networks, Lines, and Fields*, Prentice-Hall Inc., Englewood Cliffs, 1957.

Schwartz, L., *Théorie des Distributions*, Hermann et Cie, Paris, 1950–51.

Van Valkenburg, M. E., *Network Analysis*, Prentice-Hall Inc., Englewood Cliffs, 1955.

INDEX